THE BIRDWATCHE
AND DIARY

Designed and published by
Hilary Cromack

Edited by
David Cromack

BUCKINGHAM PRESS LTD

In association with

Published in 2007 by
Buckingham Press Ltd
55 Thorpe Park Road, Peterborough
Cambridgeshire PE3 6LJ
United Kingdom

(Tel/Fax) 01733 561 739
e-mail: admin@buckinghampress.com
www.birdsillustrated.com

ISBN 978-0-955033-96-4
ISSN 0144-364 X

Cover image: Grey Partridges by Ernest Leahy
Address: 32 Ben Austins, Redbourn, Herts, AL3 7DR; 01582 793 144;
e-mail: ernest.leahy@ntlworld.com
www.wildlifewatercolours.co.uk

Black and white illustrations: By Mabel Cheung
E-mail: chinita@talk21.com

Printed and bound in Great Britain by
Cambridge University Press, Cambridge, UK

CONTENTS

CONTENTS

PREFACE

BIRDWATCHERS have quickly learnt the benefits of having information available to them through the myriad channels of the Internet, so it is perhaps not surprising that I'm sometimes asked if this new digital resource will make the *The Birdwatcher's Yearbook* redundant. Happily, the answer is a resounding 'no'!

Research conducted among buyers of the 2007 Edition revealed that when offered the option of having *Yearbook* information available on-line, an overwhelming percentage of respondents (more than 95%) still prefer having it available in a single handy book.

I can't say I'm particularly surprised at these results. As someone who now uses the Internet on a daily basis when researching articles or checking facts for *Birds Illustrated* magazine, I'm constantly frustrated by the time it takes to sift the wheat from the chaff. Properly edited books and magazine perform that filtering service so that time-pressured readers don't have to. At a rough estimate, I reckon that Hilary and I spend five months a year in assembling and checking the information within the pages of each edition of the *Yearbook*.

The *Yearbook's* original editor and publisher John Pemberton declared in his first Preface in 1981 that he was launching the *Yearbook* with the aim of providing a comprehensive and convenient work of reference for all sectors of the birdwatching community in Great Britain and for visitors from overseas.

He also expressed the hope that the feature articles would build into an interesting and useful 'library', recording the growth and changing patterns of the hobby of watching wild birds. He ended by thanking people for their ideas about content for future editions and said it would be the policy of BYB to respond as positively as possible to the wishes of its readers.

We have tried to stay true to these laudable principles since buying Buckingham Press in 2001 and I always welcome correspondence from readers if it will enhance the value of the book to a modern-day audience.

Our research underlined the fact that birdwatchers are becoming increasingly interested in broadening their appreciation of nature. So, for the first time, we have included checklists of dragonflies and butterflies to enable you to keep an annual tally of your sightings alongside your bird records. We have also included information about key flora and fauna species in the Reserves section.

PREFACE

Time for groups to get more help

BY COMMUNICATING with all bird and wildlife organisations on an annual basis, we get a feel for what is happening across the country, and in the case of RSPB local groups, there does appear to be cause for concern. A number are currently without leaders, while others with aging committees are questioning how long they can continue to operate if younger members don't materialise.

I only hope that the powers-that-be at RSPB headquarters and in the regional offices are giving urgent consideration to ways of giving greater support to the groups, as they not only raise funds for the Society's conservation work but represent it in the community. Without groups being on hand to connect with ordinary members of the public, a burgeoning interest in wild birds could easily wither away.

The *Yearbook* is obviously the first place to look if you want to join your local bird club or RSPB local group and if you've not already signed up, I hope 2008 is the year you put that right.

Happy retirement

FINALLY, I want to pay tribute to John Brinkley, who retires as Managing Director of Swarovski Optik UK at the end of 2007, though happily we can look forward to continuing our long friendship, because the company is retaining John as a consultant.

He joined the company with the intention of making it a leader in sports optics and it is a testament to his vision and hard work that John's ambition has been realised. He was quick to appreciate that the views of users needed to be taken into account when developing new products, and as a result of this consultative policy, birders around the globe now covet the company's innovative and stylish binoculars and telescopes.

We are very appreciative of the sponsorship support John has given to Buckingham Press to develop the *Yearbook* and our growing range of *Best Birdwatching Sites* books. We are by no means the only beneficiaries: this commitment to making a positive contribution to 'good causes' is well-established at Swarovski and the company now supports many conservation projects, art awards and other sponsorships in the UK and overseas.

David Cromack

EDITOR

A MESSAGE FROM THE SPONSORS OF THIS BOOK

FOR 28 YEARS *The Birdwatcher's Yearbook & Diary* has provided the essential facts and figures relating to the birdwatching scene in Britain. If you are buying this valuable resource for the first time, you can be assured that every effort has been made to check and update every single piece of information for each edition.

Every journalist, company director, bird club leader, field trip organiser and ordinary birdwatcher who puts his or her faith in the accuracy of the book owes publisher Hilary Cromack a debt of gratitude for months of work she dedicates each year to the task of compiling the content.

You will discover within its pages so many useful features, it's hard to know where to look first. In terms of practical benefits, the Reserves section is particularly valuable because it has up-to-date information on more than 400 sites, plus contact information on scores more sites recorded in more detail in previous editions.

The Diary element and Log Charts will enable you to keep track of your outings and bird sightings and this year Checklists for Butterflies and Dragonflies have been included to reflect the growing interest in these insects.

The special features produced by guest writers address important birding topics of the day and, taken together since 1981, provide a useful social history of the activity. This year Dawn Balmer discusses the New Atlas of Birds in Britain, the biggest project of its kind and one worthy of your support.

Swarovski UK was first invited to sponsor the 2002 edition and it has been our pleasure to support the publication ever since, as we believe that Buckingham Press shares our own ethos of 'improving through innovation and attention to detail'. Put *The Yearbook* to the test and I'm sure you will not find it wanting.

Let me end by wishing you a successful year of birdwatching in 2008.

John Brinkley
Managing Director, Swarovski Optik

Key contributors in this Edition

GRAHAM APPLETON is a former teacher who now heads the BTO's Fundraising and Publicity Department. A trained ringer and participant in many surveys, he is particularly interested in migration and co-operated with Jim Flegg in the development of the Time To Fly book.

DAWN BALMER works in the Habitats Section of BTO and has been appointed as the Co-ordinator for the New Bird Atlas 2007-11. Since joining the Trust in 1992 she has worked on a number of projects including the successful BirdTrack on-line recording scheme. Dawn has contributed to many scientific papers and gives talks to bird clubs.

MABEL CHEUNG was originally from Newton Abbot in Devon, and has now returned to the county to work as a Countryside Ranger. Amongst her varied work history, highlights include working with sea turtle conservation charities in Costa Rica and BirdWatch Ireland. She works in pencil, ink pens, charcoal, pastels and acrylics, from life and/or photos and has contributed illustrations to *Birds of Inishbofin Connemara* by Tim Gordon.

RICHARD FACEY is a keen birder and photographer and is a regular contributor to Buckingham Press' quarterly magazine *Birds Illustrated*. He has a degree in zoology, with his main interests being bird behaviour and evolution.

GORDON HAMLETT, a freelance writer, is a regular contributor to *Bird Watching* magazine, both as a reviewer of books, DVDs and computer software and also as sub-editor of the UK Bird Sightings section. Gordon is the author of the acclaimed *Best Birdwatching Sites in the Highlands of Scotland* (Buckingham Press) and in his spare time is a dedicated internet browser.

ERNEST LEAHY is a full-time professional artist who has contributed work to numerous books and magazines. He works mainly in watercolour but uses other media when appropriate. Ernest is happy to accept commissions (ernest.leahy@ntlworld.com) and if you visit his website (www.wildlifewatercolours.co.uk) you can see more of his work.

ROGER RIDDINGTON edits British Birds magazine from his home in Shetland, where he has lived for more than a decade. A former warden of the Fair Isle Bird Observatory, he founded and managed the Shetland Biological Records Centre. He is a co-author of Rare Plants of Shetland and of the forthcoming Birds of Shetland, a member of the Scottish Birds Rarities Committee and a Trustee of Fair Isle Bird Observatory.

BOB SCOTT, a former warden at Dungeness and RSPB Northward Hill, held the post of Chief Reserves Officer for the RSPB until his retirement. Together with his wife Anne, he leads birding tours to various destinations, but with a particular interest in Bulgaria and Poland. Bob is currently a British Birds Trustee and regularly gives talks to birding groups.

OUR SPECIAL THANKS go to Derek Toomer and David Ballance for their help with putting this edition of the *Yearbook* together. We would also like to thank all of our information providers in the various bird groups and clubs, bird reserves and national organisations as it would be impossible to produce this book without their continued support and assistance.

FEATURES

Satellite tracking has revealed that Glossy Ibises that breed in Syria, spend their winters in Ethiopia.

KEY ORNITHOLOGICAL NEWS OF 2007

Richard Facey reviews key reports and scientific literature from around the globe to provide a digest of the most significant bird news.

Newly-discovered species in Asia and South America

IN AN ERA when many species are being threatened with extinction, it is good to hear that new species are still being discovered. One such example is the wonderfully named Bugun Liocichia (*Liocichla bugunorum*), which was found in at the Eaglenest Wildlife Sanctuary, Arunachal Pradesh, India.

This babbler was discovered not by an ornithologist, but by professional astronomer Ramana Athreya, and represents the most thrilling ornithological discovery from India in the last half century.

Athreya first glimpsed the Bugun Liocichia in 1995 but could not confirm its identity until May 2006 when he and his colleagues in the Eaglenest Biodiversity Project returned to the area armed with mist nets in an attempt to catch the new species. They were successful, catching two specimens.

When a new species is discovered and described, the norm is to preserve a dead specimen in a museum. This so called "type" specimen acts as a template to show the features that distinguish this from other species and act as proof of the species' existence. However as the known population of the Bugun Liocichia consists of 14 individuals (including three breeding pairs), the species was deemed too rare for a type specimen to be taken. Instead, it is documented by a series of photographs, feather samples and recordings of its song. The species was named in honour of the local tribe from the area.

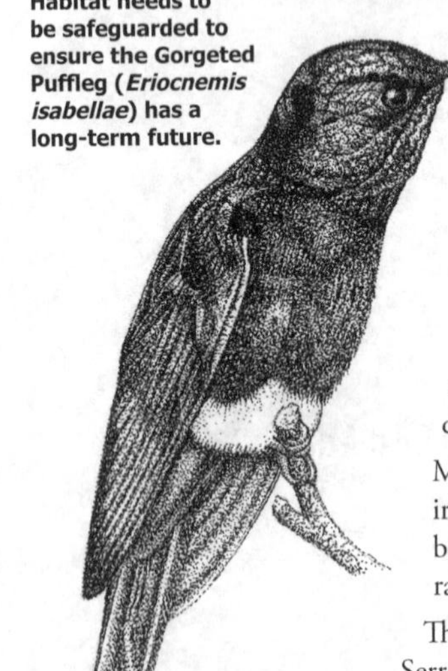

Habitat needs to be safeguarded to ensure the Gorgeted Puffleg (*Eriocnemis isabellae*) has a long-term future.

Another recently discovered species also bears a fantastic name but the Gorgeted Puffleg (*Eriocnemis isabellae*), a species of hummingbird from Colombia, unfortunately does not reside in a protected area.

Males of the new species sport an enlarged dual-coloured iridescent throat patch and white tufts above the legs. It's believed that the new puffleg has a small population and range.

The species was found in the montane cloud forest in the Serrania del Pinche, an unprotected area that is under threat from habitat clearance, causing major concerns for the bird's future.

A number of organisations, including the Hummingbird Conservancy, Fundación Echohabitat and BirdLife International, have sprung into action to start efforts to safeguard the future of the Gorgeted Puffleg.

Sources:
Bugun Liocichla – *Indian Birds*, volume 2, pages 82-94.
Gorgeted Puffleg – *Ornitologia Neotropical*, volume 18, pages 161-170.

Breeding trends in British birds

MORE THAN one million birds were counted by 2,647 British Trust for Ornithology volunteers as part of the last Breeding Bird Survey (BBS) to be published. No fewer than 223 species were counted in 2006, and, as always, the results revealed a mixed bag, with 29 species declining and 46 increasing.

Of the 16 red-listed species (high conservation concern), 11 continued to decline, while four continued their way to recovery. The Turtle Dove, the UK's only migratory dove, continues to cause concern, with numbers declining by 61% over the last 12 years. Habitat changes in wintering grounds, hunting on migration and agricultural intensification have all played a part in the decline.

However it is hoped that Government-funded agri-environment schemes will help reverse the trend, as they have done in other species, such as the Tree Sparrow (*Passer montanus*). Having undergone a massive 97% overall decline, the Tree Sparrow has surged back since 1994 (66% growth between 2005 and 2006) but still has a long way to go until its population recovers to its former levels.

The Song Thrush (*Turdus philomelos*) is another red list species on the up and up, showing a 17% increase. Reed Bunting (*Emberiza schoeniclus*) numbers have increased by 39%, but its close relative, the Yellowhammer (*Emberiza citrinella*), dropped by 16%.

The results from two other specific BTO surveys into Wood Lark (*Lullula arborea*) and Dartford Warbler were released in 2007 and both revealed encouraging upturns in fortunes after years of dramatic decline. The Wood Lark's estimated population has risen nearly 90% since 1997, while the Dartford Warbler's (*Sylvia undata*) is up 70%.

The lark's rise was mainly confirmed within its traditional strongholds, but Dartford Warblers have struck out to colonise new areas. It can now be found along the coast of South Wales and some Welsh Valleys, into the West Midlands and East Anglia, as well as expanding west to Cornwall.

2006 was a landmark year for one of Britain's colourful, albeit adopted species, the Ring-necked Parakeet (*Psittacula*

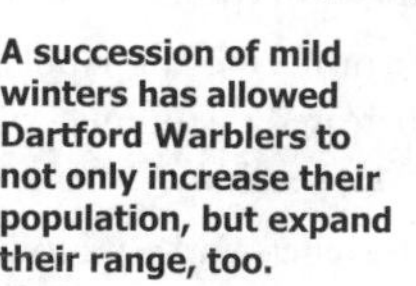

A succession of mild winters has allowed Dartford Warblers to not only increase their population, but expand their range, too.

krameri), which has achieved coverage in 30 or more BBS squares – the requisite number to allow population changes to be monitored. Not bad for a species that only made it on to the British list in 1983.

Sources:
Breeding Bird Survey: BTO,
see http://www.bto.org/bbs/results/BBSreport06.pdf

Britain's Tawny Owls remain stable

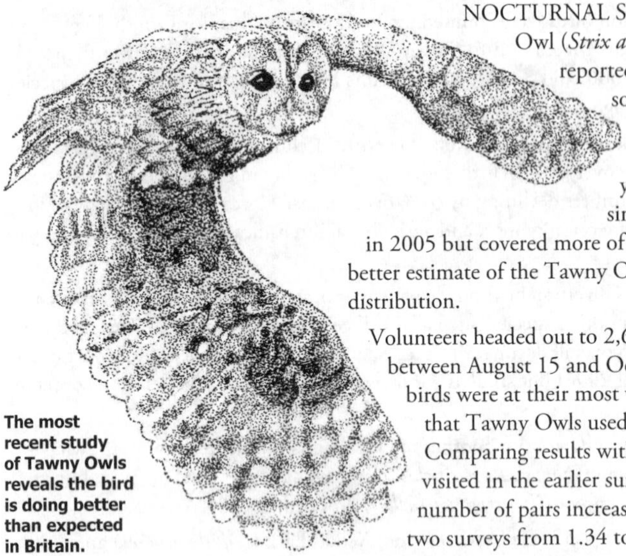

NOCTURNAL SPECIES such as Tawny Owl (*Strix aluco*) tend to be under-reported in general bird surveys, so there was great interest in the BTO's specific study published last year. The survey, the first since 1989, was conducted in 2005 but covered more of the UK, giving a much better estimate of the Tawny Owl's population and distribution.

The most recent study of Tawny Owls reveals the bird is doing better than expected in Britain.

Volunteers headed out to 2,652 tetrads across Britain between August 15 and October 15, when the birds were at their most vocal. It was estimated that Tawny Owls used 63% of the tetrads. Comparing results with the 1,286 tetrads visited in the earlier survey showed the average number of pairs increased slightly between the two surveys from 1.34 to 1.42 pairs per tetrad.

So it appears the Tawny Owl is holding its own – good news as BBS, which doesn't cater well for nocturnal species, showed a 38% decline in the Tawny Owl population between 1994 and 2004.

Sources:
BTO News 268

Change of scene for Cirl Buntings

BIRDS THAT LIVE in isolated pockets are particularly vulnerable and sometimes they need a helping hand to extend their range. That is the case with Cirl Bunting (*Emberiza cirlus*), a species which has been restricted to a few sites in Devon for many years.

Changes in agriculture had sent the overall population plummeting until the RSPB's Cirl Bunting Recovery Project increased the number of pairs from 120 in 1989 to 700 in 2003 but during that time the species' range didn't increase.

Cirl Buntings are reluctant travellers and tend to move no further than 2km between breeding and wintering quarters, so a joint project between the RSPB, Natural England, the National

Trust and Paignton Zoo decided to give the birds a helping hand in expanding their horizons.

In 2004 young Cirl Buntings were taken from their nest (under licence) in land owned by the National Trust in South Devon, and taken to Paignton Zoo where they were hand reared. Once old enough, they were released close to where they had been collected.

This trial operation proved a success, and in 2006 more than 70 birds were released in areas of Cornwall that could support the species. Cornwall clearly agreed with the released birds, as several of them bred in 2007 – the first time in 15 years the species has bred in the county. The project aims to release a minimum of 60 birds each year for the next three years.

Long-lost species make a comeback

STILL MORE species have resurfaced from zoological obscurity. The Madagascar Pochard (*Aythya innotata*) was considered "possibly extinct" until nine adults and four recently hatched young were discovered. The previous last sighting of the species was a male seen in 1991 and the last record of a group of birds came from 1960.

Having not being seen for 70 years, the Manipur Bush-quail (*Perdicula manipurensis*) decided that it was time to put in an appearance at Manas National Park, Assam, India. The bird was flushed by the Embankment and Drainage Department as they drove to do some engineering work in the reserve.

Luckily they were accompanied by Dr Anwaruddin Choudhury, the region's Deputy Commissioner and an ornithologist, who was able to identify the bird. The last authentic records for the species date back to around 1905.

Our third species to make a reappearance, the Large-billed Reed-warbler (*Acrocephalus orinus*) was originally discovered in 1867 in the Sutlej Valley, India. However as only one individual was collected, doubt surrounded the validity of the species – was it a proper species or just an aberrant Reed Warbler (*A.scripaceus*)?

In 2002 Professor Staffan Bensch of the Lund University, examined its mitochondrial DNA and confirmed it represented a valid species, but the fact still remained that the species had not been seen for 139 years

However that was about to change – thanks to Philip Round, Assistant Professor in the Department of Biology, Mahidol University. Round was bird ringing in a waste treatment centre near Bangkok, when he noticed something rather unusual in one of his mist nets.

To confirm the bird's identity, Round took photographs, and feathers for DNA analysis. The results, along with the photographs, were sent to Bensch who confirmed the identification. The rediscovery of the Large-billed Reed-warbler, so far from the initial site of its discovery, suggests the species could be quite widespread in South East Asia, particularly during the winter months.

However, six months after the rediscovery of the Large-billed Reed-warbler in Thailand, another specimen was discovered, lurking in a drawer of Blyth's Reed Warblers (*A. dumetorum*) in the collections of the Natural History Museum at Tring. The specimen had been collected from a different part of India, in the 19th Century.

Sources:

Madagascar Pochard – BirdLife International

Manipur Bush-quail - BirdLife International
Large-billed Reed-warbler - *Journal of Avian Biology* Volume 38 Issue 2 pages 133-246 and BirdLife International

US bird declines mirrored across the globe

ACCORDING to BirdLife International's annual Red List update, the situation for many of the world's birds grows ever more gloomy, with 1,221 species threated with extinction. When combined with the 812 species considered to be Near Threatened, this mean that more than a fifth of the world's species are in urgent need of conservation measures.

Several vulture and albatross species were re-listed to higher categories of concern, while birds restricted to islands are among the most threatened groups. For instance, the St Helena Plover (*Charadrius sanctaehelenae*) is now Critically Endangered, due to continued habitat degradation and predation by feral cats.

However all is not doom and gloom. What goes down can also go up – and that includes the infamous Mauritius Parakeet (*Psittacula eques*), which is now only considered Endangered, thanks to a highly successful recovery programme. The Spectacled Petrel (*Procellaria conspicillata*) is now considered Vulnerable rather than Critically Endangered.

However more localised reports illustrated declines and success. Combining data from its Christmas Bird Count and the U.S. Geological Survey's breeding bird survey, the National Audubon Society's study revealed alarming declines in some of America's common and familiar birds.

Once-common species have declined by more than 50% and in the case of the Evening Grosbeak (*Coccothraustes vespertinus*), the drop is as high as 78%. The Northern Bobwhite (*Colinus virginianus*) has fared even worse, with an 82% decline. Other common species in peril include the Eastern Meadowlark (*Sturnella magna*), which is down 71% and Pintail (*Anas acuta*), down 78%.

Declines of these and other species in America are attributed to habitat degradation, climate change, agricultural intensification and urbanisation.

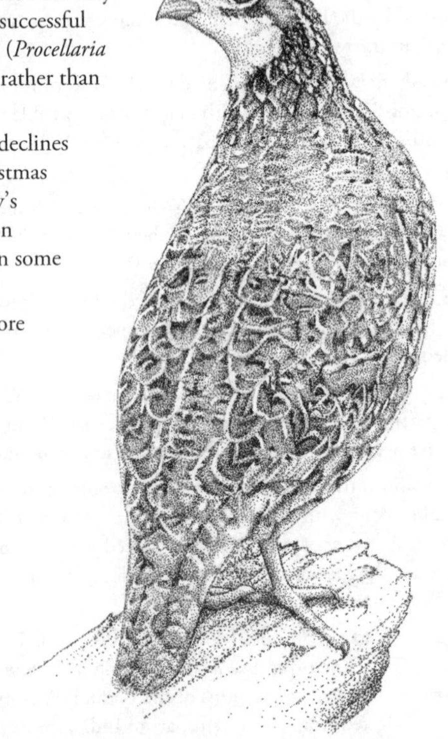

Northern Bobwhite, a quail species that is largely confined to the eastern states of America, has suffered a massive decline in recent years.

KEY ORNITHOLOGICAL NEWS OF 2007

Bald Eagles and Turkeys reverse the trend

GOOD NEWS from across the pond reveals Wild Turkey (*Meleagris gallopavo*) increasing by 14% annually, while numbers of the Double-crested Cormorant (*Phalacrocorax auritus*) have risen by 8%.

One bird is doing particulary well – the Collared Dove (*Streptopelia decaocto*). Not content with expanding its range from Asia through Europe, the species made is way to the US in the 1980s.

The Bald Eagle has been removed from the Endangered Species Act's list of threatened species. Hunting and poisoning meant the species underwent a dramatic decline until by 1963 only 4,176 pairs remained in the USA's lower 48 states.

The situation worsened with the introduction and widespread use of DDT, which caused all but Alaska's population to dive. However, the banning of DDT in 1972 and a huge conservation effort has resulted in the Bald Eagle's population reaching a staggering 11,040 pairs.

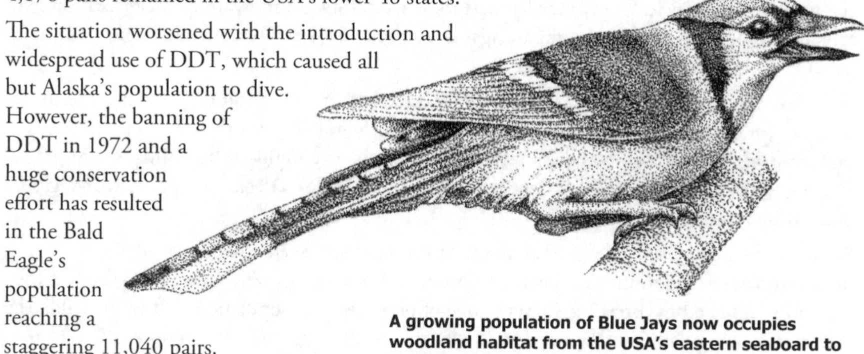

A growing population of Blue Jays now occupies woodland habitat from the USA's eastern seaboard to the Rockies.

Though it was one of the seven American bird species most affected by an outbreak of the mosquito-borne West Nile Virus in 1997, Blue Jays have proved very resilient and the latest Audubon Society figures indicate its population is recovering strongly.

Sources:

Bald Eagle – American Bird Conservancy
American Bird Declines – the Audubon Society
Red List update – BirdLife International

Great Bustards ahead of schedule

THE Great Bustard Group (GBC) is a charitable organisation dedicated to restoring this charismatic species to the UK. The original population was hunted to extinction in this country but in 2004 the first batch of new birds was imported from Russia.

GBC predicted that the new population of Great Bustards (*Otis tarda*) would produce their first eggs in 2008, so there was jubilation when this landmark arrived in 2007. However, the champagne had to be put on ice as the nest was abandoned, and when examined the eggs proved to be infertile.

Nevertheless this first British breeding attempt for 175 years goes to show that these birds have settled in and are thriving enough to consider expending energy on breeding. Reintroductions are scheduled to continue until 2014, but hopefully they'll be augmented by homegrown birds in the not-too-distant future.

Sources:
The Great Bustard Group www.greatbustard.com

Migration mysteries solved by technology

THE QUESTION of where Aquatic Warblers (*Acrocephalus paludicola*) go in winter has been a question that has occupied many scientists and conservationist for years. But now they know – Senegal.

Combining traditional field techniques, with more modern ones, scientists were able to crack the mystery. The species grows new feathers in its wintering grounds, so scientists used these to look for isotopic signatures to compare against isotopic maps of West Africa, an area that had produced a handful of ringing recoveries.

Next came some fancy modelling of areas with suitable climatic conditions, and hey presto an area next to the Senegal River was revealed as a likely hide-out for the species when it was not breeding. A field team was deployed and found between 5,000-10,000 birds within the Djoudj National Park, northwest Senegal; a vital discovery for a declining species with a global population estimated at 15,000 pairs.

Scientists have also been able to track the Bald Ibis (*Geronticus eremita*) to its previously unknown wintering grounds in the last 12 months. Satellite tags were attached to three of the remaining seven adults breeding in Syria, one of two breeding populations left in the wild. The tagged trio, along with another bird, were relocated in the highlands of Ethiopia, 30 years after the last records for that area.

Satellite tracking has also revealed some record breakers. A Bar-tailed Godwit (*Limosa lapponica*) has set a new world record for the longest non-stop flight, flying from North Island, New Zealand, to Yalu Jiang, at the northern end of China's Yellow Sea, a journey of 10,200km which the bird completed non-stop in nine days.

A Barnacle Goose (*Branta leucopsis*) named Barbow, one of 13 geese currently being GPS satellite-tracked by the Wildfowl and Wetlands Trust (WWT), from their wintering grounds at the Caerlaverock centre in Scotland, to their breeding grounds in High Arctic, has set a new speed record.

Reaching speeds of 127kph, Bardow completing the journey from the Solway Firth and across the North Sea in five hours. However as the transmitter can only record a maximum speed of 127kph, Bardow could have been travelling even faster. To find out more visit the WWT's website at www.wwt.org.uk

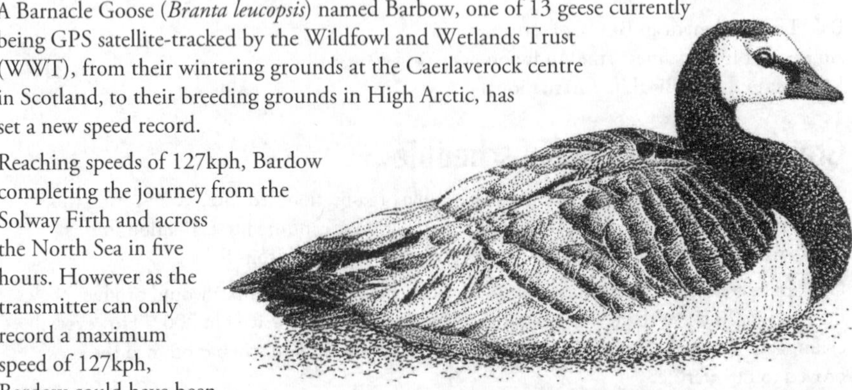

When seen resting on the ground, it is hard to believe that ungainly species such as Barnacle Goose are capable of setting avian speed records.

BB – 100 NOT OUT!

Bob Scott and Roger Riddington look back over the history of *British Birds*, a treasured publication for ornithologists and birdwatchers for the past century.

EARLY in 1907, H.F. (Harry) Witherby, one of the leading lights of British ornithology, approached several like-minded people to support his idea of a monthly magazine devoted to the study of British birds – an idea that he had been developing for several years

Even though birdwatching in the early years of the 20th Century was still a minority interest, the numbers of people involved was growing slowly but surely. At that time, egg-collecting and collecting birds for museum specimens were still commonplace but gradually birdwatchers began to turn increasingly to their binoculars (still of poor quality compared with modern standards) rather than their guns.

Among many supporters of Witherby's grand scheme was the Hon. Walter Rothschild and he offered financial assistance to ensure the project was born. Though the name *British Birds* has been used for every issue throughout its 100 years, there was much debate before the first copy left the print room – also under consideration were *The Magazine of British Ornithology* and *The British Ornithologists' Magazine*. It is perhaps not surprising that, as the trend was towards the study of birds rather than the pastime of ornithology, the title was simplified and became very succinct – a decision that has stood the test of time.

BRITISH BIRDS
AN·ILLUSTRATED·MAGAZINE DEVOTED·TO·THE·BIRDS·ON THE·BRITISH·LIST
JUNE 1, 1907.
Vol. I. No. 1.
MONTHLY·ONE·SHILLING·NET
326 HIGH·HOLBORN·LONDON
WITHERBY & Co

The cover of the first issue, published in June 1907

The title may not have changed but birdwatchers certainly have. Their behaviour, interests and approach, their mobility and equipment, and not least their numbers have all changed dramatically over the 100 years that *BB* has been published.

Over the years, the key objectives of *British Birds* have broadened. Initially, the journal was 'To be devoted to the study of birds on the British list and mainly to the study of them in the British Islands, but notes and articles on observations abroad of birds rare in Britain would be allowable.'

Today, *BB*'s mission statement reads '...

provide a forum for contributions of interest to all birdwatchers in the Western Palearctic; publish material on behaviour, conservation, distribution, ecology, identification, movements, status and taxonomy embrace new ideas and research; maintain its position as the respected journal of record and interpret good scientific research on birds for the interest of the non-scientist.'

The Red Grouse has been the jounal's logo throughout its history though the design has been udated several times.

Nonetheless, Witherby's plans for the journal have survived extremely well, with articles, notes, letters, photographs and reviews continuing to expand our ornithological knowledge, much as they had in 1907.

Production methods and costs, of course, have changed dramatically. In advance of the first issue appearing, in June 1907, it was contemplated that there would be a monthly sale of 200 or 300 copies at 6d (2.5p) each. Each issue would have 32 pages and one plate and the production costs of each issue would be some £14. This would have produced a significant deficit, however, and as a result the sale price was settled at one shilling (5p) with the statement that any profit would go back into expanding the production.

The Red Grouse *Lagopus lagopus* was elected as the journal's logo, though of course the word logo (probably a shortening of the word logogram) did not arrive in the English language until 1937, so would have been completely unknown to Witherby.

However, he was looking for a symbol to represent British birds and selected the only species then considered endemic to the British Isles and nesting in all four countries. We now know that it is the British subspecies of the Willow Grouse – but it has nonetheless stood the journal in good stead for 100 years in the various formats in which it has been reproduced – facing left, facing right, standing on rocks, in outline only and, for a time, in flight. Today's modern logo was drawn for *BB* by the journal's art consultant, Robert Gillmor, in 2002.

Marine foraging by Ospreys in southwest Scotland: implications for the species' distribution in western Europe

Mick Marquiss, Lynne Robinson and Elizabeth Tindal

ABSTRACT Most breeding Ospreys *Pandion haliaetus* in the UK are in Scotland and feed on freshwater fish. Some east-coast pairs use estuarine fish in summer but still depend on freshwater foraging in spring. However, a pair in southwest Scotland fed predominantly on marine fish in both 2004 and 2005. This pair took freshwater fish early in the breeding season, but fed mainly marine fish to their young. The marine prey, grey mullet *Chelon/Liza*, Garfish *Belone belone* and flatfish (Pleuronectidae), were taken at different stages of the tidal cycle, so these Ospreys could feed from the sea almost throughout the day. A review of dietary studies of Palearctic Ospreys shows that most birds in the north

The modern BB is still keen to publish material about aspects of bird behaviour.

The opening paper in Vol 1, No 1 (edited by H. F. Witherby, assisted by W. P. Pycraft of the Natural History Museum) was by Howard Saunders and described numerous species that had been added to the British List during the preceding eight years – many of which were subsequently exposed as fraudulent claims as part of the 'Hastings Rarities Affair', the whole event being thoroughly analysed and reported in *BB* in August 1962.

Right from the start, *BB* set out with a pioneering spirit. In that very first issue, W. Eagle Clarke contributed a note reporting the first records of Arctic Terns *Sterna paradisaea* wintering in Antarctica – information that we now accept as commonplace but in 1907 this was dramatic and new.

Among the pages of the early issues is a fantastic wealth of historical data, pioneering ornithology, classic errors and the infancy of many aspects of birdwatching now taken as everyday features of the modern hobby.

Discussions on marking birds to study migration led to the start of the 'British Birds Marking Scheme' in 1909, with the issue of rings marked 'Witherby High Holborn London'. Those early days of ringing, almost exclusively of nestling birds, produced results that included the first Barn Swallow *Hirundo rustica* recovered in South Africa.

The scheme was passed to the fledgling British Trust for Ornithology (BTO) in 1937 with the rings carrying the new address 'British Museum Nat. Hist. London' – an address far more likely to produce results! *BB* was closely involved with the formation of the BTO – launching an appeal in 1933 with the then editors taking a leading role in the new Trust.

Harry Witherby sold his extensive collection of bird skins to the British Museum and donated the proceeds to the BTO to help them through their formative years. Some of the BTO's most venerable surveys – notable the Heronries Census – had their origins in enquiries launched in *BB*.

Of course not everything has gone smoothly – an early article on the breeding of Hen Harriers *Circus cyaneus* in Surrey soon proved to be about Montagu's Harriers *C. pygargus*! One 1959 cover depicted a Common Buzzard *Buteo buteo*, drawn by a technically capable but ornithologically inexperienced artist, which could not have flown as the primary feathers overlapped the wrong way on one wing!

British Birds

Established 1907; incorporating 'The Zoologist', established 1843

Unequal sex-ratio, mortality causes and pollutant residues in Long-eared Owls in Britain

I. Wyllie, L. Dale and I. Newton

ABSTRACT Recent reports have indicated an uneven sex-ratio among wintering Long-eared Owls *Asio otus*, in favour of males in Norway and females in Britain. Harvey & Riddiford (1990)

A breeding record of Moustached Warblers *Acrocephalus melanopogon* in Cambridgeshire has now been rejected after virtually every leading ornithologist of the day had (at times reluctantly) accepted them! On the theme of assessment of records, the 1950s and 1960s brought not only plans for a new handbook – *The Birds of the Western Palearctic* (or *BWP*), but also the formation of the British Birds Rarities Committee.

BB – 100 NOT OUT!

Underwater images from bird-borne cameras provide clue to poor breeding success of Shags in 2005

Yutaka Watanuki, Akinori Takahashi, Francis Daunt, Katsufumi Sato, Nobuyuki Miyazaki and Sarah Wanless

ABSTRACT The first underwater digital photographs obtained by cameras carried by Shags *Phalacrocorax aristotelis* showed the birds diving in areas dominated by soft coral *Alcyonium digitatum* and feeding on butterfish *Pholis gunnellus*, which were brought to the surface before being swallowed. Prey capture rates were markedly lower than previous estimates for birds feeding on sandeels *Ammodytes*. This reduced foraging performance probably contributed to the very poor breeding success at the colony on the Isle of May in 2005.

BB is dedicated to making scientific discoveries accesible to the modern birdwatcher.

No longer would the acceptance (or rejection) of records relating to rare birds be a matter for the editor of *BB*; now the decision would become one of assessment by leading field ornithologists of the day and the annual report would be published in *BB*. The BBRC report, together with, the report of the Rare Breeding Birds Panel from the early 1970s, helped to firmly establish *BB* as the recognised journal of record in British ornithology. This remains one of its core themes today, though in the past 10–15 years, with the advent of digital photography and the communications revolution, a new, electronic, era in record assessment has arrived.

Like all journals and magazines, *BB* has had difficult times – paper shortages in the second world war; excessively late publication in the 1950s; competition with other publications as birdwatching grew ever more popular in the 1980s and 1990s; and, at various times in its history, changes of publisher/owner and attendant financial problems.

Typically, the periods of crisis have come with the departure of a particularly long-standing or influential editor or publisher, and the deaths of both Harry Witherby and Bernard Tucker shook the very foundations of *BB*. Now in its 100th year, *BB* is, once again, on a sound footing, under new directorship and owners since 2000 and with exciting new projects in the pipeline.

As we look to the future, it is unclear whether, in 50 or 100 years time, the format of *BB* will remain as a paper-based journal or (more likely) be available in some form of electronic media; but whatever its format, there will still be a demand for its key functions, as journal of record and a forum for well-researched contributions on all aspects of ornithology. Everyone involved with *BB* believes that, at the very least, Harry Witherby's vision for the journal remains intact. We hope that subscribers and readers agree.

For more details of *BB*, visit the website — www.britishbirds.co.uk — where you can download a sample copy of *BB* or request a sample copy. Alternatively, phone Hazel Jenner on (01424) 755 155.

Bob Scott is currently a *British Birds* trustee and director. Roger Riddington is Editor.

ENGLISH LANGUAGE BIRD MAGAZINES

RECOGNISING that birdwatchers in Great Britain increasingly want information about birds and birding opportunities overseas, we have compiled this Directory of English language magazines (a mix of commercial and society-based titles). We welcome further reader recommendations for future Editions of *The Yearbook*.

GREAT BRITAIN

BirdingASIA

Described as the bulletin of the Oriental Bird Club, *BirdingASIA* is published twice a year for the group's expanding membership in Britain and around the globe. It provides a forum for articles on the avifauna of the Oriental zoogeographic area (from Indonesia in the south to Russia's Kamchatka region and west to Pakistan).

Regular features include bird identification, taxonomy, birding hotspots, species under threat, pioneers of Oriental ornithology, news, book reviews and letters.

Editor: OBC Publications Committee.
Contact details: Oriental Bird Club, PO Box 324 Bedford MK42 0WG.
E-mail: mail@orientalbirdclub.org
www.orientalbirdclub.org

Birding World

A full-colour monthly magazine that caters for keener birders interested in rarities, identification, status, taxonomy and overseas birding. Each monthly issue details the most significant bird sightings in Britain and the remainder of the Western Palearctic. Other regulars features include ground-breaking identification articles and accounts of overseas birding trips.

Editor: Steve Gantlett.
Contact details: *Birding World*, Sea Lawn, Coast Road, Cley-next-the-Sea, Holt, Norfolk NR25 7RZ. Tel: 01263 740 913.
E-mail: Steve@birdingworld.co.uk
www.birdingworld.co.uk

Birds

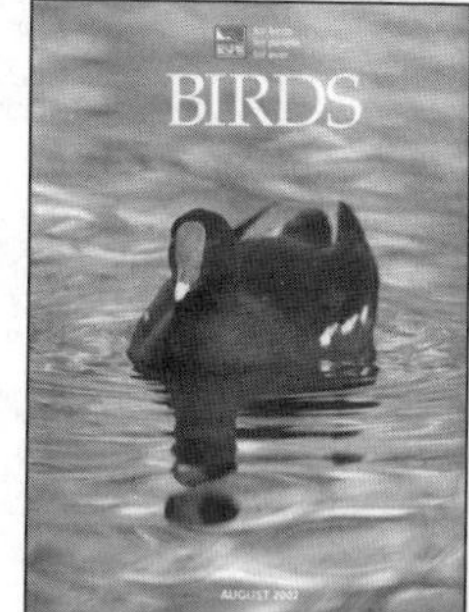

The quarterly members-only magazine issued by the Royal Society for the Protection of Birds is a full-colour super-A4 magazine that promotes the organisation's work in conservation and education.

In addition to an extensive general news section, the magazine carries features on RSPB reserves, international initiatives with partner organisations, tips on developing birdwatching skills, members' letters and book reviews. *Birds* is available on tape for visually-impaired members.

Editor: Rob Hume.
Contact details: Birds magazine, The Lodge, Sandy, Bedfordshire SG19 2DL.
Tel: 01767 680 551. www.rspb.org.uk

Birds Illustrated

A subscription-only quarterly A4 publication, *Birds Illustrated* strives to be different to the practical advice magazines in Britain with its emphasis on the aesthetic appreciation of wild birds anywhere in the world.

In-depth articles cover a broad range of ornithological topics, both current and historical, with regular features on leading

ENGLISH LANGUAGE BIRD MAGAZINES

bird artists and photographers. A regular column on secondhand books is a unique feature.

The publishers sponsor a number of art awards at exhibitions staged by the Society of Wildlife Artists, the British Decoy and Bird Carving Association, British Birdwatching Fair and the National Exhibition of Wildlife Art.

Editor: David Cromack.

Contact details: Buckingham Press Ltd, 55 Thorpe Park Road, Peterborough PE3 6LJ. 01733 561 739.
E-mail: editor@ buckinghampress.com
www.birdsillustrated.com

Bird Table

This quarterly A4 magazine is sent free to all participants in the British Trust for Ornithology's Garden Birdwatch survey, which is sponsored by CJ Wildbird Foods.

It presents a seasonal round-up of the most significant garden bird sightings, plus features on individual species, bird behaviour, bird feeding, migration, items from Garden Birdwatch participants, news and Q&A pages.

Editors: Graham Appleton, Dawn Balmer, Nigel Clark, Su Gough, Peter Lack, Mike Toms and Derek Toomer.

Contact details: To join the BTO/CJ Garden Birdwatch survey, write to British Trust for Ornithology, The Nunnery, Thetford, Norfolk IP24 2BR or phone 01842 750 050.
Website: www.bto.org/gbw

Birdwatch

A monthly full-colour A4 magazine, *Birdwatch* is available on subscription and from a limited number of newsagents and specialist outlets such as bird reserves. Contains a range

of features on identification, birding tips, UK and foreign birding areas and taxonomic issues.

Also contains news, events, readers' letters, product reviews and summaries of British, Irish and Western Palearctic bird sightings. The magazine organises the Swarovski-sponsored Bird Artist of the Year competition.

Editor: Dominic Mitchell.

Contact details: Solo Publishing Ltd, The Chocolate Factory, 5 Clarendon Road, London N22 6XJ. Tel: 020 8881 0550. Fax: 020 8881 0990. Email: editorial@birdwatch.co.uk
www.birdwatch.co.uk

Bird Watching

Britain's best-selling monthly bird magazine since its launch in 1986, *Bird Watching* is available from all leading newsagents and on subscription. This A4 full-colour title caters for all active birdwatchers and underwent a major revamp in October 2006 under the direction of its new editor, Kevin Wilmot.

Every issue contains articles on garden birds and identification, plus news, readers' letters, and the *Go Birding* pull-out guide to bird walks and reserves. Individual product reviews, plus surveys of leading optical products. The annual travel supplement *Destinations* appears with the November issue. The magazine is a co-organiser of the International Wildbird Photographer competition.

Editor: Kevin Wilmot.

Contact details: *Bird Watching,* Media House, Lynchwood, Peterborough PE2 6EA. Tel: 01733 468 201. E-mail: kevin.wilmot@emap.com
www.birdwatching.co.uk

ENGLISH LANGUAGE BIRD MAGAZINES

British Birds

This well respected subscription-only A5 journal of record celebrated its centenary of publication in 2007. Throughout its long history it has always aimed to publish material on behaviour, conservation, distribution, ecology, identification, status and taxonomy for birders throughout the Western Palearctic.

Organises the BB Bird Photograph of the Year competition. Publishes the annual report of the British Birds Rarities Committee.

Editor: Roger Riddington.

Contact details: Editor, *British Birds*, Spindrift, Eastshore, Virkie, Shetland ZE3 9JS. Tel: 01950 460 080.
E-mail: editor@britishbirds.co.uk
www.britishbirds.co.uk

BTO News

A bi-monthly A4 colour magazine sent to all members of the British Trust for Ornithology. Features include articles about the full range of BTO research projects, articles of general interest based on BTO research, plus the status of various species, book reviews and an events guide.

Editor: Derek Toomer.

Contact details: BTO, The Nunnery, Thetford, Norfolk IP24 2PU. Tel; 01842 750 050.
E-mail: btonews@bto.org
Website: www.bto.org

Forktail

Described as the journal of Asian ornithology, *Forktail* is published annually by the Oriental Bird Club. It contains original papers in the English language (occasionally also English translations of papers in Oriental languages) treating any aspect of the ornithology (e.g. distribution, biology, conservation, identification) of the same region covered by its sister publication *BirdingASIA*.
All submissions are reviewed by referees and the *Forktail* editorial committee.

Senior Editor: Suhel Quader.

Contact details: Oriental Bird Club, PO Box 324 Bedford MK42 0WG.
E-mail: mail@orientalbirdclub.org
Website: www.orientalbirdclub.org

Sandgrouse

This journal is produced twice yearly and is sent to all members of the Ornithological Society of the Middle East in Britain and overseas. Content is very varied and includes the latest birding and conservation news from the Middle East, Caucausus and central Asia, recent sightings as well as major feature articles on birding, identification, research and guides to birding sites in the region.

Some of the feature articles from past bulletins may be found on the OSME website.

Editor: Michael Blair.

Contact: www.osme.org

World Birdwatch

The long-established quarterly subscription-only magazine from BirdLife International promotes global bird conservation activities.

An extensive round-up of world bird-related news regularly includes exciting reports of new bird species discoveries and rediscoveries, and is supported by features on birdwatching hotspots, Red Data species profiles, and articles

on all aspects of conservation.
Editor: Martin Fowlie.
Contact details: BirdLife International, Wellbrook Court, Girton Road, Cambridge CB3 0NA.
E-mail: birdlife@birdlife.org www.birdlife.org

FINLAND

Alula

Started in 1995, Alula is an independent journal for people interested in birds and bird identification. Regular topics include ID papers by field experts, articles about birding sites, tests of optical equipment, literature reviews, competitions and current birding issues.

In order to widen its sales appeal, this high-quality quarterly A4 magazine is now available in an English-language edition as well as Finnish.
Editor: Rami Lindroos.
Contact details: Alula Oy, P.O. Box 68, FI-02101 Espoo, Finland. E-mail: alula@alula.fi www.alula.fi

HOLLAND

Dutch Birding

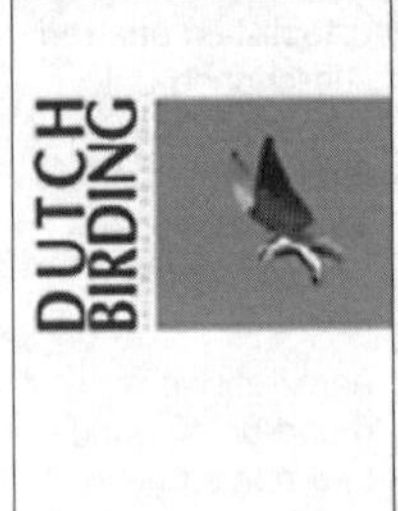

Many of the articles in this long-established bi-monthly A5 journal catering for serious birders and twitchers are published in English, and the Dutch pieces generally have an English summary.
Regular topics include ID papers by field experts, extensive coverage of scarcer birds in Holland and the Western Palearctic generally, literature reviews, competitions and current birding issues. Good range of quality rarity photographs.
Editor: Arnoud van den Berg.
Contact details:
E-mail: editors@dutchbirding.nl
www.dutchbirding.nl

INDIA

Indian Birds

Despite its name, this bi-monthly A4 journal (colour cover/mono inside), publishes articles on bird behaviour, ecology and conservation, birding sites, plus notes about birds throughout Afghanistan, Bangladesh, Bhutan, India, the Maldives, Myanmar, Nepal, Pakistan and Sri Lanka.

First published in 2005, *Indian Birds* provides details of Indian bird conservation groups and web-based e-mail groups in each issue, as part of its mission to encourage awareness of birdwatching among the general public in the region.
Editor: Aasheesh Pittie.
Contact details: Indian Birds, c/o The New Ornis Foundation, PO Box 2, Banjar Hills, Hyderabad 500034, India. E-mail: editor@indianbirds.in

SOUTH AFRICA

Africa Birds & Birding

This award-winning glossy A4 bi-monthly colour magazine, first published in 1994, enjoys support from BirdLife South Africa and several other non-governmental groups but remains totally independent.
The publishers (Africa Geographic

ENGLISH LANGUAGE BIRD MAGAZINES

Pty Ltd) strives to foster an awareness of the continent's birdlife and encourages birdwatching as a pastime and for its ecotourism potential.

High quality photographic features on birds and habitats, mainly in southern Africa, are included along with articles on sites, book and product reviews, news and letters.

Editor: Eve Gracie.

Contact details: P O Box 44223, Claremont 7735, Cape Town, South Africa.

E-mail: eve@africageographic.com

Website: www.africageographic.com

USA

Birder's World

A bi-monthly magazine for birdwatchers who actively look for wild birds in the field. It concentrates on where to find, how to attract, and how to identify wild birds, and on how to understand what they do.

It carries features on individual bird species, hotspots across the globe, local birding hotspots in North America, conservation issues, bird behaviour, book and product reviews. Also features a question-and-answer column, and readers' letters and photography.

Editor: Charles J. Hagner.

Contact details: Kalmbach Publishing Co., Birder's World editorial dept, PO Box 1612, Waukesha, WI 53187-1612, USA.

E-mail: mail@birdersworld.com

www.birdersworld.com

Birding

Issued exclusively to members six times a year by the American Birders Association, a not-for-profit organisation that aims to help field birders develop their knowledge, skills and enjoyment of wild birds.

The organisation (membership open to all birdwatchers) also encourages the conservation of birds and their habitats. In practice this means the magazine carries full-colour features on bird-finding in the USA and Canada, in-depth ID articles, book and product reviews, photo quizzes, fieldcraft, taxonomy and conservation articles.

Birding now features substantial online content, available free of charge at www.americanbirding.org/pubs/birding/archives/.

Editor: Ted Floyd.

Contact details: American Birding Association, PO Box 7974, Boulder, CO 80306 - 7974, USA.

www.americanbirding.org

Bird Watcher's Digest

This pocket-sized full-colour bi-monthly magazine is unashamedly populist in its approach and features a high proportion of articles about backyard birding and readers' birding tales as well as helpful advice on ID and fieldcraft.

Top birding areas in North America and abroad are spotlighted and Book Notes covers the latest publications.

Subscribers get free access to additional material on the magazine's website, which also features a birding blog (Bill of the Birds) and a series of podcasts, called This Birding Life.

Editor: William H Thompson III.

Contact details: Bird Watcher's Digest, PO Box 110, Marietta, Ohio 45750, USA.

E-mail: editor@birdwatchersdigest.com

www.birdwatchersdigest.com

MAKE IT COUNT

JOINING IN THE NEW BIRD ATLAS

BTO staff members Dawn Balmer and Graham Appleton explain the scope and importance of the new Atlas of Birds of Britain and Ireland and urge all birdwatchers to get involved.

EFFECTIVE bird conservation depends on reliable data and the organisers of the new Bird Atlas have worked hard to make it easier for recreational birdwatchers to get involved. 2008 is the first full year of the new Atlas, so if you have Willow Tits breeding close by, there are Tawny Owls hooting in a local wood or you spot a Whinchat while walking in the hills, then the Atlas team want to hear from you.

New technologies have allowed a change of emphasis; equal attention will be paid to systematic surveys of specified tetrads (2km by 2km squares) and to the every-day birdwatching records ('Roving Records') that we all collect in our notebooks and that many of us store electronically.

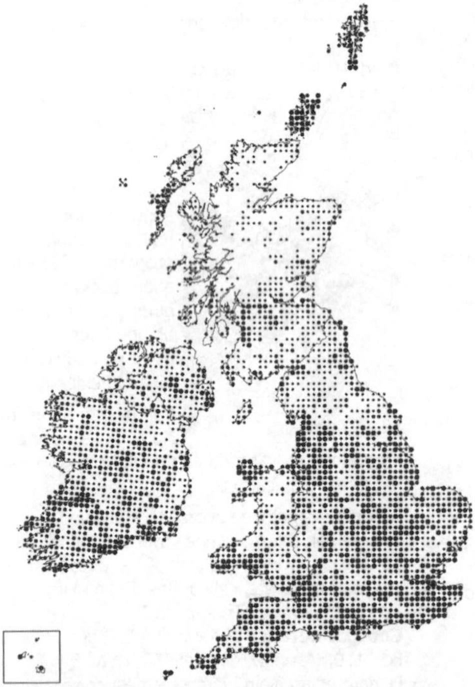

Working in partnership once more, the British Trust for Ornithology, Scottish Ornithologists Club and BirdWatch Ireland launched a combined winter and breeding Atlas of the Birds of Britain and Ireland in November 2007.

This is the first 'where and what' update since the New Breeding Atlas (1988-91) and the Winter Atlas (1981-84), so it will provide a chance to see how climate and habitat changes have affected bird distributions for every county of Britain and Ireland.

As in previous Atlases, birdwatchers who take on tetrads will also be contributing information on bird numbers, which will provide updates on hot-spots for individual

Where are we going to find wintering Snipe? The 1981-84 Winter Atlas shows Snipe as a widespread wintering bird, with local populations bolstered by arrivals from Iceland, Scandinavia and Europe. Do you still see Snipe in your square - just 25 years later?

species and for guilds of birds that rely on key habitats. Sadly, we can predict some results; for example, the red areas for Swallow will have disappeared from much of East Anglia and the Willow Tit map for the south-east of England will be almost totally devoid of colour.

The changes in distribution between the first Breeding Atlas of 1968-72 and the second in 1988-91 pinpointed several species of common birds that were silently disappearing. The timing of the two surveys encapsulated the period of massive decline for species such as Sky Larks, Corn Buntings and Tree Sparrows, and the alarming changes highlighted in the second Atlas helped to set new farmland conservation priorities.

The new Atlas will evaluate whether the contraction of the ranges of farmland species has been arrested and look for new patterns. We expect to see big changes for woodland species, based on local reports of declines but an expansion of species that have enjoyed our milder winters.

Most conservation targets in this country relate to breeding birds, with only the Wetland Bird Survey (organised by BTO staff on behalf of a BTO, Wildfowl and Wetlands Trust, Royal Society for the Protection of Birds & Joint Nature Conservancy Council partnership), and the WWT's Goose Monitoring Programme, providing annual information about winter bird populations, and only for specific sites.

The British Isles provide vital winter habitats for other species too, such as finches, buntings, thrushes, Starlings, plovers and Woodcock, drawn here from across Europe and Scandinavia, from Iceland, Greenland and eastern Canada. Information about how numbers and distributions have changed since the last winter Atlas project in the period 1981 to 1984 will attract much international interest.

Plotting changes in distribution

The Atlas Project will draw upon all of the records that are held within the BTO database, including BirdTrack (www.birdtrack.net) and Garden BirdWatch. As the Atlas project starts to unfold, new maps of bird distributions will become available on the Atlas website.

Many of the three million or more British people who profess to be interested in birds will be fascinated to see how distributions have changed. We know that we will see the shrinkage of breeding areas of Corn Crake but there will be a massive spread of Buzzards to balance the picture, and there will be less obvious changes that we can only guess at.

Closer to home, we hope that Bird Atlas 2007-11 will give us a much better picture of what is happening to urban birds than its predecessors. Across the UK, the area taken up by gardens is twice that within nature reserves, providing the potential for wildlife-friendly gardeners to make a real difference for red-listed species such as Song Thrush and Spotted Flycatcher.

Mild winters since the Atlas of 1988-91 have been good for species such as Nuthatch, Great Spotted Woodpecker and Green Woodpecker and garden birdwatchers, particularly those who submit their records through the BTO/CJ Garden BirdWatch scheme, will be able to show just how many new areas have been colonised in the last 20 years. There is no better way to prove that Great Spotted Woodpeckers are breeding in a particular square than to mark the box which says "family party seen".

According to recent Breeding Bird Survey results, covering just a few squares where Wood Warblers breed, we may have lost up two-thirds of breeding pairs since 1994. How many spots will have disappeared from this map, taken from the 1988-91 Breeding Atlas?

How can you join in Bird Atlas 2007-11? If you feel like taking responsibility for surveying a tetrad, either locally or one that you visit on your holidays, you can find the local Atlas organiser by visiting www.birdatlas.net or by contacting Dawn Balmer (Atlas Co-ordinator) at BTO headquarters in Thetford.

To submit your 'Roving Records', either use the input facilities on the website or simply ask for a supply of record forms and, if you want your garden to be part of the next Bird Atlas, why not consider joining BTO/CJ Garden BirdWatch?

Taking on both winter and breeding Atlases at the same time makes this a particularly ambitious project. However, there are advantages, in terms of an ability directly to compare summer and winter results, and we hope that birdwatchers will find it interesting to report on their 'patches' across complete years. If earlier patterns are repeated, new people will get involved in bird and habitat monitoring and they will maintain their commitment for years to come – hopefully through to the next Atlas in 2027!

Local Atlases in the pipeline

Rob Fuller, Head of the BTO's Habitat Research Department, has been talking about the plans for the 2007-11 Bird Atlas for several years. Early notice of the timing of fieldwork has enabled many local bird clubs to plan their own local Atlases, with the aim of achieving complete coverage of tetrads, during the same time period.

The following Atlas projects are hoping to take place during 2008, though at the time of writing, some plans are still tentative: Bedfordshire, Berkshire, Buckinghamshire, Cambridgeshire, Carmarthenshire, Ceredigion, Cumbria, Glamorgan, Gloucestershire, Hampshire, Herefordshire, Hertfordshire, Isle of Wight, Kent, Kinross, Lancashire and North Merseyside, London, North Wales (Clwyd, Caernarfonshire, Anglesey, Merioneth), Northumberland, Oxfordshire, Peterborough, Shetland, Shropshire, Suffolk, Surrey, Sussex, and South-East Scotland (Lothian and Borders).

WEBSITES OF VALUE TO BIRDWATCHERS

Keeping abreast of the rapid growth in bird-related websites can seem a daunting task, so take advantage of Gordon Hamlett's trawling of the Internet to find the sites most worth visiting.

THE IMPACT of the Internet on the world of birdwatching has been as far-reaching as in any other field of human activity. A multitude of websites cater for our specific information needs, while more general travel sites can help us plan that perfect holiday.

As years pass, technological innovation accelerates but what does this mean for birders? It is hard to pick up a newspaper at the moment without finding some reference to 'Web 2.0 or Internet 2.0'. When software developers bring out a new product, it is known as version 1.0. Minor upgrades then become versions 1.1, 1.2 etc. When you get a complete rewrite, then you get version 2.0 and so on.

So far we have not seen any major breakthrough apart from the field of video. Whereas a couple of years ago, digital photography was just beginning to kick in, now everyone seems to be uploading their own bit of footage rather than a still shot. Obvious examples where this benefits birders are sequences of birds in flight and those showing unusual bits of behaviour.

A professional (non-bird) photographer I spoke to reckons that anyone can get lucky when they press a stills camera shutter; if they do it often enough, they are bound to take some decent images. It is very unlikely that anyone is going to fluke a good film, so a lot of footage may be very tedious to watch.

Having said that, there is some very good features available, including whole wildlife films that you can watch whenever it suits you. This 'video on demand' doesn't seem to have gone much further though. I have only heard of a couple of birders getting clips sent direct to their mobile phone.

While video has yet to establish itself on birding websites, it has to be said that birding has been revolutionised by digital photography. Take a look at some of the rarity photos appearing in magazines even ten years ago – blurred, grainy shots that were of minimal help in identifying a bird. Just take a look now. Everyone is taking competent shots in abundance and most websites are now full of bird pictures. The latest rarity photos appear online within hours of a bird being found.

As the image becomes increasingly dominant, so the written word continues its decline. A couple of years ago, I applauded the rise of mailing lists, where, subscribers could post a message to everyone else in the circle, and they could then respond in kind. It seemed ideal for disseminating news of bird sightings, group trips, advice on all matters pertaining to birding and so on.

In practice, the bubble has burst, with just a few diehard regulars posting with any degree of frequency. Even the most active British groups – Hampshire and Kent – have descended recently to bouts of petty bickering.

There is one massive exception though. Bird Forum (see below) continues to flourish with more than 61,500 members from around the world at the time of writing. They write on any birding matter that takes their fancy. Friendships are struck up and some of the posters have thousands of messages to their name. It becomes an all-enveloping – and friendly – community.

Blogs – online diaries – continue to appear in huge numbers and frustrate in equal measures. You find something you like, only to discover that it hasn't been updated for three months. I predict that many will disappear or migrate to somewhere like Bird Forum where there isn't the pressure to post on a regular basis.

Probably the biggest problem facing the Internet user is finding the useful sites quickly. There are so many potential websites on offer, it can take many frustrating hours before you finally latch onto the one offering genuine value.

This year's website survey, part of a three year cycle in the *Yearbook*, is designed to point you in the direction of quality sites. It covers everything that doesn't easily fit into the other two categories of 'British birding' and 'Foreign birding' so expect plenty of the arcane and trivial as well as useful.

AN INDEX TO THIS YEAR'S GUIDE

Sites are listed alphabetically under various subject headings, also listed alphabetically.

BIRD ART

www.birdsbirdsbirds.co.uk
www.birdingart.com
www.birdscapesgallery.co.uk
www.carryakroyd.co.uk
www.chrisrose-artist.co.uk
www.ian-lewington.co.uk
www.jamesmccallum.co.uk
www.langford-press.co.uk
www.larsjonsson.se
www.steve-cale-artist.co.uk
www.swla.co.uk
www.thelandgallery.co.uk

Warning! Viewing any of these sites could prove prejudicial to your bank balance. As Oscar Wilde said: "I can resist everything except temptation," and here temptation is

ANNUAL WEBSITE SURVEY

plentiful in the form of some outstanding pieces of wildlife art.

The sites above are a mixture of pages devoted to individual artists and collective sites featuring the works of several. Langford Press publishes an excellent series of books on wildlife art. As well as featuring their titles, there are a series of links to other artist's sites, plus a selection of galleries.

Website browsing allows you to compare and contrast various styles of expression and work out which most appeals to you.Though some sites allow you to buy online, there are usually details of exhibitions and birdfairs where you can view the work in the flesh.

Another word of warning. Drooling over your keyboard does not improve its efficiency.

BIRD RINGING

www.bto.org/ringing/index.htm
This section of the British Trust for Ornithology's web site explains why birds are ringed as well as giving advice if you want to train as a ringer or buy your ringing supplies.

www.eastdalesringinggroup.org.uk/
Among their other activities, the East Dales Ringing Group is involved in colour-ringing the necks of local Greylags and there is a newsletter you can download. Other schemes include local Merlins, Wood Warblers and Pied Flycatchers.

www.euring.org/
This site has details of all the various ringing schemes across Europe so if you find a colour-ringed bird and want to report it, this is the place to start.

BLOGS

Given the ephemeral nature of these beasts, there is no guarantee that these will still be active when you read this section but fingers crossed.

www.birder.pwp.blueyonder.co.uk/
The Gloster Birder is one of those sites that you stumble across occasionally that makes web surfing worthwhile. Nothing too fancy, but the enthusiasm bubbles through. As well as a diary, there are trip reports, recent sightings and site guides.

http://deesidedlybirds.blogspot.com/
Scotland's Deeside gets very little attention compared to the Speyside area, so it's interesting to hear about trials and tribulations of a self-confessed 'Mr Average' of birding exploring areas unfamiliar to most.

www.hi.is/~yannk/diary.htm
This Icelandic diary is part of an excellent website covering all aspects of birding in that country. It is interesting to compare their birding scene – about 15 active birders for the whole country – with ours.

www.peregrinesbirdblog.blogspot.com/
Peregrine's Bird Blog covers the author's birding life in Northern Ireland. He has a huge interest in bird photography and there are links to hundreds of bird photography sites around the world. A browser's delight.

www.skills-bills.co.uk/2007.htm
Tom McKinney's birding diary takes an irreverent look at the Manchester birding scene. Not one to read if you are easily offended.

www.thenaturalstone.blogspot.com/
I know Brian Stone well from my Peterborough birding days and it is interesting to see how his tastes have evolved over the years – the emphasis has now shifted away from birds to encompass other wildlife. A fascinating series of moth and insect pictures.

BOOKS

www.birdbooksdirect.com/index.htm

www.callunabooks.co.uk/

www.cleybirds.com/StopPress1.htm

www.nhbs.com/

www.wildlifebooks.com/

www.wildsounds.com/

Here are some sites to help you keep track of all the new releases.

The last four sites all specialise in selling new wildlife books while the first has a good selection of secondhand books too. Calluna is one of the few dealers in secondhand natural history books to have a website

www.birdjournals.com/
This site specialises in buying and selling old copies of bird reports and other journals, so if you desperately need a 1958 copy of the Cambridge Bird Report to complete your collection, this is a good place to try.

www.eurobirding.com/birdingmagazines/articlesearch.php
If you are looking for literature on a particular species, this site searches the content pages of 12 European magazines, including *British Birds*, *Alula* and *Dutch Birding*, to see if any articles have appeared recently. You can search for a species or family, by English or scientific name, or for the author of the paper.

www.hbw.com/
As well as being one of the defining reference books of the age, *Handbook of the Birds of the World* is also one of the most sumptuously produced. Here on the website, you can see sample plates and articles as well as details of forthcoming volumes.

CELEBRITIES

www.mcq.org/audubon/menu.html
Explore John James Audubon's bird prints in this joint French/English site. The multimedia presentations won't be to everyone's taste but all the plates are there, together with a mini-biography and a selection of useful links.

www.simonkingwildlife.com/
Everything you wanted to know about wildlife film maker Simon King, star of *Springwatch* and *Autumnwatch* on the BBC. There is an online diary, details of the equipment he uses, loads of top quality wildlife photos, discussion groups and a monthly competition.

http://en.wikipedia.org/wiki/Bill_Oddie

http://en.wikipedia.org/wiki/David_Attenborough

The online encyclopaedia Wikipedia, in which anyone can edit the entries, has come in for a lot of stick from academics with respect to the total veracity of some of its entries. That said, here are biographies of Bill Oddie and David Attenborough, together with plenty of links to their programmes on the BBC.

DISCUSSION SITES

www.birdcallonline.com
There is a forums section on this site run by Focalpoint Optics but it was undergoing a major revamp at the time of writing. In its previous incarnation, there were about 4,500 members, though traffic was fairly light.

www.birdforum.net
There are typically 250-350 active threads or discussion subjects each day with topics including advice sought/offered, optics, trip reports, reviews, news, recent sightings, photography, behaviour and just about anything else you care to discuss. The tone is very friendly with offensive posts not tolerated. They even send you an email when someone else replies to a thread you have already contributed to. All the old messages are archived so you can search a huge database of information.

http://dir.groups.yahoo.com/dir/Recreation___Sports/Outdoors/Birding
Many of the discussion groups are hosted by Yahoo and more than 650 are listed here. You can preview each group's activity before you sign up: you will soon find that some groups are quite active with plenty of members, e.g. 936 members of the digiscoping group but only ten members of the Jerusalem Bird Observatory. Tables show the number of messages posted each month and it is noticeable with most groups that these are well down on a couple of years ago.

www.fatbirder.com/links/signpost_and_discussion/mailing_lists.html
Here are details of hundreds of e-mail discussion groups. The groups listed here are devoted to specific ornithological matters or groups of birds such as penguins. For lists dealing with a specific geographical area, check out the relative pages on the Fatbirder site or see below.

www.wildaboutbritain.co.uk
There are 10,000 members and subjects cover all sorts of wildlife topics. Look and feel is much the same as Bird Forum's but there isn't the same level of depth of discussion and expertise.

ANNUAL WEBSITE SURVEY

FOLKLORE

www.owlpages.com/articles.php?section=Owl+Mythology
Owls are one the major bird families when it comes to folklore, with myths and stories from just about every culture. This section of the 'owlpages' site examines many of these stories. The rest of the site contains much useful information about owls in general.

www.mudcat.org/@displaysong.cfm?SongID=1420

http://mysongbook.de/msb/songs/c/cutywren.html

http://tinyurl.com/2khucp

In Celtic mythology, the Wren – the King of the Birds – was hunted on St Stephen's Day (December 26). Here you can find details of the stories, from biblical times onward, and various folk songs concerning Wrens. The first and second links are a discussion on the origins of one of the traditional wren songs and a parody by Les Barker involving Kentucky Fried Wren!

http://urbanlegends.about.com/od/birds/Birds.htm
Today's urban myths (I was told by a friend of friend... is a typical beginning) could well become the folklore of tomorrow. This site discusses some very strange stories that are doing the rounds including 'why doesn't a duck's 'quack' echo?' and various versions of group outings to a zoo with penguins replacing children on the return journey!

INDIVIDUAL SPECIES

www.blackgrouse.info/
www.blackredstarts.org.uk/

www.goldenoriolegroup.org.uk/
Three sites devoted to individual species from groups devoted to their conservation.

www.geocities.com/RainForest/Canopy/6181/gulls.htm
There are probably more gull fanatics than for any other group of birds. As well as discussion, photos and quizzes, there are plenty of links to other gull sites.

www.piskulka.net/Satellite%20tracking.htm
With satellite tracking becoming an increasingly useful tool in understanding the movements of birds, this site looks at a study involving Lesser White-fronted Geese.

http://research.amnh.org/ornithology/crossbills/contents.html
As if it wasn't hard enough separating Crossbills anyway (does the Scottish Crossbill really exist?) there are some Americans who want to split Common (Red) Crossbill even further, with seven types identified. Here you can find sonograms and recordings.

www.roydennis.org/index.htm
The Highland Foundation for Wildlife is involved with radio-tracking Scottish Honey Buzzards and Marsh Harriers. They are also interested in the possible reintroduction of various mammals such as beaver, lynx, wolf and brown bear to the Highlands.

www.seawatch-sw.org/
Collecting data on a variety of species including basking sharks and Mediterranean Shearwaters, Seawatch SW present monthly distribution maps and invites you to submit all your sightings.

LITERATURE

www.bellaonline.com/subjects/3884.asp
www.poetseers.org/themes/poetic_themes/poems_about_birds/
Though neither site is particularly comprehensive, each has a dozen or so bird poems to get you started, including Poe's 'Raven', Lear's 'Owl and the Pussycat' and Keats' 'Ode to a Nightingale'. There is a long-running poetry thread on Bird Forum that is also worth exploring.

http://petcaretips.net/famous-bird.html

http://en.wikipedia.org/wiki/List_of_fictional_birds
It is only when you see lists of birds in literature like this that you start to realise just what sort of impact birds have made on the cultural life of mankind. Subjects here include everything from ancient mythology to comics. Large American bias.

ANNUAL WEBSITE SURVEY

LINKS

http://birdingonthe.net/

www.bsc-eoc.org/links/

www.camacdonald.com/birding/birding.htm

In a time when Google has become a near-universal search engine, sites detailing huge numbers of birding links perhaps don't hold the dominant position they did a couple of years ago. These sites with huge numbers of links are geared more towards North America than Europe.

www.fatbirder.com/
Fatbirder is an excellent starting point whatever you are researching, especially for the UK. It remains the links site of choice.

MISCELLANEOUS

www.birdforum.net/opus
I remain to be convinced by Opus, Bird Forum's new birding encyclopaedia. Anyone can contribute/edit/amend an entry for different birds/locations/optics reviews and in a Utopian world, they will. But I suspect that the initial enthusiasm for contributing will soon dissipate. Listing optics by numbers e.g. 10x42 EL rather than Swarovski 10x42 EL doesn't add to the user friendliness.

www.nzbirds.com/more/nouns.html
I have a friend who insists that the only collective noun for an assembly of birds is 'flock' and that anything else is mere Victorian whimsy. But then he has no romance in his soul and is useless at pub quizzes. This is my favourite list of collective nouns and is sure to include some you haven't come across, such as an 'incontinence' of yellowlegs.

www.rarebooks.nd.edu/digital/heraldry/charges/birds.html

www.sca.org/heraldry/primer/birds.html
Birds have adorned heraldic devices for many hundreds of years. These sites explore some of the devices used, explaining why storks and cranes are shown holding rocks - and arcane names, e.g. a martlet, usually shown without feet and depicting a fourth son.

www.stigc.dk/projects/countinggame/index.asp
How good are you at estimating flock sizes? This wonderfully silly yet addictive game shows various numbers of birds flying across five different backgrounds. All you have to do is work out how many there are. Practice certainly does help. My initial guesses were out by more than 30% but rather too much time later, I had reduced this to under 20% – still rubbish but a better 'rubbish' than before.

http://en.wikipedia.org/wiki/List_of_official_city_birds

http://en.wikipedia.org/wiki/List_of_U.S._state_birds

http://en.wikipedia.org/wiki/National_bird
These are lists of the official (and some unofficial) birds of assorted countries/cities and American states – ideal for quiz nights and crosswords. It does throw up some interesting questions, such as who decided that the Robin was going to be the UK's national bird and the reinforcement of the USA's reputation for problems with irony: the state bird of Utah is the California Gull!

PREHISTORIC BIRDS

www.ucmp.berkeley.edu/diapsids/birds/birdfr.html

www.bhigr.com/pages/info/info_bird.htm

http://en.wikipedia.org/wiki/Fossil_birds

The trouble with researching fossil birds is that evidence is fairly scanty and theories are diverse, if not outright contradictory. And that's just among the scientists. There are also many Creationist, intelligent design and anti-evolution sites and if you research this topic, you could well find yourself involved in religious rather than scientific arguments.

ONLINE MAGAZINES

www.birdsofbritain.co.uk/
Aimed at beginners and improvers, Birds of Britain is beginning to feel its age. There are fewer and fewer new articles and sections that were incomplete a couple of years ago, such as British nature reserves (which still only includes England) haven't been updated. The passion's gone I'm afraid.

ANNUAL WEBSITE SURVEY

www.surfbirds.com/
Just because they trytocramasmuchaspossible ontoonepagewithoutanygreatthoughttolayout doesn't mean that there isn't a lot of good stuff here on Surfbirds. In particular, this is the best place to see pictures of the latest rarities, which often appear within a couple of hours of a bird being found. There are news stories, blogs, features and trip reports too.

OPTICS

www.alula.fi/GB/index.htm
The optic reviews from the respected Finnish magazine *Alula* are probably the most stringent of any published by commercial publications.

www.betterviewdesired.com/
The trouble with most optics reviews is that they are to a greater or lesser extent the subjective opinion of the reviewer. Better View Desired attempts to measure resolution etc. objectively. Some of the results might surprise you.

www.europe-nikon.com/home/en_GB/homepage/broad/site.html

www.kowascope.com/frontend/landing_sports.asp

www.leica-camera.co.uk/nature_observation/

www.opticron.co.uk/

http://steiner-binoculars.co.uk/

www.swarovskioptik.at/index.php?l=en

www.swift-sportoptics.com/

www.zeiss.com/
These are the pages of the major optics suppliers and are good sites to check if you need to know or compare the exact specifications of a particular eyepiece for example. They often have general pages on using and choosing optics.

ORGANISATIONS

www.bou.org.uk/
A facelift has improved the pages of the British Ornithologists' Union's website immeasurably. There are a few scientific papers that can be downloaded free but the main interest is always going to be the official British list. The BOU is guardian of the list and you can read about various changes brought about by taxonomic research as well as viewing the full up-to-date listing of (currently) all 572 species.

www.bto.org/
The British Trust for Ornithology monitors Britain's bird populations via a series of surveys and you are encouraged to take part online. No great skill is needed for example in the garden bird survey but you can also volunteer for full fieldwork. Of most interest to casual visitors is the superb Bird Track, which features animated maps as sightings of winter and summer migrants are entered. You can also download the latest *State of the UK's Birds* report.

www.rspb.org.uk/
This site has improved beyond all recognition since I described it as 'the worst birding website' a few years ago. Well laid out, it has immediate appeal to the casual visitor with the front page offering news stories, surveys, blogs, podcasts etc. Delving deeper brings details of all the reserves (still some work needed here) and British bird species, complete with video clips and sound recordings.

www.the-soc.org.uk/
The pages of the Scottish Ornithologists' Club look much as they did several years ago. They feel really dated, totally lacking in dynamic impact and are in need of a massive make-over. Even something as basic as a few photos wouldn't go amiss. The 'recent sighting' section is six months old, though there is a special section – for members only – which is only a couple of months old. Enough said.

www.wwt.org.uk/
Initial feeling is a good, clean appearance, but where's the content? The bland leading the bland, springs to mind. It's only when you start to look a little deeper that you find something other organisations would do well to copy. All the Wildfowl & Wetland Trust reserves submit regular updated sightings, so you know what you can expect to see at any given time.

PHOTOGRAPHY

www.aabirdpix.com

www.alanmurphyphotography.com

www.avesphoto.com/website/home.htm

www.benhallphotography.com/gallery.htm

www.birds-photos.com

www.birdphotos.dk/indexuk.htm

www.birdphoto.fi

www.juzaphoto.com

www.kitday-uk.com

www.pbase.com/alibenn

www.pbase.com/liquidstone

www.pbase.com/tonbenrob

There are endless numbers of bird photographers with websites. Peregrine's Blog alone (see above) lists more than 400. As you might expect, quality ranges from the mundane to the extraordinary. Three of four years ago, digiscoping – taking pictures through your telescope– was all the rage. As with all things digital though, technology has moved on apace and there has been a wholesale rush to switch to digital SLR cameras, bringing with it a marked increase in the standard of bird photography.

Many sites have one or two pictures that you look at and say 'I wish I had taken that'. The dozen sites listed above cover a wide range of geographic areas and topics; one is devoted to seabirds for example, surely one of the most difficult subjects to shoot well. The quality is so consistently high that you will go one of two ways: either you give up your own dismal attempts in disgust, or you will be truly inspired.

STAMPS

www.bird-stamps.org

Not every species on stamps is identifiable, either through poor labelling, poor artwork or simply no identification given at all. As well as detailing all available bird stamps, some 50 or so identification problems are also addressed here.

www.birdtheme.org

Collecting birds on stamps is by far the most popular theme in philately. This site lists birds by country of issue and species. One nice touch is that hovering your cursor over a thumbnail illustration of the stamp automatically brings up a full sized picture.

VIDEOS

www.birdcinema.com

This is a sort of YouTube but just for bird videos with nearly 600 clips - most lasting well under a minute - at the time of writing. You can upload you own footage or simply watch and rate the efforts of others. Quality tends towards home video rather than professional standard.

www.hbw.com/ibc/

Enjoy 15,000 clips of nearly 4,000 species. There is some amazing stuff here and the overall quality is excellent. The first clip I picked at random showed a huge flock of migrating Black-throated (Pacific) Divers flying past - a fantastic sight when you are used to seeing just ones and twos in Britain. You will need to turn off your pop-up blocker if you have it enabled.

http://uk.youtube.com/watch?v=wfvEgWINUFc

Ourselves as others see us. Not to be taken too seriously.

http://uk.youtube.com/watch?v=X30eJjDZlJ0

Ten brief video clips of birds interfering with sporting events. Warning – contains material that might be distressing to some.

www.wildlifechannel.tv/

This is the video arm of Bird Forum and the unique selling point here is that you can watch entire wildlife films rather than just video clips. And all for free. Quality isn't compromised either, with film producers including the RSPB, Bird Images and Malcolm Rymer. You can change channels as easily as you can on a TV and at the click of a button, you can visit the likes of Alaska, Costa Rica, Cyprus, Taiwan...

DIARY 2008

Red-legged Partridge by Bob Glover

EVENTS DIARY 2008

JANUARY

6 – 27: Slimbridge Celebration of Birds
Illustrated lectures by noted bird experts followed by Sunday lunch in the water's edge restaurant.
6: Swan expert and author Eileen Rees.
13: UK geese and swan populations by Richard Hearn; 20: Birds of Wiltshire by Peter Cranswick
27: Wildlife Health by Ruth Cromie, top wildlife vet. All at WWT Slimbridge (off M5), Glos.
Contact: Caryn Davies on 01453 891 145.

19: Sussex Ornithological Society annual conference
Clare Hall, Haywards Heath, Sussex, by prior booking only.
Contact: E-mail: adrianrspb@btinternet.com

26-27: RSPB Big Garden Birdwatch
Nationwide survey.
Contact: RSPB on 01767 680 551.
www.rspb.org.uk

FEBRUARY

14-21: National Nest Box Week
Contact: E-mail: jeff.baker@bto.org

23: South West England Ringers' Conference. Exeter, Devon
For further details contact Kate Risely – e-mail: kate.risely@bto.org

23: Berkshire & Oxfordshire BTO Members' Conference
Didcot Civic Centre, Didcot.
For further details contact Gemma Baldwin – e-mail: gemma.baldwin@bto.org

MARCH

8: African Bird Club AGM
Venue to be announced.
Contact: E-mail: info@africanbirdclub.org

8: South East England Ringers' Conference, Sussex
For further details contact Kate Risely – e-mail: kate.risely@bto.org

15: BTO/SOC Scottish Birdwatchers Conference
Birnam Arts & Conference Centre, Birnam.
For further details contact Jacqui Kaye – e-mail: jacqui.kaye@bto.org

APRIL

4-6: RSPB Members Weekend
York University.
Contact: E-mail: Anna.saunders@rspb.org.uk

8-10: BOU 150th Anniversary Conference
University of Leicester.
Bookings: Call 01733 844 820 or e-mail: conferences@bou.org.uk

TBC: Lee Valley Birdfair
Lee Valley Park farms, near Fishers Green, Essex. Dates not fixed at time of going to press.
Contact: 01929 702 200 or e-mail: info@leevalleypark.org.uk

MAY

31- June 1: Birdwatcher's Spring Fair & Digital Photo Fair
Middleton Hall, near Tamworth, West Midlands
Contact: Alan Richards at: e-mail: thatruddyduck@hotmail.co.uk or phone 01527 852 357.

JULY

18 – Aug 3: NEWA (National Exhibition of Wildlife Art)
Gordale Nursery, Burton, The Wirral.
Contact: E-mail: NEWA@mtuffrey.freeserve.co.uk or visit: www.newa-uk.com

TBC: Ornithological Society of the Middle East (OSME) AGM
The Nunnery, BTO Thetford – date to be confirmed.
Contact: The Secretary, W J Bartley on 01636 703 512.

AUGUST

15 - 17: British Birdwatching Fair
Egleton Nature Reserve, Rutland Water, Rutland.
Contact: Tel: 01572 771 079 or e-mail: info@birdfair.org.uk
www.birdfair.org.uk

23 – 24: Dutch Birdfair (Vogelfestival)
De Oostvaardersplassen near Lelystad.
Contact: Anna Kemp on +31 30 69 377 64 or e-mail: anna.kemp@vogelbescherming.nl

EVENTS DIARY 2008

TBC: Marwell International Wildlife Art Society annual exhibition
Marwell Zoological Park, Hampshire. Date to be confirmed.
Contact: The Chairman, Pip McGarry at e-mail: pip@pipmcgarry.com
www.miwas.co.uk

SEPTEMBER

6-7: Scottish Nature Photography Fair
Battleby, Perth.
Contact: E-mail: Lorne.Gill@snh.gov.uk
www.snh.org.uk

7 – 13: 12th Pan-African Ornithological Congress
Goudini Spa Conference Center, Western Cape, South Africa
Theme: Birds and People: interaction, utilisation and conservation
Contact: Doug Harebottle, e-mail: info@paoc12.org
www.paoc12.org

TBC: Peterborough Bird Club Birdfest
Ferry Meadows Country Park, Peterborough, Cambs. Date to be confirmed.
Contact: Jane Williams at e-mail: oldrectory@oldrectory.screaming.net
www.pbc.codehog.co.uk

TBC: German Birdfair (Fokus Natur)
Radolfzell, Lake Constance.
Contact: Mrs. Marion Hammerl
e-mail: info@bodensee-stiftung.org.
www.bodensee-stiftung.org

24 – October 5: Society of Wildlife Artists' annual exhibition
The Mall Galleries, Pall Mall, London SW1.
Contact: E-mail: info@mallgalleries.com

OCTOBER

4: RSPB AGM & Members Day
Queen Elizabeth II conference centre, Westminster, London
Contact: E-mail: Anna.saunders@rspb.org.uk

TBC: North-west Bird Fair
WWT Martin Mere, Lancashire
Contact: www.wwt.org.uk

TBC: Hawk & Owl Trust AGM
Skippings Barn, Chiltern open air Museum. Call 0870 990 3889 for details.

25: RSPB Feed The Birds Day
Contact: RSPB on 01767 680 551.
www.rspb.org.uk

NOVEMBER

13 – 16: Australian Birdfair
Leeton, New South Wales.
Contact: E-mail: trust@fivebough.org.au

8: Oriental Bird Club AGM
Venue to be confirmed.
Contact: E-mail: mail@orientalbirdclub.org

DECEMBER

5-7: BTO Annual Conference
Celebrating BTO's 75th anniversary and BOU's 150th anniversary. Theme: Birds in A Changing Environment. Swanwick, Derbyshire.
Contact: E-mail: chris.morley@bto.org

BTO TRAINING COURSES 2008

RESIDENTIAL COURSES

These give a firm grounding in the course topics, and involve extensive practical sessions in the field, plus two day's full board. All held at Field Studies Council centres.

March 14-16: Malham Tarn FSC, Yorkshire;

March 28-30: Derrygonnelly FSC, Co Fermanagh;

April 11-13: Rhyd-y-Creuau FSC, N Wales;

May 28-30: Flatford Mill FSC, Suffolk.

BTO will also stage four Beginners and four Intermediate one-day bird identification courses, scattered through England, Scotland and Wales, plus one-day Bird Survey/BBS/Atlas courses. Dates and venues not fixed at time of going to press.

Visit www.bto.org or contact Su Gough (e-mail: su.gough@bto.org) 01842 750 050.

DIARY – JANUARY 2008

1 Tue	New Year's Day
2 Wed	Holiday (Scotland)
3 Thu	
4 Fri	
5 Sat	
6 Sun	
7 Mon	
8 Tue	
9 Wed	
10 Thu	
11 Fri	
12 Sat	
13 Sun	
14 Mon	
15 Tue	
16 Wed	
17 Thu	
18 Fri	
19 Sat	
20 Sun	
21 Mon	
22 Tue	
23 Wed	
24 Thu	
25 Fri	
26 Sat	
27 Sun	
28 Mon	
29 Tue	
30 Wed	
31 Thu	

DIARY – FEBRUARY 2008

1	Fri	
2	Sat	
3	Sun	
4	Mon	
5	Tue	
6	Wed	
7	Thu	
8	Fri	
9	Sat	
10	Sun	
11	Mon	
12	Tue	
13	Wed	
14	Thu	
15	Fri	
16	Sat	
17	Sun	
18	Mon	
19	Tue	
20	Wed	
21	Thu	
22	Fri	
23	Sat	
24	Sun	
25	Mon	
26	Tue	
27	Wed	
28	Thu	
29	Fri	

DIARY – MARCH 2008

1	Sat	
2	Sun	Mothering Sunday
3	Mon	
4	Tue	
5	Wed	
6	Thu	
7	Fri	
8	Sat	
9	Sun	
10	Mon	
11	Tue	
12	Wed	
13	Thu	
14	Fri	
15	Sat	
16	Sun	
17	Mon	
18	Tue	
19	Wed	
20	Thu	
21	Fri	Good Friday
22	Sat	
23	Sun	Easter Day
24	Mon	Easter Monday
25	Tue	
26	Wed	
27	Thu	
28	Fri	
29	Sat	
30	Sun	British Summertime begins
31	Mon	

DIARY – APRIL 2008

1	Tue	
2	Wed	
3	Thu	
4	Fri	
5	Sat	
6	Sun	
7	Mon	
8	Tue	
9	Wed	
10	Thu	
11	Fri	
12	Sat	
13	Sun	
14	Mon	
15	Tue	
16	Wed	
17	Thu	
18	Fri	
19	Sat	
20	Sun	
21	Mon	
22	Tue	
23	Wed	
24	Thu	
25	Fri	
26	Sat	
27	Sun	
28	Mon	
29	Tue	
30	Wed	

DIARY – MAY 2008

1	Thu	
2	Fri	
3	Sat	
4	Sun	
5	Mon	May Day
6	Tue	
7	Wed	
8	Thu	
9	Fri	
10	Sat	
11	Sun	
12	Mon	
13	Tue	
14	Wed	
15	Thu	
16	Fri	
17	Sat	
18	Sun	
19	Mon	
20	Tue	
21	Wed	
22	Thu	
23	Fri	
24	Sat	
25	Sun	
26	Mon	Spring Bank Holiday
27	Tue	
28	Wed	
29	Thu	
30	Fri	
31	Sat	

DIARY – JUNE 2008

1 Sun	
2 Mon	
3 Tue	
4 Wed	
5 Thu	
6 Fri	
7 Sat	
8 Sun	
9 Mon	
10 Tue	
11 Wed	
12 Thu	
13 Fri	
14 Sat	
15 Sun	
16 Mon	
17 Tue	
18 Wed	
19 Thu	
20 Fri	
21 Sat	
22 Sun	
23 Mon	
24 Tue	
25 Wed	
26 Thu	
27 Fri	
28 Sat	
29 Sun	
30 Mon	

DIARY – JULY 2008

1 Tue	
2 Wed	
3 Thu	
4 Fri	
5 Sat	
6 Sun	
7 Mon	
8 Tue	
9 Wed	
10 Thu	
11 Fri	
12 Sat	
13 Sun	
14 Mon	
15 Tue	
16 Wed	
17 Thu	
18 Fri	
19 Sat	
20 Sun	
21 Mon	
22 Tue	
23 Wed	
24 Thu	
25 Fri	
26 Sat	
27 Sun	
28 Mon	
29 Tue	
30 Wed	
31 Thu	

DIARY – AUGUST 2008

1 Fri	
2 Sat	
3 Sun	
4 Mon	
5 Tue	
6 Wed	
7 Thu	
8 Fri	
9 Sat	
10 Sun	
11 Mon	
12 Tue	
13 Wed	
14 Thu	
15 Fri	
16 Sat	
17 Sun	
18 Mon	
19 Tue	
20 Wed	
21 Thu	
22 Fri	
23 Sat	
24 Sun	
25 Mon	Summer Bank Holiday
26 Tue	
27 Wed	
28 Thu	
29 Fri	
30 Sat	
31 Sun	

DIARY – SEPTEMBER 2008

1	Mon	
2	Tue	
3	Wed	
4	Thu	
5	Fri	
6	Sat	
7	Sun	
8	Mon	
9	Tue	
10	Wed	
11	Thu	
12	Fri	
13	Sat	
14	Sun	
15	Mon	
16	Tue	
17	Wed	
18	Thu	
19	Fri	
20	Sat	
21	Sun	
22	Mon	
23	Tue	
24	Wed	
25	Thu	
26	Fri	
27	Sat	
28	Sun	
29	Mon	
30	Tue	

DIARY – OCTOBER 2008

1	Wed	
2	Thu	
3	Fri	
4	Sat	
5	Sun	
6	Mon	
7	Tue	
8	Wed	
9	Thu	
10	Fri	
11	Sat	
12	Sun	
13	Mon	
14	Tue	
15	Wed	
16	Thu	
17	Fri	
18	Sat	
19	Sun	
20	Mon	
21	Tue	
22	Wed	
23	Thu	
24	Fri	
25	Sat	
26	Sun	British Summertime ends
27	Mon	
28	Tue	
29	Wed	
30	Thu	
31	Fri	

DIARY – NOVEMBER 2008

1	Sat	
2	Sun	
3	Mon	
4	Tue	
5	Wed	
6	Thu	
7	Fri	
8	Sat	
9	Sun	Remembrance Sunday
10	Mon	
11	Tue	
12	Wed	
13	Thu	
14	Fri	
15	Sat	
16	Sun	
17	Mon	
18	Tue	
19	Wed	
20	Thu	
21	Fri	
22	Sat	
23	Sun	
24	Mon	
25	Tue	
26	Wed	
27	Thu	
28	Fri	
29	Sat	
30	Sun	

DIARY – DECEMBER 2008

1	Mon	
2	Tue	
3	Wed	
4	Thu	
5	Fri	
6	Sat	
7	Sun	
8	Mon	
9	Tue	
10	Wed	
11	Thu	
12	Fri	
13	Sat	
14	Sun	
15	Mon	
16	Tue	
17	Wed	
18	Thu	
19	Fri	
20	Sat	
21	Sun	
22	Mon	
23	Tue	
24	Wed	
25	Thu	Christmas Day
26	Fri	Boxing Day
27	Sat	
28	Sun	
29	Mon	
30	Tue	
31	Wed	

YEAR PLANNER 2009

January
February
March
April
May
June
July
August
September
October
November
December

LOG CHARTS

Kingfisher by Tony Bates

CHANGES TO ORDER OF THE BRITISH LIST

an explanation

NEWCOMERS to birdwatching are sometimes baffled when they examine their first fieldguide as it is not immediately clear why the birds are arranged the way they are. The simple answer is the order is meant to reflect the evolution of the included species. If one were to draw an evolutionary tree of birds, those families that branch off earliest (i.e are the most ancient) should be listed first.

Previously the British List was based on Voous Order (BOU 1977), the work of an eminent Dutch taxonomist. However, more than 26 phylogenetic studies, many using DNA analysis, have been published in recent years that together form a large body of evidence showing that the order of birds in the British List did not properly reflect their evolution. A change in order was required.

The British Ornithologists' Union's Records Committee (BOURC) is responsible for maintaining the British List and it relies on its Taxonomic Sub-Committee (BOURC-TSC) to advise on taxonomic issues relating to the species that form the British List. This advice usually takes the form of recommendations relating to the status of a species or sub-species, which sometimes results in 'splitting' (creating two or more species from a single species) and 'lumping' (creating a single species from two or more).

At the end of 2002, BOURC-TSC recommended that the order of species on the British List be changed as it accepted the most likely hypotheses for bird evolution stemmed from the following key characters:

1.That the deepest branch point in the evolutionary tree of birds splits them into the Palaeognathae (tinamous and 'ratites') and the Neognathae (all other birds).

2.That within the Neognathae, the deepest branch-point splits them into Galloanserae (composed of two 'sister' groups – Anseriformes (waterfowl) and Galliformes (turkeys, guineafowl, megapodes, grouse, pheasants etc) and Neoaves (all remaining birds).

3.The World list would therefore start with Palaeognathae, but because only Neognathae occur in Britain, the new British List starts with the Galloanserae, as the deepest split from all other birds (Neoaves).

Within the Galloanserae there are fewer species of Anseriformes than Galliformes, therefore Anseriformes are listed first in accordance with normal custom. The orders of families within these groups remains unchanged, so the British List now starts with Anatidae (swans, ducks, geese), followed by Tetraonidae and Phasianidae (grouse, pheasants, quail and partridges), followed by all remaining families as in the old order (divers, grebes etc).

These recommendations have been accepted by the British Ornithologists' Union who have advised all book, magazine and bird report editors and publishers to begin using the new order as soon as possible and preferably no later than the publication of reports covering the year 2003.

Martin Collinson & Steve Dudley - British Ornithologists' Union

SPECIES, CATEGORIES, CODES AND GUIDE TO USE

Species list
The charts include all species from categories A, B and C on the British List, based on the latest BOU listing. Selected species included in categories D and E are listed separately at the end of the log chart.

Vagrants which are not on the British List, but which may have occurred in other parts of the British Isles, are not included. Readers who wish to record such species may use the extra rows provided on the last page. In this connection it should be noted that separate lists exist for Northern Ireland (kept by the Northern Ireland Birdwatchers' Association) and the Isle of Man (kept by the Manx Ornithological Society), and that Irish records are assessed by the Irish Rare Birds Committee.

The commoner species in the log charts are indicated by the * symbol to help make record-keeping easier.

Taxonomic changes introduced in 2002 mean there is a new order of species (as outlined above). The species names are those most widely used in the current fieldguides (with some proposed changes shown in parentheses); each is followed by its scientific name, printed in italics.

Species categories
The following categories are those assigned by the British Ornithologists' Union.

A Species which have been recorded in an apparently natural state at least once since January 1, 1950.

B Species which would otherwise be in Category A but have not been recorded since December 31, 1949.

C Species that, although originally introduced by man, either deliberately or accidentally, have established breeding populations derived from introduced stock that maintain themselves without necessary recourse to further introduction. (This category has been subdivided to differentiate between various groups of naturalised species, but these subdivisions are outside the purpose of the log charts).

D Species that would otherwise appear in Categories A or B except that there is reasonable doubt that they have ever occurred in a natural state. (Species in this category are included in the log charts, though they do not qualify for inclusion in the British List, which comprises species in Categories A, B and C only. One of the objects of Category D is to note records of species which are not yet full additions, so that they are not overlooked if acceptable records subsequently occur. Bird report editors are encouraged to include records of species in Category D as appendices to their systematic lists).

E Species that have been recorded as introductions, transportees or escapees from captivity, and whose populations (if any) are thought not to be self-sustaining. They do not form part of the British List.

EU Species not on the British List, or in Category D, but which either breed or occur regularly elsewhere in Europe.

Life list

Ticks made in the 'Life List' column suffice for keeping a running personal total of species. However, added benefit can be obtained by replacing ticks with a note of the year of first occurrence. To take an example: one's first-ever Marsh Sandpiper, seen on April 14, 2006, would be logged with '06' in the Life List and '14' in the April column (as well as a tick in the 2006 column). As Life List entries are carried forward annually, in years to come it would be a simple matter to relocate this record.

First and last dates of migrants

Arrivals of migrants can be recorded by inserting dates instead of ticks in the relevant month columns. For example, a Common Sandpiper on March 11 would be recorded by inserting '11' against Common Sandpiper in the March column. The same applies to departures, though dates of last sightings can only be entered at the end of the year after checking one's field notebook.

Unheaded columns

The three unheaded columns at the right hand end of each chart are for special (personal) use. This may be, for example, to cater for a second holiday, a particular county or a 'local patch'. Another use could be to indicate species on, for example, the Northern Ireland List or the Isle of Man List.

BTO species codes

British Trust for Ornithology two-letter species codes are shown in brackets in the fourth column from the right. They exist for many species, races and hybrids recorded in recent surveys. Readers should refer to the BTO if more codes are needed. In addition to those given in the charts, the following are available for some well-marked races or forms - Whistling Swan (WZ), European White-fronted Goose (EW), Greenland White-fronted Goose (NW), dark-bellied Brent Goose (DB), pale-bellied Brent Goose (PB), Black Brant (BB), domestic goose (ZL), Green-winged Teal (TA), domestic duck (ZF), Yellow-legged Gull (YG), Kumlien's Gull (KG), Feral Pigeon (FP), White Wagtail (WB), Black-bellied Dipper (DJ), Hooded Crow (HC), intermediate crow (HB).

Rarities

Rarities are indicated by a capital letter 'R' immediately preceding the 'Euring No.' column.

EURING species numbers

EURING species numbers are given in the last column. As they are taken from the full Holarctic bird list there are many apparent gaps. It is important that these are not filled arbitrarily by observers wishing to record species not listed in the charts, as this would compromise the integrity of the scheme. Similarly, the addition of a further digit to indicate sub-species is to be avoided, since EURING has already assigned numbers for this purpose. The numbering follows the Voous order of species so some species are now out of sequence following the re-ordering of the British List.

Rare breeding birds

Species monitored by the Rare Breeding Birds Panel (see National Directory) comprise all those on Schedule 1 of the Wildlife and Countryside Act 1981 (see Quick Reference) together with all escaped or introduced species breeding in small numbers. The following annotations in the charts (third column from the right) reflect the RBBP's categories:

A Rare species. All breeding details requested.

B Less scarce species. Totals requested from counties with more than 10 pairs or localities; elsewhere all details requested.

C Less scarce species (specifically Barn Owl, Kingfisher, Crossbill). County summaries only requested.

D Escaped or introduced species. County summaries only requested.

	SWANS, GEESE, DUCKS		Life list	2008 list	24 hr	Garden	Holiday	Jan	Feb	Mar	Apr	May	Jun	Jul	Aug	Sep	Oct	Nov	Dec			BTO	RBBP	BOU	EU No
* AC	**Mute Swan**	*Cygnus olor*																				MS			0152
* A	**Bewick's (Tundra) Swan**	*C. columbianus*																				BS	A		0153
* A	**Whooper Swan**	*C. cygnus*																				WS	AD		0154
* A	**Bean Goose**	*Anser fabalis*																				BE			0157
* A	**Pink-footed Goose**	*A. brachyrhynchus*																				PG	D		0158
* A	**White-fronted Goose**	*A. albifrons*																				WG	D		0159
A	**Lesser White-fronted Goose**	*A. erythropus*																				LC	D	R	0160
* AC	**Greylag Goose**	*A. anser*																				GJ			0161
A	**Snow Goose**	*A. caerulescens*																				SJ	D		0163
* AC	**Canada Goose**	*Branta canadensis*																				CG			0166
* A	**Barnacle Goose**	*B. leucopsis*																				BY	D		0167
* A	**Brent Goose**	*B. bernicla*																				BG	D		0168
A	**Red-breasted Goose**	*B. ruficollis*																				EB	D	R	0169
* C	**Egyptian Goose**	*Alopochen aegyptiacus*																				EG	D		0170
B	**Ruddy Shelduck**	*Tadorna ferruginea*																				UD	D		0171
* A	**Shelduck**	*T. tadorna*																				SU			0173
* C	**Mandarin Duck**	*Aix galericulata*																				MN			0178
* A	**Wigeon**	*Anas penelope*																				WN	A		0179
A	**American Wigeon**	*A. americana*																				AW		R	0180
* AC	**Gadwall**	*A. strepera*																				GA	B		0182
* A	**Eurasian Teal**	*A. crecca*																				T			0184
A	**Green-winged Teal**	*A. carolinensis*																					A		1842
* AC	**Mallard**	*A. platyrhynchos*																				MA			0186
A	**American Black Duck**	*A. rubripes*																				BD		R	0187
	Sub total																								

DUCKS CONTINUED			Life list	2008 list	24 hr	Garden	Holiday	Jan	Feb	Mar	Apr	May	Jun	Jul	Aug	Sep	Oct	Nov	Dec				BTO	RBBP	BOU	EU No
* A	**(Northern) Pintail**	*A. acuta*																					PT	A		0189
* A	**Garganey**	*A. querquedula*																					GY	A		0191
A	**Blue-winged Teal**	*A. discors*																					TB	D	R	0192
* A	**(Northern) Shoveler**	*A. clypeata*																					SV	A		0194
A	**Red-crested Pochard**	*Netta rufina*																					RQ	D		0196
* A	**Pochard**	*Aythya ferina*																					PO	B		0198
A	**Redhead**	*A. americana*																					AZ		R	0199
A	**Canvasback**	*A. valisineria*																							R	0197
A	**Ring-necked Duck**	*A. collaris*																					NG	A		0200
A	**Ferruginous Duck**	*A. nyroca*																					FD			0202
* A	**Tufted Duck**	*A. fuligula*																					TU			0203
* A	**(Greater) Scaup**	*A. marila*																					SP	A		0204
* A	**Lesser Scaup**	*A. affinis*																					AY		R	0205
* A	**Eider**	*Somateria mollissima*																					E			0206
* A	**King Eider**	*S. spectabilis*																					KE	A	R	0207
A	**Steller's Eider**	*Polysticta stelleri*																					ES		R	0209
A	**Harlequin**	*Histrionicus histrionicus*																					HQ		R	0211
* A	**Long-tailed Duck**	*Clangula hyemalis*																					LN	A		0212
* A	**Common Scoter**	*Melanitta nigra*																					CX	A		0213
A	**Black Scoter**	*M. americana*																								2132
* A	**Surf Scoter**	*M. perspicillata*																					FS			0214
A	**Velvet Scoter**	*M. fusca*																					VS	A		0215
A	**Bufflehead**	*Bucephala albeola*																					VH		R	0216
A	**Barrow's Goldeneye**	*B. islandica*																							R	0217
	Sub total																									

LOG CHARTS

DUCKS, GAMEBIRDS, DIVERS, GREBES			Life list	2008 list	24 hr	Garden	Holiday	Jan	Feb	Mar	Apr	May	Jun	Jul	Aug	Sep	Oct	Nov	Dec				BTO	RBBP	BOU	EU No
* A	**Goldeneye**	*B. clangula*																					GN	AD		0218
* A	**Smew**	*Mergellus albellus*																					SY	A		0220
* A	**Red-breasted Merganser**	*Mergus serrator*																					RM			0221
* A	**Goosander**	*M. merganser*																					GD			0223
* C	**Ruddy Duck**	*Oxyura jamaicensis*																					BY			0225
* A	**Red (Willow) Grouse**	*Lagopus lagopus*																					RG			0329
* A	**(Rock) Ptarmigan**	*L. muta*																					PM			0330
* A	**Black Grouse**	*Tetrao tetrix*																					BK			0332
* BC	**(Western) Capercaillie**	*T. urogallus*																					CP	A		0335
* C	**Red-legged Partridge**	*A. rufa*																					RL			0358
* AC	**Grey Partridge**	*Perdix perdix*																					P			0367
* A	**(Commom) Quail**	*Coturnix coturnix*																					Q	B		0370
* C	**(Common) Pheasant**	*Phasianus colchicus*																					PH			0394
C	**Golden Pheasant**	*Chrysolophus pictus*																					GF	D		0396
C	**Lady Amherst's Pheasant**	*C. amherstiae*																					LM	D		0397
* A	**Red-throated Diver**	*Gavia stellata*																					RH	B		0002
* A	**Black-throated Diver**	*G. arctica*																					BV	A		0003
* A	**Great Northern Diver**	*G. immer*																					ND	A		0004
A	**White-(Yellow) billed Diver**	*G. adamsii*																					IW	A	R	0005
A	**Pied-billed Grebe**	*Podilymbus podiceps*																					PJ	A	R	0006
* A	**Little Grebe**	*Tachybaptus ruficollis*																					LG			0007
* A	**Great Crested Grebe**	*Podiceps cristatus*																					GG			0009
* A	**Red-necked Grebe**	*P. grisegena*																					RX	A		0010
* A	**Slavonian Grebe**	*P. auritus*																					SZ	A		0011
	Sub total																									

	ALBATROSS, FULMAR, PETRELS, SHEARWATERS, CORMORANTS, FRIGATE BIRDS		Life list	2008 list	24 hr	Garden	Holiday	Jan	Feb	Mar	Apr	May	Jun	Jul	Aug	Sep	Oct	Nov	Dec				BTO	RBBP	BOU	EU No
* A	**Black-necked Grebe**	*P. nigricollis*																					BN	A		0012
A	**Black-browed Albatross**	*Thalassarche melanophris*																					AA	A	R	0014
* A	**Fulmar**	*Fulmarus glacialis*																					F			0020
A	**Fea's Petrel**	*Pterodroma feae*																							R	0026
B	**Capped Petrel**	*P. hasitata*																							R	0029
A	**Cory's Shearwater**	*Calonectris diomedea*																					CQ			0036
* A	**Great Shearwater**	*Puffinus gravis*																					GQ			0040
* A	**Sooty Shearwater**	*P. griseus*																					OT			0043
* A	**Manx Shearwater**	*P. Puffinus*																					MX			0046
A	**Balearic Shearwater**	*P. mauretanicus*																								0046
A	**Macaronesian Shearwater**	*P. baroli*																							R	0048
* A	**Wilson's Storm-petrel**	*Oceanites oceanicus*																							R	0050
B	**White-faced Storm-petrel**	*Pelagodroma marina*																							R	0051
* A	**European Storm-petrel**	*Hydrobates pelagicus*																					TM			0052
* A	**Leach's Storm-petrel**	*Oceanodroma leucorhoa*																					TL	A		0055
A	**Swinhoe's Storm-petrel**	*O. monorhis*																							R	0056
B	**Madeiran Storm-petrel**	*O. castro*																							R	0058
A	**Red-billed Tropicbird**	*Phaethon aethereus*																								0064
* A	**(Northern) Gannet**	*Morus bassanus*																					GX			0071
* A	**(Great) Cormorant**	*Phalacrocorax carbo*																					CA			0072
A	**Double-crested Cormorant**	*P. auritus*																							R	0078
* A	**(European) Shag**	*P. aristotelis*																					SA			0080
A	**Magnificent Frigatebird**	*Fregata magnificens*																								0093
A	**Ascension Frigatebird**	*F. aquila*																							R	
	Sub total																									

LOG CHARTS

	BITTERNS, HERONS, STORKS, SPOONBILL, RAPTORS		Life list	2008 list	24 hr	Garden	Holiday	Jan	Feb	Mar	Apr	May	Jun	Jul	Aug	Sep	Oct	Nov	Dec				BTO	RBBP	BOU	EU No
* A	**(Great) Bittern**	*Botaurus stellaris*																					BI	A		0095
A	**American Bittern**	*B. lentiginosus*																					AM		R	0096
A	**Little Bittern**	*Ixobrychus minutus*																					LL	A	R	0098
A	**Black-crowned Night Heron**	*Nycticorax nycticorax*																					NT	D	R	0104
A	**Green Heron**	*Butorides virescens*																					HR		R	0107
A	**Squacco Heron**	*Ardeola ralloides*																					QH		R	0108
A	**Cattle Egret**	*Bubulcus ibis*																					EC		R	0111
A	**Snowy Egret**	*Egretta thula*																								0115
* A	**Little Egret**	*E. garzetta*																					ET	A		0119
A	**Great Egret**	*Ardea alba*																					HW		R	0121
* A	**Grey Heron**	*A. cinerea*																					H			0122
A	**Purple Heron**	*A. purpurea*																					UR	A		0124
A	**Black Stork**	*Ciconia nigra*																					OS		R	0131
A	**White Stork**	*C. ciconia*																					OR	A		0134
A	**Glossy Ibis**	*Plegadis falcinellus*																					IB			0136
* A	**(Eurasian) Spoonbill**	*Platalea leucorodia*																					NB	A		0144
* A	**Honey Buzzard**	*Pernis apivorus*																					HZ	A		0231
A	**Black Kite**	*Milvus migrans*																					KB	A	R	0238
* AC	**Red Kite**	*M. milvus*																					KT	A		0239
* A	**White-tailed Eagle**	*Haliaeetus albicilla*																					WE	A		0243
BD	**Egyptian Vulture**	*Neophron percnopterus*																							R	0247
A	**Short-toed Eagle**	*Circaetus gallicus*																								0256
* A	**(Eurasian) Marsh Harrier**	*Circus aeruginosus*																					MR	A		0260
* A	**Hen Harrier**	*C. cyaneus*																					HH	B		0261
	Sub total																									

RAPTORS, RAILS AND CRAKES			Life list	2008 list	24 hr	Garden	Holiday	Jan	Feb	Mar	Apr	May	Jun	Jul	Aug	Sep	Oct	Nov	Dec				BTO	RBBP	BOU	EU No
A	**Pallid Harrier**	*C. macrourus*																						A	R	0262
* A	**Montagu's Harrier**	*C. pygargus*																					MO	A		0263
* AC	**Goshawk**	*Accipiter gentilis*																					GI	B		0267
* A	**(Eurasian) Sparrowhawk**	*A. nisus*																					SH			0269
* A	**Buzzard**	*Buteo buteo*																					BZ			0287
* A	**Rough-legged Buzzard**	*B. lagopus*																					RF	A		0290
B	**Greater Spotted Eagle**	*A. clanga*																							R	0293
* A	**Golden Eagle**	*A. chrysaetos*																					EA	B		0296
* A	**Osprey**	*Pandion haliaetus*																					OP	A		0301
A	**Lesser Kestrel**	*Falco naumanni*																							R	0303
* A	**Kestrel**	*F. tinnunculus*																					K			0304
A	**American Kestrel**	*F. sparverius*																							R	0305
* A	**Red-footed Falcon**	*F. vespertinus*																					FV		R	0307
* A	**Merlin**	*F. columbarius*																					ML	B		0309
* A	**(Eurasian) Hobby**	*F. subbuteo*																					HY	B		0310
A	**Eleonora's Falcon**	*F. eleonorae*																							R	0311
* A	**Gyr Falcon**	*F. rusticolus*																					YF	A	R	0318
* A	**Peregrine Falcon**	*F. peregrinus*																					PE	B		0320
* A	**Water Rail**	*Rallus aquaticus*																					WA	A		0407
* A	**Spotted Crake**	*Porzana porzana*																					AK	A		0408
A	**Sora**	*P. carolina*																							R	0409
A	**Little Crake**	*P. parva*																					JC		R	0410
A	**Baillon's Crake**	*P. pusilla*																					VC	A	R	0411
* A	**Corn Crake**	*Crex crex*																					CE	A		0421
	Sub total																									

GALLINULES AND WADERS			Life list	2008 list	24 hr	Garden	Holiday	Jan	Feb	Mar	Apr	May	Jun	Jul	Aug	Sep	Oct	Nov	Dec				BTO	RBBP	BOU	EU No
* A	**Moorhen**	*Gallinula chloropus*																					MH			0424
B	**Allen's Gallinule**	*Porphyrula alleni*																							R	0425
A	**American Purple Gallinule**	*P. martinica*																							R	0426
* A	**Coot**	*Fulica atra*																					CO			0429
A	**American Coot**	*F. americana*																							R	0430
* A	**Crane**	*Grus grus*																					AN	A		0433
A	**Sandhill Crane**	*G. canadensis*																							R	0436
A	**Little Bustard**	*Tetrax tetrax*																							R	0442
B	**Macqueen's Bustard**	*Chlamydotis macqueenii*																							R	0444
A	**Great Bustard**	*Otis tarda*																					US	A	R	0446
* A	**(Eurasian) Oystercatcher**	*Haematopus ostralegus*																					OC			0450
* A	**Black-winged Stilt**	*Himantopus himantopus*																					IT	A	R	0455
* A	**(Pied) Avocet**	*Recurvirostra avosetta*																					AV	A		0456
* A	**Stone-curlew**	*Burhinus oedicnemus*																					TN	A		0459
A	**Cream-coloured Courser**	*Cursorius cursor*																							R	0464
A	**Collared Pratincole**	*Glareola pratincola*																							R	0465
A	**Oriental Pratincole**	*G. maldivarum*																					GM		R	0466
A	**Black-winged Pratincole**	*G. nordmanni*																					KW		R	0467
* A	**Little (Ringed) Plover**	*Charadrius dubius*																					LP	B		0469
* A	**Ringed Plover**	*C. hiaticula*																					RP			0470
A	**Semipalmated Plover**	*C. semipalmatus*																					TV		R	0471
A	**Killdeer**	*C. vociferus*																					KL		R	0474
A	**Kentish Plover**	*C. alexandrinus*																					KP	A		0477
A	**Lesser Sand Plover**	*C. mongolus*																							R	0478
	Sub total																									

	WADERS CONTINUED		Life list	2008 list	24 hr	Garden	Holiday	Jan	Feb	Mar	Apr	May	Jun	Jul	Aug	Sep	Oct	Nov	Dec				BTO	RBBP	BOU	EU No
A	**Greater Sand Plover**	*C.leschenaultii*																								0479
A	**Caspian Plover**	*C. asiaticus*																							R	0480
* A	**(Eurasian) Dotterel**	*C. morinellus*																					DO	B		0482
A	**American Golden Plover**	*Pluvialis dominica*																					ID		R	0484
A	**Pacific Golden Plover**	*P. fulva*																					IF		R	0484
* A	**Golden Plover**	*P. apricaria*																					GP			0485
* A	**Grey Plover**	*P. squatarola*																					GV			0486
A	**Sociable Lapwing**	*Vanellus gregarius*																					IP		R	0491
A	**White-tailed Lapwing**	*V. leucurus*																							R	0492
* A	**(Northern) Lapwing**	*V. vanellus*																					L			0493
A	**Great Knot**	*Calidris tenuirostris*																					KO		R	0495
* A	**(Red) Knot**	*C. canutus*																					KN			0496
* A	**Sanderling**	*C. alba*																					SS	A		0497
A	**Semipalmated Sandpiper**	*C. pusilla*																					PZ		R	0498
A	**Western Sandpiper**	*C. mauri*																					ER		R	0499
A	**Red-necked Stint**	*C. ruficollis*																							R	0500
* A	**Little Stint**	*C. minuta*																					LX			0501
* A	**Temminck's Stint**	*C. temminckii*																					TK	A		0502
A	**Long-toed Stint**	*C. subminuta*																							R	0503
A	**Least Sandpiper**	*C. minutilla*																					EP		R	0504
A	**White-rumped Sandpiper**	*C. fuscicollis*																					WU		R	0505
A	**Baird's Sandpiper**	*C. bairdii*																					BP		R	0506
A	**Pectoral Sandpiper**	*C. melanotos*																					PP	A		0507
A	**Sharp-tailed Sandpiper**	*C. acuminata*																					VV		R	0508
	Sub total																									

	WADERS CONTINUED		Life list	2008 list	24 hr	Garden	Holiday	Jan	Feb	Mar	Apr	May	Jun	Jul	Aug	Sep	Oct	Nov	Dec				BTO	RBBP	BOU	EU No
* A	**Curlew Sandpiper**	*C. ferruginea*																					CV			0509
A	**Stilt Sandpiper**	*C. himantopus*																								
* A	**Purple Sandpiper**	*C. maritima*																					PS	A		0510
* A	**Dunlin**	*C. alpina*																					DN			0512
A	**Broad-billed Sandpiper**	*Limicola falcinellus*																					OA	A	R	0514
A	**Buff-breasted Sandpiper**	*Tryngites subruficollis*																					BQ			0516
* A	**Ruff**	*Philomachus pugnax*																					RU	A		0517
* A	**Jack Snipe**	*Lymnocryptes minimus*																					JS	A		0518
* A	**Snipe**	*Gallinago gallinago*																					SN			0519
A	**Great Snipe**	*G. media*																					DS		R	0520
A	**Short-billed Dowitcher**	*Limnodromus griseus*																								0526
A	**Long-billed Dowitcher**	*L. scolopaceus*																					LD		R	0527
* A	**(Eurasian) Woodcock**	*Scolopax rusticola*																					WK			0529
* A	**Black-tailed Godwit**	*Limosa limosa*																					BW	A		0532
A	**Hudsonian Godwit**	*L. haemastica*																					HU		R	0533
* A	**Bar-tailed Godwit**	*L. lapponica*																					BA	A		0534
A	**Little Whimbrel (Curlew)**	*Numenius minutus*																							R	0536
B	**Eskimo Curlew**	*N. borealis*																							R	0537
* A	**Whimbrel**	*N. phaeopus*																					WM	B		0538
A	**Slender-billed Curlew**	*N. tenuirostris*																								0540
* A	**(Eurasian) Curlew**	*N. arquata*																					CU			0541
A	**Upland Sandpiper**	*Bartramia longicauda*																					UP		R	0544
* A	**Spotted Redshank**	*Tringa erythropus*																					DR			0545
* A	**Redshank**	*T. totanus*																					RK			0546
	Sub total																									

	WADERS (continued), SKUAS, GULLS		Life list	2008 list	24 hr	Garden	Holiday	Jan	Feb	Mar	Apr	May	Jun	Jul	Aug	Sep	Oct	Nov	Dec				BTO	RBBP	BOU	EU No
* A	**Marsh Sandpiper**	*T. stagnatilis*																					MD		R	0547
* A	**Greenshank**	*T. nebularia*																					GK	A		0548
A	**Greater Yellowlegs**	*T. melanoleuca*																					LZ		R	0550
A	**Lesser Yellowlegs**	*T. flavipes*																					LY		R	0551
A	**Solitary Sandpiper**	*T. solitaria*																					I		R	0552
* A	**Green Sandpiper**	*T. ochropus*																					GE	A		0553
* A	**Wood Sandpiper**	*T. glareola*																					OD	A		0554
A	**Terek Sandpiper**	*Xenus cinereus*																					TR		R	0555
* A	**Common Sandpiper**	*Actitis hypoleucos*																					CS			0556
A	**Spotted Sandpiper**	*A. macularia*																					PQ	A	R	0557
A	**Grey-tailed Tattler**	*Heteroscelus brevipes*																					YT		R	0558
* A	**(Ruddy) Turnstone**	*Arenaria interpres*																					TT	A		0561
A	**Wilson's Phalarope**	*Phalaropus tricolor*																					WF		R	0563
* A	**Red-necked Phalarope**	*P. lobatus*																					NK	A		0564
* A	**Grey Phalarope**	*P. fulicarius*																					PL			0565
* A	**Pomarine Skua**	*Stercorarius pomarinus*																					PK			0566
* A	**Arctic Skua**	*S. parasiticus*																					AC			0567
* A	**Long-tailed Skua**	*S. longicaudus*																					OG			0568
* A	**Great Skua**	*Catharacta skua*																					NX			0569
B	**(Gt Black-headed) Pallas's Gull**	*Larus ichthyaetus*																							R	0573
* A	**Mediterranean Gull**	*L. melanocephalus*																					MU	A		0575
A	**Laughing Gull**	*L. atricilla*																					LF		R	0576
A	**Franklin's Gull**	*L. pipixcan*																					FG		R	0577
* A	**Little Gull**	*L. minutus*																					LU	A		0578
	Sub total																									

GULLS AND TERNS			Life list	2008 list	24 hr	Garden	Holiday	Jan	Feb	Mar	Apr	May	Jun	Jul	Aug	Sep	Oct	Nov	Dec				BTO	RBBP	BOU	EU No
* A	**Sabine's Gull**	*L. sabini*																					AB			0579
A	**Bonaparte's Gull**	*L. philadelphia*																					ON		R	0581
* A	**Black-headed Gull**	*L. ridibundus*																					BH			0582
A	**Slender-billed Gull**	*L. genei*																					EI	A		0585
A	**Audouin's gull**	*L. audouinii*																								0589
A	**Ring-billed Gull**	*L. delawarensis*																					IN			0588
* A	**Common (Mew) Gull**	*L. canus*																					CM			0590
* A	**Lesser Black-backed Gull**	*L. fuscus*																					LB			0591
* A	**Yellow-legged Gull**	*L. michahellis*																						A		5927
* A	**Herring Gull**	*L. argentatus*																					HG			0592
* A	**Iceland Gull**	*L. glaucoides*																					IG			0598
* A	**Glaucous Gull**	*L. hyperboreus*																					GZ	A		0599
* A	**Great Black-backed Gull**	*L. marinus*																					GB			0600
A	**Ross's Gull**	*Rhodostethia rosea*																					QG		R	0601
* A	**(Black-legged) Kittiwake**	*Rissa tridactyla*																					KI			0602
A	**Ivory Gull**	*Pagophila eburnea*																					IV		R	0604
A	**Aleutian Tern**	*Onychoprion aleutica*																							R	0617
A	**Sooty Tern**	*O.fuscata*																							R	0623
A	**Bridled Tern**	*O.anaethetus*																							R	0622
* A	**Little Tern**	*Sternula albifrons*																					AF	B		0624
A	**Gull-billed Tern**	*Gelochelidon nilotica*																					TG		R	0605
A	**Caspian Tern**	*Hydroprogne caspia*																					CJ		R	0606
* A	**Whiskered Tern**	*Chlidonias hybrida*																					WD		R	0626
* A	**Black Tern**	*C. niger*																					BJ	A		0627
	Sub total																									

	TERNS continued, AUKS, DOVES		Life list	2008 list	24 hr	Garden	Holiday	Jan	Feb	Mar	Apr	May	Jun	Jul	Aug	Sep	Oct	Nov	Dec				BTO	RBBP	BOU	EU No
* A	**White-winged Black Tern**	*C. leucopterus*																					WJ		R	0628
* A	**Sandwich Tern**	*Sterna sandvicensis*																					TE			0611
A	**Royal Tern**	*S.maxima*																					QT		R	0607
A	**Lesser Crested Tern**	*S.bengalensis*																					TF	A	R	0609
A	**Forster's Tern**	*S.forsteri*																					FO		R	0618
* A	**Common Tern**	*S.hirundo*																					CN			0615
* A	**Roseate Tern**	*S.dougallii*																					RS	A		0614
* A	**Arctic Tern**	*S.paradisaea*																					AE			0616
* A	**Guillemot**	*Uria aalge*																					GU			0634
A	**Brünnich's Guillemot**	*U. lomvia*																					TZ		R	0635
* A	**Razorbill**	*Alca torda*																					RA			0636
B	**Great Auk**	*Pinguinus impennis*																								
* A	**Black Guillemot**	*Cepphus grylle*																					TY			0638
A	**Long-billed Murrelet**	*Brachyramphus perdix*																								
A	**Ancient Murrelet**	*Synthliboramphus antiquus*																							R	0645
* A	**Little Auk**	*Alle alle*																					LK			0647
* A	**(Atlantic) Puffin**	*Fratercula arctica*																					PU			0654
A	**Pallas's Sandgrouse**	*Syrrhaptes paradoxus*																							R	0663
* AC	**Rock (Pigeon) Dove**	*Columba livia*																					DV			0665
* A	**Stock (Pigeon) Dove**	*C. oenas*																					SD			0668
* A	**Woodpigeon**	*C. palumbus*																					WP			0670
* A	**(Eurasian) Collared Dove**	*Streptopelia decaocto*																					CD			0684
* A	**(European) Turtle Dove**	*S. turtur*																					TD			0687
A	**Rufous (Oriental) Turtle Dove**	*S. orientalis*																							R	0689
	Sub total																									

DOVES continued, CUCKOOS, OWLS, NIGHTJARS, SWIFTS,			Life list	2008 list	24 hr	Garden	Holiday	Jan	Feb	Mar	Apr	May	Jun	Jul	Aug	Sep	Oct	Nov	Dec				BTO	RBBP	BOU	EU No
A	**Mourning Dove**	*Zenaida macroura*																							R	0695
* C	**Rose-ringed Parakeet**	*Psittacula krameri*																					RI	D		0712
A	**Great Spotted Cuckoo**	*Clamator glandarius*																					UK		R	0716
* A	**Cuckoo**	*Cuculus canorus*																					CK			0724
A	**Black-billed Cuckoo**	*Coccyzus erythrophthalmus*																							R	0727
A	**Yellow-billed Cuckoo**	*C. americanus*																							R	0728
* A	**Barn Owl**	*Tyto alba*																					BO	C		0735
A	**(Eurasian) Scops Owl**	*Otus scops*																							R	0739
A	**Snowy Owl**	*Nyctea scandiaca*																					SO	A	R	0749
A	**(Northern) Hawk Owl**	*Surnia ulula*																							R	0750
* c	**Little Owl**	*Athene noctua*																					LO			0757
* A	**Tawny Owl**	*Strix aluco*																					TO			0761
* A	**Long-eared Owl**	*Asio otus*																					LE			0767
* A	**Short-eared Owl**	*A. flammeus*																					SE			0768
A	**Tengmalm's Owl**	*Aegolius funereus*																							R	0770
* A	**(European) Nightjar**	*Caprimulgus europaeus*																					NJ			0778
B	**Red-necked Nightjar**	*C. ruficollis*																							R	0779
A	**Egyptian Nightjar**	*C. aegyptius*																							R	0781
A	**Common Nighthawk**	*Chordeiles minor*																							R	0786
A	**Chimney Swift**	*Chaetura pelagica*																							R	0790
A	**White-throated Needletail**	*Hirundapus caudacutus*																					NI		R	0792
* A	**(Common) Swift**	*Apus apus*																					SI			0795
A	**Pallid Swift**	*A. pallidus*																							R	0796
A	**Pacific Swift**	*A. pallidus*																							R	0797
	Sub total																									

	SWIFTS continued, KINGFISHERS, BEE-EATERS, WOODPECKERS, LARKS		Life list	2008 list	24 hr	Garden	Holiday	Jan	Feb	Mar	Apr	May	Jun	Jul	Aug	Sep	Oct	Nov	Dec			BTO	RBBP	BOU	EU No
A	**Alpine Swift**	*A. pacificus*																				AI		R	0798
A	**Little Swift**	*A. affinis*																						R	0800
* A	**Kingfisher**	*Alcedo atthis*																				KF	C		0831
A	**Belted Kingfisher**	*Ceryle alcyon*																						R	0834
A	**Blue-cheecked Bee-eater**	*Merops superciliosus*																						R	0839
* A	**(European) Bee-eater**	*M. apiaster*																				MZ	A		0840
A	**(European) Roller**	*Coracias garrulus*																						R	0841
* A	**(Eurasian) Hoopoe**	*Upupa epops*																				HP	A		0846
* A	**(Eurasian) Wryneck**	*Jynx torquilla*																				WY	A		0848
* A	**Green Woodpecker**	*P. viridis*																				G			0856
A	**Yellow-bellied Sapsucker**	*Sphyrapicus varius*																						R	0872
* A	**Great Spotted Woodpecker**	*Dendrocopos major*																				GS			0876
* A	**Lesser Spotted Woodpecker**	*D. minor*																				LS			0887
A	**Eastern Phoebe**	*Sayornis phoebe*																						R	0909
A	**Calandra Lark**	*Melanocorypha calandra*																						R	0961
A	**Bimaculated Lark**	*M. bimaculata*																						R	0962
A	**White-winged Lark**	*M. leucoptera*																						R	0965
A	**Black Lark**	*M. yeltoniensis*																							0966
A	**Short-toed Lark**	*Calandrella brachydactyla*																				VL			0968
A	**Lesser Short-toed Lark**	*C. rufescens*																						R	0970
A	**Crested Lark**	*Galerida cristata*																						R	0972
* A	**Wood Lark**	*Lullula arborea*																				WL	B		0974
* A	**Sky Lark**	*Alauda arvensis*																				S			0976
* A	**Shore (Horned) Lark**	*Eremophila alpestris*																				SX	A		0978
	Sub total																								

	MARTINS, SWALLOWS, PIPITS, WAGTAILS, WAXWING		Life list	2008 list	24 hr	Garden	Holiday	Jan	Feb	Mar	Apr	May	Jun	Jul	Aug	Sep	Oct	Nov	Dec				BTO	RBBP	BOU	EU No
* A	**Sand Martin**	*Riparia riparia*																					SM			0981
A	**Tree Swallow**	*Tachycineta bicolor*																							R	0983
A	**Purple Martin**	*Progne subis*																								0989
A	**(Eurasian) Crag Martin**	*Ptyonoprogne rupestris*																							R	0991
* A	**(Barn) Swallow**	*Hirundo rustica*																					SL			0992
* A	**House Martin**	*Delichon urbica*																					HM			1001
A	**Red-rumped Swallow**	*H. daurica*																					VR		R	0995
A	**Cliff Swallow**	*H. pyrrhonota*																							R	0998
A	**Richard's Pipit**	*Anthus richardi*																					PR			1002
A	**Blyth's Pipit**	*A. godlewskii*																							R	1004
A	**Tawny Pipit**	*A. campestris*																					TI			1005
A	**Olive-backed Pipit**	*A. hodgsoni*																					OV		R	1008
* A	**Tree Pipit**	*A. trivialis*																					TP			1009
A	**Pechora Pipit**	*A. gustavi*																							R	1010
* A	**Meadow Pipit**	*A. pratensis*																					MP			1011
A	**Red-throated Pipit**	*A. cervinus*																					VP		R	1012
* A	**Rock Pipit**	*A. petrosus*																					RC			1014
* A	**Water Pipit**	*A. spinoletta*																					WI			1014
A	**Buff-bellied Pipit**	*A. rubescens*																							R	1014
* A	**Yellow Wagtail**	*Motacilla flava*																					YW			1017
A	**Citrine Wagtail**	*M. citreola*																						A	R	1018
* A	**Grey Wagtail**	*M. cinerea*																					GL			1019
* A	**Pied (White) Wagtail**	*M. alba*																					PW			1020
A	**Cedar Waxing**	*Bombycilla cedrorum*																							R	1046
	Sub total																									

WAXWING, DIPPER, WREN, CHATS, WHEATEAR			Life list	2008 list	24 hr	Garden	Holiday	Jan	Feb	Mar	Apr	May	Jun	Jul	Aug	Sep	Oct	Nov	Dec				BTO	RBBP	BOU	EU No
* A	**(Bohemian) Waxwing**	*B. garrulus*																					WX	A		1048
* A	**(White-throated) Dipper**	*Cinclus cinclus*																					DI			1050
* A	**(Winter) Wren**	*Troglodytes troglodytes*																					WR			1066
A	**Northern Mockingbird**	*Mimus polyglottos*																							R	1067
A	**Brown Thrasher**	*Toxostoma rufum*																							R	1069
A	**Gray Catbird**	*Dumetella carolinensis*																								1080
* A	**Dunnock (Hedge Accentor)**	*Prunella modularis*																					D			1084
A	**Alpine Accentor**	*P. collaris*																							R	1094
A	**Rufous-tailed Scrub Robin**	*Cercotrichas galactotes*																							R	1095
* A	**Robin**	*Erithacus rubecula*																					R			1099
A	**Rufous-tailed Robin**	*Luscinia sibilans*																								1102
A	**Thrush Nightingale**	*L. luscinia*																					FN	A	R	1103
* A	**Nightingale**	*L. megarhynchos*																					N			1104
A	**Siberian Rubythroat**	*L. calliope*																							R	1105
A	**Bluethroat**	*L. svecica*																					BU	A		1106
A	**Siberian Blue Robin**	*L. cyane*																								1112
A	**Red-flanked Bluetail**	*Tarsiger cyanurus*																							R	1113
A	**White-throated Robin**	*Irania gutturalis*																							R	1117
* A	**Black Redstart**	*Phoenicurus ochruros*																					BX	A		1121
* A	**Redstart**	*P. phoenicurus*																					RT			1122
A	**Moussier's Redstart**	*P. moussieri*																							R	1127
* A	**Whinchat**	*Saxicola rubetra*																					WC			1137
* A	**Stonechat**	*S. torquata*																					SC			1139
A	**Isabelline Wheatear**	*Oenanthe isabellina*																							R	1144
	Sub total																									

	WHEATEARS continued, THRUSHES,		Life list	2008 list	24 hr	Garden	Holiday	Jan	Feb	Mar	Apr	May	Jun	Jul	Aug	Sep	Oct	Nov	Dec				BTO	RBBP	BOU	EU No
* A	**(Northern) Wheatear**	*O. oenanthe*																					W			1146
A	**Pied Wheatear**	*O. pleschanka*																					PI		R	1147
A	**Black-eared Wheatear**	*O. hispanica*																							R	1148
A	**Desert Wheatear**	*O. deserti*																							R	1149
A	**White-crowned(-tailed) Black Wheatear**	*O. leucopyga*																								1157
A	**(Rufous-tailed) Rock Thrush**	*Monticola saxatilis*																					OH		R	1162
A	**Blue Rock Thrush**	*M. solitarius*																							R	1166
A	**White's Thrush**	*Zoothera dauma*																							R	1170
A	**Siberian Thrush**	*Z. sibirica*																							R	1171
A	**Varied Thrush**	*Z. naevia*																					VT		R	1172
A	**Wood Thrush**	*Hylocichla mustelina*																							R	1175
A	**Hermit Thrush**	*Catharus guttatus*																							R	1176
A	**Swainson's Thrush**	*C. ustulatus*																							R	1177
A	**Grey-cheeked Thrush**	*C. minimus*																							R	1178
A	**Veery**	*C. fuscescens*																							R	1179
* A	**Ring Ouzel**	*Turdus torquatus*																					RZ			1186
* A	**(Common) Blackbird**	*T. merula*																					B			1187
A	**Eyebrowed Thrush**	*T. obscurus*																								1195
A	**Dusky Thrush**	*T. naumanni*																							R	1196
A	**Dark-throated Thrush**	*T. ruficollis*																					XC		R	1197
* A	**Fieldfare**	*T. pilaris*																					FF	A		1198
* A	**Song Thrush**	*T. philomelos*																					ST			1200
* A	**Redwing**	*T. iliacus*																					RE	A		1201
* A	**Mistle Thrush**	*T. viscivorus*																					M			1202
	Sub total																									

	WARBLERS		Life list	2008 list	24 hr	Garden	Holiday	Jan	Feb	Mar	Apr	May	Jun	Jul	Aug	Sep	Oct	Nov	Dec				BTO	RBBP	BOU	EU No
A	**American Robin**	*T. migratorius*																					AR		R	1203
* A	**Cetti's Warbler**	*Cettia cetti*																					CW	A		1220
A	**Zitting Cisticola (Fan-tailed Warbler)**	*Cisticola juncidis*																							R	1226
A	**Pallas's Grasshopper Warbler**	*Locustella certhiola*																							R	1233
A	**Lanceolated Warbler**	*L.lanceolata*																							R	1235
* A	**Grasshopper Warbler**	*L.naevia*																					GH			1236
A	**River Warbler**	*L.fluviatilis*																					VW	A	R	1237
A	**Savi's Warbler**	*L.luscinioides*																					VI	A	R	1238
A	**Aquatic Warbler**	*A. paludicola*																					AQ			1242
* A	**Sedge Warbler**	*A. schoenobaenus*																					SW			1243
A	**Paddyfield Warbler**	*A. agricola*																					PY		R	1247
A	**Blyth's Reed Warbler**	*A. dumetorum*																						A	R	1248
* A	**Marsh Warbler**	*A. palustris*																					MW	A		1250
* A	**(Eurasian) Reed Warbler**	*A. scirpaceus*																					RW			1251
A	**Great Reed Warbler**	*A. arundinaceus*																					QW	A	R	1253
A	**Thick-billed Warbler**	*A. aedon*																							R	1254
A	**Eastern Olivaceous Warbler**	*Hippolais pallida*																							R	1255
A	**Booted Warbler**	*H. caligata*																						A		1256
A	**Syke's Warbler**	*H. rama*																								
* A	**Icterine Warbler**	*H. icterina*																					IC	A		1259
* A	**Melodious Warbler**	*H. polyglotta*																					ME			1260
* A	**Blackcap**	*Sylvia atricapilla*																					BC			1277
* A	**Garden Warbler**	*S. borin*																					GW			1276
A	**Barred Warbler**	*S. nisoria*																					RR			1273
	Sub total																									

	WARBLERS continued		Life list	2008 list	24 hr	Garden	Holiday	Jan	Feb	Mar	Apr	May	Jun	Jul	Aug	Sep	Oct	Nov	Dec				BTO	RBBP	BOU	EU No
* A	**Lesser Whitethroat**	*S. curruca*																					LW			1274
A	**Orphean Warbler**	*S. hortensis*																								1272
A	**Desert Warbler**	*S. nana*																								1270
* A	**(Common) Whitethroat**	*S. communis*																					WH			1275
A	**Spectacled Warbler**	*S. conspicillata*																								1264
* A	**Dartford Warbler**	*S. undata*																					DW	B		1262
A	**Marmora's Warbler**	*S. sarda*																					MM			1261
A	**Rüppell's Warbler**	*S. rueppelli*																						A		1269
A	**Subalpine Warbler**	*S. cantillans*																						A		1265
A	**Sardinian Warbler**	*S. melanocephala*																						A		1267
A	**Greenish Warbler**	*Phylloscopus trochiloides*																					NP			1293
A	**Arctic Warbler**	*P. borealis*																					AP			1295
A	**Pallas's Warbler**	*P. proregulus*																					PA			1298
* A	**Yellow-browed Warbler**	*P. inornatus*																					YB			1300
A	**Hume's Leaf Warbler**	*P. humei*																								1300
A	**Radde's Warbler**	*P. schwarzi*																								1301
A	**Dusky Warbler**	*P. fuscatus*																					UY		R	1303
A	**Western Bonelli's Warbler**	*P. bonelli*																					IW		R	1307
A	**Eastern Bonelli's Warbler**	*P. orientalis*																							R	1307
* A	**Wood Warbler**	*P. sibilatrix*																					WO			1308
* A	**(Common) Chiffchaff**	*P. collybita*																					CC			1311
A	**Iberian Chiffchaff**	*P. ibericus*																							R	1311
* A	**Willow Warbler**	*P. trochilus*																					WW			1312
* A	**Goldcrest**	*Regulus regulus*																					GC			1314
	Sub total																									

	FLYCATCHERS, TITS, CREEPERS, SHRIKES		Life list	2008 list	24 hr	Garden	Holiday	Jan	Feb	Mar	Apr	May	Jun	Jul	Aug	Sep	Oct	Nov	Dec				BTO	RBBP	BOU	EU No
* A	**Firecrest**	*R. ignicapilla*																					FC	A		1315
* A	**Spotted Flycatcher**	*Muscicapa striata*																								1335
A	**Red-breasted Flycatcher**	*Ficedula parva*																					FY			1343
A	**Taiga Flycatcher**	*F. albicilla*																								1343
A	**Collared Flycatcher**	*F. albicollis*																							R	1348
* A	**Pied Flycatcher**	*F. hypoleuca*																					PF			1349
* A	**Bearded Tit (Bearded Reedling)**	*Panurus biarmicus*																					*BR*	B		1364
* A	**Long-tailed Tit**	*Aegithalos caudatus*																					LT			1437
* A	**Blue Tit**	*Cyanistes caeruleus*																					BT			1462
* A	**Great Tit**	*Parus major*																					GT			1464
* A	**Crested Tit**	*Lophophanes cristatus*																					CI	B		1454
* A	**Coal Tit**	*Periparus ater*																					CT			1461
* A	**Willow Tit**	*Poecile montanus*																					WT			1442
* A	**Marsh Tit**	*Parus palustris*																					MT			1440
A	**Red-breasted Nuthatch**	*Sitta canadensis*																							R	1472
* A	**(Wood) Nuthatch**	*S. europaea*																					NH			1479
A	**Wallcreeper**	*Tichodroma muraria*																							R	1482
* A	**(Eurasian) Treecreeper**	*Certhia familiaris*																					TC	A		1486
A	**Short-toed Treecreeper**	*C. brachydactyla*																					TH		R	1487
A	**(Eurasian) Penduline Tit**	*Remiz pendulinus*																					DT	A	R	1490
* A	**(Eurasian) Golden Oriole**	*Oriolus oriolus*																					OL	A		1508
A	**Brown Shrike**	*Lanius cristatus*																							R	1513
A	**Isabelline Shrike**	*L. isabellinus*																					IL		R	1514
* A	**Red-backed Shrike**	*L. collurio*																					ED	A		1515
	Sub total																									

	SHRIKES continued, CROWS, SPARROWS, VIREOS		Life list	2008 list	24 hr	Garden	Holiday	Jan	Feb	Mar	Apr	May	Jun	Jul	Aug	Sep	Oct	Nov	Dec			BTO	RBBP	BOU	EU No
A	**Long-tailed Shrike**	*L. schach*																							1517
* A	**Lesser Grey Shrike**	*L. minor*																						R	1519
* A	**Great Grey Shrike**	*L. excubitor*																				SR	A		1520
A	**Southern Grey Shrike**	*L. meridionalis*																						R	1520
A	**Woodchat Shrike**	*L. senator*																				OO			1523
A	**Masked Shrike**	*L. nubicus*																							1524
* A	**(Eurasian) Jay**	*Garrulus glandarius*																				J			1539
* A	**(Black-billed) Magpie**	*Pica pica*																				MG			1549
A	**(Spotted) Nutcracker**	*Nucifraga caryocatactes*																				NC		R	1557
* A	**(Red-billed) Chough**	*P. pyrrhocorax*																				CF	B		1559
* A	**(Eurasian) Jackdaw**	*Corvus monedula*																				JD			1560
* A	**Rook**	*C. frugilegus*																				RO			1563
* A	**Carrion Crow**	*C. corone*																				C			1567
* A	**Hooded Crow**	*C. cornix*																							1567
* A	**Raven**	*C. corax*																				RN			1572
* A	**Starling**	*S. vulgaris*																				SG			1582
A	**Rose-coloured (Rosy) Starling**	*Sturnus roseus*																				OE		R	1594
* A	**House Sparrow**	*Passer domesticus*																				HS			1591
A	**Spanish Sparrow**	*P. hispaniolensis*																						R	1592
* A	**(Eurasian) Tree Sparrow**	*P.r montanus*																				TS			1598
A	**Rock Sparrow**	*Petronia petronia*																						R	1604
A	**Yellow-throated Vireo**	*Vireo flavifrons*																						R	1628
A	**Philadelphia Vireo**	*V. philadelphicus*																						R	1631
A	**Red-eyed Vireo**	*V.olivaceus*																				EV		R	1633
	Sub total																								

	FINCHES continued, NEW WORLD WARBLERS		Life list	2008 list	24 hr	Garden	Holiday	Jan	Feb	Mar	Apr	May	Jun	Jul	Aug	Sep	Oct	Nov	Dec				BTO	RBBP	BOU	EU No
* A	**Chaffinch**	*Fringilla coelebs*																					CH			1636
* A	**Brambling**	*F. montifringilla*																					BL	A		1638
* A	**(European) Serin**	*Serinus serinus*																					NS	A		1640
* A	**(European) Greenfinch**	*Carduelis chloris*																					GR			1649
* A	**(European) Goldfinch**	*C carduelis*																					GO			1653
* A	**(Eurasian) Siskin**	*C. spinus*																					SK			1654
* A	**Linnet**	*C. cannabina*																					LI			1660
* A	**Twite**	*C. flavirostris*																					TW			1662
* A	**(Common) Mealy Redpoll**	*C. flammea*																						A		1663
* A	**Lesser Redpoll**	*C. cabaret*																					LR			1663
A	**Arctic Redpoll**	*C. hornemanni*																					AL		R	1664
* A	**Two-barred Crossbill**	*Loxia leucoptera*																					PD		R	1665
* A	**Crossbill**	*L. curvirostra*																					CR	C		1666
* A	**Scottish Crossbill**	*L. scotica*																					CY	A		1667
* A	**Parrot Crossbill**	*L. pytyopsittacus*																					PC	A	R	1668
A	**Trumpeter Finch**	*Bucanetes githagineus*																							R	1676
* A	**Common Rosefinch**	*Carpodacus erythrinus*																					SQ	A		1679
A	**Pine Grosbeak**	*Pinicola enucleator*																							R	1699
* A	**Bullfinch**	*Pyrrhula pyrrhula*																					BF			1710
* A	**Hawfinch**	*Coccothraustes coccothraustes*																					HF	A		1717
A	**Evening Grosbeak**	*Hesperiphona vespertina*																							R	1718
A	**Black-and-white Warbler**	*Mniotilta varia*																							R	1720
A	**Golden-winged Warbler**	*Vermivora chrysoptera*																							R	1722
A	**Tennessee Warbler**	*V. peregrina*																							R	1724
	Sub total																									

NEW WORLD WARBLERS continued, SPARROWS			Life list	2008 list	24 hr	Garden	Holiday	Jan	Feb	Mar	Apr	May	Jun	Jul	Aug	Sep	Oct	Nov	Dec				BTO	RBBP	BOU	EU No
A	**Northern Parula**	*Parula americana*																							R	1732
A	**Yellow Warbler**	*Dendroica petechia*																							R	1733
A	**Chestnut-sided Warbler**	*D. pensylvanica*																							R	1734
A	**Blackburnian Warbler**	*D. fusca*																							R	1747
A	**Cape May Warbler**	*D. tigrina*																							R	1749
A	**Magnolia Warbler**	*D. magnolia*																							R	1750
A	**Yellow-rumped Warbler**	*D. coronata*																							R	1751
A	**Blackpoll Warbler**	*D. striata*																							R	1753
A	**Bay-breasted Warbler**	*D. castanea*																							R	1754
A	**American Redstart**	*Setophaga ruticilla*																					AD		R	1755
A	**Ovenbird**	*Seiurus aurocapilla*																							R	1756
A	**Northern Waterthrush**	*S. noveboracensis*																							R	1757
A	**Yellowthroat**	*Geothlypis trichas*																							R	1762
A	**Hooded Warbler**	*Wilsonia citrina*																							R	1771
A	**Wilson's Warbler**	*W. pusilla*																							R	1772
A	**Summer Tanager**	*Piranga rubra*																							R	1786
A	**Scarlet Tanager**	*P. olivacea*																							R	1788
A	**Eastern Towhee**	*Pipilo erythrophthalmus*																							R	1798
A	**Lark Sparrow**	*Chondestes grammacus*																							R	1824
A	**Savannah Sparrow**	*Passerculus sandwichensis*																							R	1826
A	**Song Sparrow**	*Melospiza melodia*																							R	1835
A	**White-crowned Sparrow**	*Zonotrichia leucophrys*																							R	1839
A	**White-throated Sparrow**	*Z. albicollis*																							R	1840
A	**Dark-eyed Junco**	*Junco hyemalis*																					JU		R	1842
	Sub total																									

	BUNTINGS		Life list	2008 list	24 hr	Garden	Holiday	Jan	Feb	Mar	Apr	May	Jun	Jul	Aug	Sep	Oct	Nov	Dec				BTO	RBBP	BOU	EU No
A	**Lapland (Longspur) Bunting**	*Calcarius lapponicus*																					LA	A		1847
* A	**Snow Bunting**	*Plectrophenax nivalis*																					SB	A		1850
A	**Black-faced Bunting**	*Emberiza spodocephala*																							R	1853
A	**Pine Bunting**	*E. leucocephalos*																					EL		R	1856
* A	**Yellowhammer**	*E. citrinella*																					Y			1857
* A	**Cirl Bunting**	*E. cirlus*																					CL	A		1958
A	**Rock Bunting**	*E. cia*																							R	1860
A	**Ortolan Bunting**	*E. hortulana*																					OB			1866
A	**Cretzschmar's Bunting**	*E. caesia*																							R	1868
A	**Yellow-browed Bunting**	*E. chrysophrys*																						A	R	1871
A	**Rustic Bunting**	*E. rustica*																							R	1873
A	**Chestnut-eared Bunting**	*E. fucata*																								1869
A	**Little Bunting**	*E. pusilla*																					LJ			1874
A	**Yellow-breasted Bunting**	*E. aureola*																							R	1876
* A	**Reed Bunting**	*E. schoeniclus*																					RB			1877
A	**Pallas's Bunting**	*E. pallasi*																							R	1878
A	**Black-headed Bunting**	*E. melanocephala*																							R	1881
* A	**Corn Bunting**	*Miliaria calandra*																					CB			1882
A	**Rose-breasted Grosbeak**	*Pheucticus ludovicianus*																							R	1887
A	**Indigo Bunting**	*Passerina cyanea*																							R	1892
A	**Bobolink**	*Dolichonyx oryzivorus*																							R	1897
A	**Brown-headed Cowbird**	*Molothrus ater*																							R	1899
A	**Baltimore Oriole**	*Icterus galbula*																							R	1918
	Sub total																									

CATEGORY D & E SPECIES PLUS EUROPEAN SPECIES			Life list	2008 list	24 hr	Garden	Holiday	Jan	Feb	Mar	Apr	May	Jun	Jul	Aug	Sep	Oct	Nov	Dec			BTO	RBBP	BOU	EU No
D	**Ross's Goose**	*Anas Vosii*																							
D	**Falcated Duck**	*A. falcata*																				FT		R	0181
D	**Baikal Teal**	*A. formosa*																				IK		R	0183
D	**Marbled Duck**	*Marmaronetta angustirostris*																						R	0195
EU	**White-headed Duck**	*0. Leucocephala*																				WQ			0226
EU	**Hooded Merganser**	*Lophodytes cucullatus*																							
EU	**Rock Partridge**	*Alectoris graeca*																							0357
EU	**Barbary Partridge**	*A. barbara*																							0359
EU	**Pygmy Cormorant**	*P. pygmeus*																							0082
D	**Great White Pelican**	*Pelecanus onocrotalus*																				YP		R	0088
EU	**Dalmatian Pelican**	*P. crispus*																							0089
D	**Greater Flamingo**	*Phoenicopterus roseus*																				FL		R	0147
EU	**Black-winged Kite**	*Elanus caeruleus*																							0235
D	**Bald Eagle**	*H. leucocephalus*																						R	0244
EU	**Lammergeier**	*Gypaetus barbatus*																							0246
D	**Black (Monk) Vulture**	*Aegypius monachus*																						R	0255
EU	**Levant Sparrowhawk**	*A. brevipes*																							0273
EU	**Long-legged Buzzard**	*B. rufinus*																							0288
EU	**Lesser Spotted Eagle**	*Aquila pomarina*																							0292
EU	**Imperial Eagle**	*A. heliaca*																							0295
EU	**Booted Eagle**	*Hieraaetus pennatus*																							0298
EU	**Bonelli's Eagle**	*H. fasciatus*																							0299
EU	**Lanner Falcon**	*Falco biarmicus*																				FB			0314
D	**Saker Falcon**	*F. cherrug*																				JF		R	0316
	Sub total																								

CATEGORY D & E SPECIES PLUS EUROPEAN SPECIES			Life list	2008 list	24 hr	Garden	Holiday	Jan	Feb	Mar	Apr	May	Jun	Jul	Aug	Sep	Oct	Nov	Dec				BTO	RBBP	BOU	EU No
EU	**Andalusian Hemipode**	*Turnix sylvatica*																								0400
EU	**Purple (Swamp-hen) Gallinule**	*Porphyrio porphyrio*																								0427
EL	**Crested Coot**	*F. cristata*																								0431
FA	**Greater Sand Plover**	*C. leschenaultii*																					DP		R	0479
EU	**Spur-winged Plover**	*Hoplopterus spinosus*																					UW			0487
EU	**Black-bellied Sandgrouse**	*Pterocles orientalis*																								0661
EU	**Pin-tailed Sandgrouse**	*P. alchata*																								0662
EU	**(Eurasian) Eagle Owl**	*Bubo bubo*																					EO	bD		0744
EU	**Pygmy Owl**	*Glaucidium passerinum*																								0751
EU	**Ural Owl**	*S. uralensis*																								0765
EU	**Great Grey Owl**	*S. nebulosa*																								0766
EL	**White-rumped Swift**	*A. melba*																								0799
EU	**Grey-headed Woodpecker**	*Picus canus*																								0855
EU	**Black Woodpecker**	*Dryocopus martius*																								0863
EU	**Syrian Woodpecker**	*D. syriacus*																								0878
EU	**Middle Spotted Woodpecker**	*D. medius*																								0883
EU	**White-backed Woodpecker**	*D. leucotos*																								0884
EU	**Three-toed Woodpecker**	*Picoides tridactylus*																								0898
EU	**Dupont's Lark**	*Chersophilus duponti*																								0959
EU	**Thekla Lark**	*G. theklae*																								0973
EU	**Black Wheatear**	*0. Leucura*																							R	1158
IA	**Eyebrowed Thrush**	*T. obscurus*																							R	1195
EU	**Olive-tree Warbler**	*H. olivetorum*																								1258
EU	**Cyprus Warbler**	*S. melanothorax*																								1268
	Sub total																									

CATEGORY D & E SPECIES PLUS EUROPEAN SPECIES			Life list	2007 list	24 hr	Garden	Holiday	Jan	Feb	Mar	Apr	May	Jun	Jul	Aug	Sep	Oct	Nov	Dec			BTO	RBBP	BOU	EU No
D	**Asian Brown Flycatcher**	*Muscicapa dauurica*																							1335
D	**Mugimaki Flycatcher**	*F. mugimaki*																						R	1344
EU	**Semi-collared Flycatcher**	*F. semitorquata*																							1347
EU	**Sombre Tit**	*P. lugubris*																							1441
EU	**Siberian Tit**	*P. cinctus*																							1448
EU	**Krüper's Nuthatch**	*Sitta krueperi*																							1469
EU	**Corsican Nuthatch**	*S. whiteheadi*																							1470
EU	**Rock Nuthatch**	*S. neumayer*																							1481
EU	**Masked Shrike**	*L. nubicus*																							1524
EU	**Siberian Jay**	*Perisoreus infaustus*																							1543
EU	**Azure-winged Magpie**	*Cyanopica cyana*																							1547
EU	**Alpine Chough**	*Pyrrhocorax graculus*																							1558
D	**Daurian Starling**	*Sturnus sturninus*																						R	1579
EU	**Spotless Starling**	*S. unicolor*																							1583
D	**(White-winged) Snow Finch**	*Montifringilla nivalis*																						R	1611
D	**Palm Warbler**	*D. palmarum*																						R	1752
D	**Yellow-headed Blackbird**	*Xanthocephalus xanthocephalus*																							1911
EU	**Cinereous Bunting**	*E. cineracea*																							1865
D	**Chestnut Bunting**	*E. rutila*																						R	1875
D	**Red-headed Bunting**	*E. bruniceps*																							1880
D	**Blue Grosbeak**	*Guiraca caerulea*																						R	1891
	TOTAL																								

BRITISH DRAGONFLY LIST

SPECIES	2008 list	Life list
DAMSELFLIES		
Calopterygidae (Demoiselles)		
Banded Demoiselle		
Beautiful Demoiselle		
Lestidae (Emerald damselflies)		
Scarce Emerald Damselfly		
Emerald Damselfly		
Southern Emerald Damselfly		
Coenagrionidae (Blue, blue-tailed & red damselflies)		
Small Red Damselfly		
Norfolk Damselfly		
Northern Damselfly		
Irish Damselfly		
Southern Damselfly		
Azure Damselfly		
Variable Damselfly		
Dainty Damselfly		
Common Blue Damselfly		
Red-eyed Damselfly		
Small Red-eyed Damselfly		
Blue-tailed Damselfly		
Scarce Blue-tailed Damselfly		
Large Red Damselfly		
Platycnemididae (White-legged damselflies)		
White-legged Damselfly		
DRAGONFLIES		
Gomphidae (Club-tailed Dragonflies)		
Common Club-tail		
Aeshnidae (Hawkers and Emperors)		
Southern Migrant Hawker		
Southern Hawker		
Brown Hawker		

SPECIES	2008 list	Life list
Norfolk Hawker		
Azure Hawker		
Common Hawker		
Migrant Hawker		
Emperor		
Lesser Emperor		
Green Darner		
Hairy Dragonfly		
Vagrant Emperor		
Cordulegastridae (Golden-ringed Dragonflies)		
Golden-ringed Dragonfly		
Corduliidae (Emerald dragonflies)		
Downy Emerald		
Brilliant Emerald		
Northern Emerald		
Libellulidae (Chasers, Skimmers and Darters)		
Broad-bodied Chaser		
Scarce Chaser		
Four-spotted Chaser		
Black-tailed Skimmer		
Keeled Skimmer		
Scarlet Dragonfly		
Black Darter		
Yellow-winged Darter		
Red-veined Darter		
Ruddy Darter		
Common Darter		
Highland Darter		
Vagrant Darter		
Banded Darter		
White-faced Darter		
TOTAL		

BRITISH BUTTERFLY LIST

SPECIES	2008 list	Life list
Hesperiidae - Skippers		
Chequered Skipper		
Dingy Skipper		
Grizzled Skipper		
Lulworth Skipper		
Essex Skipper		
Small Skipper		
Silver-spotted Skipper		
Large Skipper		
Papilionidae		
Swallowtail		
Pieridae - The Whites		
Wood White		
Clouded Yellow		
Brimstone		
Large White		
Small White		
Green-veined White		
Orange Tip		
Lycaenidae - Hairstreaks, Coppers and Blues		
Green Hairstreak		
Brown Hairstreak		
Purple Hairstreak		
White-letter Hairstreak		
Black Hairstreak		
Small Copper		
Small Blue		
Silver-studded Blue		
Northern Brown Argus		
Brown Argus		
Common Blue		
Chalkhill Blue		
Adonis Blue		

SPECIES	2008 list	Life list
Holly Blue		
Large Blue		
Duke of Burgundy		
Nymphalidae - The Nymphalids		
White Admiral		
Purple Emperor		
Painted Lady		
Small Tortoiseshell		
Red Admiral		
Peacock		
Comma		
Nymphalidae -- The Fritillaries		
Small Pearl-bordered Fritillary		
Pearl-bordered Fritillary		
High Brown Fritillary		
Dark Green Fritillary		
Silver-washed Fritillary		
Marsh Fritillary		
Glanville Fritillary		
Heath Fritillary		
Nymphalidae - The Browns		
Speckled Wood		
Wall		
Mountain Ringlet		
Scotch Argus		
Marbled White		
Grayling		
Gate Keeper		
Meadow Brown		
Ringlet		
Small Heath		
Large Heath		
TOTAL		

DIRECTORY OF ARTISTS, PHOTOGRAPHERS AND LECTURERS

Great Crested Grebe and chick by Nick Williams

DIRECTORY OF WILDLIFE ART GALLERIES

BIRDS BIRDS BIRDS

Paul and Sue Cumberland opened Birds Birds Birds in June 2001. Now it is becoming one of the nation's leading bird art galleries. A steady increase in sales, has encouraged professional wildlife artists to join the roster. Prints are now being produced and published in-house, using the giclee system.
Address: 4, Limes Place, Preston St, Faversham, Kent ME13 8PQ; 01795 532 370;
email: birdsbirdsbirds@birdsbirdsbirds.co.uk
www.birdsbirdsbirds.co.uk

BIRDSCAPES

Offers top quality bird art all year round, plus landscapes and other wildlife originals, sculptures, prints, wildlife art books and cards. More than 30 regular artists, including SWLA members, are represented, with new exhibitions each month. Located next to the Cley Spy optical dealership and offering the opportunity of exploring the Farmland Bird Project on the Bayfield Estate.
Opening times: Mon-Sat, (10am-5pm), Sunday, (10am-4pm). The gallery may be closed for part of the day before a new exhibition.
Address: The BIRDscapes Gallery, Manor Farm Barns, Glandford, Holt, Norfolk. NR25 7JP. 01263 741 742. (Follow the brown signs to Cley Spy from Blakeney Church) .

NATURE IN ART

The world's first museum dedicated exclusively to art inspired by nature. The collection spans 1,500 years, covers 60 countries and includes work by Tunnicliffe, Harrison, Thorburn, Scott and other bird artists. See work being created by artists in residence (see website for dates), plus a vibrant exhibitions programme. Sculpture garden, coffee shop, gift shop and children's activity areas.
Opening times: 10am-5pm (Tuesday to Sunday and bank holidays).
Address: Wallsworth Hall, Twigworth, Gloucester GL2 9PA (two miles N of city on A38). 01452 731 422. e-mail: enquiries@nature-in-art.org.uk
www.nature-in-art.org.uk

THE WILDLIFE ART GALLERY

Opened in 1988 as a specialist in 20th Century and contemporary wildlife art. It exhibits work by many of the leading European wildlife artists, both painters and sculptors, and has published several wildlife books.
Opening times: Mon-Sat (10am-4.30pm) and Sun (2pm-4.30pm).
Address: 97 High Street, Lavenham, Suffolk CO10 9PZ; 01787 248 562; (Fax) 01787 247 356.
E-mail: wildlifeartgallery@btinternet.com
www.wildlifeartgallery.com

DIRECTORY OF WILDLIFE ARTISTS

CALE, Steve

Steve is a keen naturalist and specialises in painting in acrylics. His paintings have gone as far afield as Hong Kong and New Zealand. Undertakes work for The Mareeba Wetland Foundation in Australia and for Pensthorpe waterfowl park. Steve produced the cover image for *Best Birdwatchng Sites in Norfolk* and *Best Birdwatching Sites in North Wales*, and is happy to consider commission requests.
Address: Bramble Cottage, Westwood Lane, Gt Rysburgh, Fakenham, Norfolk, NR21 7AP. 01328 829 589; e-mail: steveshrike@aol.com

CHEUNG, Mabel
Mabel is a Countryside Ranger in her home county of Devon. In the past she has worked for a number of conservation organisations in the UK, Ireland and Costa Rica.
Products for sale: Works in pencil, ink, charcoal, pastels and acrylics, from life and/or photos and has contributed illustrations to previous editions of *The Birdwatcher's Yearbook* and the recently published *Birds of Inishbofin Connemara* by Tim Gordon.
Address: E-mail: chinita@talk21.com

DOODY, Dee
Dee paints finely detailed portraits on pure rag paper of British and world bird of prey, (Red Kite a speciality), as well as powerful, large scale portraits on canvas of big cats - snow leopards, tigers, African wildlife.
Products for sale: Dee paints almost exclusively to commission. The work itself can be seen at www.deedoodywildlife.co.uk, at exhibitions or at his lectures.
Address: The Studio, 2 Fan Terrace, Fan, Llanidloes, Powys, SY18 6NW. (Day) 01686 413 819; (eve) 01686 412 163;
e-mail: dee.doody@virgin.net

GARNER FRSA, Jackie
Original paintings based on field sketches, mostly British or Falkland Islands birds. Particularly interested in camouflage and natural pattern. Contributor to *Birds Illustrated* magazine. See website for details of talks and workshops.
Exhibitions for 2008: British Birdwatching Fair, SWLA, NEWA, Nature in Art residency (see website for details).
Products for sale: Originals, limited edition prints, cards. Commissions accepted.
Address: c/o Nature in Art, Wallsworth Hall, Twigworth, Glos, GL2 9PA; 01452 730 159.
e-mail: artist@jackiegarner.co.uk
www.jackiegarner.co.uk

GILLMOR, Robert
Original watercolours, linocut prints and line drawings, mainly of British birds. Illustrator of many books. His book *Cutting Away, The Linocuts of Robert Gillmor*, is published by Langford Press.
Exhibitions for 2008: Work available at Wildlife Art Gallery, Suffolk; BIRDscapes Gallery, Holt, Norfolk. SWLA annual exhibition.
Address: North Light, Hilltop, Cley-next-the-Sea, Holt, Norfolk, NR25 7SE; 01263 740 729.

GREENHALF, Robert
Fulltime painter and printmaker. Member of SWLA. Work features in many books including *Modern Wildlife Painting* (Pica Press 1998), *Artists for Nature Foundation* books on Poland and Extremadura and *Towards the Sea* (Pica Press 1999) – first solo book.
Exhibitions for 2008: Bircham Gallery, Holt, Norfolk (Nov 8 - Dec 3).
Products for sale: Watercolours, oils and woodcuts, sold mainly through galleries but some commissions undertaken.
Address: Romney House, Saltburn Lane, Playden, Rye, East Sussex, TN33 7PH; 01797 222 381.
Search internet on 'Robert Greenhalf' for links to galleries showing examples of work.

HAMILTON, Lorna
Full-time artist, specialising in wildlife and portrait art. Associate member of Society of Animal Artists, member of Marwell International Wildlife Art Society.
Exhibitions for 2008: Vist website.
Products for sale: Private commissions undertaken, artwork for sale on website.
Address: 157 Crossgar Road, Saintfield, Ballynahinch, Co Down, BT24 7JJ; 028 4483 0479.
e-mail: info@lornahamilton.com
www.lornahamilton.com

JONES, Chris
Painter of all wildlife subjects (primarily in oils), especially birds and poultry. International Young Artist of the Year 1998. Gold Award Winner, the Wildlife Art Society 2000.
Exhibitions for 2008: WWT Slimbridge, (Jan 13-Mar 2). See website for more.
Products for sale: Original paintings and drawings, prints, cards (by Medici) and postcards. Commission and illustration work undertaken. See website for examples.
Address: 47 Church Lane, North Bradley, Trowbridge, Wilts, BA14 0TE; 01225 769 717.
e-mail: chrisjonesart@yahoo.co.uk
www.chrisjonesart.com

DIRECTORY OF WILDLIFE ARTISTS

LEAHY, Ernest

Original watercolours and drawings of Western Palearctic birds, wildlife and country scenes. Illustrations for many publications including Poysers. Wide range of framed and unframed originals available. Commissions accepted and enquiries welcome.
Exhibitions for 2008: BBWF and e-mail for details of further exhibitions.
Products for sale: E-mail for details of current work available and for quotations on commissioned work.
Address: 32 Ben Austins, Redbourn, Herts, AL3 7DR; 01582 793 144;
e-mail: ernest.leahy@ntlworld.com
www.wildlifewatercolours.co.uk

LINGHAM, Steven

Fulltime wildlife and landscape artist, private collectors worldwide. Short-listed in the *Daily Mail*'s 'Not the Turner Prize' competition.
Exhibitions for 2008: Solo exhibitions once every two years. British Falconry Fair and galleries throughout the UK.
Products for sale: Originals, limited edition prints and greeting cards. All commissions undertaken.
Contact: 0779 694 576.
e-mail: info@stevenlingham.com
www.stevenlingham.com

POMROY, Jonathan

Works in watercolour and oils, always from field sketches, made on trips across the British Isles, most recently to Norfolk, the Isles of Scilly, Anglesey & Snowdonia, North West Scotland and Slimbridge as well as around home in North Yorkshire. Recent exhibitions at WWT Slimbridge and Barnes and Birdscapes Gallery, Cley, Norfolk.
Exhibitions for 2008: West Barn, Bradford on Avon August 1-5, work constantly on display at BIRDscapes Gallery, North Norfolk. See website for latest exhibition details.
Products for sale: Chiefly selling original watercolours and oils at one man exhibitions and from website.
Address: Rose Cottage, Thornton-in-Craven, Skipton, North Yorkshire BD23 3TJ; 01282 841 117; e-mail: jonathanpomroy@supanet.com
www.jonathanpomroy.co.uk

ROSE, Chris

Originals in oils and acrylics of birds and animals in landscapes. Particular interest in painting water and its myriad effects. Limited edition reproductions available. *In a Natural Light – the Wildlife Art of Chris Rose* published 2005. Illustrated many books including *Grebes of the World* (publ. 2002) and *Handbook to the Birds of the World.*
Exhibitions for 2008: SWLA annual exhibition, Mall Galleries, London.
Products for sale: Original drawings and paintings, linocuts, illustrations, limited edition reproductions, postcards.
Address: 6 Whitelee Cottages, Newton St Boswells, Melrose, Scotland TD6 0SH; (Tel) 01835 822 547. e-mail: chris@chrisrose-artist.co.uk
www.chrisrose-artist.co.uk

SMART, Adrian

Full-time artist and illustrator. First illustrated book due in 2008 on British garden birds. MIWAS member, Wildscape Artist of the Year (outright winner), commended at NEWA in 2007.
Exhibitions for 2008: British Birdwatching Fair, August 2008, local gallery exhibitions, Northmoor Trust, November 2008.
Products for sale: Private commissions, Darryl Davies fine art greetings cards, Cachet UK Ltd, limited edition prints, RSPB, BTO.
Address: 31 Sinodun Road, Didcot, Oxon, OX11 8HW; 01235 815 375; (M) 07751 365 134.
e-mail: ads.smart@btopenworld.com

WARREN, Michael

Original watercolour paintings of birds, all based on field observations. Books, calendars, cards and commissions.
Exhibitions for 2008: Will have work in SWLA exhibitions at FeFieFoFum Gallery, nr. Corbridge, Northumberland, Feb/Mar and at BIRDscapes Gallery, Glandford, Norfolk in May. Birdfair, Rutland in Aug and SWLA annual exhibition in Sept.
For other information see website.
Products for sale: Original watercolour paintings of birds, all based on field observations. Books, calendars, cards and commissions welcomed.
Address: The Laurels, The Green, Winthorpe, Nottinghamshire, NG24 2NR; 01636 673 554;
e-mail: mike.warren@tiscali.co.uk
www.mikewarren.co.uk

WOODHEAD, Darren MA(RCA), SWLA
Original watercolours and woodcuts of birds, butterflies, mammals and other wildlife subjects, as well as landscapes and cloudscapes. All subjects painted direct in the field. Commissions undertaken.
Exhibitions for 2008: McHardy's Art and Framing Gallery, (May 11-Jun 2), Wildlife Art Gallery, Lavenham, Suffolk (Oct), SWLA exhibition, Mall Galleries, London (Sept).
Products for sale: Original watercolour paintings and brush drawings, sketches and pen drawings.
Address: 36 Stoneybank Road, Musselburgh, East Lothian, EH21 6HJ; 0131 665 6802.
e-mail: darren.woodhead@virgin.net
www.darrenwoodheadartist.co.uk

WOOLF, Colin
Beautiful original watercolour paintings. The atmosphere of a landscape and the character of his subject are his hallmark, also the pure watercolour technique that imparts a softness to the natural subjects he paints. Owls, birds of prey and ducks are specialities. Wide range of limited editions and greetings cards, special commissions also accepted.
Exhibitions for 2008: Please check the website for an up-to-date show calendar.
Products for sale: Original paintings, limited edition prints and greetings cards.
Address: Tremallt, Penmachno, Betws y Coed, Conwy, LL24 0YL; +44 (0) 1690 760 308;
e-mail: colin@wildart.co.uk www.wildart.co.uk

DIRECTORY OF WILDLIFE PHOTOGRAPHERS

BASTON, Bill
Photographer, lecturer.
Subjects: East Anglian rarities and common birds, Mediterranean birds and landscapes, UK wildlife and landscapes, Florida birds and landscapes, Northern Greece, Spain, western Turkey.
Products for sale: Prints, slides, digital, mounted/unmounted.
Address: 86 George Street, Hadleigh, Ipswich, IP7 5BU; 01473 827 062; e-mail: bill.baston@bt.com
www.billbaston.com

BATES, Tony
Photographer and lecturer.
Subjects: Mainly British wildlife, landscapes and astro landscapes.
Products for sale: Prints (mounted or framed), original handmade photo greetings cards.
Address: 22 Fir Avenue, Bourne, Lincs, PE10 9RY; 01778 425 137; e-mail: mtr@masher.f9.co.uk

BELL, Graham
Professional ornithologist, photograher, cruise lecturer worldwide.
Subjects: Birds, animals, flowers, landscapes worldwide from Arctic to Antarctic.
Products for sale: Original slides for sale, £2 each.
Address: Ros View, South Yearle, Wooler, Northumberland, NE71 6RB; 01668 281 310;
e-mail: seabirdsdgb@hotmail.com

BRIGGS, Kevin
Freelance ecologist.
Subjects: Raptors, Oystercatcher, Ringed Plover, Goosander, Yellow Wagtail, Ring Ouzel, Lune Valley.
Address: The Bramblings, 1 Washington Drive, Warton, Carnforth, LA5 9RA; 01254 730 533;
e-mail: kbbriggs@yahoo.com

DIRECTORY OF WILDLIFE PHOTOGRAPHERS

BROADBENT, David
Professional photographer.
Subjects: UK birds and wild places.
Products for sale: Top quality photographic prints.
Address: Rose Cottage, Bream Road, Whitepool, St Briavels, Lydney, GL15 6TL; 07771 664 973; e-mail: info@davidbroadbent.com
www.davidbroadbent.com

BROOKS, Richard
Wildlife photographer, writer, lecturer.
Subjects: Owls (Barn especially), raptors, Kingfisher and a variety of European birds (Lesvos especially) and landscapes.
Products for sale: Mounted and unmounted computer prints (6x4 to A3+ size), framed pictures, A5 greetings cards, surplus slides for sale.
Address: 24 Croxton Hamlet, Fulmodeston, Fakenham, Norfolk, NR21 0NP; 01328 878 632; e-mail: email@richard-brooks.co.uk
www.richard-brooks.co.uk

BUCKINGHAM, John
Worldwide bird and wildlife photographer.
Subjects: Huge range of birds, botany and wildlife in UK and Europe, plus great coverage from Africa, Americas, Australia and worldwide.
Products for sale: Original slides for lectures and personal use.
Address: 3 Cardinal Close, Tonbridge, Kent, TN9 2EN; (Tel/fax) 01732 354 970;
e-mail: john@buckingham7836.freeserve.co.uk

COSTER, Bill
Professional wildlife photographer, writer and photographic tour leader.
Subjects: Wildlife and landscape from around the world.
Products for sale: Images for publication, prints for sale. See my website for details. Stunning new digital shows (see Directory of Lecturers).
Address: 17 Elm Road, South Woodham Ferrers, Chelmsford, Essex CM3 5QB; 01245 320 066;
e-mail: billcoster@hotmail.com
www.billcoster.com

DENNING, Paul
Wildlife photographer, lecturer.
Subjects: Birds, mammals, reptiles, butterflies and plants from UK, Europe, Canaries, North and Central America.
Products for sale: 35mm transparencies and digital images.
Address: 17 Maes Maelwg, Beddau, Pontypridd, CF38 2LD; (H) 01443 202 607; (W) 02920 673 243; e-mail: pgdenning.naturepics@virgin.net

HAMBLIN, Mark
Freelance nature and landscape photographer and tour leader for Wildshots.
Subjects: British wildlife and Scottish landscapes.
Products for sale: Photographic commissions, photo tours, books, greetings cards, fine art prints.
Address: Ballinlaggan Farm, Duthil, Carr-bridge, Inverness-shire, PH23 3ND; 01479 841 547;
e-mail: mark@markhamblin.com
www.markhamblin.com

LANGLEY, John and Tracey
Wildlife photographers, workshop tutors and lecturers.
Subjects: Birds, mammals, butterflies and other wildlife. European plus Indian (especially tigers).
Products for sale: Digital images for publication and commercial use. Mounted images, framed images, greeting cards, bookmarks and calendars.
Address: 16 Carrick Road, Curzon Park, Chester CH4 8AW; 01244 678 781;
e-mail: little.owl@btopenworld.com
www.ourwildlifephotography.co.uk

LANGSBURY, Gordon FRPS
Professional wildlife photographer, lecturer, author.
Subjects: Birds and mammals from UK, Europe, Scandinavia, N America, Gambia, Kenya, Tanzania, Morocco and Falklands.
Products for sale: Digital and 35mm transparencies for publication, lectures and prints.
Address: Sanderlings, 80 Shepherds Close, Hurley, Maidenhead, Berkshire, SL6 5LZ; (Tel/fax) 01628 824 252;
e-mail: gordonlangsbury@birdphoto.org.uk
www.birdphoto.org.uk

McKAVETT, Mike
Wildlife photographer and lecturer.
Subjects: Birds and mammals from India, Kenya, The Gambia, Lesvos, N.America and UK.
Products for sale: 35mm transparencies and digital images for publication and commercial use, prints and lectures.

Address: 34 Rectory Road, Churchtown, Southport, PR9 7PU; 01704 231 358; e-mail: mike.mckavett@btinternet.com

MOCKLER, Mike

Safari guide, tour leader, writer and photographer.
Subjects: Birds and wildlife of Britain, Europe, Central and South America, India and several African countries.
Products for sale: 35mm transparencies and digital images.
Address: Gulliver's Cottage, Chapel Rise, Avon Castle, Ringwood, Hampshire, BH24 2BL; 01425 478 103; e-mail: mikemockler@lineone.net

OFFORD, Keith

Photographer, writer, tour leader, conservationist.
Subjects: Birds, other wildlife and scenery of UK, USA, Africa, Spain, Australia, India, Costa Rica.
Products for sale: Conventional prints, greetings cards, framed pictures.
Address: Yew Tree Farmhouse, Craignant, Selattyn, Nr Oswestry, Shropshire, SY10 7NP; 01691 718 740; e-mail: keith.offord@virgin.net www.keithofford.co.uk

PARKER, Susan and Allan ARPS

Professional photographers (ASPphoto - Images of Nature) lecturers and tutors.
Subjects: Birds plus other flora and fauna from the UK, Spain, Lesvos, Cyprus, Florida and Texas.
Products for sale: 35mm and digital images, mounted digital images, greetings cards and digital images on CD/DVD for reproduction (high quality scans up to A3+).
Address: Ashtree House, 51 Kiveton Lane, Todwick, Sheffield, South Yorkshire, S26 1HJ; 01909 770 238; e-mail: aspphoto@tiscali.co.uk

READ, Mike

Photographer (wildlife and landscapes), tour leader, writer.
Subjects: Birds, mammals, plants, landscapes, and some insects. UK, France, USA, Ecuador (including Galapagos).
Products for sale: Prints, greetings cards, books.
Address: Claremont, Redwood Close, Ringwood, Hampshire, BH24 1PR; 01425 475 008; e-mail: mike@mikeread.co.uk
www.mikeread.co.uk

SWASH, Andy

Photographer, author, tour leader.
Subjects: Birds, habitats/landscapes and general wildlife from all continents; photographic library currently 1,700 bird species.
Products for sale: Slides for publication and duplicates for lectures. High resolution scans on CD-Rom. Conventional and digital prints, unmounted, mounted or framed.
Address: Stretton Lodge, 9 Birch Grove, West Hill, Ottery St Mary, Devon, EX11 1XP; (Tel/Fax) 01404 815 383.
e-mail: andy_swash@wildguides.co.uk
www.wildguides.co.uk

WARD, Chris

Lecturer, N Bucks RSPB Local Group Leader.
Subjects: Primarily birds (and some other wildlife) and landscapes from UK and worldwide (Spain, Americas, S. Africa, Goa, Australisia).
Products for sale: Digital images and prints on request.
Address: 41 William Smith Close, Woolstone, Milton Keynes, Bucks MK15 0AN; 01908 669 448; e-mail: cwphotography@hotmail.com
www.cwardphotography.co.uk

WILKES, Mike FRPS

Professional wildlife photographer, tour leader.
Subjects: Florida and Texas, Ecuador and Galapagos wildlife, Kenya, Tanzania, Gambia, Lesvos, Spain.
Products for sale: Organises and leads wildlife photograhic trips to Tanzania and Ecuador and Galapagos Islands.
Address: 43 Feckenham Road, Headless Cross, Redditch, Worcestershire, B97 5AS; 01527 550 686; e-mail: wilkes@photoshot.com

WILLIAMS, Nick

Photographer, lecturer, author.
Subjects: W.Palearctic also Cape Verde Islands and Falkland Islands.
Products for sale: Duplicate slides, some originals, prints also available.
Address: Owl Cottage, Station Street, Rippingale, Lincs, PE10 0TA; (Tel/Fax) 01778 440 500;
e-mail: birdmanandbird@hotmail.com
www.nickwilliams.eu

DIRECTORY OF LECTURERS

APPLETON, Tim

Reserve Manager, Rutland Water
Subjects: Rutland Water, British Birdwatching Fair, Return of Ospreys to England, Trips and birds of Spain, Australia, Papua New Guinea, various African countries, Argentina and more.
Fees: Negotiable. **Limits:** Preferably within 2hrs of Rutland. **Times:** Winter preferred but can be flexible.
Address: Fishponds Cottage, Stamford Road, Oakham, Rutland, LE15 8AB; (H) 01572 724 101, (W) 01572 770 651: (Fax) 01572 755 931.

BATES, Tony

Photographer and lecturer.
Subjects: Seven disolve projection shows (all include some music), 'A Woodland Walk', 'Seasons and Sayings', 'From a Puddle to the Sea', 'Favourite Places', 'USA, East and West', 'Folklore of Woodland and Hedgerow', 'The Hare and the Owls', 'A Wildlife Garden'.
Fees: £75 plus travel. **Limits:** None.
Times: To suit.
Address: 22 Fir Avenue, Bourne, Lincs, PE10 9RY; 01778 425 137; e-mail: mtr@masher.f9.co.uk

BELL, Graham

Cruise lecturer worldwide, photographer, author, former BBRC.
Subjects: Arctic, Antarctic, Siberia, Australia, Canada, Iceland, Seychelles, UK - identification, behaviour, seabirds, garden birds, entertaining bird sound imitations, birds in myth and fact, bird names etc.
Fees: £30 plus travel. **Limits:** None. **Times:** Any.
Address: Ros View, South Yearle, Wooler, Northumberland, NE71 6RB; 01668 281 310; e-mail: seabirdsdgb@hotmail.com

BOND, Terry

International consultant, ex-bank director, conference speaker worldwide, photographer, group field leader, lecturer on birds for more than thirty years.
Subjects: 8 talks – including Scilly Isles, Southern Europe, North America, Scandinavia, 'Birdwatching Identification - a New Approach' (an audience participation evening).
Fees: By arrangement (usually only expenses).
Limits: Most of UK. **Times:** Evenings.
Address: 3 Lapwing Crescent, Chippenham, Wiltshire, SN14 6YF; 01249 462 674; e-mail: terryebond@btopenworld.com

BRIGGS, Kevin

Freelance ecologist.
Subjects: General wildlife in NW England; specialist topics – Raptors, Oystercatcher, Ringed Plover, Goosander, Yellow Wagtail, Ring Ouzel, Lune Valley, 'Confessions of a Lunatic'.
Fees: £60 + petrol. **Limits:** None. **Times:** Any.
Address: The Bramblings, 1 Washington Drive, Warton, Carnforth, LA5 9RA; 01254 730 533; e-mail: kbbriggs@yahoo.com

BROADBENT, David

Photographer.
Subjects: UK birds and wild places. In praise of natural places.
Fees: £70 plus travel. **Limits:** 50mls without o.n accom, anywhere otherwise. **Times:** Any.
Address: Rose Cottage, Bream Road, Whitepool, St Briavels, Lydney, GL15 6TL; e-mail: info@davidbroadbent.com www.davidbroadbent.com

BROOKS, David

Freelance naturalist.
Subjects: Various talks on wildlife, principally birds, in UK and overseas.
Fees: £50 plus petrol. **Limits:** 50 mls without o.n. accom. **Times:** Any.
Address: 2 Malthouse Court, Green Lane, Thornham, Norfolk, PE36 6NW; 01485 512 548; e-mail: brooks472@btinternet.com

BROOKS, Richard

Wildlife photographer, writer, lecturer.
Subjects: 12 talks (including Lesvos, Evros Delta, Israel, Canaries, E.Anglia, Scotland, Wales, Oman).
Fees: £75 plus petrol. **Limits:** None if accom provided. **Times:** Any.
Address: 24 Croxton Hamlet, Fulmodeston, Fakenham, Norfolk, NR21 0NP; 01328 878 632; e-mail: email@richard-brooks.co.uk www.richard-brooks.co.uk

BUCKINGHAM, John
Lecturer, photographer, tour leader.
Subjects: 60+ titles covering birds, wildlife, botany, ecology and habitats in UK, Europe, Africa, Australia, India and the Americas.
Fees: £70 plus expenses. **Limits:** None.
Times: Any.
Address: 3 Cardinal Close, Tonbridge, Kent, TN9 2EN; (Tel/Fax) 01732 354 970;
e-mail: john@buckingham7836.freeserve.co.uk

BURROWS, Ian
Tour leader.
Subjects: Papua New Guinea, Cape Clear Island and Food from the Wild.
Fees: £70 plus mileage over 100. **Limits:** Anything considered. **Times:** Evenings preferable but other times considered.
Address: Trefor, Creake Road, Sculthorpe, Fakenham, Norfolk, NR21 9NQ. 01328 856 925;
e-mail: Ian@sicklebill.demon.co.uk
www.sicklebill.com

CARRIER, Michael
Lifelong interest in natural history.
Subjects: 1) Birds in Cumbria, 2) The Solway and its Birds and 3)The Isle of May, 4)A look at Bird Migration, 5)A Lifetime of Birds.
Fees: £20. **Limits:** None but rail connection helpful. **Times:** Sept-March inc., afternoons or evenings.
Address: Lismore Cottage, 1 Front Street, Armathwaite, Carlisle, Cumbria, CA4 9PB; 01697 472 218; e-mail: m.carrier131@btinternet.com

CLEAVE, Andrew MBE
Wildlife photographer, author, lecturer and tour leader.
Subjects: More than 30 talks (including Galapagos, Iceland, Mediterranean birds and wildlife, Lundy, Shetland, ancient woodlands, dormice and seashore). Full list available.
Fees: £65 plus petrol. **Limits:** Approx. 60 mls without o.n accom. **Times:** Afternoons and evenings, not school holidays.
Address: 31 Petersfield Close, Chineham, Basingstoke, Hampshire, RG24 8WP; 01256 320 050; e-mail: andrew@bramleyfrith.co.uk

COOMBER, Richard
Tour leader, photographer, writer.
Subjects: Australia, Botswana, Namibia, Seychelles, Falklands, Galapagos, Ring of Fire, S America, USA, Zambia, seabirds (all are digital presentations).
Fees: £65 plus petrol. **Limits:** 50 mls without o.n. accom, 150 mls otherwise.
Times: Afternoons or evenings.
Address: 1 Haglane Copse, Lymington, Hampshire, SO41 8DT; 01590 674 471;
e-mail: rfcoomber@btinternet.com

COSTER, Bill
Professional wildlife photographer, writer and photographic tour leader.
Subjects: Stunning new digital shows provide a unique look at subjects around the world, including: Pacific Northwest USA, Antarctica, Shetland, Birds and Landscape of USA Deserts, Florida, Britain and more. See my website for full details (www.billcoster.com). Even if you have seen shows from the same location, my shows will be different.
Fees: £75 plus 25p per mile. **Limits:** None.
Times: Any.
Address: 17 Elm Road, South Woodham Ferrers, Chelmsford, Essex CM3 5QB; 01245 320 066;
e-mail: billcoster@hotmail.com
www.billcoster.com

COUZENS, Dominic
Full-time birdwatcher, tour leader (UK and overseas), writer and lecturer.
Subjects: The Secret Lives of Garden Birds, Birds Behaving Badly - the trials and tribulations of birds through the year, Bird Sounds - As You've Never Heard Them Before, Have Wings Will Travel -the marvel of bird migration, Vive la Difference - a look at the lives of some European birds.
Fees: £80 plus travel . **Limits:** London and south.
Times: Any.
Address: 3 Clifton Gardens, Ferndown, Dorset, BH22 9BE; (Tel/Fax) 01202 874 330.
e-mail: dominic.couzens@btinternet.com
www.birdwords.co.uk

CROMACK, David
Editor of *Birds Illustrated* magazine, co-publisher of Buckingham Press Ltd, chairman of Peterborough Bird Club.
Subjects: 1) Bird magazines and the art of bird photography, 2) Birds of Arizona and California, 3) World class bird images (International Wildbird Photographer competition), 4) Birdwatching For

Beginners, 5) Garden Bird Survival Guide. Leaflet available on request.
Fees: £60 plus expenses (20p per mile). **Limits:** 200 mls. **Times:** All requests considered from Jan 2008 onwards.
Address: 55 Thorpe Park Road, Peterborough PE3 6LJ. 01733 566 815; (Fax) 01733 561 739; e-mail: editor@buckinghampress.com

CROUCHER, Roy
Tour leader, lecturer, former RSPB member of staff, former Local Authority ecologist.
Subjects: The wildlife of Northern France, The birds of Montenegro, Managing the countryside for wildlife.
Fees: £50 + cost of petrol from Leicester (return) at £12 per 100 miles. **Limits:** Anywhere on mainland Britain. **Times:** November and December.
Address: Place de l'église, 53700, Averton, France. 00 33 243 00 6969; e-mail: nfwt@online.fr www.northernfrancewildlifetours.com

DENNING, Paul
Wildlife photographer, lecturer.
Subjects: 15 talks, (birds, mammals, reptiles, butterflies etc, UK, western and eastern Europe, north and central America, Canaries).
Fees: £40 plus petrol. **Limits:** 100 mls.
Times: Evenings, weekends.
Address: 17 Maes Maelwg, Beddau, Pontypridd, CF38 2LD; (H) 01443 202 607; (W) 02920 673 243; e-mail: pgdenning.naturepics@virgin.net

DOODY, Dee
Wildlife artist, television wildlife cameraman, presenter (radio and TV), bird of prey expert. Dee brings with him a good collection of wildlife art.
Subjects: 'Wild Wales'– birdlife from mountain to coasts, 'The Red Kite', 'The Birds of Prey of Wales'.
Fees: £85 plus cost of petrol. **Limits:** None.
Times: Any.
Address: The Studio, 2 Fan Terrace, Fan, Llanidloes, Powys, SY18 6NW; (Day) 01686 413 819; (eve) 01686 412 163;
e-mail: dee.doody@virgin.net

DUGGAN, Glenn
Ex-Commander Royal Navy, tour leader, researcher.
Subjects: Ten talks including, birds of paradise and bower birds, history of bird art (caveman to present day), modern day bird art, famous Victorian bird artists (John Gould, the Birdman and John James Audubon), Trogons and Tanagers.
Fees: £60 plus expenses. **Limits:** none with o.n accom. **Times:** Any.
Address: 25 Hampton Grove, Fareham, Hampshire, PO15 5NL; 01329 845 976, (M) 07771 605 320; e-mail: glenn.m.duggan@ntlworld.com www.birdlectures.com

EYRE, John
Author, photographer, conservationist and chairman Hampshire Ornithological Society.
Subjects: Many talks covering birding around the world (Europe, Africa, Australasia and the Americas), plus special Hampshire subjects (eg. Gilbert White's birds and the changing fortunes of Hampshire birds).
Fees: £60 plus travel. **Limits:** Any location negotiable. **Times:** Any.
Address: 3 Dunmow Hill, Fleet, Hampshire, GU51 3AN; 01252 677 850;
e-mail: John.Eyre@ntlworld.com

FURNELL, Dennis
Natural history writer, radio and television broadcaster, artist and wildlife sound recordist.
Subjects: British and European wildlife, France, (*The Nature of France*). Wildlife sound recording, wildlife and disability access issues.
Fees: £100. **Limits:** 50 miles, further with o.n. accom. **Times:** Afternoons or evenings according to commitments.
Address: 19 Manscroft Road, Gadebridge, Hemel Hempstead, Hertfordshire, HP1 3HU; 01442 242 915, (Fax) 01442 242 032;
e-mail; dennis.furnell@btinternet.com
www.natureman.co.uk

GALLOP, Brian
Speaker, photographer, tour leader.
Subjects: 35 talks covering UK, Africa, India, Galapagos and Europe - all natural history subjects.
Fees: £50 plus 20p per ml. **Limits:** None - o.n acc. if over 100 mls. **Times:** Any.
Address: 13 Orchard Drive, Tonbridge, Kent, TN10 4LT; 01732 361 892;
e-mail: brian_gallop@hotmail.co.uk

GARNER, David
Wildlife photographer.
Subjects: 19 live talks and audio-visual shows on all aspects of wildlife in UK and some parts of Europe – list available.
Fees: £40 plus 20p per ml. **Limits:** None.
Times: Any.
Address: 73 Needingworth Road, St Ives, Cambridgeshire, PE27 5JY; (H) 01480 463 194; (W) 01480 463 194;
e-mail: david@hushwings.co.uk
www.hushwings.co.uk

GARTSHORE, Neil
23-years working in nature conservation (National Trust, South Africa, RSPB) now a freelance contractor, writer, lecturer, tour guide and natural history bookseller.
Subjects: Various talks including South Africa; Sub-Antarctic Prince Edward Islands; Japan; Farne Islands; Heathlands; Poole Harbour.
Fees: Negotiable. **Limits:** Anything considered.
Times: Flexible
Address: 54 Corfe Road, Stoborough, Wareham, Dorset, BH20 5AF. 01929 552 560;
e-mail: neil&yuki@onaga54.freeserve.co.uk

GLENN, Neil
Author of *Best Birdwatching Sites in Norfolk*; regular contributor to *Birds Illustrated* and *Bird Watching* magazines; bird tour leader for Avian Adventures.
Subjects: Wildlife of the Lower Rio Grande Valley, Texas. More to follow!
Fees: Negotiable. **Limits:** None. **Times:** Any day.
Address: 13 Gladstone Avenue, Gotham, Nottingham NG11 0HN; 0115 983 0946;
e-mail: n.glenn@ntlworld.com

GUNTON, Trevor
Ex.RSPB Staff, recruitment advisor, lecturer and consultant.
Subjects: 15 different talks, featuring places such as Shetland, other UK islands, Yorkshire from dales to coast, and Viking lands (four different talks on Viking history). New talks are 'A Norwegian coastal voyage' and 'Wild goose chase (Holland and Romania)', 'Starting Birdwatching', Great Gardens and Houses of East Anglia'. Other topics include wildlife on National Trust properties and gravel pits.
Fees: Variable (basic £60 plus expenses).
Limits: None. **Times:** Anytime, anywhere.
Address: 15 St James Road, Little Paxton, St Neots, Cambs, PE19 6QW; (tel/Fax)01480 473562; e-mail: trevor.gunton@tesco.net

HAMBLIN, Mark
Wildlife photographer, writer and tour leader.
Subjects: Tooth & Claw – Living alongside Britain's predators, plus other talks on Scottish wildlife and nature photography.
Fees: £250 plus actual travel costs. **Limits:** None.
Times: Lunchtime, afternoons and evenings.
Address: Ballinlaggan Farm, Duthil, Carr-bridge, Inverness-shire, PH23 3ND; 01479 841 547;
e-mail: mark@markhamblin.com
www.markhamblin.com

HASSELL, David
Birdwatcher and photographer.
Subjects: Six talks (including British Seabirds, Shetland Birds, British Birds, USA Birds, including Texas, California, Florida etc.).
Fees: £45 plus petrol. **Limits:** None. **Times:** Any.
Address: 15 Grafton Road, Enfield, Middlesex, EN2 7EY; 020 8367 0308;
e-mail: dave@davehassell.com
www.davehassell.com

LANGLEY, John and Tracey
Wildlife photographers, workshop tutors and lecturers.
Subjects: Various talks on UK wildlife, wildlife photography and Indian wildlife (with special emphasis on tigers).
Fees: Variable. **Limits:** None. **Times:** Any.
Address: 16 Carrick Road, Curzon Park, Chester CH4 8AW; 01244 678 781;
e-mail: little.owl@btopenworld.com
www.ourwildlifephotography.co.uk

LANGSBURY, Gordon FRPS
Professional wildlife photographer, lecturer, author.
Subjects: 20 talks - Africa, Europe, USA, Falklands and UK. Full list provided.
Fees: £90 plus travel expenses. **Limits:** None.
Times: Any.
Address: Sanderlings, 80 Shepherds Close, Hurley, Maidenhead, Berkshire, SL6 5LZ; (Tel/Fax)01628 824 252;
e-mail: gordonlangsbury@birdphoto.org.uk
www.birdphoto.org.uk

DIRECTORY OF LECTURERS

LINN, Hugh ARPS

Experienced lecturer, photographer.
Subjects: 12 talks, covering UK, Europe, Africa and bird-related subjects. List available.
Fees: £40 plus petrol. **Limits:** 100 mls without o.n. accom 150 mls otherwise. **Times:** Flexible.
Address: 4 Stonewalls, Rosemary Lane, Burton, Rossett, Wrexham, LL12 0LG; 01244 571 942.

LOVELL, Stephen

Naturalist, RSPB lecturer, photographer.
Subjects: 18 topics including the natural history of several European destinations including Lesvos, Mallorca, Britain. Other talks available on New Zealand, Australia, St Lucia, Tanzania, Sri Lanka and Southern India.
Fees: According to distance – on request.
Limits: None. **Times:** Any.
Address: 6 Abingdon Close, Doddington Park, Lincoln LN6 3UH; 01522 689 456; (M) 07957 618 684; e-mail: stephen.lovell7@btinternet.com

MATHER, John Robert

Ornithologist, writer, tour guide, lecturer.
Subjects: Birds and wildlife of: Kenya, Tanzania, Uganda, Ethiopia, Namibia, South Africa, Costa Rica, Romania/Bulgaria, India, Nepal, Algonquin to Niagara – a tour around the Great Lakes; Landscapes, Flowers and Wildlife of the American West; Bird on the Bench – a fascinating account of bird biology.
Fees: £65 plus 20p per ml. **Limits:** 100 mls.
Times: Evenings.
Address: Eagle Lodge, 44 Aspin Lane, Knaresborough, North Yorkshire, HG5 8EP; 01423 862 775.

McKAVETT, Mike

Photographer.
Subjects: Six talks, Birds and Wildlife of India, North and Western Kenya and the Gambia, Bird Migration in North America, Birds of the Eastern Mediterranean.
Fees: £50 plus expenses. **Limits:** None.
Times: Any.
Address: 34 Rectory Road, Churchtown, Southport, PR9 7PU; 01704 231 358;
e-mail: mike.mckavett@btinternet.com

MOCKLER, Mike

Safari guide, tour leader, writer and photographer.
Subjects: Birds and other wildlife of: Botswana, Kenya, Tanzania, Zambia, Spain, Finland, Norway, Costa Rica, Antarctica and South Georgia, India and Brazil.
Fees: Negotiable. **Limits:** None.
Times: Evenings.
Address: Gulliver's Cottage, Chapel Rise, Avon Castle, Ringwood, Hampshire, BH24 2BL; 01425 478 103; e-mail: mikemockler@lineone.net

NOBBS, Brian

Amateur birdwatcher and photographer.
Subjects: Wildlife of the Wild West, Israel, Mediterranean, Florida, Wildlife Gardening, Reserved for Birds.
Fees: £40 plus 25p per ml. **Limits:** Kent, Surrey, Sussex. **Times:** Any.
Address: The Grebes, 36 Main Road, Sundridge, Sevenoaks, Kent, TN14 6EP; 01959 563 530;
e-mail: Brian.nobbs@tiscali.co.uk

OFFORD, Keith

Photographer, writer, Wild Insights tour leader, conservationist.
Subjects: 16 talks covering raptors, uplands, woodlands, gardens, migration, flight, Australia, Southern USA, Morocco, Tanzania, Gambia, Spain, Namibia, Western Cape.
Fees: £90 plus travel costs. **Limits:** None.
Times: Sept-April.
Address: Yew Tree Farmhouse, Craignant, Selattyn, Nr Oswestry, Shropshire, SY10 7NP; 01691 718 740; e-mail: keith.offord@virgin.net
www.keithofford.co.uk

PALMER, Phil

Tour leader for Bird Holidays.
Subjects: Mostly birds, but includes mammals, insects, reptiles, whale watching etc. Many foreign trips including Alaska, Midway Atoll, Antarctica and India. British birds – 'First for Britain' from Phil's book, The Secret Life of the Nightjar, twitching in the UK and bird photography.
Fees: To suit all club budgets. **Limits:** None.
Times: Any.
Address: 43 Grove Coach Road, Retford, Nottinghamshire DN22 7HB; (Tel/Fax) 0113 391 0510; e-mail: Phil@birdholidays.fsnet.co.uk

PARKER, Susan and Allan ARPS

Professional photographers, (ASPphoto – Images of Nature), lecturers and tutors.
Subjects: 16 plus talks on birds and natural

history, natural history photography - countries include UK, USA (Texas, Florida), Spain, Greece, Cyprus.
Fees: On application. **Limits:** Any distance with o.n accom or up to 120 mls without. **Times:** Any.
Address: Ashtree House, 51 Kiveton Lane, Todwick, Sheffield, South Yorkshire, S26 1HJ; 01909 770 238. e-mail: aspphoto@tiscali.co.uk

READ, Mike

Photographer, tour leader, writer.
Subjects: 12 talks featuring British and foreign subjects (list available on receipt of sae).
Fees: £70 plus travel. **Limits:** 125 mls.
Times: Any.
Address: Claremont, Redwood Close, Ringwood, Hampshire, BH24 1PR; 01425 475 008;
e-mail: mike@mikeread.co.uk
www.mikeread.co.uk

ROBINSON, Peter

Consultant ornithologist and former Scilly resident, author of *Birds of the Isles of Scilly*.
Subjects: Spring Watch - The Real Story' and various subjects including 'Sea and Landbirds of Scilly - Life in an Island Environment'.
Fees: £80 plus petrol. **Limits:** None. **Times:** Any.
Address: 19 Pine Park Road, Honiton, Devon, EX14 2HR; 01404 549 873 (M) 07768 538 132.
e-mail: pjrobinson2@aol.com

RUMLEY-DAWSON, Ian

Wildlife photographer, course leader, cruise lecturer.
Subjects: 96 talks using twin dissolving projectors or digital Power Point and some with natural wildlife sounds as well. Birds, mammals, insects, plants, habitats, ethology. Arctic, Antarctic, Falklands, N and S America, N.Z, Seychelles, North Pacific islands, Albatrosses, penguins, Snowy Owls, polar bears etc. List available.
Fees: £60 plus expenses. **Limits:** None.
Times: Any.
Address: Oakhurst, Whatlington Road, Battle, East Sussex, TN33 0JN; 01424 772 673.

SCOTT, Ann and Bob

Ex-RSPB staff, tour leaders, writers, lecturers, tutors, trainers.
Subjects: 16+ talks (including nature reserves, RSPB, tours, gardening, Europe, Africa, S America, after-dinner talks etc).
Fees: £60 plus travel over 50 mls. **Limits:** None (by arrangement). **Times:** Any.
Address: 8 Woodlands, St Neots, Cambridgeshire, PE19 1UE; 01480 214 904; (Fax)01480 473 009;
e-mail: abscott@tiscali.co.uk

SMART, Oliver

Photographer and lecturer.
Subjects: 1) Birds of Lesvos; 2) Grizzly Bears of Alaska; 3) Wildlife on Handa Island, NW Scotland.
Fees: £60 plus mileage over 50 miles.
Limits: None but o.n. accom. may be needed.
Times: Any.
Address: 78 Aspen Park Road, Weston-Super-Mare, Somerset BS22 8ER; 01934 628 888; (M) 07802 417 810;
e-mail: oliver@smartimages.co.uk
www.smartimages.co.uk

STEPHEN, Gerry

Subjects: More than 28 talks, mainly about wild flowers and their habitats but including natural history of all types and covering areas of the USA, Canada, Europe and Africa. All about 60 minutes duration but can be tailored to your needs. **Fees:** £30 plus travel expenses at cost. **Times:** Any.
Address: 10 Birch Way, Poulton-le-Fylde, Blackpool, FY6 7SF; 01253 895 195;
e-mail: melodystephen@hotmail.com

SWASH, Andy

Photographer, author, tour leader.
Subjects: Birds, general wildlife, scenery and tales from travels in: Antarctica, Argentina, Australia, Brazil, Chile, China, Costa Rica, Cuba, Galápagos, Kenya, Namibia, South Africa, USA or Venezuela .
Fees: £85 plus petrol. **Limits:** None.
Times: Evenings.
Address: Stretton Lodge, 9 Birch Grove, West Hill, Ottery St Mary, Devon, EX11 1XP; (Tel/ Fax) 01404 815 383;
e-mail: andy_swash@wildguides.co.uk
www.wildguides.co.uk

TAYLOR, Mick

Co-ordinator South Peak Raptor Group, photographer, ornithologist, writer.
Subjects: Several talks including (Merlins, Peak District birds, Peak District raptors, Alaskan wildlife).
Fees: £60 plus petrol. **Limits:** Negotiable.
Times: Evenings preferred.
Address: 76 Hawksley Avenue, Chesterfield, Derbyshire, S40 4TL; 01246 277 749.

DIRECTORY OF LECTURERS

TODD, Ralph

Lecturer & photographer, course tutor and former tour leader.

Subjects: 13 talks incl. Galapagos Wildlife, On the Trail of the Crane, Polar Odyssey, Operation Osprey, Iceland & Pyrenees, Man & Birds – Travels through time, A Summer in Northern Landscapes, Where Yeehaa meets Ole.

Fees: £60 plus expenses. **Limits:** None, neg over 120 miles. **Times:** Any - also short notice.

Address: 9 Horsham Road, Bexleyheath, Kent, DA6 7HU; (Tel/Fax) 01322 528 335; e-mail: rbtodd@todds9.fsnet.co.uk

WARD, Chris

Photographer, N Bucks RSPB Local Group Leader.

Subjects: 20 talks on UK and worldwide topics (Spain, Americas, Africa, Goa, Australasia) – primarily birds, some other wildlife.

Fees: £45 plus petrol. **Limits:** 100 mls. **Times:** Evenings only.

Address: 41 William Smith Close, Woolstone, Milton Keynes, MK15 0AN; 01908 669 448; e-mail: cwphotography@hotmail.com www.cwardphotography.co.uk

WILKES, Mike FRPS

Professional wildlife photographer, tour leader.

Subjects: 13 talks - natural history - Africa, America, South America, Europe, Gt Britain.

Fees: On request according to distance.

Limits: None. **Times:** Any.

Address: 43 Feckenham Road, Headless Cross, Redditch, Worcestershire, B97 5AS; 01527 550 686; e-mail: wilkes@photoshot.com

WILLIAMS, Nick

Photographer, lecturer, author.

Subjects: Several audio visual shows (including Spain, N.Germany, Camargue, Turkey, N.Norway, Cape Verde Islands, Falklands and Birds of Prey).

Fee: £90-£110 depending on group size and distance. **Limits:** None. **Times:** Any.

Address: Owl Cottage, Station Street, Rippingale, Lincs, PE10 0TA; (Tel/Fax) 01778 440 500; e-mail: birdmanandbird@hotmail.com www.nickwilliams.eu

WREN, Graham J. ARPS

Wildlife photographer, lecturer, tour guide.

Subjects: 22 talks: birds – UK and Scandinavia, the environment – recent habitat changes and effect on bird populations, wildlife – Ohio and Kenya. Detailed information package supplied on request.

Fees: £50-80 plus petrol. **Limits:** None. **Times:** Any.

Address: The Kiln House, Great Doward, Whitchurch, Ross-on-Wye, Herefordshire, HR9 6DU; 01600 890 488; e-mail: grahamjwren@aol.com

BTO SPEAKERS

BTO speakers can be contacted by post at BTO, The Nunnery, Thetford, Norfolk IP24 2PU
Tel: 01842 750 050; Fax: 01842 750 030; www.bto.org

Fees for BTO talks are £40, plus travel expenses and distances are negotiable with the speaker. Some speakers also offer talks in a private capacity and fees for these are shown where applicable.

APPLETON, Graham
Head of Fundraising and Publicity.
Subjects: The work of the BTO; Flyway to Iceland; Time to fly - bird migration; House Sparrows: what's the problem?
E-mail: graham.appleton@bto.org

AUSTIN, Dr Graham
Wetland & Coastal Ecology Unit Team Leader.
Subjects: Wetland Bird Survey
E-mail: graham.austin@bto.org

BAILLIE, Dr Stephen
Director of Populations Research.
Subjects: BirdTrack; population monitoring.
E-mail: stephen.baillie@bto.org

BAKER, Jeff (Kevin)
Head of Membership.
Subjects: 'Little brown jobs' - warblers and how to identify them; The work of the BTO.
E-mail: jeff.baker@bto.org
Tel: 01842 768243 (Direct Line).

BALMER, Dawn
Demography Unit Population Biologist.
Subjects: Bird ringing; BirdTrack; BTO work in General. E-mail: dawn.balmer@bto.org

BANKS, Alex
Wetland & Coastal Ecology Unit Research Ecologist.
Subjects: Wetland Bird Survey; Aerial monitoring of waterbirds.
E-mail: alex.banks@bto.org

BARIMORE, Carl
Nest Records Officer.
Subjects: Nest Record Scheme; Barn Owl monitoring programme.
E-mail: carl.barimore@bto.org

BLACKBURN, Jez
Ringing Unit Recoveries and Licencing Team Leader.
Subjects: Bird Moult suitable for ringers; Sule Skerry.
Distance: East Anglia.
E-mail: jez.blackburn@bto.org

CARTER, Dr Nick
Director of Development.
Subjects: Farmland birds.
Fee: £40 donated to current BTO Appeal.
E-mail: nick.carter@bto.org

CHAMBERLAIN, Dr Dan
Senior Research Ecologist.
Subjects: Garden BirdWatch; Breeding Bird Survey.
E-mail: dan.chamberlain@bto.org

CLARK, Jacquie
Head of Ringing Unit.
Subjects: Waders and severe weather; Ringing for conservation.
Distance: 100 mile radius of Thetford.
E-mail: jaquie.clark@bto.org

CLARK, Dr Nigel
Head of Projects Development Unit.
Subjects: Waders, man and estuaries; Horseshoe crabs and waders; Migration through Delaware in spring.
Distance: 100 mile radius of Thetford.
E-mail: nigel.clark@bto.org

COLLIER, Mark
Wetland Bird Survey Research Officer.
Subjects: Wetland Bird Survey
E-mail: mark.collier@bto.org

DIRECTORY OF LECTURERS

CONWAY, Greg
Terrestrial Ecology Unit Research Ecologist.
Subjects: Nightjars; Woodlarks & Dartford Warblers; Wintering warblers.
Distance: 100 miles from Thetford.
E-mail: greg.conway@bto.org

CRICK, Dr Humphrey
Head of Demography Unit.
Subjects: Climate change and birds; One million nests.
Fee: £50 for private. **Expenses:** Mileage @ 25p per mile. **Distance:** Prefer less than 100 miles from Cambridge.
E-mail: humphrey.crick@bto.org

DAVID, Dr Sarah
Census Unit Population Biologist.
Subjects: Food availability and Arctic Skuas.
E-mail: sarah.david@bto.org

FULLER, Dr Rob
Director of Habitats Research.
Subjects: Nightingales; Woodland management and birds; Changing times for woodland birds.
Distance: Anywhere.
E-mail: rob.fuller@bto.org

GILLINGS, Dr Simon
Terrestrial Ecology Unit Research Ecologist.
Subjects: Winter Golden Plovers and Lapwings; Winter farmland birds.
E-mail: simon.gillings@bto.org

GOUGH, Su
Terrestrial Ecology Unit Research Ecologist.
Subjects: Bird Biology; The work of the BTO; urban birds. Non-BTO talks: Wildlife of Canada, Wildlife of southwestern USA, Wildlife of European mountains.
Fee: BTO fee £40, plus expenses for private talks.
E-mail: su.gough@bto.org

GRANTHAM, Mark
Ringing Unit Recoveries Officer.
Subjects: A range of general talks on ringing, migration and bird observatories; Oiled sea-birds.
Distance: 100 miles.
E-mail: mark.grantham@bto.org

GREENWOOD, Professor J J D
Former BTO Director.
Subjects: How to change government policy by counting birds; Why ring birds?; The future for birds and people; Purposeful birdwatching around the world.
Fee: BTO fee £40, £50 for private talks.
Expenses: Public transport or 25p/mile.
Distance: 100 miles from Thetford, further by arrangement.
E-mail: jeremy.greenwood@bto.org

HENDERSON, Dr Ian
Terrestrial Ecology Unit Research Manager.
Subjects: Arable farming and birds.
E-mail: ian.henderson@bto.org

HOLLOWAY, Steve
Wetland & Coastal Ecology Unit Research Ecologist.
Subjects: Wetland Bird Survey.
E-mail: steve.holloway@bto.org

LACK, Dr Peter
Head of Information Systems Unit.
Subjects: Bird atlassing; Palearctic migrants in Africa; On foot in Rwanda and Zambia; Bird ecology in East African savannahs; General natural history of Eastern Africa - All are given as non-BTO talks.
Fee: Negotiable. **Expenses:** Travel. **Distance:** 60 miles from Bury St Edmunds.
E-mail: peter.lack@bto.org

MARCHANT, John
Census Unit Team Leader.
Subjects: Heronries; Waterways Bird Survey/ Waterways Breeding Bird Survey; Breeding bird trends in the UK.
E-mail: john.marchant@bto.org

McCLEAN, Dr Ilya
Wetland & Coastal Ecology Unit Research Ecologist.
Subjects: Waterbird trends in protected areas; African wetland conservation.
E-mail: ilya.mcclean@bto.org

DIRECTORY OF LECTURERS

MUSGROVE, Dr Andy
Wetland & Coastal Ecology Unit Research Manager.
Subjects: The Wetland Bird Survey; Little Egrets in the UK; Recording moths in your garden (non-BTO).
Fee: BTO fee £40, £30 for private talk.
Expenses: Travel. **Distance:** By agreement.
E-mail: andy.musgrove@bto.org

NEWSON, Dr Stuart
Demography Unit Population Biologist.
Subjects: Tree-nesting Cormorants.
E-mail: stuart.newson@bto.org

NOBLE, Dr David
Head of Census Unit.
Subjects: The Farmland Bird Indicator; Population trends.
E-mail: david.noble@bto.org

RAVEN, Mike
Breeding Bird Survey Organiser.
Subjects: Latest findings from the Breeding Bird Survey.
E-mail: mike.raven@bto.org

REHFISCH, Dr Mark
Head of Wetland & Coastal Ecology Unit.
Subjects: Wetland work at the BTO; Water quality & waterbirds; Waterbird alerts; Climate change; Habitat loss and waterbirds; Monitoring waterbirds; Sea level rise and climate change; Introduced species including Golden Pheasant.
Fee: BTO fee £40, up to £40 for private talk.
Expenses: Travel. **Distance:** By agreement.
E-mail: mark.rehfisch@bto.org

ROBINSON, Dr Rob
Demography Unit Senior Population Biologist.
Subjects: Farming and birds; House Sparrows.
E-mail: rob.robinson@bto.org

SIRIWARDENA, Dr Gavin
Terrestrial Ecology Unit Research Manager.
Subjects: Marsh and Willow Tits - analysis of BTO data; Evidence of impacts of nest predation and competition; Quantifying migratory strategies; Winter feeding of farmland birds - currently all short talks.
Distance: 50 miles from Thetford, further with accommodation.
E-mail: gavin.siriwardena@bto.org

TOMS, Mike
Garden BirdWatch Organiser.
Subjects: The BTO Garden BirdWatch.
Distance: 50 miles from Thetford, further by arrangement.
E-mail: mike.toms@bto.org

TOOMER, Dr Derek
Membership Development Officer.
Subjects: Making your birding count - the work of the BTO.
E-mail: derek.toomer@bto.org

VICKERY, Dr Juliet
Head of Terrestrial Ecology Unit.
Subjects: Farmland birds.
E-mail: juliet.vickery@bto.org

WERNHAM, Dr Chris
Senior Research Ecologist, BTO Scotland.
Subjects: The BTO's migration research including the Migration Atlas and later developments; The work of BTO Scotland.
Fee: £40. **Expenses:** Petrol. **Distance:** Scotland and northeast England.
E-mail: chris.wernham@bto.org

the bird magazine that dares to be different

Birds Illustrated is a high quality subscription-only quarterly magazine that blends

- intelligent, in depth articles on wide range of topics of interest to birdwatchers
- profiles on leading wildlife artists and bird photographers
- unique features on secondhand bird books and forthcoming wildlife art exhibitions

An annual subscription costs £20 but as a reward to existing Buckingham Press customers, simply quote this reference (NB3) with your subscription order and you will receive two extra Back Issues completely free.

To order, please call the Buckingham Press Credit Card Hotline on 01733 561 739 or write to: Birds Illustrated Offer (NB3), Buckingham Press Ltd, 55 Thorpe Park Road, Peterborough PE3 6LJ. Please make cheques payable to Buckingham Press Ltd.

BE PREPARED!

ID Insights Pocket Cards are handy postcard-sized guides to help you identify 113 common but difficult bird species. You no longer need to carry a heavyweight fieldguide to solve your ID dilemmas – the ten ID Insights cards feature excellent artwork by Dave Nurney and key written tips from Dominic Couzens.

Buy one pack of ten full colour, high quality coated cards for £5.95 (postage included). Pay only £5 per pack for orders of three or more packs.

To order, please call the Buckingham Press Credit Card Hotline on 01733 561 739 or write to: Pocket Card Offer (NB2), Buckingham Press Ltd, 55 Thorpe Park Road, Peterborough PE3 6LJ. Please make cheques payable to Buckingham Press Ltd.

ID Insights Pocket cards are produced in association with Zeiss and *Bird Watching* magazine.

TRADE DIRECTORY

Lesser Spotted Woodpecker by Steve Knell

BIRD GARDEN SUPPLIERS

BIRD GARDEN SUPPLIES

BAMFORDS TOP FLIGHT

Company ethos: Family-owned manufacturing company providing good quality bird foods via a network of UK stockists or mail-order. RSPB Corporate Member, BTO Business Ally, Petcare Trust Member.
Key product lines: A range of wild bird mixtures containing the revolutionary new 'Pro-tec Health Aid', developed by Bamfords, to protect and promote the welfare of wild birds. Vast array of other foods and seeds for birds.
New for 2008: New formula Four Seasons Wild Bird Food now with added aniseed and more nutritious seeds.
Other services: Trade suppliers of bulk and pre-packed bird and petfoods. Custom packing/own label if required.
Opening times: Mon - Fri (8am-5.30pm); Sat (8am-12 noon); Sunday (10am-12 noon), Mill Shop only.
Address; Globe Mill, Midge Hall, Leyland, Lancashire, PR26 6TN: 01772 456 300; (Fax) 01772 456 302. email: sales@bamfords.co.uk
www.bamfords.co.uk

BIRD VENTURES

Company ethos: A comprehensive stock of wildlife products for everyone from garden bird enthusiasts to keen birdwatchers. The business operates as an online shop and retail outlet based in Holt, Norfok. The business helps support Natural Surrounding, a wildlife centre with eight acres of gardens and education facilities for all ages. This won the District Council's Environmental Small Business of the Year for north Norfolk.
Key product lines: Nest box cameras, moth traps, butterfly nets, wildbird food, bird feeders, nest boxes, hedgehog homes, insect habitats, bat boxes, squirrel-proof feeders, wildflower seeds, children's nature study equipment and much more.
Other services: On-line 24 hours.
Opening times: Mon-Sat (9am-5.30pm).
Contact: Bird Ventures, 9B Chapel Yard, Albert Street, Holt, Norfolk, NR25 6HG; 01263 710 203; (Fax) 01263 711 091.
e-mail: paullaurie100@aol.com
www.birdventures.co.uk

CJ WILDBIRD FOODS LTD

Company ethos: High quality products, no-quibble guarantee, friendly, professional service.
Key product lines: Complete range of CJ Wildlife bird feeders, bird food, nest boxes, bird tables and accessories, alongside a collection of other wildlife related products.
Other services: Mail-order company, online ordering, 24hr delivery service. Free *Handbook of Garden Wildlife* to all enquirers.
Opening times: Mon-Fri (9am-5pm). Sat (9am-12pm).
Address: The Rea, Upton Magna, Shrewsbury, Shropshire, SY4 4UR; 0800 731 2820; (Fax) 01743 709 504.
e-mail: enquiries@birdfood.co.uk
www.birdfood.co.uk

ERNEST CHARLES

Company ethos: Member of Birdcare Standards Assoc. ISO 9001 registered. Offering quality bird foods/wildlife products through a friendly mail-order service.
Key product lines: Bird foods, feeders, nest boxes and other wildlife products.
Other services: Own label work for other companies considered and trade enquiries.
Opening times: Mon to Fri (8am-5pm).
Contact: Stuart Christophers, Copplestone Mills, Crediton, Devon EX17 5NF; 01363 84 842; (Fax) 01363 84 147.
e-mail: stuart@ernest-charles.com
www.ernest-charles.com

FIELD AND GARDEN LTD

Company ethos: To provide an inspirational range of quality garden wildlife products to attract and care for creatures great and small.
Key product lines: Wild bird food, feeders and accessories, wildlife habitats and attractants.
Opening times: Telephone and internet mail-order 24/7.
Address; Neil Spinks. 01553 844 055; (Fax) 01553 842 162.
email: info@fieldandgarden.co.uk
www.fieldandgarden.co.uk

foodforbirds.co.uk

Company ethos: Specialist mail-order company supplying high quality wild bird foods via a fast and friendly next day service. Supporter of RSPB

and BTO through parent company.
Key product lines: A great range of tried and tested, freshly made wild bird mixtures, together with a whole host of straight foods - peanuts, sunflowers, niger seed, fat foods etc.
New for 2008: New formula Four Seasons Wild Bird Food now with added aniseed and more nutritious seeds.
Other services: Vast array of bird feeders for peanuts and seed, plus other wildlife foods, all of which can be ordered via a secure on-line website. Send for free catalogue.
Opening times: Telesales (freephone) 8am-5.30pm (order before midday for next day delivery). Answer phone outside these hours. On-line ordering and Fax, 24 hours.
Contact: Foodforbirds, Leyland PR26 6TN; (Freephone) 0800 043 9022; (Fax) 01772 456 302. e-mail: sales@foodforbirds.co.uk
www.foodforbirds.co.uk

JACOBI JAYNE & CO.

Company ethos: Supplying market-leading products of highest quality and proven conservation worth for almost 20 years. Offering expertise and special prices to wildlife groups, schools and colleges.
Key product lines: Birdfeeders, birdfoods, nest boxes & accessories. UK distributor of Schwegler woodcrete nest boxes, Droll Yankees feeders and Jacobi Jayne wildlife foods.
Other services: *Wild Bird News* mail-order catalogue.
Opening times: 24hrs (use websites or answering service when office is closed).
Contact: Graham Evans/Sally Haynes, Jacobi Jayne & Co, Wealden Forest Park, Canterbury, Kent, CT6 7LQ; 0800 072 0130; (Fax) 01227 719 235. e-mail: enquiries@jacobijayne.com
www.jacobijayne.com

JAMIE WOOD LTD

Company ethos: A comprehensive range of quality hand-made products at competitive prices as supplied to the RSPB, universities, film units, householders. Thirty years' experience.
Key products: Owl boxes, nest boxes, bird tables. High quality bird food supplier, feeders, hides, photographic electronics.
Other services: Mail-order, delivery ex-stock, within seven days. Hides and screens. Individual items can be made to order.
Opening times: Mon to Fri (9am-6pm), Sat (9am-12.30pm).
Contact: John Miller, Unit 17, Oaks Farm Workshops, Blackboys Road, Framfield, East Sussex TN22 5PN. 01825 890 990.
e-mail: sales@birdbox.co.uk
www.birdbox.co.uk

VINE HOUSE FARM BIRD FOODS

Company ethos: Growing and selling wild bird food on their family run farm. A full range of high quality bird foods and accessories direct to the customer through our mail-order service and farm shop.
Key product lines: A full range of bird food including home grown black sunflowers and a range of specialist mixes and feeder accessories.
Other services: A number of farm walks and open days in early summer for people to view the conservation award-winning farm. A range of products available for wholesale customers.
Opening times: Mon to Fri (8am-5pm), Sat (8am-4pm).
Contact: Nicholas Watts, Vine House Farm, Deeping St Nicholas, Spalding, PE11 3DG; 01775 630 208; (Fax) 01775 630 244 .
e-mail:birdseed@vinehousefarm.co.uk
www.vinehousefarm.co.uk

BOOK PUBLISHERS

BUCKINGHAM PRESS LTD

Imprints: Single imprint company - publishers of *The Birdwatcher's Yearbook* since 1980, *Who's Who in Ornithology* (1997), *Best Birdwatching Sites* series covering Norfolk, Sussex, Highlands of Scotland and North Wales. Plus sets of identification cards for British birds and British butterflies. Also publishes *Birds Illustrated*, a quarterly, subscription-only magazine (see survey of English language bird magazines page 22).
New for 2008: *Best Birdwatching Sites in Cornwall and The Isles of Scilly, ID Insights Pocket Cards for British Dragonflies.*
Address: 55 Thorpe Park Road, Peterborough, PE3 6LJ. Tel/Fax: 01733 561 739.
e-mail: admin@buckinghampress.com
www.birdsillustrated.com

BOOK SELLERS

CHRISTOPHER HELM PUBLISHERS

Imprints: Christopher Helm – the leading publisher of ornithology books in the world; includes many field guides, identification guides, family guides, county and country avifaunas, and a Where to Watch Birds series. T & AD Poyser – an acclaimed series of respected ornithology monographs. Birds of Africa – the standard series of handbooks on African birds. A & C Black – publisher of definitive natural history books.
New for 2008: *Secret Lives of Garden Wildlife* by Dominic Couzens and Peter Partington, *Birds by Colour* by Marc Duquet, *Birds of Argentina* by Mark Pearman, *Fieldguide to the Birds of East Asia* by Mark Brazil, *Albatrosses* by Tui de Roy, Mark Jones and Julian Fitter, *RSPB Handbook of Garden Wildlife* by Peter Holden and Geoffrey Abbott, *British Moths: A Photographic Guide* by Chris Manley, *Reed and Bush Warblers* by Peter Kennerley and David Pearson.
Address: 38 Soho Square, London, W1D 3HB; 020 7758 0200; (Fax) 020 7758 0222.
e-mail: nredman@acblack.com
www.acblack.com/naturalhistory

HARPER COLLINS PUBLISHERS

Imprints: Collins Natural History -- the leading publisher of fieldguides to the natural world. Collins New Naturalist Series, the encyclopaedic reference for all areas of British natural history. HarperCollins, publisher of the best illustrated books.
New for 2008: *New Naturalist: Wye Valley* by George Peterken, *Dragonflies* by Philip Corbett and Stephen Brooks, *Grouse* by Adam Watson and Robert Moss, *Southern England* by Peter Friend. *Collins Flower Guide* by David Streeter, *Collins Butterfly Guide* by Tom Tolman and Richard Lewington, *Collins/Readers Digest What is that? - a complete guide to British wildlife* by Paul Sterry, *Britain's Greatest Wildlife Spectacles* by Mike Dilger.
Address: 77-85 Fulham Palace Rd, Hammersmith, London, W6 8JB; 020 8307 4998; (Fax) 020 8307 4037. e-mail: Myles.Archibald@harpercollins.co.uk
www.fireandwater.com www.collins.co.uk

NEW HOLLAND PUBLISHERS (UK) LTD

Imprints; New Holland, illustrated bird books, general wildlife and personality-led natural history.
Address: Garfield House, 86-88 Edgware Road, London, W2 2EA; 020 7724 7773; (Fax) 020 7258 1293. e-mail: postmaster@nhpub.co.uk
www.newhollandpublishers.com

WILDGuides LTD

Imprints; WILD*Guides* – definitive natural history fieldguides. Hardback and flexicover.
OCEAN*Guides* – definitive identification guides to marine wildlife. Hardback and flexicover.
WILD eARTh – lavishly illustrated celebrations of wildlife and natural places. Hardback.
Your Countryside Guides – regional heritage guides for walkers. Hardback. Sales of all books benefit conservation.
New for 2008: *Whales and Dolphins of the North American Pacific, Endemic Plants of the Altai Mountains, Nightjars of the World.*
Address: PO Box 680, Maidenhead, Berkshire, SL6 9ST; 01628 529 297; (Fax) 01628 525 314.
e-mail: info@wildguides.co.uk
www.wildguides.co.uk

BOOK SELLERS

ATROPOS

Company ethos: Lively magazine for butterfly, moth and dragonfly enthusiasts. Mail-order book service providing key titles swiftly at competitive prices.
Key subjects: Butterflies, moths, dragonflies and other insects.
Address: 36 Tinker Lane, Methan, Holmfirth, West Yorkshire HD9 4EX;
e-mail: atropos@atroposed.freeserve.co.uk
www.atropos.info

CALLUNA BOOKS

Company ethos: Specialising in buying and selling out-of-print natural history titles, with an emphasis on quality stock at competitive prices.
Key subjects: Birds, mammals, flora, invertebrates in the UK and worldwide, including the Poyser and New Naturalist series, and general natural history, conservation and countryside titles including some reports and journals. Stock of 1,500+ titles maintained.
Other services: Catalogues issued (usually 3 p.a). Exhibitor at some bird fairs including Rutland and Slimbridge. Wants lists welcomed – no obligation to buy.

Opening hours: Mail-order but viewing by appointment possible.
Address: 54 Corfe Road, Stoborough, Wareham, Dorset, BH20 5AF. 01929 552 560.
e-mail: neil&yuki@onaga54.freeserve.co.uk
www.callunabooks.co.uk

NHBS ENVIRONMENT BOOKSTORE

Company ethos: A unique natural history, conservation and environmental bookstore.
Key subjects: Natural history, conservation, environmental science, zoology, habitats and ecosystems, botany, marine biology.
Other services: www.nhbs.com offers a searchable and browsable web catalogue with more than 95,000 titles.
Opening times: Mon-Fri (9am-5pm), for mail-order service.
Address; 2-3 Wills Road, Totnes, Devon, TQ9 5XN; 01803 865 913; (Fax) 01803 865 280.
e-mail: nhbs@nhbs.co.uk www.nhbs.com

ORNITHOLIDAYS BOOK STOP

Company ethos: Friendly and helpful staff on hand to assist in the purchase of ornithological and natural history books.
Key subjects: Ornithology and natural history books by mail-order.
Other services; Though primarily a tour operator sending birdwatching and natural history tours worldwide since 2000, we have complemented our business by successfully supplying a wide range of books, published by the leading companies, at a 10% discount with free postage and packing within the UK.
Opening times: Mail-order/internet only. Telephone lines are open Mon-Fri (9am-5pm).
Address: 29 Straight Mile, Romsey, Hampshire SO51 9BB; 01794 523 500; (Fax) 01794 523 544.
e-mail: ruth@ornitholidays.co.uk
www.ornitholidays.co.uk

PICTURE BOOK

Company ethos: General bookshop with specialist interest in bird books.
Key subjects: Birdwatching, natural history, local history.
Other services: Mail-order, new and secondhand books.
Opening times: Tue-Fri (10am-5pm), Sat (9am-5pm).
Address; Picture Book, 6 Stanley Street, Leek ST13 5HG; 01538 384 337; (Fax) 01538 399 696.
e-mail: info@leekbooks.co.uk
www.birdbooksonline.co.uk

PORTLAND OBSERVATORY BOOK SHOP

Company ethos: To meet the needs of amateur and professional naturalists.
Key subjects: Ornithology, general natural history, topography, art and local history. New and secondhand.
Other services: Mail-order, discount on new books, increased discount for observatory members.
Opening times: Wed, Thur, Sat and Sunday; (10am-4pm). Other times on request.
Address; Bird Observatory, Old Lower Light, Portland Bill, Dorset, DT5 2JT; 01305 820 553, (shop) 01305 826 625, (home) 01225 700 728.
e-mail: petermowday@tiscali.co.uk
www.portlandbirdobs.btinternet.co.uk

SECOND NATURE

Company ethos: Buying and selling out-of-print/secondhand/antiquarian books on natural history, topography and travel.
Key subjects: Birds, mammals and travel with a natural history interest. Very large specialist stock.
Other services: Occasional catalogues issued. Often exhibiting at bird/natural history fairs.
Opening times: Mail-order only.
Address; Knapton Book Barn, Back Lane, Knapton, York, YO26 6QJ; (Tel/Fax) 01904 339 493. e-mail: SecondnatureYork@aol.com

SUBBUTEO BOOKS

Company ethos: Specialist knowledge on all aspects of wildlife, travel and natural history books, friendly service.
Key subjects: Wildlife, natural history and travel books.
Other services: Source any natural history book from around the world. Online ordering, free delivery for orders over £50 (in-print titles and UK orders only), free catalogue and email newsletter.
Opening times: Mon-Fri (9am-5pm). Sat (9am-12pm).
Address: The Rea, Upton Magna, Shrewsbury, Shropshire, SY4 4UR; 0870 010 9700; (Fax) 0870 010 9699. e-mail: info@wildlifebooks.com
www.wildlifebooks.com

BOOK SELLERS AND CLOTHING SUPPLIERS

WAXWINGS NATURAL HISTORY BOOKS

Company ethos: Friendly, helpful and personal service. All levels of interest catered for, from beginner to professional.
Key subjects: Ornithology, all aspects of natural history and ecology.
Other services: Freelance ornithological research, bird survey and monitoring, ecological surveys and environmental assessment.
New for 2008: Massive stock sale (see website), autumn 2007-winter 2008.
Opening times: Mail-order only, orders or enquiries at any reasonable time.
Address: Sunny Bank Cottage, Ruston Parva, Driffield, East Yorkshire YO25 4DG; 01377 254 775; e-mail: books@waxwings.co.uk
www.waxwings.co.uk

WILDSOUNDS

Company ethos: Committed to sound environmental practice. Donates a significant portion of profit to bird conservation (Associate sponsor of the annual British Birdwatching Fair). Official bookseller to African Bird Club.
Key product lines: Mail-order, post-free books, DVDs, multi-media guides and eGuides for PDAs - mobile versions of popular fieldguides complete with bird sounds and listing software e.g. *Collins Bird eGuide* and *Sasol eBirds of Southern Africa.* Publisher and distributor of *Birding in Eastern Europe* by Gerard Gorman.
New for 2008: eGuides for North America (Sibley) and Australia.
Opening times: Weekdays (9.30am-5pm).
Address: Cross Street, Salthouse, Norfolk, NR25 7XH; +44(UK) (0)1263 741 100; (Fax) +44 (0)1263 741 838. e-mail: duncan@wildsounds.com
www.wildsounds.com

WYSEBY HOUSE BOOKS

Company ethos: We stock rare, out-of-print, second-hand and unusual titles which are on display in our shop or can be found on our website. Informed and friendly staff always ready to help personal shoppers or answer telephone and e mail inquiries.
Key subjects: Bird books, gardening, forestry and natural history, art, architecture, design.
Other services: A well designed website with easy to use search facility where books can be located by author, title, keyword or subject.
Opening times: Mon-Sat (9am-5pm), but we suggest you ring beforehand just in case you are travelling some distance.
Address: Kingsclere Old Bookshop, 2a, George Street, Kingsclere, Nr Newbury, Berks. RG20 5NQ. 01635 297 995; (Fax) 01635 297 677; e-mail: info@wyseby.co.uk
www.wyseby.co.uk

CLOTHING

COUNTRY INNOVATION

Company ethos: Friendly advice by well-trained staff.
Key product lines: Full range of outdoor wear; jackets; smock; fleeces; trousers; Brasher boots, poles & accessories; Tilley hats; healthy back bags; lightweight clothing; hats; gloves; rucksacks and pouches. Ladies fits available.
Other services: Mail-order and website.
Opening times; Mon-Fri (9am-5pm), Sat (10am-4pm).
Address: 1 Broad Street, Congresbury, North Somerset , BS49 5DG; 01934 877 333.
e-mail: sales@countryinnovation.com
www.countryinnovation.com

PÁRAMO DIRECTIONAL CLOTHING SYSTEMS

Company ethos: Innovators of technical mountain, birding and travel clothing using revolutionary Nikwax fabrics, functional design to provide performance and comfort for all outdoor enthusiasts and professionals, whatever their activity. Ethical manufacture.
Key product lines: Waterproof jackets and trousers, technical base layers and insulating overlayers. Of particular note: the Pájaro birdwatching jacket and Cascada waterproof trousers and the Andy Rouse Limited Edition range of Aspira smock, Cascada trousers and mountain vent pull-on.
Other services: Repair and service of Páramo garments.
Opening times For independent retailers, consult website or ring 01892 786 444 for a stockist list and catalogue pack.
Address: Unit F, Durgates Industrial Estate, Wadhurst, East Sussex, TN5 6JL, UK
e-mail: info@paramo.co.uk
www.paramo.co.uk

EQUIPMENT SUPPLIERS AND SERVICES

ALWYCH BOOKS

Company ethos: The Bird Watcher's All-weather Flexible Pocket Book.
Key product lines: Alwych all-weather notebooks.
Address: Janette Scott, Wishaw Printing Company, 84 Stewarton Street, Wishaw, ML2 8AG; 0845 270 2828; (admin) 01698 357 223.

BIRD IMAGES

Company ethos: High quality products at affordable prices.
Key product lines: Bird DVDs.
New for 2008: *Birdwatching in England.*
Opening times: Telephone first.
Address: 28 Carousel Walk, Sherburn in Elmet, North Yorkshire LS25 6LP; 01977 684 666.
www.birdvideodvd.com

BIRDGUIDES LTD

Company ethos: Better birding through technology. A range of web and e-mail services for birders, DVD-roms, CD-roms and MP3 sound guides.
Key product lines: DVD-ROM, CD-ROM, DVD, sound and video guides to British, European and American birds. Rare bird news services via e-mail, website and SMS.
New for 2008: *British Birds Interactive*, Best of BirdGuides series.
Address: Birdguides Ltd, PO Box 4104, Sheffield, S25 9BS; 01909 560 992; order line (freephone) 0800 919 391. e-mail: contact@birdguides.com
www.birdguides.com

FLAGHEAD PHOTOGRAPHIC LTD

Company ethos: Importer and distributor of quality products for the photographer and optics user.
Key product lines: Walkstool - the only three-legged stool with telescopic legs in the world! Quantum - external battery power for portable flash units, specialist high power flash units and radio remote triggers. Expodisc - digital white balance filters. Green Clean - sensor cleaning for digital cameras and air dusting equipment for all photographic and optics equipment. Gigicover - protection screens for LDC screens.
Address: PO Box 6143, Poole, Dorset BH12 9AS. 01202 733 123; (Fax) 01202 737 428.
e-mail: info@flaghead.co.uk
www.flaghead.co.uk

GOLDEN VALLEY INSURANCE SERVICES

Company ethos: Knowledgeable, friendly insurance services. Free information pack on request. Freephone telephone number for all enquiries.
Key product lines: Insurance for optical/photographic/video/computer equipment for birdwatchers. Also, public liability for ornithological clubs and societies.
Opening times: Mon-Fri (9am-5pm), answering machine at other times
Address: Sharron or Marion, Golden Valley Insurance Services, The Olde Shoppe, Ewyas Harold, Herefordshire HR2 0ES; 0800 015 4484; (Fax) 01981 240 451. e-mail: gvinsurance@aol.com
www.insuranceforcameras.co.uk

HARVEY MAPS

Company ethos: Over 30 years, Harvey has gained a reputation for high quality maps for outdoor recreation. These award-winning maps are compiled from original aerial surveys and field checked by experienced surveyors, themselves hill-walkers.
Key product lines: Detailed maps for walking
New for 2008: South West Coast Path, Plymouth to Exmouth & South West Coast Path, Exmouth to Poole.
Opening times: Mon-Fri (8.30am-5.30pm).
Address: 12-22 Main Street, Doune, Perthshire FK16 6BJ; 01786 841 202; (Fax) 01786 841 098.
e-mail: sales@harveymaps.co.uk
www.harveymaps.co.uk

OPTREP Optical Repairs

Company ethos: To give a speedy, economical and effective repair service.
Key services: Servicing and repair of binoculars, telescopes etc. Conversant with the special needs of birdwatchers.
Opening times: Mon-Thu (9am-5pm), Fri (9am-3pm).
Address: 16 Wheatfield Road, Selsey, West Sussex PO20 0NY; 01243 601 365;
e-mail: info@opticalrepairs.com
www.opticalrepairs.com

WILDLIFE WATCHING SUPPLIES

Company ethos: To bring together a comprehensive range of materials, clothing and equipment covers, making it easier and more comfortable for users to blend in with the environment. We always aim to provide a quick and friendly service and are happy to make up specials.

Key product lines: Camera and scope covers, digi-scope covers, hides, camouflage, bean bags, lens and camera covers, clothing etc.etc.

New for 2008: Scope and digi-scope covers, updated on-line shop, see new products page on website.

Opening times: Mon to Fri (9am-5pm), mail-order. Visitors by appointment.

Address: Town Living Farmhouse, Puddington, Tiverton, Devon, EX16 8LW; 01884 860 692 (24hr); (Fax) 01884 860 994.
e-mail: enquiries@wildlifewatchingsupplies.co.uk
www.wildlifewatchingsupplies.co.uk

WILDSOUNDS

Company ethos: Committed to sound environmental practice. Donates a significant portion of profit to bird conservation (Associate sponsor of the annual British Birdwatching Fair). Official bookseller to African Bird Club.

Key product lines: Mail-order, post-free books, DVDs, multi-media guides and eGuides for PDAs - mobile versions of popular fieldguides complete with bird sounds and listing software e.g. *Collins Bird eGuide* and *Sasol eBirds of Southern Africa*. Publisher and distributor of *Birding in Eastern Europe* by Gerard Gorman.

New for 2008: eGuides for North America (Sibley) and Australia.

Opening times: Weekdays (9.30am-5pm).

Address: Cross Street, Salthouse, Norfolk, NR25 7XH; +44(UK) (0)1263 741 100; (Fax) +44 (0)1263 741 838. e-mail: duncan@wildsounds.com
www.wildsounds.com

HOLIDAY COMPANIES

AIGAS QUEST LTD

Company ethos: Scotland's longest running nature holiday provider delivers outstanding wildlife watching holidays for groups and individuals. From birdwatching to pine martin, badger or beaver viewing - we've got the lot!

Types of tours: Birdwatching and wildlifewatching for all levels.

Destinations: Highlands and Islands of Scotland.

New for 2008: Skye, Orkney, Shetland, Highlands.

Opening times: Mon-Fri (8.30am-5pm).

Brochure from: Aigas Field Centre, Aigas, Beauly, Inverness-shire IV4 7AD; 01463 782 443; (Fax) 01463 782 097. e-mail: info@aigas.co.uk
www.aigas.co.uk

AVIAN ADVENTURES

Company ethos: Top quality, value for money tours, escorted by friendly, experienced leaders at a fairly relaxed pace. ATOL 3367.

Types of tours: Birdwatching, birds and wildlife photography and wildlife safaris, all suitable for both the first-time and the more experienced traveller.

Destinations: More than 70 tours worldwide.

Brochure from: 49 Sandy Road, Norton, Stourbridge, DY8 3AJ; 01384 372 013; (Fax) 01384 441 340. e-mail: aviantours@argonet.co.uk
www.avianadventures.co.uk

BIRD HOLIDAYS

Company ethos: Relaxed pace, professional leaders, small groups, exciting itineraries.

Types of tours: Birdwatching for all levels, beginners to advanced.

Destinations: Worldwide (40 tours, 6 continents).

New for 2008: Czech Republic, Taiwan, Transylvania, Drakensberg, Cape to Cape (Tierra del Fuego to Cape Town cruise via Antarctica, S. Georgia, Triston da Cunha, Gough Island).

Brochure from: 10 Ivegate, Yeadon, Leeds, LS19 7RE; (Tel/Fax) 0113 3910 510.
e-mail: info@birdholidays.co.uk
www.birdholidays.co.uk

BIRDFINDERS

Company ethos: Top-value birding tours to see all specialities/endemics of a country/area, using leading UK and local guides. ATOL 5406.

Types of tours: Birdwatching holidays for all abilities.

Destinations: More than 50 tours in UK, Europe, Africa, Asia, Australasia, North and South America and Antarctica.

New for 2008: Australia, Egypt, Falkland Islands and Chile, Japan, Madeira, Paraguay, Russia-

Kamchatka and Commander Islands, Turkey.
Brochure from: Vaughan Ashby, Westbank, Cheselbourne, Dorset, DT2 7NW. 01258 839 066; e-mail: info@birdfinders.co.uk
www.birdfinders.co.uk
Our office is open seven days a week (8am-8pm).

BIRDWATCHING BREAKS

Company ethos: Birdwatching breaks and Black Isle birding.
Types of tours: Birding tours around the world to little-known destinations, along with more traditional destinations, using local guides in addition to our own. These tours are aimed at all abilities and are limited to a maximum of eight clients to one leader. We also specialise in Northern Scotland including the Highlands and Islands under the Black Isle Birding banner. Our tours main interest is aimed at birds but we also take in mammals and other wildlife. Many of our tours are suitable for photography.
Destinations: Argentina, Azores, Bulgaria, Canada, Chile, China, Ethiopia, Ghana, Iceland, India, Ireland, Japan, Madagascar, Malawi, Malaya, Scotland, Spain, Syria, Thailand, U.A.E.
New for 2008: Borneo, French Polynesia, New Caledonia and Fiji, Madeira, Tibet.
Brochure from: Birdwatchinig Breaks, Cygnus House, Gordon's Mill, Balblair, Ross-shire IV7 8LQ; 01381 610 495; (Fax) 01381 610 452.
e-mail: enquiries@birdwatchingbreaks.com
www.birdwatchingbreaks.com

BRITISH-BULGARIAN FRIENDSHIP SOCIETY

Company ethos: To introduce people to the beauty of Bulgarian wildlife at exceptional value prices with expert leaders.
Types of tours: Birdwatching tours in spring and autumn, also butterfly, wild flower and natural history tours. Group size 12-14 persons.
Destinations: Specialists to Bulgaria, with more than 30 years experience. The first to send birdwatching tours to Bulgaria and organisers of the first butterfly tour.
New for 2008: Wildlife photography tour with Gordon Langsbury.
Brochure from: Our ATOL-bonded agents, Balkania Travel Ltd, Suite 3.40, Morley House, 320 Regent Street, London W1B 3BE. 020 7538 8654 or email: ognian@balkaniatravel.com
Enquiries: Dr Annie Kay 020 7237 7616; email: annie.kay@btinternet.com
www.bbfs.org.uk

CLASSIC JOURNEYS

Company ethos: Professional and friendly company, providing well organised and enjoyable birdwatching holidays.
Types of tours: General birdwatching and wildlife holidays on the Indian sub-continent and beyond.
Destinations: Nepal, India, Bhutan, Sri Lanka, Tibet, Ecuador, Galapagos, Tanzania, Spitsbergen, Finland.
Brochure from: 33 High Street, Tibshelf, Alfreton, Derbyshire, DE55 5NX; 01773 873 497; (Fax) 01773 590 243.
e-mail: info@classicjourneys.co.uk
www.classicjourneys.co.uk

DORSET BIRDING & WILDLIFE EXPERIENCE

Company ethos: To provide local knowledge and an expertise of Dorset's birds and wildlife, catering for all levels of experience and tailor-made to your requirements.
Types of tours: A guiding service for individuals and small groups aimed at providing an experience of Dorset's birds, wildlife and landscapes. Although there is a particular emphasis on birds, all species groups are covered. Half-day, full-day, weekends or longer breaks are available. Local accommodation can be arranged.
Destinations: Dorset, New Forest.
Brochure from: 54 Corfe Road, Stoborough, Wareham, Dorset, BH20 5AF. 01929 552 560; e-mail: neil&yuki@onaga54.freeserve.co.uk

EXPEDITION CRUISES & CRUISES FOR NATURE

Company ethos: We are specialists in cruises on expedition ships, with expertise for birdwatchers, photographers and naturalists. We also have escorted cruises, using professional guides, to amazing destinations. ATOL no 6934.
Types of cruises: Both escorted and unescorted wildlife cruises on expedition ships.
Destinations: Worldwide including Antarctica, Spitsbergen, Pacific and the North Pole.
New for 2008: New Zealand to Japan cruise.

HOLIDAY COMPANIES

Brochure from: 29 Straight Mile, Romsey, Hampshire, SO51 9BB; 01794 523 500; (Fax) 01794 523 544.
e-mail: info@expeditioncruising.co.uk
www.expeditioncruising.co.uk

HEATHERLEA

Company ethos: Exciting holidays to see all the birds of Scotland and worldwide. Experienced guides and comfortable award-winning hotel to give great customer service.
Types of tours: Birdwatching and other wildlife watching tours, awarded 4 stars by VisitScotland.
Destinations: Scottish Highlands, including holidays from our base in Nethybridge, plus Outer Hebrides, Orkney, Shetlands, Coll and more. Selected overseas destinations include Pyrenees, Lesvos, Galapagos, Kenya and Trinidad.
New for 2008: Yellowstone/Grand Tetons, Spitsbergen, Guyana, and High Season across the Highlands.
Brochure from: The Mountview Hotel, Nethybridge, Inverness-shire, PH25 3EB; 01479 821 248; (Fax) 01479 821 515;
e-mail: hleabirds.aol.com
www.heatherlea.co.uk

LIMOSA HOLIDAYS

Company ethos: The very best in birdwatching and wildlife holidays – expertly-led, fun, friendly and packed with great birding and wildlife. ATOL 2950. AITO member. AITO Trust 1049.
Types of tours: Birdwatching and wildlife tours and cruises.
Destinations: More than 100 departures worldwide.
Brochure from: Limosa Holidays, Suffield House, Northrepps, Norfolk, NR27 0LZ; 01263 578 143; (Fax) 01263 579 251.
e-mail: info@limosaholidays.co.uk
www.limosaholidays.co.uk

NATURETREK

Company ethos: Friendly, gentle-paced, birdwatching holidays with a broad-brush approach. Sympathetic to other wildlife interests, history and local culture. Also operate faster-paced, bargain birdwatching selection. ATOL no 2692.
Types of tours: Escorted birdwatching, botanical and natural history holidays worldwide.
Destinations: Worldwide – see brochure.
Brochure from: Cheriton Mill, Cheriton, Alresford, Hampshire, SO24 0NG; 01962 733 051; (Fax) 01962 736 426.
e-mail: info@naturetrek.co.uk
www.naturetrek.co.uk

NORTHERN FRANCE WILDLIFE TOURS

Company ethos: Friendly personal attention. Normally a maximum of five in a group. Totally flexible.
Types of tours: Mini-bus trips catering for all from beginners to experienced birders. Local birds include Bluethroat, Black Woodpecker, Melodious Warbler.
Destinations: Brittany, Normandy and Pays de la Loire.
Brochure from: Place de l'église, 53700, Averton, France; 00 33 243 00 6969. e-mail: nfwt@online.fr
www.northernfrancewildlifetours.com

ORIOLE ADVENTURES

Company ethos: Enhancing your ID skills and enjoyment of birding.
Types of tours: Norfolk-based birding tours year round, covering all the best sites and species, plus a selection of Britain's best destinations.
Destinations: Norfolk (11 tours), South Wales, Solway, Extremadura, NE England, Cornwall, Mull and Iona.
New for 2008: North Wales, Scilly, Dorset, Romania, South Africa.
Brochure from: Oriole Adventures, White Horse Inn, Fakenham Road, East Barsham, Fakenham, Norfolk NR21 0LH; 01328 821 795.
e-mail: ashley.saunders1@btinternet.com
www.orioleadventures.com

ORKNEY ISLAND HOLIDAYS

Company ethos: Providing high quality holidays for discerning travellers to learn about Orkney and Shetland and beyond, from knowledgeable local experts, with an emphasis on fun and enjoyment, in a relaxed informal atmosphere.
Types of tours: Multi-interest holidays, exploring all aspects of Orkney and Shetland (and other destinations); their birds, flowers, archaeology, history and culture.
Destinations: Specialising in Orkney and Shetland, with some trips abroad too.

New for 2008: Celebrating 20 years of guided holidays.
Brochure from: Paul and Louise Hollinrake, Orkney Island Holidays, Furrowend, Balfour, Shapinsay 19, Orkney, KW17 2DY; 01856 711 373. e-mail: holidays@orkney.com www.orkneyislandholidays.com

ORNITHOLIDAYS

Company ethos: Oldest bird tour company in the world - established 1965. Friendly and fun holidays led by full-time tour leaders. ABTA V2378, ATOL no 0743.
Types of tours: Escorted birdwatching and natural history tours.
Destinations: Worldwide including Trinidad and Tobago, Costa Rica, Bolivia, South Africa and Vietnam.
New for 2008: Guyana, Papua New Guinea, Crete.
Brochure from: 29 Straight Mile, Romsey, Hampshire, SO51 9BB; 01794 519 445; (Fax) 01794 523 544; e-mail: info@ornitholidays.co.uk www.ornitholidays.co.uk

SICKLEBILL SAFARIS LTD

Company ethos: Highly qualified and very experienced, genial leader, to show you the birds and the natural world you have always wanted to see. Under ATOL 9212.
Types of tours: Highly specific and carefully planned birdwatching tours; also general natural history tours, including mammals, larger insects, higher plants and macrofungi.
Destinations: East Anglia, Papua New Guinea, Papua Indonesia and Myanmar.
Brochure from: Trefor, Creake Road, Sculthorpe, Fakenham, Norfolk, NR21 9NQ; 01328 856 925. e-mail: Ian@sicklebill.demon.co.uk
www.sicklebill.com www.pngphototours.com

SPEYSIDE WILDLIFE

Company ethos: We deliver outstanding wildlife experiences where you are always treated as an individual, not one of a crowd. Expert leaders, personal attention and a sense of fun - it's your holiday. ATOL no 4259.
Types of tours: Experts in Scotland and leaders worldwide – birdwatching, mammals and whale watching.
Destinations: Speyside and the Scottish Islands, Scandinavia, the Arctic, Europe, N America, Africa and India.
New for 2008: Sri Lanka, Bulgaria, Hungary, return of Estonia, Namibia, Florida and Mallorca.
Brochure from: Garden Office, Inverdruie House, Inverdruie, Aviemore, Inverness-shire, PH22 1QH; (Tel/Fax) 01479 812 498.
e-mail: enquiries@speysidewildlife.co.uk
www.speysidewildlife.co.uk

SUNBIRD

Company ethos: Enjoyable birdwatching tours led by full-time professional leaders. ATOL no 3003.
Types of tours: Birdwatching, Birds & Music, Birds & History, Birds & Butterflies.
Destinations: Worldwide.
New for 2008: Japan in winter, Egypt – Birds & History, Estonia, Slovenia and Croatia, Ghana, Panama.
Brochure from: P.O. Box 76, Sandy, Bedfordshire, SG19 1DF; (Tel) 01767 262 522; (Fax) 01767 262 168.
e-mail: sunbird@sunbirdtours.co.uk
www.sunbirdtours.co.uk

THE TRAVELLING NATURALIST

Company ethos: Friendly, easy-going, expertly-led birdwatching and wildlife tours. ATOL no.3435. AITO 1124.
Types of tours: Tours include birds and history, birds and bears, whale-watching, birds and flowers.
Destinations: Worldwide.
New for 2008: Japan, Canadian Rockies, bats in Hungary, California, Brazil for mammals, Guyana.
Brochure from: PO Box 3141, Dorchester, Dorset, DT1 2XD; 01305 267 994; (Fax) 01305 265 506. e-mail: jamie@naturalist.co.uk
www.naturalist.co.uk

THE ULTIMATE TRAVEL COMPANY

Company ethos: Quality wildlife experiences and shared enjoyment of the natural world.
Types of tours: Relaxed, escorted wildlife and birdwatching holidays with friendly groups and Britain's most experienced leaders. Often good photographic opportunities as well.
Destinations: Various locations in Africa, South America, India and the Indian Ocean and Europe

New for 2008: Spitsbergen.
Brochure from: The Ultimate Travel Company, 25-27 Vanston Place, London, SW6 1AZ; 020 7386 4676; (Fax) 020 7381 0836.
email: enquiry@theultimatetravelcompany.co.uk

WILD INSIGHTS

Company ethos: Friendly, no-rush tours designed to savour, understand and enjoy birds and wildlife fully, rather than simply build large tick lists. Emphasis on quality ATOL no 5429 (in association with Wildwings).
Types of tours: Reader breaks for *Bird Watching* magazine, skills-building UK courses and workshops, plus selected overseas tours.
Destinations: Various UK locations, plus Spain, Holland, Estonia, Morocco, Gambia, Namibia, Western Cape, Texas, Florida, Costa Rica and Northern India.
Calender brochure from: Yew Tree Farmhouse, Craignant, Selattyn, Oswestry, Salop SY10 7NP. (Tel/Fax) 01691 718 7401;
e-mail: keith.offord@virgin.net
www.wildinsights.co.uk

WILDWINGS

Company ethos: Superb value holidays led by expert guides.
Types of tours: Birdwatching Holidays, whale and dolphin watching holidays, wildlife cruises worldwide.
Destinations: Europe, Arctic, Asia, The Americas, Antarctica, Pacific Region, Trinidad and Tobago.
New for 2008: Scotland to Iceland, Hungarian Bird Festival, Thailand, Panama, Chile for pumas and birds.
Brochure from: 577-579 Fishponds Road, Fishponds, Bristol, BS16 3AF; 0117 9658 333; (Fax) 0117 9375 681;
e-mail: wildinfo@wildwings.co.uk
www.wildwings.co.uk

OPTICAL IMPORTERS AND MANUFACTURERS

ACE OPTICS

Company ethos: To be the best - service, price and stock.
Product lines: Importers of Avian, Optolyth, Questar and main suppliers of Leica, Swarovski, Zeiss and Kowa. All the best tripods and an array of optical related accessories.
Address: 16 Green Street, Bath, BA1 2JZ; 01225 466 364; (Fax) 01225 469 761.
e-mail: optics@acecameras.co.uk
www.acecameras.co.uk

CARL ZEISS LTD

Company ethos: World renowned, high quality performance and innovative optical products.
Product lines: Victory FL, Conquest, Stabilised, Victory and Classic compacts and Diascope FL telescopes.
Address: PO Box 78, Woodfield Road, Welwyn Garden City, Hertfordshire, AL7 1LU; 01707 871 350; (Fax) 01707 871 287.
e-mail: binos@zeiss.co.uk
www.zeiss.co.uk

INTRO 2020 LTD

Company ethos: Experienced importer of photo and optical products.
Product lines: Steiner binoculars, Summit (binoculars and scopes), Velbon and Slik (tripods), Kenko (range of scopes), Hoya and Cokin (filters), Tamrac + Crumpler (bags), Tamron lenses, Metz flashguns
Address: Unit 1, Priors Way, Maidenhead, Berkshire, SL6 2HP; 01628 674 411; (Fax) 01628 771 055. e-mail: sales@intro2020.co.uk
www.intro2020.co.uk www.cokin.co.uk
www.steiner-binoculars.co.uk
www.metzflash.co.uk

LEICA CAMERA LTD

Company ethos: Professional advice from Leica factory-trained staff.
Product line: Leica Ultravid HD full-size binoculars, Leica Ultravid and Trinovid compacts. Leica Televid APO and HD 82 and 65 spotting scopes with a choice of 3 eyepieces, a photo-adapter and digital adapter for D-LUX and C-LUX cameras. Leica Duovid dual magnification and Geovid rangefinder binoculars.
Address: Leica Camera Limited, Davy Avenue, Knowlhill, Milton Keynes, Bucks. MK5 8LB 01908 256 400; (Fax) 01908 671 316.
www.leica-camera.co.uk

OPTICAL DEALERS

NEWPRO UK LTD

Company ethos: A very old brand name with new company technology and attitude.
Product lines: Minox binoculars, telescopes and cameras, Op/tech straps and harnesses.
New for 2008: Hoodman accessories for D-SLRs.
Address: Old Sawmills Road, Faringdon, Oxon SN7 7DS; 01367 243 535; (Fax) 01367 241 124. e-mail: sales@newprouk.co.uk www.newprouk.co.uk

OPTICRON

Company ethos: To continuously develop high quality optics and accessories that are useful, ergonomically sound and exceptional value for money.
Product lines: Opticron binoculars, monoculars, telescopes, telephotography/digi-scoping equipment and accessories.
Address: Unit 21, Titan Court, Laporte Way, Luton, LU4 8EF; 01582 726 522: (Fax) 01582 273 559. e-mail: sales@opticron.co.uk www.opticron.co.uk

PYSER-SGI LTD

Company ethos: Our primary aim is customer/ dealer care and satisfaction, achieved through technological leadership, quality technical assistance and post-sales service/support.
Product lines: Pyser-SGI quality binoculars at competitive prices, Kowa Prominar exceptional quality spotting scopes and binoculars, including the new TSN-770 and TSN-880 series scopes and Prominar XD binoculars. Swift Sport Optics wide range of binoculars and spotting scopes, including the renowned original Audobon binoculars, Niggeloh straps, Pyser-SGI microscopes.
New for 2008: Continuing enhancements to the product ranges.
Address; Fircroft Way, Edenbridge, Kent TN8 6HA. 01732 864 111; (Fax) 01732 865 544; e-mail: sales@pyser-sgi.com www.pyser-sgi.com

SWAROVSKI UK

Company ethos: Constantly improving on what is good in terms of products and committed to conservation world-wide.
Product lines: ATS 65 spotting scope and EL 8x32 and 10x32 binoculars, the latest additions to a market-leading range of telescopes and binoculars. Swarovski tripods and digiscoping attachments also available.
Address: Perrywood Business Park, Salfords, Surrey RH1 5JQ; 01737 856 812: (Fax) 01737 856 885. e-mail: christine.percy@swarovskioptik.co.uk www.swarovskioptik.com

VICKERS SPORTS OPTICS

Company ethos: Sole UK distributors of world renowned products from American company, Bushnell as well as Premierlight LED Torches.
Product lines: The extensive Bushnell list includes market leading binoculars, including the Natureview and H20 range, spotting scopes and nightvision equipment.
Address: Unit 9, 35 Revenge Road, Lordswood, Kent, ME5 8DW; Tel: 01634 201 284, (Fax) 01634 201 286; e-mail: www.jjvickers.co.uk, e-mail: info@jjvickers.co.uk

EAST MIDLANDS AND EAST ANGLIA

BIRDNET OPTICS LTD

Company ethos: To provide the birdwatcher with the best value for money on optics, books and outdoor clothing.
Viewing facilities: Clear views to distant hills for comparison of optics at long range and wide variety of textures and edges for clarity and resolution comparison.
Optical stock: Most leading binocular and telescope ranges stocked. If we do not have it in stock we will endeavour to get it for you.
Non-optical stock: Books incl. New Naturalist Series and Poysers, videos, CDs, audio tapes, tripods, hide clamps, accessories and clothing.
Opening times: Mon-Sat (9:30am-5:30pm). Sundays (9:30am-5pm).
Address: 5 London Road, Buxton, Derbyshire, SK17 9PA; 01298 71 844; (Fax) 01298 27 727. e-mail: paulflint@birdnet.co.uk www.birdnet.co.uk

IN-FOCUS

Company ethos: The binocular and telescope specialists, offering customers informed advice

at birdwatching venues throughout the country. Leading sponsor of the British Birdwatchng Fair.
Viewing facilities: Available at all shops (contact your local outlet), or at field events (10am-4pm) at bird reserves (see *Bird Watching* magazine or website www.at-infocus.co.uk for calendar)
Optical stock: Many leading makes of binoculars and telescopes, plus own-brand Delta range of binoculars and tripods.
Non-optical stock: Wide range of tripods, clamps and other accessories. Repair service available.
Opening times: Vary - please contact local shop or website before travelling.

NORFOLK
Address: Main Street, Titchwell, Nr King's Lynn, Norfolk, PE31 8BB; 01485 210 101.

RUTLAND
Address: Anglian Water Birdwatching Centre, Egleton Reserve, Rutland Water, Rutland, LE15 8BT; 01572 770 656.

LONDON CAMERA EXCHANGE
Company ethos: To supply good quality optical equipment at a competitive price, helped by knowlegeable staff.
Viewing facilities: In shop and at local shows. Contact local branch.
Optical stock: All leading makes of binoculars and scopes.
Non-optical stock: All main brands of photo, digital and video equipment.
Opening times: All leading makes of binoculars and scopes.

CHESTERFIELD
Address: 1A South Street, Chesterfield, Derbyshire, S40 1QZ; 01246 211 891; (Fax) 01246 211 563;
e-mail: chesterfield@lcegroup.co.uk

COLCHESTER
Address: 12 Led Lane, Colchester, Essex CO1 1LS; 01206 573 444.

DERBY
Address: 17 Sadler Gate, Derby, Derbyshire, DE1 3NH; 01332 348 644; (Fax) 01332 369 136;
e-mail: derby@lcegroup.co.uk

LINCOLN
Address: 6 Silver Street, Lincoln, LN2 1DY; 01522 514 131; (Fax) 01522 537 480;
e-mail: lincoln@lcegroup.co.uk

NORWICH
Address: 12 Timber Hill, Norwich, Norfolk NR1 3LB; 01603 612 537.

NOTTINGHAM
Address: 7 Pelham Street, Nottingham, NG1 2EH; 0115 941 7486; (Fax) 0115 952 0547;
e-mail: nottingham@lcegroup.co.uk

PEAK DISTRICT BINOCULARS
Company ethos: Family-run business offers good service and value with a well defined range of birdwatching optics.
Viewing facilities: Viewing facilities in beautiful rural National Park village.
Optical stock: Stockists of Opticron, optical hardware, Olivon and a wide range of outdoor clothing and footwear.
Opening times: Mon-Sun (9am-5pm), between April and October, all weekends - please phone midweek in winter to make sure.
Address: The Old Barn, Market Place, Castleton, Hope Valley, Derbyshire SS3 8WQ; 01433 620 999; e-mail: theoldbarn1@btconnect.com
www.oldbarncastleton.co.uk

WAREHOUSE EXPRESS
Company ethos: Mail-order and website.
Optical stock: All major brands including, Leica, Swarvoski, Opticron, Kowa, Zeiss, Nikon, Bushnell, Canon, etc.
Non-optical stock: All related accessories including hides, tripods and window mounts etc.
Opening times: Mon-Fri (9am-5pm).
Address: PO Box 659, Norwich, Norfolk, NW3 2WN; 01603 258 012; (Fax) 01603 258 950.
www.warehouseexpress.com

NORTHERN ENGLAND

FOCALPOINT
Company ethos: Friendly advice by well-trained staff, competitive prices, no "grey imports".
Viewing facilities: Fantastic open countryside for superb viewing from the shop, plenty of wildlife. Parking for up to 20 cars.
Optical stock: All leading brands of binoculars and telescopes from stock, plus many pre-owned binoculars and telescopes available.
Non-optical stock: Bird books, outdoor clothing, boots, tripods, plus full range of Skua products etc. available from stock.

Opening times: Mon-Sat (9:30am-5pm).
Address: Marbury House Farm, Bentleys Farm Lane, Higher Whitley, Warrington, Cheshire, WA4 4QW; 01925 730 399; (Fax) 01925 730 368; e-mail: focalpoint@dial.pipex.com www.fpoint.co.uk

IN-FOCUS

(see entry in Eastern England).

LANCASHIRE

Address: WWT Martin Mere, Burscough, Ormskirk, Lancs, L40 0TA: 01704 897 020.

WEST YORKSHIRE

Address: Westleigh House Office Est. Wakefield Road, Denby Dale, West Yorks, HD8 8QJ: 01484 864 729.

LONDON CAMERA EXCHANGE

Company ethos: To supply good quality optical equipment at a competitive price, helped by knowlegeable staff.
Viewing facilities: In shop and at local shows. Contact local branch.
Optical stock: All leading makes of binoculars and scopes.
Non-optical stock: All main brands of photo, digital and video equipment.
Opening times: Mon-Sat (9am-5.30pm).

CHESTER

Address: 9 Bridge Street Row, CH1 1NW; 01244 326 531.

MANCHESTER

Address: 37 Parker Street, Picadilly, M1 4AJ; 0161 236 5819.

ROTHER VALLEY OPTICS

Company ethos: Selling and distributing binoculars, spotting scopes, telescopes and accessories, we aim to offer very competitive prices and an excellent customer service.
Viewing facilities: Potential buyers can test and try out binoculars and scopes on the premises.
Optical stock: Large stock levels of Nikon, Optricron, Hawke, Audubon, Leupold, Minox, Leica, Swarovski and more.
Opening times: Mon-Fri (9am-5pm); Sat (9.30pm-3pm).
Address: 36 Bridge Street, Killamarsh, Sheffield, South Yorks S21 1AH; (Tel/Fax) 0114 247 6024; e-mail: ian@rothervalleyoptics.com www.rothervalleyoptics.com

WILKINSON CAMERAS

Company ethos: The widest range of photographic and birdwatching equipment available at competitive prices at all times.
Viewing facilities: Optical field days at selected nature reserves in northern England. See website for details of photographic courses and other events.
Optical stock: Binoculars from Bushnell, Canon, Hawke, Leica, Nikon, RSPB, Steiner, Swarovski, Vanguard and Viking. Spotting scopes from Bushnell, Hawke, Leica, Nikon, Summit, Swarovski and Vanguard. Wide range of bags, digital cameras, lenses and video equipment.
Opening times: Branches open 9am to 5:30pm Monday to Saturday. Sunday 11am to 4pm (Preston only).
e-mail: sales@wilkinson.co.uk
www.wilkinson.co.uk

BLACKBURN

42 Northgate, Blackburn, Lancs BB2 1JL: 01254 581 272; (Fax) 01254 695 867.

BURNLEY

95 James Street, Burnley, Lancs BB11 1PY; 01282 424 524; (Fax) 01282 831 722.

BURY

61 The Rock, Bury, Greater Manchester BL9 0NB; 01617 643 402; (Fax) 01617 615 086.

CARLISLE

13 Grapes Lane, Carlisle, Cumbria CA3 8NQ; 01228 538 583; (Fax) 01228 514 699.

KENDAL

19A The Westmorland Centre, Kendal, Cumbria LA9 4AB; 01539 735 055; (Fax) 01539 734 929.

LANCASTER

6 James Street, Lancaster, Lancs LA1 1UP; 01524 380 510; (Fax) 01524 380 512.

PRESTON

27 Friargate, Preston, Lancs PR1 2NQ; 01772 556 250; (Fax) 01772 259 435.

SOUTHPORT

38 Eastbank Street, Southport, Merseyside, PR8 1ET. 01704 534 534; (Fax) 01704 501 546;
e-mail: southport@wilkinson.co.uk

OPTICAL DEALERS

SOUTH EAST ENGLAND

IN-FOCUS

(see entry in Eastern England).

ST ALBANS

Address: Bowmans Farm, London Colney, St Albans, Herts, AL2 1BB: 01727 827 799: (Fax) 01727 827 766.

SOUTH WEST LONDON

Address: WWT The Wetland Centre, Queen Elizabeth Walk, Barnes, London, SW13 9WT: 020 8409 4433.

LONDON CAMERA EXCHANGE

Company ethos: To supply good quality optical equipment at a competitive price, helped by knowlegeable staff.
Viewing facilities: In shop and at local shows. Contact local branch.
Optical stock: All leading makes of binoculars and scopes.
Non-optical stock: All main brands of photo, digital and video equipment.
Opening times: Mon-Sat (9am-5.30pm).

FAREHAM

Address: 135 West Street, Fareham, Hampshire, PO16 0DU; 01329 236 441; (Fax) 01329 823 294;
e-mail: fareham@lcegroup.co.uk

GUILDFORD

Address: 8/9 Tunsgate, Guildford, Surrey, GU1 2DH; 01483 504 040; (Fax) 01483 538 216;
e-mail: guildford@lcegroup.co.uk

PORTSMOUTH

Address: 40 Kingswell Path, Cascados, Portsmouth, PO1 4RR; 023 9283 9933; (Fax) 023 9283 9955;
e-mail: portsmouth@lcegroup.co.uk

READING

Address: 7 Station Road, Reading, Berkshire, RG1 1LG; 0118 959 2149; (Fax) 0118 959 2197;
e-mail: reading@lcegroup.co.uk

SOUTHAMPTON

Address: 10 High Street, Southampton, Hampshire, SO14 2DH; 023 8022 1597; (Fax) 023 8023 3838; e-mail: southampton@lcegroup.co.uk

STRAND, LONDON

Address: 98 The Strand, London, WC2R 0AG; 020 7379 0200; (Fax) 020 7379 6991;
e-mail: strand@lcegroup.co.uk

WINCHESTER

Address: 15 The Square, Winchester, Hampshire, SO23 9ES; 01962 866 203; (Fax)01962 840 978;
e-mail: winchester@lcegroup.co.uk

SOUTH WEST ENGLAND

ACE CAMERAS

Company ethos: To be the best - service, price and stock.
Viewing facilities: Bird of prey and Leica test card to check quality at 100 metres.
Optical stock: All the top brands, including Questar and Avian.
Non-optical stock: All the best tripods and an array of optical related accessories.
Opening times: Mon-Sat (8:45am-6pm).
Address: 16 Green Street, Bath, BA1 2JZ; 01225 466 364; (Fax) 01225 469 761.
e-mail: optics@acecameras.co.uk
www.acecameras.co.uk

LONDON CAMERA EXCHANGE

Company ethos: To supply good quality optical equipment at a competitive price, helped by knowlegeable staff.
Viewing facilities: In shop and at local shows. Contact local branch.
Optical stock: All leading makes of binoculars and scopes.
Non-optical stock: All main brands of photo, digital and video equipment.
Opening times: Mon-Sat (9am-5.30pm).

BATH

Address: 13 Cheap Street, Bath, Avon, BA1 1NB; 01225 462 234; (Fax) 01225 480 334.
e-mail: bath@lcegroup,co.uk

BOURNEMOUTH

Address: 95 Old Christchurch Road, Bournemouth, Dorset, BH1 1EP; 01202 556 549; (Fax) 01202 293 288;
e-mail: bournemouth@lcegroup.co.uk

OPTICAL DEALERS

BRISTOL
Address: 53 The Horsefair, Bristol, BS1 3JP; 0117 927 6185; (Fax) 0117 925 8716;
e-mail: bristol.horsefair@lcegroup.co.uk

EXETER
Address: 174 Fore Street, Exeter, Devon, EX4 3AX; 01392 279 024/438 167; (Fax) 01392 426 988. e-mail: exeter@lcegroup.co.uk

PAIGNTON
Address: 71 Hyde Road, Paington, Devon, TQ4 5BP;01803 553 077; (Fax) 01803 664 081.
e-mail: paignton@lcegroup.co.uk

PLYMOUTH
Address: 10 Frankfort Gate, Plymouth, Devon, PL1 1QD; 01752 668 894; (Fax) 01752 604248.
e-mail: plymouth@lcegroup.co.uk

SALISBURY
Address: 6 Queen Street, Salisbury, Wiltshire, SP1 1EY; 01722 335 436; (Fax) 01722 411 670;
e-mail: salisbury@lcegroup.co.uk

TAUNTON
Address: 6 North Street, Taunton, Somerset, TA1 1LH; 01823 259955; (Fax) 01823 338 001.
e-mail: taunton@lcegroup.co.uk

WESTERN ENGLAND

FOCUS OPTICS
Company ethos: Friendly, expert service. Top quality instruments. No 'grey imports'.
Viewing facilities: Our own pool and nature reserve with feeding stations.
Optical stock: Full range of leading makes of binoculars and telescopes.
Non-optical stock: Waterproof clothing, fleeces, walking boots and shoes, bird food and feeders. Books, videos, walking poles.
Opening times: Mon-Sat (9am-5pm). Some bank holidays.
Address: Church Lane, Corley, Coventry, CV7 8BA; 01676 540 501/542 476; (Fax) 01676 540 930. e-mail: focopt1@aol.com
www.focusoptics.co.uk

IN-FOCUS
(see entry in Eastern England).

GLOUCESTERSHIRE
Address: WWT Slimbridge, Gloucestershire, GL2 7BT: 01453 890 978. 22314; (Fax) 01905 724 585;
e-mail: worcester@lcegroup.co.uk

LONDON CAMERA EXCHANGE
Company ethos: To supply good quality optical equipment at a competitive price, helped by knowlegeable staff.
Viewing facilities: In shop and at local shows. Contact local branch.
Optical stock: All leading makes of binoculars and scopes.
Non-optical stock: All main brands of photo, digital and video equipment.
Opening times: Mon-Sat (9am-5.30pm).

CHELTENHAM
Address: 10-12 The Promenade, Cheltenham, Gloucestershire, GL50 1LR; 01242 519 851; (Fax) 01242 576 771;
e-mail: cheltenham@lcegroup.co.uk

GLOUCESTER
Address: 12 Southgate Street, Gloucester, GL1 2DH; 01452 304 513; (Fax) 01452 387 309;
e-mail: gloucester@lcegroup.co.uk

LEAMINGTON
Address: Clarendon Avenue, Leamington, Warwickshire, CV32 5PP; 01926 886 166; (Fax)01926 887 611;
e-mail: leamington@lcegroup.co.uk

WORCESTER
Address: 8 Pump Street, Worcester, WR1 2QT; 01905 22314; (Fax) 01905 724 585;
e-mail: worcester@lcegroup.co.uk

BIRD RESERVES AND OBSERVATORIES

Scotland's Findhorn Valley by David Cromack

Why not widen your birdwatching horizons by visiting some new reserves in 2008? Here we detail more than 400 sites for you to explore – the information is updated each year, making it the most up-to-date guide covering the whole of Britain.

To reflect birdwatchers' growing interest in other flora and fauna, we have asked information providers for each site to highlight key mammal, insect and plant species – and elsewhere in this edition (pages 97 to 98) you can record your butterfly and dragonfly sightings.

With every new edition, our goal is to provide details of newly-created reserves or little known gems that have previously been neglected and this year there are 28 newcomers to the listings. Previously listed reserves, where information has not altered year-on-year are listed under Other Sites for each county. A contact number is provided to help group leaders plan visits.

Bedfordshire

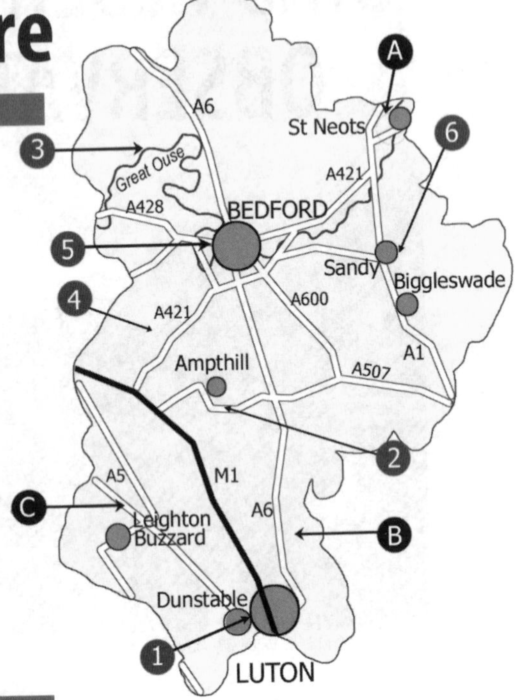

1. BLOW'S DOWNS

Beds, Cambs, Northants and Peterborough Wildlife Trust.
Location: TL 033 216. On the outskirts of Dunstable, W of Luton. Parking is at Skimpot roundabout, off Hatters Way on A505, and in Half Moon Lane, Dunstable.
Access: Open all year.
Facilities: None.
Public transport: None.
Habitat: Chalk downland, scrub and grassland, that is a traditional resting place for incoming spring migrants.
Key birds: *Spring/summer*: Hobby, Turtle Dove, Grasshopper Warbler, Lesser Whitethroat, Cuckoo, Spotted Flycatcher, Golden Plover. *Winter*: Buzzard, winter thrushes, possible Brambling. *Passage*: Ring Ouzel, Wheatear, Redstart. *All year*: Marsh and Willow Tits, Bullfinch, Sparrowhawk.
Contact: Trust HQ, 01954 713 500; (Fax) 01954 710 051.
e-mail: bedfordshire@wildlifebcnp.org
www.wildlifebcnp.org

2. FLITWICK MOOR

Beds, Cambs, Northants and Peterborough Wildlife Trust.
Location: TL 046 354. SE of Ampthill. From Flitwick town centre, take the road towards Greenfield. After approx 0.8km turn L into Maulden Road. Head N to Folly Farm (approx 0.8km), opposite an industrial estate. Turn R at the farm and follow road to car park.
Access: Open all year.
Facilities: Car park. Please stick to public paths.
Public transport: None.
Habitat: SSSI, valley fen, woodland, sedge, reed.
Key birds: *Spring/summer*: Turtle Dove, possible Grasshopper Warbler, Chiffchaff, Cuckoo, warblers. *Winter*: Teal, Lapwing, Woodcock, Siskin. *All year*: Water Rail, Little Owl, Great Spotted and Lesser Spotted Woodpeckers, possible Willow and Marsh Tits, Jay.
Other notable flora and fauna: Marsh pennywort, good variety of butterflies and dragonflies.
Contact: Trust HQ, 01954 713 500; (Fax) 01954 710 051. e-mail:bedfordshire@wildlifebcnp.org
www.wildlifebcnp.org

3. HARROLD ODELL COUNTRY PARK

Harrold Odell Country Park.
Location: SP 960 570. 10 miles NW of Bedford off the Harrold to Carlton road.
Access: Open at all times. Disabled parking available. Wheelchair access to lake side and hide in favourable weather conditions. Call park to check availability of coach parking.
Facilities: Visitor centre. Cafe open 9am-5.30pm every day. Hide.
Public transport: United Counties bus service, 124, 125 and 126 stop at entrance. Call 01234 228 337 for timetable information.
Habitat: Lakes (one with island), lagoons, osier beds, meadows adjacent River Great Ouse, woodland.
Key birds: *Summer*: Breeding Reed and Sedge Warblers, Lesser Whitethroat. Passage waders, Common and Black Terns, late summer Hobby. *Winter*: Wildfowl, Water Rail.

Contact: Ed Burnett, Country Park, Carlton Road, Harrold, Bedford MK43 7DS. 01234 720 016. e-mail: holp@bedscc.gov.uk www.ivelandouse.co.uk

4. MARSTON VALE MILLENNIUM CP

Marston Vale Trust (Regd Charity No 1069229).
Location: SW of Bedford off A421 at Marston Moretaine. Only five mins from J13 of M1.
Access: Park and forest centre open seven days. Summer 10am-6pm, winter 10am-4pm. No dogs in wetlands reserve, rest of site OK for dogs and horses. Main 8km trail surfaced for wheelchair and pushchair access. All-terrain wheelchairs available for free loan. Coaches fine.
Facilities: Cafe bar, gift shop, art gallery, exhibition. Free parking.
Public transport: Marston Vale Line – trains direct from Millbrook and Stewartby station. Bus route to Marston Moretaine, contact Bedfordshire bus line on 01234 228 337, (8.30am-5pm) Monday to Friday.
Habitat: Lake – 610 acres/freshwater marsh (man-made), reedbed, woodland, hawthorn scrub and grassland.
Key birds: *Winter*: Iceland and Glaucous Gulls (regular), gull roost, wildfowl, Great Crested Grebe. *Spring*: Passage waders and terns (Black Tern, Arctic Tern), Garganey. *Summer*: Nine species of breeding warblers, Hobby, Turtle Dove, Nightingale, Bearded Tit. *Autumn*: Passage waders and terns. *Rarities*: White-winged Black Tern, Laughing Gull, divers, Manx Shearwater, Bittern.
Other notable flora and fauna: Dingy and grizzled skipper butterflies, excellent for dragonflies, red-veined darter in 2006. Also otter and brown hare plus bluebells, bee orchid, pyramidal orchid and stoneworts.
Contact: Forest Centre, Station Road, Marston Moretaine, Beds MK43 0PR. 01234 767 037. e-mail: info@marstonvale.org www.marstonvale.org

5. PRIORY MARINA COUNTRY PARK

Bedford Borough Council.
Location: TL 071 495. 1.5 miles SE from Bedford town centre. Signposted A428 and A421.
Access: Open at all times.
Facilities: Toilets, visitor centre, hides, nature trail. Provision for disabled visitors. Coaches welcome.
Public transport: Stagecoach bus service 3 and 4 pass Barkers Lane (main) entrance.
Habitat: Lakes, reedbeds, scrub/plantations, meadows adjoining River Great Ouse.
Key birds: *Winter*: Grebes, wildfowl, Merlin, Sparrowhawk, Water Rail, Stonechat, Chiffchaff, thrushes, corvid, finch and bunting roosts. *Summer*: Terns, Hobby, woodpeckers, Kingfisher, Swift, warblers. *Passage*: Raptors, gulls, terns, waders, hirundines, pipits, wagtails.
Other notable flora and fauna: Dragonflies, butterflies and otter.
Contact: Jon Bishop, Wardens Office, Visitor Centre, Priory CP, Barkers Lane, Bedford MK41 9SH. 01234 211 182.

6. LODGE (THE)

RSPB Eastern England Office
Location: TL 190 479. Reserve lies 1 mile/1.6km E of Sandy on the B1042 to Potton.
Access: Reserve is open daily 9am-9pm (or sunset when earlier); shop 9am-5pm weekdays, 10am-5pm weekends.
Facilities: Nature trails, up to 5 miles, 1 bridleway (0.5 miles) and gardens wheelchair/pushchair accessible. Hides, (one wheelchair accessible) - parking 50 yards.
Public transport: Buses from Bedford to Sandy, infrequent service. One mile from Sandy train station on B1042 or 0.5 miles on trail through new part of reserve, Sandy Warren. By bicycle, view the National Cycle Network map of The Lodge.
Habitat: This reserve is a mixture of woodland, heathland, and includes the formal gardens of the RSPB's UK headquarters. New land being restored to heathland.
Key birds: *Spring/summer*: Hobby, Spotted Flycatcher. *All year*: Woodpeckers, woodland birds.
Contact: Peter Bradley, RSPB Eastern England Office, 46 Stalham House, The Green, 65 Thorpe Road, Norwich, Norfolk NR1 1UD.

OTHER SITES

Full details in previous editions, (year indicated in brackets).

A. Begwary Brook – BC & P Wildlife Trust, 01954 713 500 (04).

B. Pegsden Hill – BC & P Wildlife Trust, 01954 713 500 (04).

C. Stockgrove Country Park – 01525 237 760.

Berkshire

1. DINTON PASTURES

Wokingham District Council.
Location: SU 784 718. Country Park, E of Reading off B3030 between Hurst and Winnersh.
Access: Open all year, dawn to dusk.
Facilities: Hides, information centre, car park, café, toilets. Suitable for wheelchairs.
Habitat: Mature gravel pits and banks of River Loddon.
Key birds: Kingfisher, Water Rail, Little Ringed Plover, Common Tern, Nightingale. *Winter*: Wildfowl (inc. Goldeneye, Wigeon, Teal, Gadwall).
Contact: Dave Webster, Ranger, Dinton Pastures CP, Davis Street, Hurst, Berks. 0118 934 2 016. e-mail:countryside@wokingham.gov.uk

2. LAVELL'S LAKE

Wokingham District Council.
Location: SU 781 729. Via Sandford Lane off B3030 between Hurst and Winnersh, E of Reading.
Access: Dawn to dusk. No permit required.
Facilities: Hides.
Public transport: Information not available.
Habitat: Gravel pits, two wader scapes, although one congested with crassula helmsii, rough grassland, marshy area, between River Loddon, Emm Brook. To N of Lavell's Lake, gravel pits are being restored and attract birds. A lake is viewable walking N along River Lodden from Lovell's Lake over small green bridge. The lake is in a field immediately on R but is only viewable through hedge. No access is permitted.
Key birds: *All year*: Sparrowhawk. *Summer*: Garganey, Common Tern, Redshank, Lapwing, Hobby, Red Kite, Peregrine, Buzzard. Passage waders. *Winter*: Green Sandpiper, ducks (inc. Smew), Bittern.
Contact: Dave Webster, Ranger, Dinton Pastures Country Park, Davis Street, Hurst, Berks. 0118 934 2 016.

3. MOOR GREEN LAKES

Blackwater Valley Countryside Partnership.
Location: SU 805 628. Main access and parking off Lower Sandhurst Road, Finchampstead. Alternatively, Rambler's car park, Mill Lane, Sandhurst (SU 820 619).
Access: Car parks open dawn-dusk. Two bird hides open to members of the Moor Green Lakes Group (contact BVCP for details). Dogs on leads. Site can be used by people in wheelchairs, though surface not particularly suitable.
Facilities: Two bird hides, footpaths around site, Blackwater Valley Long Distance Path passes through site.
Public transport: Nearest bus stop, Finchampstead (approx 1.5 miles from main entrance). Local bus companies – Stagecoach Hants & Surrey, tel 01256 464 501, First Beeline & Londonlink, tel 01344 424 938.
Habitat: Thirty-six hectares (90 acres) in total. Three lakes with gravel islands, beaches and scrapes. River Blackwater, grassland, surrounded by willow, ash, hazel and thorn hedgerows.
Key birds: *Spring/summer*: Redshank, Little Ringed Plover, Sand Martin, Willow Warbler, and of particular interest, a flock of Goosander. Also Whitethroat, Sedge Warbler, Common Sandpiper, Common Tern, Dunlin and Black Tern. Lapwings breed on site and several sightings of Red Kite. *Winter*: Ruddy Duck, Wigeon, Teal, Gadwall.
Contact: Blackwater VCP, Ash Lock Cottage,

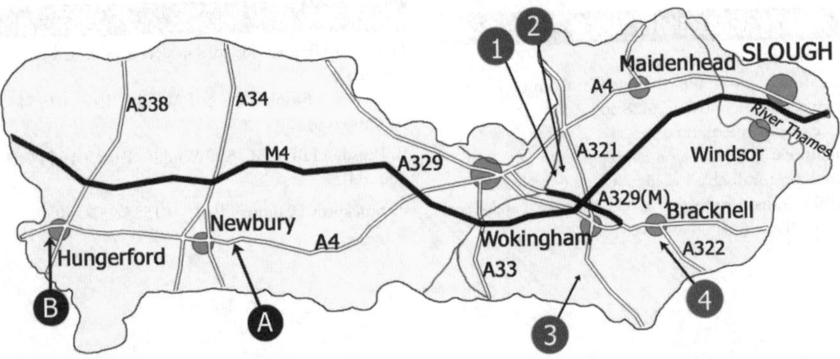

Government Road, Aldershot, Hants GU11 2PS. 01252 331 353. e-mail: blackwater.valley@hants.gov.uk www.blackwater-valley.org.uk

4. WILDMOOR HEATH

Berks, Bucks & Oxon Wildlife Trust.
Location: SU 842 627. Between Bracknell and Sandhurst. From Sandhurst shopping area, take the A321 NW towards Wokingham. Turn E at the mini-roundabout on to Crowthorne Road. Continue for about one mile through one set of traffic lights. Car park is on the R at the bottom of the hill.
Access: Open all year. No access to woodland N of Rackstraw Road at Broadmoor Bottom. Please keep dogs on a lead.
Facilities: Car park.
Habitat: Wet and dry lowland heath, bog, mixed woodland and mature Scots pine plantation.
Key birds: *Spring/summer*: Wood Lark, Nightjar, Dartford Warbler, Stonechat. Good for dragonflies.
Contact: Wildlife Trust HQ, BBOWT, 01865 775 476. www.bbowt.org.uk

OTHER SITES

Full details in previous editions, (year indicated in brackets).
A. Baynes & Bowdown Reserve – BBOWT, 01865 775 476 (04).
B. Hungerford Marsh – BBOWT, 01865 775 476 (04).

Buckinghamshire

1. BURNHAM BEECHES NATIONAL NNR

City of London.
Location: SU 950 850. N of Slough and on W side of A355, running between J2 of the M40 and J6 of M4. There are several entrances from A355. Also entrances from Hawthorn Lane and Pumpkin Hill to the S and Park Lane to the W.
Access: Open all year. Main Lord Mayor's Drive open from 8am-dusk.
Facilities: Car parks, toilets, café, seasonal refreshment kiosk. Easy access path network, suitable for wheelchairs, most start at Victory Cross. Coach parking possible, additional coach parking on request.
Public transport: Train: nearest station Slough on the main line from Paddington. Buses stop in Farnham Common (between Slough and Beaconsfield), Beeline, London and Country 0870 608 2608.
Habitat: Ancient woodland, streams, pools, heathland, grassland, scrub.
Key birds: *Spring/summer*: Cuckoo, possible Turtle Dove. *Winter*: Siskin, Crossbill, regular large flocks c100 Brambling. Possible Woodcock. *All year*: Mandarin (good population), all three woodpeckers, Sparrowhawk, Marsh Tit, possible Willow Tit.
Contact: City of London Corporation. Burnham Beeches Office, Hawthorn Lane, Farnham Common SL2 3TE . 01753 647 358. www.cityoflondon.gov.uk e-mail: burnham.beeches@cityoflondon.gov.uk

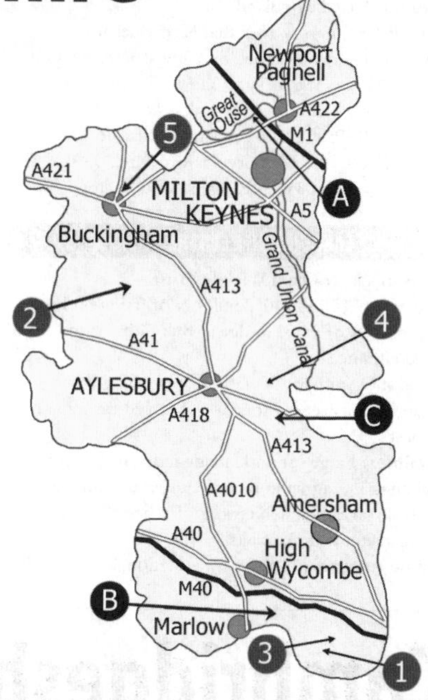

2. CALVERT JUBILEE

Berks, Bucks & Oxon Wildlife Trust.
Location: SP 849 425. Near Steeple Claydon, NW of Aylesbury, Bucks.
Access: Access by permit (free) only. Apply to Trust who provide map and information with permit. Please keep to network of paths.
Facilities: Two hides, small car park.
Public transport: None.
Habitat: Ex-clay pit, railway and landfill site. Now with deep lake, marginal reedbed and scrub habitat.

Key birds: *Summer*: Nesting Common Tern, Kingfisher, warblers, occasional Nightingale, Lapwing. Passage migrants include Black-tailed Godwit, Greenshank. *Winter*: Bittern, Water Rail, Lesser Black-backed Gull roost. Wigeon. Rarer birds turn up regularly,.
Other notable flora and fauna: Rare butterflies, including dingy and grizzled skippers.
Contact: BBOWT HQ – 01865 775 476.

3. CHURCH WOOD RSPB RESERVE

RSPB Central England Office
Location: SU 972 872. Reserve lies three miles from J2 of M40 in Hedgerley. Park in village, walk down small track beside pond for approx 200m. Reserve entrance is on L.
Access: Open all year.
Facilities: Two marked paths.
Public transport: None.
Habitat: Mixed woodland.
Key birds: *Spring/summer*: Red Kite, Buzzard, Blackcap, Garden Warbler, Swallow. *Winter*: Redpoll, Siskin. *All year*: Marsh Tit, Willow Tit, Nuthatch, Great Spotted and Green Woodpeckers.
Contact: RSPB Central England Office, 46 The Green, South Bar, Banbury, Oxfordshire, OX16 9AB. 01295 253 330. www.rspb.org.uk/wildlife/reserves

4. COLLEGE LAKE WILDLIFE CENTRE

Berks, Bucks & Oxon Wildlife Trust.
Location: SU 934 140. 2 miles N of Tring on B488, 1/4 miles N of canal bridge at Bulbourne turn L into gated entrance.
Access: Open Apr-Oct (10am-5pm); Nov-Mar (10am-4pm), except Mondays. Disabled car trail on request.
Facilities: Large car park, many hides, interpretive buildings, inc. agricultural museum, refreshments available on Sundays. Network of wheelchair-friendly paths, visitor centre, toilets.
Public transport: Tring railway station, 2 miles walk.
Habitat: Deep lake in former chalk pit, shallow pools, wet, chalk and rough grasslands, scrub.
Key birds: *Spring/summer*: Lapwing, Redshank, Little Ringed Plover, Sand Martin, Hobby, Common Tern, Corn Bunting and Sky Lark. *Winter*: Wildfowl (Wigeon, Shoveler, Teal, Gadwall), waders, inc. Snipe, Peregrine Falcon.
Contact: The Warden, College Lake Wildlife Centre, Upper Icknield Way, Bulbourne, Tring, Herts HP23 5QG. 01442 826 774; (M)07711 821 303.

5. FOXCOTE RESERVOIR

Berks, Bucks & Oxon Wildlife Trust/Anglian Water.
Location: Reservoir is one mile NE of Buckingham, off A422 on a lane between Maids Moreton and Leckhampstead. Map and details sent with permit.
Access: Open all year. Access to hide by permit only - these are available free of charge from BBOWT.
Facilities: Hides.
Public transport: None.
Habitat: Open water.
Key birds: *Spring*: Common Tern, Hobby, Common Sandpiper, Corn Bunting. *Summer*: Spotted Flycatcher at Hydelane, warblers, Common Tern, ducks, Great Crested and Little Grebes. *Winter*: Water Rail, duck, inc. Wigeon and Goldeneye, Goosander. *All year*: Sparrowhawk, Kingfisher, Little and Tawny Owls, Grey Wagtail, Green and Great Spotted Woodpeckers, Marsh Tit, Jay.
Contact: Trust HQ, BBOWT, The Lodge, 1 Armstrong Road, Littlemore, Oxford OX4 4XT. 01865 775 476. www.bbowt.org.uk

OTHER SITES

Full details in previous editions, (year indicated in brackets).
A. Hanson Environmental Study Centre – contact Andrew Stevenson, 01908 604 810 (06).
B. Little Marlow Gravel Pits – www.bucksbirdclub.co.uk/LMGP.htm (05).
C. Weston Turville – BBOWT, 01865 775 476.

Cambridgeshire

1. FERRY MEADOWS COUNTRY PARK

Nene Park Trust.
Location: TL 145 975. Three miles W of Peterborough town centre, signed off A605.
Access: Open all year. Electric scooters and wheelchair available for loan - call to book in advance. Coach parking free at all times.
Facilities: Car park (fee at weekends and bank holidays between April 1 and Oct 30). Visitor centre, toilets, café, two hides in nature reserve area.
Public transport: Tel. Traveline 0870 6082 608 or

www.traveline.org.uk
Habitat: Lakes, meadows, scrub, broadleaved woodland and small wetland nature reserve.
Key birds: *Spring*: Terns, waders, Yellow Wagtail. *Winter*: Grebes, Siskin, Redpoll, Water Rail, occasional Hawfinch. *All year*: Good selection of woodland and water birds, Kingfisher. CES ringing site,.
Contact: Chris Parks, Visitor Services Officer, Nene Park Trust, Ham Farm House, Orton, Peterborough PE2 5UU. 01733 234 443.
e-mail:services@nene-park-trust.org.uk

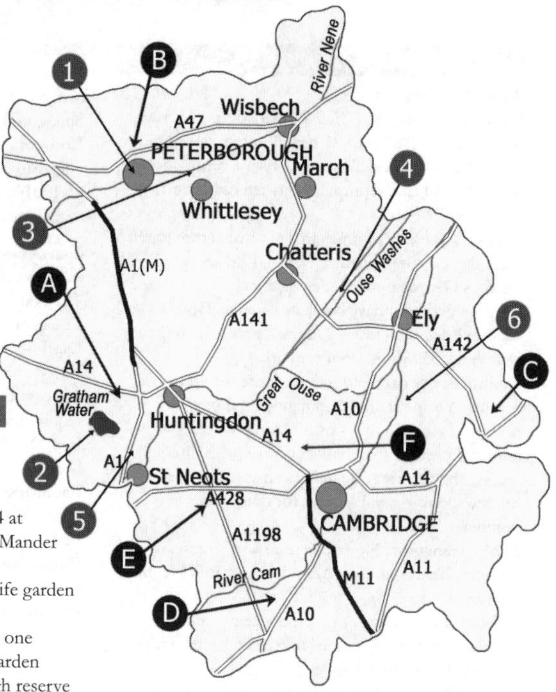

2. GRAFHAM WATER

Beds, Cambs, Northants and Peterborough Wildlife Trust.
Location: TL 143 671. Follow signs for Grafham Water from A1 at Buckden or A14 at Ellington. Nature Reserve entrance is from Mander car park, W of Perry village.
Access: Open all year. Dogs barred in wildlife garden only, on leads elsewhere.
Facilities: Five bird hides in nature reserve, one also at settlement lagoons. Two in wildlife garden accessible to wheelchairs. Cycle track through reserve also accessible to wheelchairs. Visitor centre with restaurant, shop and toilets. Disabled parking. Use Plummer car park for lagoons and Marlow car park for the dam area (good for waders and vagrants).
Public transport: None.
Habitat: Open water, settlement lagoons ranging from reedbeds, open water, wet mud and willow carr, ancient and plantation woodland, scrub, species rich grassland.
Key birds: *Resident*: Common woodland birds, wildfowl. *Winter*: Waders including Common Sandpiper and Dunlin, Great Crested Grebe, Wildfowl including large flocks of Tufted Duck and Coot, Pochard, Shoveler, Shelduck, Goldeneye, Goosander and Smew, gulls (can be up to 30,000 roosting in mid-winter). *Spring/summer*: Breeding Nightingale, Reed, Willow and Sedge Warblers, Common and Black Terns. *Autumn*: Passage waders. *Rarities*: Have included Wilson's Phalarope (2007), Ring-necked Duck, Great Northern Diver, Glaucous, Iceland and Mediterrranean Gulls.
Other notable flora and fauna: Bee and common spotted orchids, early purple orchid, common twyblade (in woods), cowslip. Common blue and marbled white butterflies.
Contact: The Warden, Grafham Water Nature Reserve, c/o The Lodge, West Perry, Huntingdon, Cambs PE28 0BX. 01480 811 075.
e-mail: matt.hamilton@wildlifebcnp.org
www.wildlifetrust.org.uk/bcnp

3. NENE WASHES

RSPB (East of England Office).
Location: TL 300 995. N of Whittlesey and six miles E of Peterborough.
Access: Open at all times along South Barrier Bank, accessed at Eldernell, one mile NE of Coates, off A605. Group visits by arrangement. No access to fields. No access for wheelchairs along bank.
Facilities: Small car park - one coach max.
Public transport: Bus and trains to Whittlesey, bus to Coates.
Habitat: Wet grassland with ditches. Frequently flooded.
Key birds: *Spring/early Summer*: Breeding waders, including Black-tailed Godwit, duck, including Garganey, Marsh Harrier and Hobby. *Winter*: Waterfowl including Bewick's Swan and Pintail, Barn Owl, Hen Harrier.
Contact: Charlie Kitchin, RSPB Nene Washes, 21a East Delph, Whittlesey, Cambs PE7 1RH. 01733 205 140.

4. OUSE WASHES

RSPB (East Anglia Office).
Location: TL 471 861. Between Chatteris and March on A141, take B1093 to Manea. Reserve signposted from Manea. Reserve office and visitor centre located off Welches Dam. Approximately ten miles from March or Chatteris.
Access: Access at all times from visitor centre (open every day except Christmas Day and Boxing Day). Welches Dam to public hides approached by marked paths behind boundary bank. No charge. Dogs to be kept on leads at all times. Disabled access to Welches Dam hide, 350 yards from car park.
Facilities: Car park and toilets. Space for up to two coaches. Visitor centre – unmanned but next to reserve office. Ten hides overlooking the reserve: nearest 350 yards from visitor centre (with disabled access) and furthest one mile from visitor centre. Boardwalk over pond – good for dragonflies in summer.
Public transport: No public transport to reserve entrance. Train station at Manea – three miles from reserve.
Habitat: Lowland wet grassland – seasonally flooded. Open pool systems in front of some hides, particularly Stockdale's hide.
Key birds: *Summer*: Around 70 species breed including Black-tailed Godwit, Lapwing, Redshank, Snipe, Shoveler, Gadwall, Garganey and Spotted Crake. Also Hobby and Marsh Harrier. *Autumn*: Passage waders including Wood and Green Sandpipers, Spotted Redshank, Greenshank, Little Stint, plus terns and Marsh and Hen Harrier. *Winter*: Large numbers of Bewick's and Whooper Swans, Wigeon, Teal, Shoveler, Pintail, Pochard.
Contact: Jon Reeves, (Site Manager), Ouse Washes Reserve, Welches Dam, Manea, March, Cambs PE15 0NF. 01354 680 212. e-mail: jon.reeves@rspb.org.uk www.rspb.org.uk

5. PAXTON PITS

Huntingdonshire District Council.
Location: TL 197 629. Access from A1 at Little Paxton, two miles N of St Neots.
Access: Free Entry. Open 24 hours. Visitor centre manned at weekends. Dogs allowed under control. Heron trail suitable for wheelchairs during summer.
Facilities: Toilets available most days 9am-5pm (including disabled), two bird hides (always open), marked nature trails.
Public transport: 565/566 run between Huntingdon and St Neots Mon-Sat. Tel: 0870 608 2608.
Habitat: Grassland, scrub, lakes.
Key birds: *Spring/summer*: Nightingale, Kingfisher, Common Tern, Sparrowhawk, Hobby, Grasshopper, Sedge and Reed Warblers, Lesser Whitethroat. *Winter*: Smew, Goldeneye, Goosander, Gadwall, Pochard.
Contact: Jim Stevenson, Ranger, The Visitor Centre, High Street, Little Paxton, St Neots, Cambs PE19 6ET. 01480 406 795. www.paxton-pits.org.uk
e-mail: mail@paxtonpits.uklinux.net

6. WICKEN FEN

The National Trust.
Location: TL 563 705. Lies 17 miles NE of Cambridge and ten miles S of Ely. From A10 drive E along A1123.
Access: Daily except Mon (9am-5pm). Permit required from visitor centre. National Trust members free. Disabled access along approx 0.75 miles boardwalk. Dogs must be on leads.
Facilities: Toilets in car park. Visitor centre with hot/cold drinks, sandwiches at weekends, three nature trails, seven hides.
Public transport: Nearest rail link either Cambridge or Ely. Buses only on Thu and Sun.
Habitat: Open Fen – cut hay fields, sedge beds, grazing marsh – partially flooded wet grassland, reedbed, scrub, woodland.
Key birds: *Spring*: Passage waders and passerines. *Summer*: Marsh Harrier, Long-eared Owl, breeding waders and warblers. *Winter*: Wigeon, Hen Harrier, Merlin.
Other notable flora and fauna: 7,800 species of pnat, fungi and animals. 28 species of butterfly including swallowtail.
Contact: Martin Lester, Lode Lane, Wicken, Cambs CB7 5XP. 01353 720 274.
e-mail: martin.lester@nationaltrust.org.uk
www.wicken.org.uk

OTHER SITES

Full details in previous editions, (year indicated in brackets).
A. Brampton Wood – Beds, Cambs & Northants Wildlife Trust – 01954 713 500 (06).
B. Dogsthorpe Star Pit – Beds, Cambs & Northants Wildlife Trust – 01954 713 500 (06).
C. Fordham Woods – Natural England, 01733 405 850 (04).
D. Fowlmere – Doug Radford (RSPB), 01763 208 978 (06).
E. Hayley Wood – Beds, Cambs & Northants Wildlife Trust – 01954 713 500 (04).
F. Mare Fen - Beds, Cambs & Northants Wildlife Trust – 01954 713 500 (04).

Cheshire

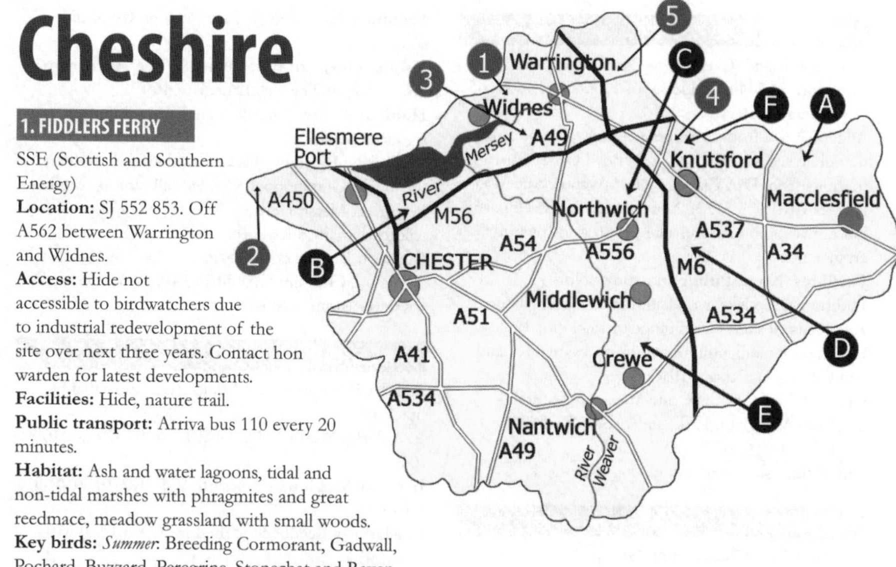

1. FIDDLERS FERRY

SSE (Scottish and Southern Energy)

Location: SJ 552 853. Off A562 between Warrington and Widnes.

Access: Hide not accessible to birdwatchers due to industrial redevelopment of the site over next three years. Contact hon warden for latest developments.

Facilities: Hide, nature trail.

Public transport: Arriva bus 110 every 20 minutes.

Habitat: Ash and water lagoons, tidal and non-tidal marshes with phragmites and great reedmace, meadow grassland with small woods.

Key birds: *Summer*: Breeding Cormorant, Gadwall, Pochard, Buzzard, Peregrine, Stonechat and Raven. *Winter*: Glaucous and Iceland Gulls, Short-eared Owl, Peregrine, Jack Snipe. *Recent rarities*: Great White Egret, Black Kite, Marsh Harrier, Hobby, Eleonora's Falcon, Yellow-legged Gull, Corn Crake.

Contact: Hon warden Keith Massey, 4 Hall Terrace, Great Sankey, Warrington WA5 3EZ. 01925 721 382. e-mail: kgmassey-4@supanet.com

2. GAYTON SANDS

RSPB Dee Estuary Office.

Location: SJ 275 785. On W side of Wirral, S of Birkenhead. View high tide activity from Old Baths car park near Boathouse pub, Parkgate off B5135.

Access: Open at all times. Viewing from public footpaths and car parks. Please do not walk on the saltmarsh, the tides are dangerous.

Facilities: Car park, picnic area, group bookings, guided walks, special events, wheelchair access. Toilets at Parkgate village opposite the Square.

Public transport: Bus – Parkgate every hour. Rail – Neston, two miles.

Habitat: Estuary – saltmarsh, pools, mud, sand.

Key birds: *Spring/summer/autumn*: Greenshank, Spotted Redshank, Curlew Sandpiper. *Winter*: Shelduck, Teal, Wigeon, Pintail, Oystercatcher, Black-tailed Godwit, Curlew, Redshank, Merlin, Peregrine, Water Rail, Short-eared Owl, Hen Harrier.

Contact: Colin E Wells, Burton Point Farm, Station Road, Burton, Nr Neston, Cheshire CH64 5SB. 0151 3367 681. e-mail: colin.wells@rspb.org.uk

3. MOORE NATURE RESERVE

Waste Recycling Group.

Location: SJ 577 854. SW of Warrington, via A56 Warrington-to-Chester road. At traffic lights at Higher Walton, follow signs for Moore. Take Moore Lane over swing bridge to reserve.

Access: Open all year. One bird hide suitable for wheelchairs, other parts of site unsurfaced or gravel paths..

Facilities: Coaches by prior arrangement. Paths, bird hides, bird feeding area. Guided walks available on request. See website for wildlife events throughout the year.

Public transport: 62 and 66 buses from Warrington and Runcorn stop in Moore village, less than 1km from reserve. Call 0870 608 2608 for times.

Habitat: Wetland, woodland, grasslands, five pools.

Key birds: More than 130 species every year, inc. occasional rarities. *Spring/summer*: Breeding wildfowl and waders, Black-necked Grebe, warblers. *Autumn/winter*: Wide variety of wildfowl, Bittern. Also good for gulls, woodpeckers, owls and raptors. See website for list and latest sightings.

Contact: Paul Cassidy/Brian Webber, c/o Waste Recycling Centre, Arpley Landfill Site, Forest Way, Sankey Bridge, Warrington, Cheshire WA4 6YZ. 01925 444 689. e-mail: paul.cassidy@wrg.co.uk www.wrg.co.uk/moorenaturereserve

4. ROSTHERNE MERE

Natural England (Cheshire to Lancashire team).
Location: SJ 744 843. Lies N of Knutsford and S of M56 (junction 8).
Access: View from Rostherne churchyard and lanes; no public access, except to A W Boyd Observatory (permits from D A Clarke, 1 Hart Avenue, Sale M33 2JY, tel: 0161 973 7122). Not suitable for coach parties but can accommodate smaller group visits by prior arrangement.
Facilities: None. **Public transport:** None.
Habitat: Deep lake, woodland, willow bed, pasture.
Key birds: *Winter*: Good range of duck (inc Ruddy Duck and Pintail), gull roost (inc. occasional Iceland and Glaucous). Passage Black Terns.
Contact: Tim Coleshaw, Site Manager, Natural England, Attingham Park, Shrewsbury SY4 4TW. 01743 282 000;(Fax) 01743 709 303; e-mail: tim.coleshaw@natural-england.org.uk.

5. WOOLSTON EYES

Woolston Eyes Conservation Group.
Location: SJ 654 888. E of Warrington between the River Mersey and Manchester Ship Canal. Off Manchester Road down Weir Lane or from Latchford to end of Thelwall Lane.
Access: Open all year. Permits required from Chairman, £8 each, £16 per family (see address below).
Facilities: No toilets or visitor centre. Good hides, some elevated.
Public transport: Buses along A57 nearest stop to Weir Lane, or Thelwell Lane, Latchford.
Habitat: Wetland, marsh, scrubland, wildflower meadow areas.
Key birds: Breeding Black-necked Grebe, warblers (including Grasshopper Warbler), all raptors (Merlin, Peregrine, Marsh Harrier). SSSI for wintering wildfowl, many duck species breed.
Contact: BR Ankers, Chairman, 9 Lynton Gardens, Appleton, Cheshire WA4 5ED. 01925 267 355. www.woolstoneyes.co.uk

OTHER SITES

Full details in previous editions, (year indicated in brackets).
A. **Alderley Woods** – National Trust, 01619 280 075 (04).
B. **Gowy Meadows** – Cheshire WT, 01270 610 180 (06).
C. **Marbury Reedbed** – Cheshire WT, 01270 610 180 (04).
D. **Rudheath Woods** – Cheshire WT, 01270 610 180 (04).
E. **Sandbach Flashes** – Patrick Whalley, 01270 624 420 (04).
F. **Tatton Park** – Cheshire WT, 01270 610 180 (04).

Cornwall

1. GOLITHA NNR

Natural England (Cornwall & Isles of Scilly Team).
Location: SX 227 690. Golitha is three miles NW of Liskeard in E Cornwall. Take minor roads N for 2.5 miles from Dobwalls on A38.
Access: Various paths from 0.5 mile to four miles. Can be muddy after rain. Limited disabled access.
Facilities: Toilets.
Public transport: None.
Habitat: Ancient woodland, deep granite gorge.
Key birds: *All year*: Sparrowhawk, Buzzard, Kingfisher, all three woodpeckers, Jay, Grey Wagtail, Dipper, Marsh Tit, Treecreeper, Nuthatch. *Summer*: Redstart, Wood Warbler, Pied Flycatcher.
Contact: Cornwall & Isles of Scilly Team, 01872 265 710. email: cornwall@naturalengland.org.uk

2. HAYLE ESTUARY

RSPB (South West England Office).
Location: SW 550 370. In town of Hayle. Follow signs to Hayle from A30.
Access: Open at all times. No permits required. No admission charges. Dogs on leads please. Sorry - no coaches.
Facilities: Eric Grace Memorial Hide at Ryan's Field has parking and viewing. Nearest toilets in town of Hayle. No visitor centre but information board at hide.
Public transport: Buses and trains at Hayle.
Habitat: Intertidal mudflats, saltmarsh, lagoon and islands, sandy beaches and sand dunes.
Key birds: *Winter*: Wildfowl, gulls, Kingfisher, Ring-billed Gull, Great Northern Diver. *Spring/summer*: Migrant waders, breeding Shelduck. *Autumn*: Rare

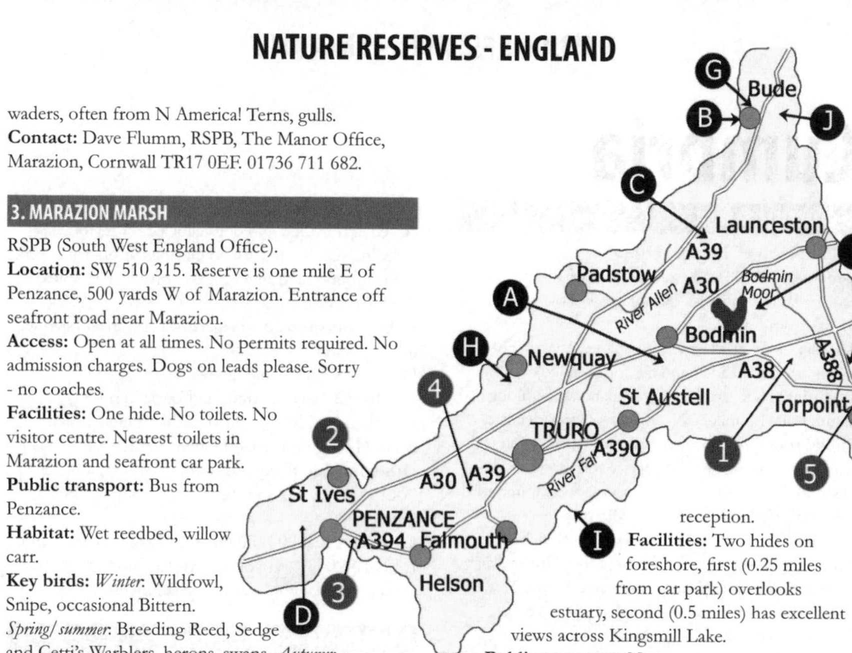

waders, often from N America! Terns, gulls.
Contact: Dave Flumm, RSPB, The Manor Office, Marazion, Cornwall TR17 0EF. 01736 711 682.

3. MARAZION MARSH

RSPB (South West England Office).
Location: SW 510 315. Reserve is one mile E of Penzance, 500 yards W of Marazion. Entrance off seafront road near Marazion.
Access: Open at all times. No permits required. No admission charges. Dogs on leads please. Sorry - no coaches.
Facilities: One hide. No toilets. No visitor centre. Nearest toilets in Marazion and seafront car park.
Public transport: Bus from Penzance.
Habitat: Wet reedbed, willow carr.
Key birds: *Winter*: Wildfowl, Snipe, occasional Bittern. *Spring/summer*: Breeding Reed, Sedge and Cetti's Warblers, herons, swans. *Autumn*: Occasional Aquatic Warbler, Spotted Crake. Large roost of swallows and martins in reedbeds, migrant warblers and waders.
Contact: Dave Flumm, RSPB, The Manor Office, Marazion, Cornwall TR17 0EF. 01736 711 682.

4. STITHIANS RESERVOIR

Cornwall Birdwatching & Preservation Society.
Location: SS 715 365. From B3297 S of Redruth.
Access: Good viewing from causeway. Hides accessible to members only.
Facilities: None. **Public transport:** None.
Habitat: Open water, marshland.
Key birds: Wildfowl and waders (inc. rarities, eg. Pectoral and Semipalmated Sandpipers, Lesser Yellowlegs).
Contact: Stuart Hutchings 5 Acres, Allet, Cornwall TR4 9DJ. 01872 273 939. e-mail: cornwt@cix.co.uk www.cornwallwildlifetrust.org.uk

5. TAMAR ESTUARY

Cornwall Wildlife Trust.
Location: SX 434 631 (Northern Boundary). SX 421 604 (Southern Boundary). From Plymouth head W on A38. Access parking at Cargreen and Landulph from minor roads off A388.
Access: Open at all times. Access bird hides from China Fleet Club car park, Saltash. Follow path alongside golf course - do not walk on course itself. Combination number for hide locks available at club reception.
Facilities: Two hides on foreshore, first (0.25 miles from car park) overlooks estuary, second (0.5 miles) has excellent views across Kingsmill Lake.
Public transport: None.
Habitat: Tidal mudflat with some saltmarsh.
Key birds: *Winter*: Avocet, Snipe, Black-tailed Godwit, Redshank, Dunlin, Curlew, Whimbrel, Spotted Redshank, Green Sandpiper, Golden Plover, Kingfisher.
Contact: Peter Kent, CWT East Cornwall Office, Cotehele Quay, Cotehele, St Dominick, Cornwall PL12 6TA. 01579 351 155.
e-mail: peter@cornwt.demon.co.uk

OTHER SITES

Full details in previous editions, (year indicated in brackets).
A. Breney Common – Cornwall WT, 01872 273 939 (06).
B. Bude Marshes – North Cornwall District Council, 01206 893 333 (04).
C. Crowdy Reservoir – SW Water, 01837 871 565 (04).
D. Drift Reservoir – Graham Hobin, 01736 362 206 (07).
E. Kit Hill Country Park – 01579 370 030 (04).
F. Loveny Reserve/Colliford Reservoir – Cornwall WT, 01872 273 939 (04).
G. Maer Lake Wetland Reserve – Cornwall WT, 01872 273 939 (05).
H. Nansmellyn Marsh – Cornwall WT, 01872 273 939 (04).
I. Nare Head – National Trust, 01208 432 691 (04).
J. Tamar Lakes – 01288 3212 262 (04).

Cumbria

1. CAMPFIELD MARSH

RSPB (North of England Office).
Location: NY 207 620. On S shore of Solway estuary, W of Bowness-on-Solway. Follow signs from B5307 from Carlisle.
Access: Open at all times, no charge. View high-tide roosts from roadside (suitable for disabled).
Facilities: Hide overlooking wetland areas, along nature trail (1.5 miles). No toilets or visitor centre.
Public transport: Nearest railway station – Carlisle (13 miles). Infrequent bus service to reserve.
Habitat: Saltmarsh/intertidal areas, open water, peat bog, wet grassland.
Key birds: *Winter*: Waders and wildfowl include Barnacle Goose, Shoveler, Scaup, Grey Plover. *Spring/summer*: Breeding Lapwing, Redshank, Snipe, Tree Sparrow and warblers. *Autumn*: Passage waders.
Contact: Dave Blackledge, North Plain Farm, Bowness-on-Solway, Wigton, Cumbria CA7 5AG. e-mail: dave.blackledge@rspb.org.uk

2 DRUMBURGH NNR

Cumbria Wildlife Trust
Location: NY 264 597. From Carlisle city centre, head W on B5307 to Kirkbride. After about one mile, turn R to Burgh by Sands. Follow road for 7.5 miles to Drumburgh village. Turn L by post office, continue down track and park on R past Moss Cottage.
Access: Open all year.
Facilities: None. **Public transport:** None.
Habitat: Raised bog, woodland, grassland.
Key birds: *Summer*: Red Grouse, Curlew, Grasshopper Warbler.
Other notable flora and fauna: Large heath butterfly, adder.
Contact: Trust HQ, Plumgarths, Kendal, Cumbria LA8 8LX, 01539 816 301.
e-mail: mail@cumbriawildlifetrust.org.uk

3. FOULNEY ISLAND

Cumbria Wildlife Trust.
Location: SD 246 640. Three miles SE of Barrow town centre on the A5087 from Barrow or Ulverston. At a roundabout 2.5 miles S of Barrow take a minor road through Rampside to Roa Island. Turn L into reserve car park. Walk to main island along stone causeway.
Access: Open all year. Access restricted to designated paths during bird breeding season. Slitch Ridge is closed at this time. No dogs allowed during bird breeding season. The island may be cut off for several hours around high-tide - please consult tide tables.
Facilities: None.
Public transport: Bus: regular service from Barrow to Roa Island.
Habitat: Shingle, sand, grassland.
Key birds: *Summer*: Arctic and Little Terns, Oystercatcher, Ringed Plover, Eider Duck. *Winter*: Brent Goose, Redshank, Dunlin, Sanderling.
Other notable flora and fauna: Sea campion, yellow horned poppy. Six spot burnet and common blue butterfly.
Contact: Trust HQ, Plumgarths, Crook Road, Kendal LA8 8LX. 01539 816 300;(Fax)01539 816 301.
e-mail: mail@cumbriawildlifetrust.org.uk

4. HARRINGTON RESERVOIR LNR

Allerdale Borough Council
Location: NX 994 257. 2 miles S of Workington. Take A597 to Harrington, turn L into Moorclose Road.
Access: Site open to the public from several points along Moorclose Road. Limited disabled access. Coaches must park on Moorclose Road.
Facilities: None.
Public transport: Bus service from the centre of Workington to Harrington and Moorclose Road.
Habitat: Small steep-sided wooded valley with streamside habitat and reservoir.
Key birds: A variety of woodland species including Willow Warbler, Chiffchaff, Sedge Warbler, Woodcock plus Redshanks, wildfowl and Kingfisher.
Contact: Patrick Joyce, Allerdale BC, Allerdale House, Workington, Cumbria CA14 3YJ. 01900 702 712; (Fax) 01900 702 716. www.allerdale.gov.uk

5. HAWESWATER

RSPB and United Utilities.
Location: NY 470 108. Golden Eagle viewpoint, near Bampton, 5 miles NW of Shap, off A6. Turn L in Bampton to car park at S of reservoir.
Access: Access at all times.
Facilities: Golden Eagle viewpoint, telescopes available Apr-end Aug (11am-4pm).
Public transport: None.
Habitat: Fells with rocky streams, steep oak and birch woodlands.

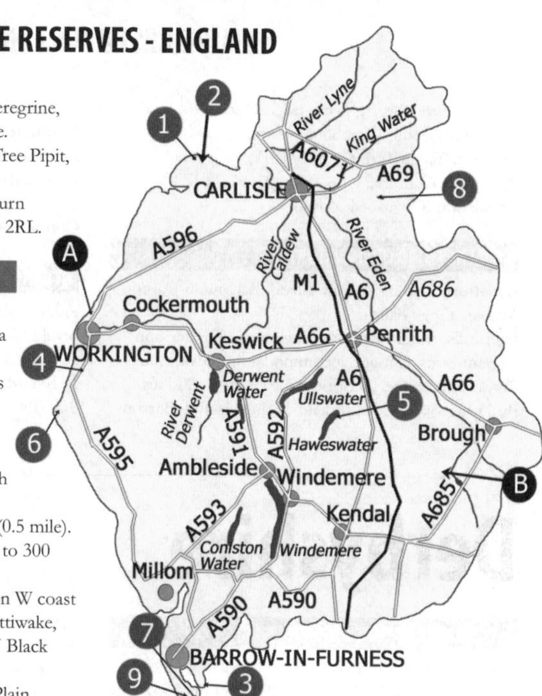

Key birds: *Upland breeders*: Golden Eagle, Peregrine, Raven, Ring Ouzel, Curlew, Redshank, Snipe. *Woodlands*: Pied Flycatcher, Wood Warbler, Tree Pipit, Redstart, Buzzard, Sparrowhawk.
Contact: Dave Shackleton, 7 Naddlegate, Burn Banks, Haweswater, Penrith, Cumbria CA10 2RL.

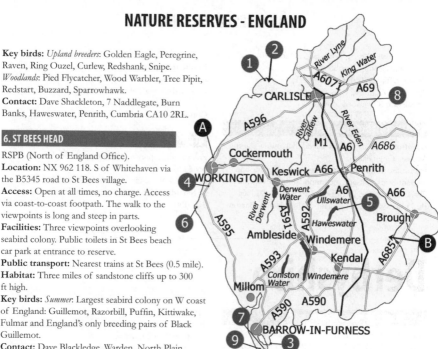

6. ST BEES HEAD

RSPB (North of England Office).
Location: NX 962 118. S of Whitehaven via the B5345 road to St Bees village.
Access: Open at all times, no charge. Access via coast-to-coast footpath. The walk to the viewpoints is long and steep in parts.
Facilities: Three viewpoints overlooking seabird colony. Public toilets in St Bees beach car park at entrance to reserve.
Public transport: Nearest trains at St Bees (0.5 mile).
Habitat: Three miles of sandstone cliffs up to 300 ft high.
Key birds: *Summer*: Largest seabird colony on W coast of England: Guillemot, Razorbill, Puffin, Kittiwake, Fulmar and England's only breeding pairs of Black Guillemot.
Contact: Dave Blackledge, Warden, North Plain Farm, Bowness-on-Solway, Wigton, Cumbria CA7 5AG. 01697 351 330. www.rspb.org.uk
e-mail: dave.blackledge@rspb.org.uk

7. SOUTH WALNEY

Cumbria Wildlife Trust.
Location: SD 215 620. Six miles S of Barrow-in-Furness. From Barrow, cross Jubilee Bridge onto Walney Island, turn L at lights. Continue through Biggar village to South End Caravan Park. Follow road for 1 mile to reserve.
Access: Open daily (10am-5pm) plus Bank Holidays. No dogs except assistance dogs. Day permits: £2 adults, 50p children. Cumbria Wildlife Trust members free.
Facilities: Toilets, nature trails, eight hides (two are wheelchair accessible), 200m boardwalk, cottage available to rent – sleeps 10.
Public transport: Bus service as far as Biggar.
Habitat: Shingle, lagoon, sand dune, saltmarsh.
Key birds: *Spring/autumn*: Passage migrants. *Summer*: 14,000 breeding pairs of Herring, Greater and Lesser Black-backed Gulls, Shelduck, Eider. *Winter*: Teal, Wigeon, Goldeneye, Redshank, Greenshank, Curlew, Oystercatcher, Knot, Dunlin, Merlin, Short-eared Owl, Twite.
Other notable flora and fauna: 450 species of flowering plants. Natterjack toad at North Walney.
Contact: The Warden, No 1 Coastguard Cottages, South Walney Nature Reserve, Walney Island, Barrow-in-Furness, Cumbria LA14 3YQ. 01229 471 066.
e-mail: mail@cumbriawildlifetrust.org.uk

8. TALKIN TARN COUNTRY PARK

Carlisle City Council
Location: NY544 591. Twelve miles E of Carlisle. From A69 E at Brampton, head S on B6413 for two miles. Talkin Tarn is on E just after level crossing.
Access: All year. Wheelchair access around tarn, two kissing gates accessible. Tearoom has lift. Coaches welcome.
Facilities: Toilets and restaurant open all year (11am-4pm Easter-Oct, limited opening times in winter). Dogs allowed around Tarn. Rowing boat hire at weekends and school holidays. Angling by day permit (with closed season).
Public transport: Bus: infrequent. Tel: 0870 608 2608. Train: nearest station is Brampton Junction. Tel: 0845 748 4950. Footpath from Brampton Junction 1 mile.
Habitat: Natural tarn, mature woodland.
Key birds: *Spring/summer*: Pied Flycatcher, Spotted Flycatcher, Redstart, Chiffchaff, Wood Warbler.

Winter: Grebes, Smew, Long-tailed Duck, Goosander, Gadwall, Wigeon, Brambling, swans.
Contact: Talkin Tarn Country Park, Tarn Road, Brampton, Cumbria, CA8 1HN. 01697 73 129.
e-mail: fionash@carlisle.gov.uk

9. WALNEY BIRD OBSERVATORY

Location: S tip of Walney Island, Barrow-in-Furness.
Access: Open daily.
Facilities: Monitoring and ringing of breeding and migrant birds. Cottage accommodation plus facilities for qualified ringers. For bookings write to Walney Bird Observatory, South End, Walney Island, Barrow-in-Furness, Cumbria LA14 3YQ.
Public transport: None.
Habitat: Mud flats, sandy beaches and dunes, pools.
Key birds: Uncommon and rare species on spring and autumn migration.
Contact: As South Walney.

OTHER SITES

Full details in previous editions, (year indicated in brackets).
A. Siddick Pond (as Harrington Reservoir) (07).
B. Smardale Gill NNR – Cumbria WT, 01539 816 300 (04).

Derbyshire

1. CARR VALE NATURE RESERVE

Derbyshire Wildlife Trust.
Location: SK 45 70. 1km W of Bolsover on A632 to Chesterfield. Turn L at roundabout into Riverside Way. Car park at end of road. Reserve is reached via footpath to R, around Peter Fidler Reserve (reclaimed colliery tip).
Access: Open all year.
Facilities: Car park, good disabled access, paths, viewing platforms. Coach parking on approach to car park.
Public transport: Various Stagecoach services from Chesterfield (Stephenson Place) all pass close to the reserve: Mon to Sat - 83 serves Villas Road, 81, 82, 82A and 83 serve the roundabout on the A632. Sun - 81A, 82A serve the roundabout on the A632.
Habitat: Lakes, wader flashes, reed bed, sewage farm, scrub, arable fields.
Key birds: *Summer*: Warblers, waders, farmland birds, wildfowl. *Winter*: Wildfowl. *Passage*: Waders, passerines.
Contact: Trust HQ, 01773 881 188.
e-mail: enquiries@derbyshirewt.co.uk
www.derbyshirewildlifetrust.org.uk

2. CARSINGTON RESERVOIR

Severn Trent Water.
Location: SK 24 51. Follow B5035 from either Ashbourne or B5036, then B5035 from Cromford.
Access: Open all year except Dec 25, (7am to sunset). There are various access points. Track is very steep in places and can be slippery in winter.
Facilities: Car parks (charge made) visitor centre, toilets, restaurant, hides.
Public transport: TM Trael operate services from Derby, Buxton and Ashbourne. Tel: 01246 477 331.
Habitat: Reservoir, woodland.
Key birds: *Spring/summer*: Gulls and wildfowl species. *Winter*: Winter thrushes, Usual woodland and farmland species, 200 plus species recorded and planned reed beds and scrapes should increase bird diversity, gulls.
Contact: Carsington Water Visitor Centre, Ashbourne, Derbyshire DE6 1ST. 01629 540 696.
e-mail: customer.relations@severntrent.co.uk
www.stwater.co.uk

3. DRAKELOW WILDFOWL RESERVE

Powergen PLC.
Location: SK 22 72 07. Drakelow Power Station, one mile NE of Walton-on-Trent.
Access: Permit holders only for the time being. Reserve is subject to closure at short notice during domolition of power station. Scheduled to last to end of 2005. Any problems, please ring warden during evenings.
Facilities: Seven hides, no other facilities.
Public transport: None.
Habitat: Disused flooded gravel pits with wooded islands and reedbeds.
Key birds: *Summer*: Breeding Reed and Sedge Warblers. Water Rail, Hobby. *Winter*: Wildfowl (Goldeneye, Gadwall, Smew), Merlin. Regular

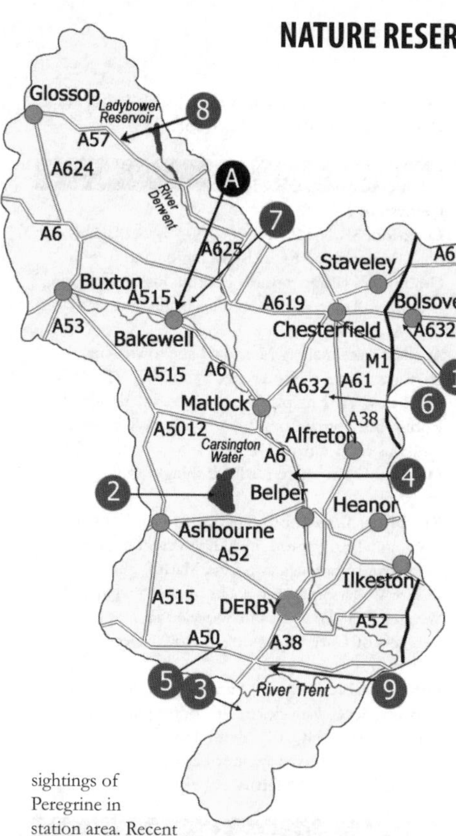

sightings of Peregrine in station area. Recent rarities include Great White and Little Egret, Cetti's Warbler and Golden Oriole, Bittern and Spotted Crake.

Other notable flora and fauna: Excellent for dragonflies and butterflies.

Contact: Tom Cockburn, Hon, Warden, 1 Dickens Drive, Swadlincote, DE11 0DX. 01283 217 146.

4. EREWASH MEADOWS

Derbyshire & Notts Wildlife Trusts

Location: SK 441 517. In three parts – Aldecar Flash, Brinsley Meadows and part of Cromford Canal. Ripley is nearest large town.

Access: Open all year – please keep to paths.

Facilities: None.

Public transport: Local bus services.

Habitat: The sites are now part of the largest floodplain grassland and wetlands in Erewash Valley.

Key birds: *Spring/summer*: Breeding Lapwing, Snipe, Reed Bunting and warblers. Raptors, waders and wildfowl seen on passage. *Winter*: Wildfowl species.

Other notable flora and fauna: Grass snake, amphibians, dragonflies, butterflies.

Contact: Derbyshire WT HQ – 017 73 881 188.

5. HILTON GRAVEL PITS

Derbyshire Wildlife Trust.

Location: SK 24 31. From Derby, take A516 from Mickleover W past Etwall onto A50 junction at Hilton. Turn R at first island onto Willow Pit Lane. Turn L next to a large white house and park next to the gate. Follow track along S side of the pools.

Access: Open all year.

Facilities: Tracks. Please observe the footpath restrictions along the side of the lakes.

Public transport: Local bus services from Derby.

Habitat: Ponds, scrub, wood, fen.

Key birds: *Spring/summer*: Great Crested Grebe, Common Tern, warblers. *Winter*: Wildfowl, Siskin, Goldcrest. *All year*: All three woodpeckers, Kingfisher, tits inc possible Willow Tit, Tawny Owl, Bullfinch.

Contact: Trust HQ, 01773 881 188.
e-mail: enquiries@derbyshirewt.co.uk
www.derbyshirewildlifetrust.org.uk

6. OGSTON RESERVOIR

Severn Trent Water Plc.

Location: From Matlock, take A615 E to B6014, just after Tansley. From Chesterfield take A61 S of Clay Cross onto B6014, towards Tansley. Cross railway, the reservoir is on L after the hill.

Access: View from roads, car parks or hides. Suitable for coaches. Heronry in nearby Ogston Carr Wood (Derbyshire Wildlife Trust) viewable from road, W of reservoir.

Facilities: Four hides (three for Ogston BC members, one public), toilets. Information pack on request.

Public transport: TM Travel 63 bus service (Chesterfield to Clay Cross) serves N end of reservoir and 64 service (Clay Cross to Matlock) not Sundays.

Habitat: Open water, pasture, mixed woodland.

Key birds: All three woodpeckers, Little and Tawny Owls, Kingfisher, Grey Wagtail, warblers. Passage raptors (inc. Osprey), terns and waders. *Winter*: Gull roost, wildfowl, tit and finch flocks.

Contact: Malcolm Hill, Treasurer, Ogston Bird Club, c/o 2 Sycamore Avenue, Glapwell, Chesterfield, S44 5LH. 01623 812 159. www.ogstonbirdclub.co.uk

7. PADLEY GORGE

The National Trust (East Midlands).

Location: From Sheffield, take A625. After eight miles, turn L on B6521 to Nether Padley. Grindleford Station is just off B6521 (NW of Nether Padley) and one mile NE of Grindleford village.

Access: All year. Not suitable for disabled people or those unused to steep climbs. Some of the paths are rocky. No dogs allowed.
Facilities: Café and toilets at Longshaw lodge.
Public transport: Bus: from Sheffield to Bakewell stops at Grindleford/Nether Padley. Tel: 01709 566 000. Train: from Sheffield to Manchester Piccadilly stops at Grindleford Station. Tel: 0161 228 2141.
Habitat: Steep-sided valley containing largest area of sessile oak woodland in south Pennines.
Key birds: *Summer*: Pied Flycatcher, Spotted Flycatcher, Redstart, Wheatear, Whinchat, Wood Warbler, Tree Pipit.
Contact: High Peak Estate Office, Edale End, Edale Road, Hope S33 2RF. 01433 670 368.
www.nationaltrust.org.uk

8. UPPER DERWENT VALLEY

National Trust (High Peak Estate)
Location: Either side of A57 from Ladybower Reservoir viaduct.
Access: Open all year but may be inaccessible in harsh winter weather. Not suitable for disabled. No dogs allowed.
Facilities: Toilets, café and visitor centre at National Park Centre, Fourholmes.
Public transport: Bus from Sheffield to Fairholmes and from Bamford train station to Kings Tree at weekends. Call Travelline on 0870 608 2608.
Habitat: Wooded valley running through extensive upland moors.
Key birds: Breeding Goshawk, Buzzard and occasional Hen Harrier, plus breeding Golden Plover, Dunlin, Curlew and Black Grouse.
Other notable flora and fauna: Mountain hare, moorland plants.
Contact: High Peak Estate Office, Edale Road, Hope, Derbyshire S33 2RF. 01433 760 368.

9. WILLINGTON GRAVEL PITS

Derbyshire Wildlife Trust.
Location: SK 285 274. From A50 'Toyota Island' turn onto Repton Road towards Willington and Repton. Go through village towards Repton. Just before bridge over River Trent, turn R onto un-made track. Park on track and walk along lane.
Access: Access along Meadow Lane to viewing platforms all year. No access on site.
Facilities: Viewing platforms. Limited parking in lane.
Public transport: Local trains stop at Willington, local bus service from Derby.
Habitat: Open water, reedbed, shingle island, grassland.
Key birds: *Summer*: Breeding Lapwing, other waders, Common Tern, raptors, including Peregrine, Kestrel, Hobby and Sparrowhawk, Sand Martin, wildfowl. *Winter*: Waders and large flocks of wildfowl including Wigeon, Teal, Pochard and Shoveler. *Passage*: Large numbers of Curlew in spring, up to 20 species of waders in spring/autumn.
Other notable flora and fauna: Short-leaved water starwort. Several species of dragonfly, plus otters.
Contact: Trust HQ, 01773 881 188.
e-mail: enquiries@derbyshirewt.co.uk
www.derbyshirewildlifetrust.org.uk

OTHER SITES

Full details in previous editions, (year indicated in brackets).
A. Great Longstone Country Park – Peak District NP, 01629 813 227 (04).

Devon

1. AYLESBEARE COMMON

RSPB (South West England Office).
Location: SY 058 897. Five miles E of J30 of M5 at Exeter, 0.5 miles past Halfway Inn on B3052. Turn R to Hawkerland, car park is on L. The reserve is on the opposite side of the main road.
Access: Open all year. One track suitable for wheelchairs and pushchairs.
Facilities: Car park, picnic area, group bookings, guided walks and special events. Disabled access via metalled track to private farm
Public transport: Buses (Exeter to Sidmouth, 52a, 52b). Request stop at Joneys Cross (reserve entrance).
Habitat: Heathland, wood fringes, streams and ponds.
Key birds: *Spring/summer*: Nightjar, Stonechat. *All year*: Dartford Warbler, Buzzard. *Winter*: Possible Hen Harrier.
Contact: Toby Taylor, Hawkerland Brake Barn, Exmouth Road, Aylesbeare, Nr Exeter, Devon, Nr Exeter, Devon EX5 2JS. 01395 233 655..

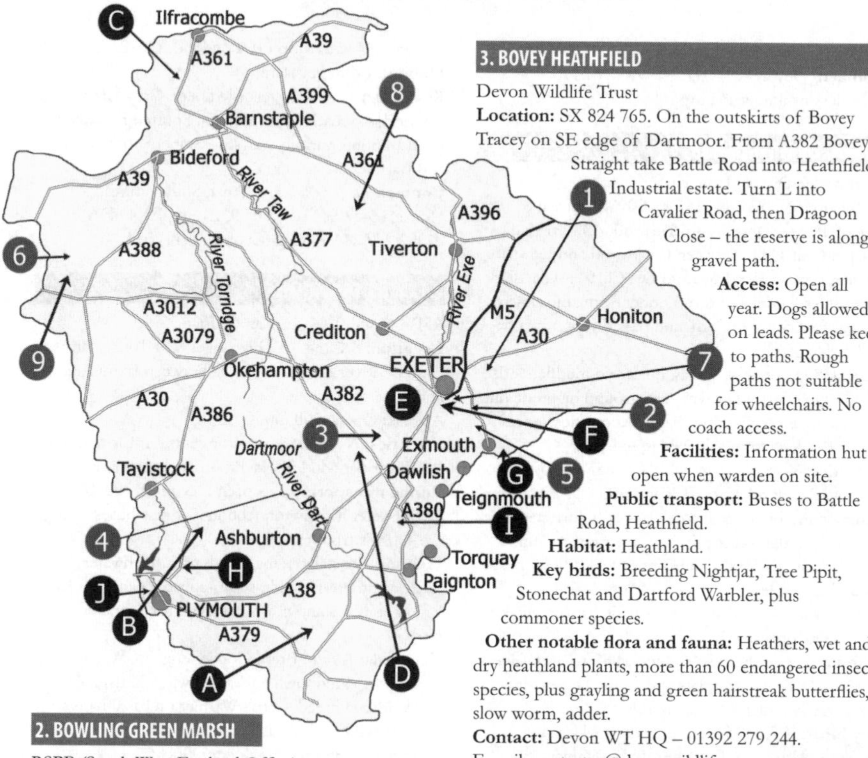

3. BOVEY HEATHFIELD

Devon Wildlife Trust

Location: SX 824 765. On the outskirts of Bovey Tracey on SE edge of Dartmoor. From A382 Bovey Straight take Battle Road into Heathfield Industrial estate. Turn L into Cavalier Road, then Dragoon Close – the reserve is along a gravel path.

Access: Open all year. Dogs allowed on leads. Please keep to paths. Rough paths not suitable for wheelchairs. No coach access.

Facilities: Information hut open when warden on site.

Public transport: Buses to Battle Road, Heathfield.

Habitat: Heathland.

Key birds: Breeding Nightjar, Tree Pipit, Stonechat and Dartford Warbler, plus commoner species.

Other notable flora and fauna: Heathers, wet and dry heathland plants, more than 60 endangered insect species, plus grayling and green hairstreak butterflies, slow worm, adder.

Contact: Devon WT HQ – 01392 279 244. E-mail: contactus@devonwildlifetrust.org

2. BOWLING GREEN MARSH

RSPB (South West England Office).

Location: SX 972 876. On the E side of River Exe, four miles SE of Exeter, 0.5 miles SE of Topsham.

Access: Open at all times. Please park at the public car parks in Topsham, not in the lane by the reserve.

Facilities: One hide suitable for wheelchair access. Viewing platform overlooking estuary reached by steps from track. No toilets or visitor centre.

Public transport: Exeter to Exmouth railway has regular (every 30 mins) service to Topsham station (half a mile from reserve). Stagecoach Devon 57 bus has frequent service (Mon-Sat every 12 mins, Sun every half-hour) from Exeter to Topsham.

Habitat: Coastal grassland, open water/marsh, hedgerows.

Key birds: *Winter*: Wigeon, Shoveler, Teal, Black-tailed Godwit, Curlew, Golden Plover. *Spring*: Shelduck, passage waders, Whimbrel, passage Garganey and Yellow Wagtail. *Summer*: Gull/tern roosts, high tide wader roosts contain many passage birds. *Autumn*: Wildfowl, Peregrine, wader roosts.

Contact: RSPB, Unit 3, Lions Rest Estate, Station Road, Exminster, Exeter EX6 8DZ. 01392 824 614. www.rspb.org.uk

4. DART VALLEY

Devon Wildlife Trust.

Location: SX 680 727. On Dartmoor nine miles NW from Ashburton. From A38 'Peartree Cross' near Ashburton, follow signs towards Princetown. Access from National Park car parks at New Bridge (S) or Dartmeet (N).

Access: Designated 'access land' but terrain is rough with few paths. It is possible to walk the length of the river (eight miles). A level, well-made track runs for a mile from Newbridge to give easy access to some interesting areas. Not suitable for large coaches (narrow bridges). Probably too rough for wheelchairs.

Facilities: Dartmoor National Park toilets in car parks at New Bridge and Dartmeet.

Public transport: Enquiry line 01392 382 800. Summer service only from Newton Abbot/Totnes to Dartmeet.

Habitat: Upland moor, wooded valley and river.

Key birds: *All year*: Raven, Buzzard. *Spring/summer*: Wood Warbler, Pied Flycatcher, Redstart in woodland, Stonechat and Whinchat on moorland, Dipper, Grey

Wagtail, Goosander on river.
Contact: Devon WT HQ, 01392 279 244. www.devonwildlifetrust.org

5. DAWLISH WARREN NNR

Teignbridge District Council.
Location: SX 983 788. At Dawlish Warren on S side of Exe estuary mouth. Turn off A379 at sign to Warren Golf Club, between Cockwood and Dawlish. Turn into car park adjacent to Lea Cliff Holiday Park. Pass under tunnel and turn L away from amusements. Park at far end of car park and pass through two pedestrian gates.
Access: Open public access, but avoid mudflats. Also avoid beach beyond groyne nine around high tide due to roosting birds. Parking charges apply. Restricted access for dogs (none allowed in hide).
Facilities: Visitor centre (tel 01626 863 980) open most weekends all year (10.30am-1pm and 2pm-5pm). Summer also open most weekdays as before, can be closed if warden on site. Toilets at entrance tunnel and in resort area only. Hide open at all times – best around high tide.
Public transport: Train station at site, also regular bus service operated by Stagecoach.
Habitat: High tide roost site for wildfowl and waders of Exe estuary on mudflats and shore. Dunes, dune grassland, woodland, scrub, ponds.
Key birds: *Winter*: Waders and wildfowl – large numbers. Also good for divers and Slavonian Grebe offshore. *Summer*: Particularly good for terns. Excellent variety of birds all year, especially on migration.
Contact: Steve Ayres/Philip Chambers, Countryside Management Section, Teignbridge District Council, Forde House, Brunel Road, Newton Abbot, Devon TQ12 4XX.
Visitor centre: 01626 863 980. Teignbridge District Council: 01626 361 101 (Ext 5754).

6. DUNSDON NATURE RESERVE

Devon Wildlife Trust
Location: SS 295 078, from A3072 take the Pancrasweek turn, W of Holsworthy. Continue on this small road for about 2 miles – entrance to reserve is on L just before Gains Cross.
Access: Open at all times. A few paths over open fields, the 400m boardwalk is suitable for wheelchairs. Please keep dogs on a short lead. Not suitable for coaches.
Facilities: Boardwalk and viewing platform. The culm fields are very rough and boggy.
Public transport: Nearest bus route is Bude to Holsworthy with drop off along the A3072.
Habitat: Culm grassland
Key birds: 50 species recorded here. Grey Heron, Buzzard, Sky Lark, Song Thrush, Spotted Flycatcher, Reed Bunting, various warblers, Snipe, Short-eared and Barn Owls.
Contact: Devon Wildlife Trust, Shirehampton House,3 5-37 St David's Hill, Exeter, EX4 4DA. 01392 279 244. e-mail: devonwt@cix.co.uk

7. EXMINSTER MARSHES

RSPB (South West England Office).
Location: SX 954 872. Five miles S of Exeter on W bank of River Exe. Marshes lie between Exminster and the estuary.
Access: Open at all times.
Facilities: No toilets or visitor centre. Information in RSPB car park and marked footpaths across reserve.
Public transport: Stagecoach Devon (01392 427 711). Exeter to Newton Abbot/Torquay buses – stops are 400 yds from car park.
Habitat: Coastal grazing marsh with freshwater ditches and pools, reeds, scrub-covered canal banks, winter stubbles and crops managed for farmland birds.
Key birds: *Winter*: Brent Goose, Wigeon, Water Rail, Short-eared Owl. *Spring*: Lapwing, Redshank and wildfowl breed, Cetti's Warbler on canal banks. *Summer*: Gull roosts, passage waders. *Autumn*: Peregrine, winter wildfowl, finch flocks.
Contact: RSPB, Unit 3, Lions Rest Estate, Station Road, Exminster, Exeter, Devon EX6 8DZ. 01392 824 614. www.rspb.org.uk

8. MESHAW MOOR

Devon Wildlife Trust
Location: SS 761 182. From Tiverton, take B3137 to Witheridge and on towards South Molton. After 3 miles turn L at Gidley Cross (telephone box on right) and then R at next crossroads. Nature reserve on L after 0.6 miles.
Access: Open all year. No access for coaches. Circular route around reserve can be uneven and wet. Boardwalks traverse most difficult sections. Dogs on leads only.
Facilities: Small car park.
Public transport: Bus from Tiverton, then walk to reserve.
Habitat: Wet acid culm grassland, drier neutral grassland, overgrown hedge banks.
Key birds: Breeding Tree Pipit, Spotted Flycatcher and warblers.
Other notable flora and fauna: Marsh fritillary,

marbled white butterflies, devil's bit scabious and heath spotted orchids, dormouse.
Contact: Devon WT HQ – 01392 279 244.
E-mail: contactus@devonwildlifetrust.org

9. VEALAND FARM NATURE RESERVE

Devon Wildlife Trust
Location: SS 288 068. E of Bude. Take A3072 and turn N to Pancrasweek immediately after Tamar bridge. Follow lane for 3km beyond Kingford. Entrance to Vealand Farm is marked. Follow access track, cross small bridge over disused canal and turn left. Park on hard standing area.
Access: Open all year. Not suitable for coaches. No set paths.
Facilities: Connected to Bude long distance path.
Public transport: None.
Habitat: Culm grassland and pasture with hedgerows. Three new ponds.
Key birds: Barn Owls frequent rush pasture fields, Tree Pipit and Reed Bunting breed in culm areas.
Other notable flora and fauna: Marbled white and marsh fritillary butterflies, otter, dragonflies.
Contact: Devon WT HQ – 01392 279 244.
E-mail: contactus@devonwildlifetrust.org

OTHER SITES

Full details in previous editions, (year indicated in brackets).
A. Andrews Wood – Devon Wildlife Trust, 01392 279 244 (04).
B. Burrator Reservoir – SW Lakes Trust, 01837 871 565 (04).
C. Chapel Wood – RSPB South-West office – 01392 432 691 (07).
D. East Dartmoor Woods & Heaths NNR – Natural England, 01626 832 330 (05).
E. Haldon Woods raptor watchpoint – Forestry Commission, 01392 832 262 (05).
F. Old Sludge Beds, Exeter – Devon Wildlife Trust, 01392 279 244 (05).
G. Otter Estuary – Devon Wildlife Trust, 01392 279 244 (05).
H. Plymbridge Woods – National Trust, 01208 432 691 (04).
I. Stover Lakes Country Park – Devon CC Rangers, 01626 835 236 (07).
J. Warleigh Point – Devon Wildlife Trust, 01392 279 244 (07).

Dorset

1. ARNE

RSPB (South West England Office).
Location: SY 973 882. Four miles SE of Wareham, turn off A351 at Stoborough.
Access: Shipstal Point and Coombe Birdwatchers' trails open all year. Bird hides available on both trails. Accessed from car park. Coaches and escorted parties by prior arrangement.
Facilities: Toilets in car park. Car park charge applies to non-members. Various footpaths. Reception hut (open end-May-early Sept).
Public transport: None.
Habitat: Lowland heath, woodland reedbed and saltmarsh, extensive mudflats of Poole Harbour.
Key birds: *All year*: Dartford Warbler, Little Egret, Stonechat. *Winter*: Hen Harrier, Red-breasted Merganser, Black-tailed Godwit. *Summer*: Nightjar, warblers. *Passage*: Spotted Redshank, Whimbrel, Greenshank, Osprey.
Contact: RSPB, Syldata, Arne, Wareham, Dorset BH20 5BJ. 01929 553 360. www.rspb.org.uk

2. BROWNSEA ISLAND

Dorset Wildlife Trust.
Location: SZ 026 883. Half hour boat rides from Poole Quay with Greenslade Pleasure Boats (01202 631 828) and Brownsea Island Ferries (01929 462 383). Ten minutes from Sandbanks Quay (next to Studland chain-ferry).
Access: Apr, May, Jun, Sept and Oct. Access by self-guided nature trail. Costs £2 adults, £1 children. Jul, Aug access by afternoon guided tour (2pm daily, duration 105 minutes). Costs £2 adults, £1 children.
Facilities: Toilets, information centre and shop, six hides, nature trail.
Public transport: Poole rail/bus station for access to Poole Quay and boats. Tel: 01202 673 555.
Habitat: Saline lagoon, reedbed, lakes, coniferous and mixed woodland.
Key birds: *Spring*: Avocet, Black-tailed Godwit, waders, gulls and wildfowl. *Summer*: Common and Sandwich Terns, Yellow-legged Gull, Little Egret, Little Grebe, Golden Pheasant. *Autumn*: Curlew

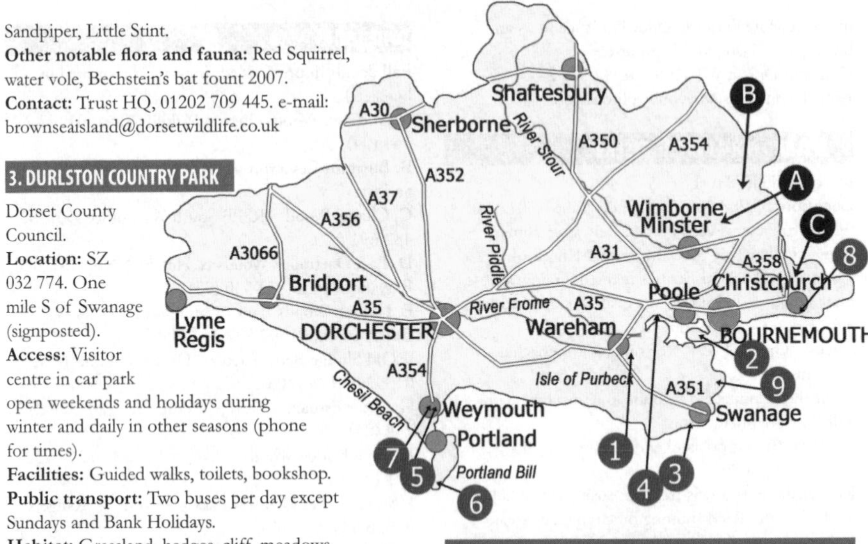

Sandpiper, Little Stint.
Other notable flora and fauna: Red Squirrel, water vole, Bechstein's bat fount 2007.
Contact: Trust HQ, 01202 709 445. e-mail: browenseaisland@dorsetwildlife.co.uk

3. DURLSTON COUNTRY PARK

Dorset County Council.
Location: SZ 032 774. One mile S of Swanage (signposted).
Access: Visitor centre in car park open weekends and holidays during winter and daily in other seasons (phone for times).
Facilities: Guided walks, toilets, bookshop.
Public transport: Two buses per day except Sundays and Bank Holidays.
Habitat: Grassland, hedges, cliff, meadows.
Key birds: Cliff-nesting seabird colonies; good variety of scrub and woodland breeding species; spring and autumn migrants; seawatching esp. Apr/May & Aug/Nov.
Contact: The Ranger, Durlston Country Park, Lighthouse Road, Swanage, Dorset BH19 2JL. 01929 424 443. e-mail: info@durlston.co.uk www.durlston.co.uk

4. HAM COMMON LNR

Poole Borough Council.
Location: SY 99. W of Poole. In Hamworthy, take the Blandford Road S along Lake Road, W along Lake Drive and Napier Road, leading to Rockley Park. Park in the beach car park by Hamworthy Pier or Rockley Viewpoint car park, off Napier Road, opposite the entrance to Gorse Hill Central Park.
Access: Open all year. Not suitable for coaches.
Facilities: None.
Habitat: Heathland, scrub, reedbeds, lake. Views over Wareham Channel and Poole Harbour.
Key birds: *Spring/summer*: Stonechat, Dartford Warbler. *Winter*: Brent Goose, Red-breasted Merganser, occasional divers, rarer grebes, Scaup. Waders inc Whimbrel, Greenshank and Common Sandpiper. *All year*: Little Egret.
Contact: Poole Borough Council, Civic Centre, Poole BH15 2RU. 01202 633 633..
e-mail: information@poole.gov.uk

5. LODMOOR

RSPB (South West England Office).
Location: SY 686 807. Adjacent Lodmoor Country Park, in Weymouth, off A353 to Wareham.
Access: Open all times.
Facilities: One viewing shelter, network of paths.
Public transport: Local bus service.
Habitat: Marsh, shallow pools, reeds and scrub, remnant saltmarsh.
Key birds: *Spring/summer*: Breeding Common Tern, warblers (including Reed, Sedge, Grasshopper and Cetti's), Bearded Tit. *Winter*: Wildfowl, waders. *Passage*: Waders and other migrants.
Contact: Nick Tomlinson, RSPB Visitor Centre, Swannery Car Park, Weymouth DT4 7TZ. 01305 778 313. www.rspb.org.uk

6. PORTLAND BIRD OBSERVATORY

Portland Bird Observatory (registered charity).
Location: SY 681 690. Six miles S of Weymouth beside the road to Portland Bill.
Access: Open at all times. Parking only for members of Portland Bird Observatory. Self-catering accommodation for up to 20. Take own towels, sheets, sleeping bags.
Facilities: Displays and information, toilets, natural history bookshop, equipped kitchen.
Public transport: Bus service from Weymouth (First Dorset Transit Route 1).
Habitat: Scrub and ponds.
Key birds: *Spring/autumn*: Migrants including many

rarities. *Summer*: Breeding auks, Fulmar, Kittiwake.
Contact: Martin Cade, Old Lower Light, Portland Bill, Dorset DT5 2JT. 01305 820 553.
e-mail: obs@btinternet.com
www.portlandbirdobs.btinternet.co.uk

7. RADIPOLE LAKE

RSPB (South West England Office).
Location: SY 677 796. In Weymouth. Enter from Swannery car park on footpaths.
Access: Visitor centre and nature trail open every day, summer (9am-5pm), winter (9am-4pm). Hide open (8.30am-4.30pm). Permit available from visitor centre required by non-RSPB members.
Facilities: Network of paths, one hide, one viewing shelter.
Public transport: Close to train station serving London and Bristol.
Habitat: Lake, reedbeds.
Key birds: *Winter*: Wildfowl. *Summer*: Breeding reedbed warblers (including Cetti's), Bearded Tit, passage waders and other migrants. Garganey regular in spring. Good for rarer gulls.
Contact: Nick Tomlinson, RSPB Visitor Centre, Swannery Car Park, Weymouth DT4 7TZ. 01305 778 313. www.rspb.org.uk

8. STANPIT MARSH LNR

Community Services, Christchurch Borough Council. (Stanpit Marsh Advisory Panel)
Location: SZ 167 924. In Christchurch, close to confluence of Rivers Avon and Stour.
Access: Public open space SSSI. Limited disabled access across marshy terrain. Nearest coach parking is at Two Riversmeet Leisure Centre, Stony Lane.
Facilities: Information centre.
Public transport: Wilts & Dorset bus no 123 (tel 01202 673 555) Stanpit recreation ground stop. Bournemouth Yellow Buses no 20 (tel 01202 636 000) Purewell Cross roundabout stop.
Habitat: Salt, fresh, brackish marsh, sand dune and scrub.
Key birds: *Estuarine*: Waders, winter wildfowl, migrants. *Reedbed*: Bearded Tit, Cetti's Warbler. Scrub: Sedge Warbler, Reed Warbler. *River/streams/bankside*: Kingfisher. Feeding and roosting site.
Contact: Peter Holloway, Christchurch Countryside Service, Steamer Point Nature Reserve, Highcliffe, Christchurch, Dorset BH23 4AU. 01425 272 479.
e-mail: countryside.service@christchurch.gov.uk

9. STUDLAND & GODLINGSTON HEATHS

National Trust.
Location: SZ 030 846. N of Swanage. From Ferry Road, N of Studland village.
Access: Open all year.
Facilities: Hides, nature trails.
Public transport: No 150 bus hourly to and from Bournemouth. 142/3 from Swanage and Wareham.
Habitat: Woodland, heath, dunes, inter-tidal mudflats, saltings, freshwater lake, reedbeds, carr.
Key birds: Water Rail, Reed and Dartford Warblers, Nightjar, Stonechat. *Winter*: Wildfowl. Studland Bay, outside the reserve, has winter Black-necked and Slavonian Grebes, Scoter, Eider.
Contact: The National Trust, Countryside Office, Middle Beach Car Park, Studland, Swanage BH19 3AX.

OTHER SITES

Full details in previous editions, (year indicated in brackets).
A. Holt Heath – Ian Nichol (Natural England), 01202 841 026 (04).
B. Moors Valley Country Park – 01425 470 721 (04).
C. Sopley Common – Dorset WT, 01305 264 620.

Durham

1. HAMSTERLEY FOREST

Forestry Commission
Location: NZ 093 315. Eight miles W of Bishop Auckland. Main entrance is five miles from A68, S of Witton-le-Wear and signposted through Hamsterley village and Bedburn.
Access: Open all year. Toll charge. Forest closes at dusk.
Facilities: Visitor Centre, toilets, shop, access for disabled. Visitors should not enter fenced farmland.
Public transport: None.
Habitat: Commercial woodland, mixed and broadleaved trees.
Key birds: *Spring/summer*: Willow Warbler, Chiffchaff, Wood Warbler, Redstart, Pied Flycatcher. *Winter*: Crossbill, Redwing, Fieldfare. *All year*: Jay, Dipper, Green Woodpecker.

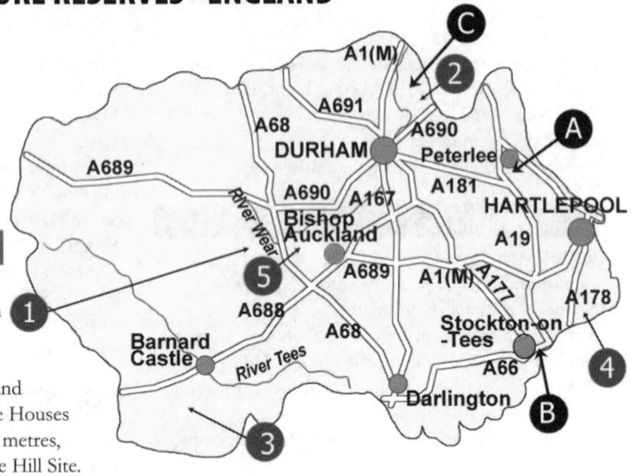

Other notable flora and fauna: Hay meadows have wide variety of plants including globe flower.
Contact: Forestry Commission, 01434 220 242. e-mail: richard.gilchrist@forestry.gsi.gov.uk

2. JOE'S POND NATURE RESERVE

Durham Wildlife Trust.
Location: NZ 32 48. Between Durham and Sunderland on A690. N from Durham, leave A690 S of Houghton-le-Spring on B21284 to Fence Houses and Hetton-le-Hole. Head W towards Fence Houses and turn L at 1st roundabout, after 800 metres, into an opencast colliery site, signed Rye Hill Site.
Access: Open all year.
Facilities: Car park, bird hide.
Public transport: None.
Habitat: Scrub, pond, grassland.
Key birds: *Spring/summer*: Ruddy Duck, hirundines, Whinchat, Lesser Whitethroat, Whitethroat, Blackcap. Possible Yellow Wagtail, Redstart, Grasshopper Warbler. *Passage*: Waders, Wheatear. *Winter*: Teal, Pochard, Water Rail, Woodcock, Short-eared Owl, Kingfisher, thrushes. Chance of Merlin, Jack Snipe.
Contact: Rainton Meadows, Chilton Moor, Houghton-le-Spring, Tyne & Wear, DH4 6PU. 01388 488 728. e-mail: info@durhamwt.co.uk

3. STANG FOREST AND HOPE MOOR

Forestry Commission
Location: NZ 022 075. The wood is six miles S of Barnard Castle. On A66 follow signs for Reeth after the turn-off to Barnard Castle on the W-bound carriageway. Stang is then about 3.5 miles from the A66 (car park for Hope Edge Walk).
Access: Open all year. Road dangerous in frost.
Facilities: Number of parking lay-bys and forest trails. Trail best for birdwatchers heads E and then N to Hope Edge.
Public transport: None.
Habitat: Woodland, moorland.
Key birds: *Spring/summer*: Whinchat, Wheatear, Cuckoo. *All year*: Red Grouse, Crossbill.
Contact: Forestry Commission, 01434 220 242.

4. TEESMOUTH

Natural England (North East Region).
Location: Two components, centred on NZ 535 276 and NZ 530 260, three and five miles S of Hartlepool, E of A178. Access to northern component from car park at NZ 534 282, 0.5 miles E of A178. Access to southern part from A178 bridge over Greatham Creek at NZ 510 254. Car park adjacent to A178 at NZ 508 251. Both car parks can accommodate coaches.
Access: Open at all times. In northern component, no restrictions over most of dunes and North Gare Sands (avoid golf course, dogs must be kept under close control). In southern component, disabled access path to public hides at NZ 516 255 and NZ 516 252 (no other access).
Facilities: Nearest toilets at Seaton Carew, one mile to the N. Disabled access path and hides (see above), interpretive panels and leaflet. Teesmouth Field Centre (Tel: 01429 264 912).
Public transport: Half-hourly bus service (service 1) operates Mon-Sat between Middlesbrough and Hartlepool (hourly on Sundays), along A178, Stagecoach Hartlepool, Tel: 01429 267 082.
Habitat: Grazing marsh, dunes, intertidal flats.
Key birds: Passage and winter wildfowl and waders. Passage terns and skuas in late summer. Scarce passerine migrants and rarities. *Winter*: Merlin, Peregrine, Snow Bunting, Twite, divers, grebes.
Contact: Mike Leakey, Natural England, c/o British Energy, Tees Road, Hartlepool TS25 2BZ. 01429 853 325. email: northumbria@naturalengland.org.uk

5. WITTON-LE-WEAR (Low Barns)

Durham Wildlife Trust.
Location: NZ 160 315. NW of Bishop Auckland. Off unclassified road between Witton-le-Wear (signposted on A68) and High Grange.
Access: Open all year.
Facilities: Five hides (four with disabled access),

observation tower above visitor centre (manned), nature trail, coffee shop.
Habitat: Former gravel workings, lake, ponds, riverbank and newly constructed reedbeds.
Key birds: *All year*: Greylag Goose, Kingfisher. *Summer*: Goosander, Grey Wagtail, Redpoll have bred. *Winter*: Wildfowl (inc. Goldeneye, Shoveler), Curlew, Redshank, Wheatear, Snipe.
Contact: Visitor Centre Manager, Low Barns Nature Reserve, Witton-le-Wear, Bishop Auckland, Co Durham DL14 0AG. 01388 488 728.
e-mail: info@durhamwt.co.uk

OTHER SITES

Full details in previous editions, (year indicated in brackets).
A. Castle Eden Dene – Natural England, 0191 586 0004 (06).
B. Maze Park/Portrack Marsh – Tees Valley WT, 01642 759 900 (04).
C. Rainton Meadows – Durham Wildlife Trust – 0191 5843 112 (06).

Essex

1. ABBERTON RESERVOIR

Essex Wildlife Trust.
Location: TL 963 185. Five miles SW of Colchester on B1026. Follow signs from Layer-de-la-Haye.
Access: Open Tue-Sun and Bank Holiday Mondays (9am-5pm). Closed Christmas Day and Boxing Day.
Facilities: Visitor centre, toilets, nature trail, five hides (3 with disabled access). Ample parking, including coaches. Also good viewing where roads cross reservoir.
Public transport: Phone Trust for advice.
Habitat: 100 acres on edge of 1200a reservoir.
Key birds: *Winter*: Nationally important for Mallard, Teal, Wigeon, Shoveler, Gadwall, Pochard, Tufted Duck, Goldeneye (most important inland site in Britain). Smew and Goosander regular. Passage waders, terns, birds of prey. Tree-nesting Cormorant colony; raft-nesting Common Tern. *Summer*: Hobby, Yellow Wagtail, warblers, Nightingale, Corn Bunting; *Autumn*: Red-crested Pochard, Water Rail.
Contact: Centre Manager, Essex Wildlife Trust, Abberton Reservoir Visitor Centre, Church Road, Layer-de-la-Haye, Colchester CO2 0EU. 01206 738 172. e-mail: abberton@essexwt.org.uk

2. BRADWELL BIRD OBSERVATORY

Essex Birdwatching Society
Location: 100 yards S of St Peter's Chapel, Bradwell-on-Sea. Mouth of Blackwater estuary, between Maldon and Foulness.
Access: Open all year.
Facilities: Accommodation for eight in hut; two rooms each with four bunks; blankets, cutlery, etc. supplied.
Public transport: None.
Habitat: Mudflats, saltmarsh.
Key birds: *Winter*: Wildfowl (inc. Brent Geese, Red-throated Diver, Red-breasted Merganser), large numbers of waders; small numbers of Twite, Snow Bunting and occasional Shore Lark on beaches, also Hen Harrier, Merlin and Peregrine. Good passage of migrants usual in spring and autumn. *Summer*: Small breeding population of terns and other estuarine species.
Contact: Graham Smith, 48 The Meads, Ingatestone, Essex CM4 0AE. 01277 354 034.

3. FINGRINGHOE WICK

Essex Wildlife Trust.
Location: TM 046 197. Colchester five miles. The reserve is signposted from B1025 to Mersea Island, S of Colchester.
Access: Open six days per week (not Mon or Christmas or Boxing Day). No permits needed. Donations invited. Centre/reserve open (9am-5pm). Dogs must be on a lead.
Facilities: Visitor centre – toilets, shop, light refreshments, car park, displays. Reserve – seven bird hides, two nature trails, plus one that wheelchair users could use with assistance.
Public transport: None.
Habitat: Old gravel pit, large lake, many ponds, sallow/birch thickets, young scrub, reedbeds, saltmarsh, gorse heathland.
Key birds: *Autumn/winter*: Brent Goose, waders, Hen

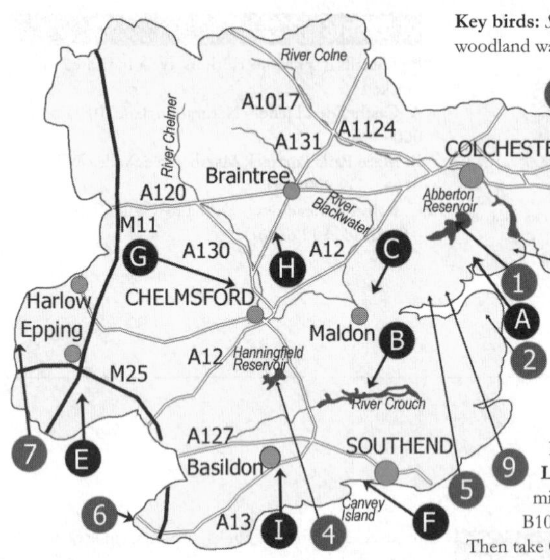

Harrier, Little Egret. *Spring*: 30 male Nightingales. Good variety of warblers in scrub, thickets, reedbeds and Turtle Dove, Green/Great Spotted Woodpeckers. *Winter*: Little Grebe, Mute Swan, Teal, Wigeon, Shoveler, Gadwall on lake.
Contact: Laurie Forsyth, Wick Farm, South Green Road, Fingringhoe, Colchester, Essex CO5 7DN. 01206 729 678. e-mail: admin@essexwt.org.uk

4. HANNINGFIELD RESERVOIR

Essex Wildlife Trust.
Location: TQ 725 972. Three miles N of Wickford. Exit off Southend Road (Old A130) at Rettendon onto South Hanningfield Road. Follow this for two miles until reaching the T-junction with Hawkswood Road. Turn R and the entrance to the Visitor Centre and reserve is one mile on the R.
Access: Open Mon-Sun (9am-5pm) all year. Disabled parking, toilets, and adapted birdwatching hide. No dogs. No cycling.
Facilities: Visitor centre, gift shop, optics, refreshments, toilets, four bird hides, nature trails, picnic area, coach parking, education room.
Public transport: Chelmsford to Wickford bus no 14 to Downham village and walk half mile down Crowsheath Lane.
Habitat: Mixed woodland (110 acres) with grassy glades and rides, adjoining 870-acre Hanningfield Reservoir, designated an SSSI due to its high numbers of wildfowl.
Key birds: *Spring*: Good numbers and mix of woodland warblers. *Summer*: Vast numbers of Swifts, Swallows and martins feeding over the water. Hobby and Osprey. *Winter*: Good numbers and mix of waterfowl. Large gull roost.
Contact: Bill Godsafe, Hanningfield Reservoir Visitor Centre, Hawkswood Road, Downham, Billericay CM11 1WT. 01268 711 001. www.essexwt.org.uk

5. OLD HALL MARSHES

RSPB (East Anglia Office).
Location: TL 97 51 25. Approx eight miles S of Colchester. From A12 take B1023, via Tiptree, to Tolleshunt D'Arcy. Then take Chapel Road (back road to Tollesbury), after one mile turn L into Old Hall Lane. Continue up Old Hall Lane, over speed ramp and through iron gates to cattle grid, then follow signs to car park.
Access: By permit only in advance from Warden, write to address below. Open 9am-9pm or dusk, closed Tues. No coaches.
Facilities: Two trails – one of three miles and one of 6.5 miles. Two viewing screens overlooking saline lagoon area at E end of reserve. No visitor centre or toilets.
Habitat: Coastal grazing marsh, reedbed, open water saline lagoon, saltmarsh and mudflat.
Key birds: *Summer*: Breeding Avocet, Redshank, Lapwing, Pochard, Shoveler, Gadwall, Garganey, Barn Owl. *Winter*: Brent Goose, Wigeon, Teal Shoveler, Goldeneye, Red-breasted Merganser, all the expected waders, Hen Harrier, Merlin, Short-eared Owl and Twite. *Passage*: All expected waders (particularly Spotted Redshank, Green Sandpiper and Whimbrel), Yellow Wagtail, Whinchat and Wheatear.
Contact: Paul Charlton, Site Manager, c/o 1 Old Hall Lane, Tolleshunt D'Arcy, Maldon, Essex CM9 8TP. 01621 869 015. e-mail: paul.charlton@rspb.org.uk

6. RSPB RAINHAM MARSHES

RSPB (East Anglian office)
Location: On N bank of River Thames, SE of Dagenham. From London take A13 to A1306 turn-off and head towards Purfleet for half a mile. At traffic lights, turn right, signposted A1090 and reserve

entrance is 300 metres along this road.
Access: Open all year. Extensive programme of guided walks - check RSPB website for details. Approx 3.5 miles of boardwalks suitable for wheelchairs and pushchairs.
Facilities: Visitor centre, disabled toilets, car park on site, picnic area, shop, refreshments available. One bird hide.
Public transport: Route 44 (Ensignbus – 01708 865 656) runs daily between Grays and Lakeside via Purfleet. Arriva service (0870 120 1088) hourly Sundays and most Public Holidays.
Habitat: A former MoD shooting range, the site is the largest remaining expanse of wetland along the upper reaches of the Thames.
Key birds: *Spring*: Marsh Harrier, Hobby, Wheatear, hirundines and other migrants. *Summer*: Many waders, including Black-tailed Godwit, Whimbrel, Greenshank, Snipe, Lapwing, Avocet. Yellow-legged Gull. Merlin and Peregrine hunt among the gathering wader flocks. *Winter*: Waders, wildfowl, Water Pipit, Short-eared owl, Little Egret.
Other notable flora and fauna: Bank and water voles, water shrew, fox, stoat, weasel, dragonflies.
Contact: For information, call 01708 899 840 or e-mail: rainham.marshes@rspb.org.uk

7. RIVER LEE COUNTRY PARK

Lee Valley Park
Location: Close to Waltham Abbey, Essex. Fishers Green entrance off B194.
Access: All hides open to public at weekends and Bank Holidays (excepting Christmas Day). Permit needed for weekday use - contact Lee Valley Park for details. Groups should also book with Info Centre. Hides and paths suitable for wheelchairs.
Facilities: Café, toilet and shop at Hayes Hill Farm. Information centre off A121 in Waltham Abbey. Bittern Watchpoint at Lee Valley Park.
Public transport: All sites served by buses - call Essex Bus Info on 0345 000 333 or Herts Travel Line on 01992 556 765.
Habitat: Former gravel pits now flooded, with wooded islands, reedbeds and marshy corners.
Key birds: *Winter*: Bittern at Fishers Green (best in winter - hide open every day). Wide variety of wildfowl inc Smew, Goosander, Shoveler and Gadwall. *Summer*: Breeding warblers, Nightingale, Little Ringed Plover, Turtle Dove. Wide variety of species on spring/autumn passage.
Contact: Lee Valley Information Centre – 01992 702 200.

8. STOUR ESTUARY

RSPB (East Anglian office)
Location: Between Manningtree and Harwich. From Manningtree, stay on B1352 past Strangers Home pub in Bradfield, then look for brown sign to reserve.
Access: Open all year. Stour wood walk (1 mile) OK for wheelchairs in dry conditions. Walks to estuary and furthest hide not suitable, due to terrain and kissing gates. Dogs only allowed in Stour Wood.
Facilities: Two hides, one viewing screen. Two picnic tables.
Public transport: Nearest train station (One Railway) at Wrabness is 1 mile away. Hourly buses (Mon - Sat) running between Colchester and Harwich will stop at entrance to woods on request.
Habitat: Extensive woodland leading down to the River Stour estuary, saltmarsh at Deep Fleet and mudflats at Copperas Bay.
Key birds: *Spring/autumn*: Black-tailed Godwit, Dunlin, Ringed Plover. *Summer*: Nightingale and warblers. *Winter*: Brent Goose, plus nationally important numbers of wildfowl and waders.
Other notable flora and fauna: Woodland wildflowers in spring.
Contact: RSPB (East Anglian office) – 01603 661 662.

9. TOLLESBURY WICK

Essex Wildlife Trust.
Location: TL 969 104. On Blackwater Estuary eight miles E of Maldon. Follow B1023 to Tollesbury via Tiptree, leaving A12 at Kelvedon. Then follow Woodrolfe Road S towards the marina. Use car park at Woodrolfe Green. Small public car park near reserve suitable for cars, mini-buses and small coaches. Wheelchair access possible to Shinglehead Point.
Access: Open all times along public footpath on top of sea wall. Motorised wheelchair access possible to Block House Bay.
Facilities: Public toilets at Woodrolfe Green car park.
Public transport: Hedingham bus services run to Tollesbury from Maldon, Colchester and Witham - call 01621 869 214 for information.
Habitat: Estuary with fringing saltmarsh and mudflats with some shingle. Extensive freshwater grazing marsh, brackish borrowdyke and small reedbeds.
Key birds: *Winter*: Wildfowl and waders, Short-eared Owl, Hen Harrier. *Summer*: Breeding Avocet, Redshank, Lapwing, Little Tern, Reed and Sedge Warblers, Barn Owl. *Passage*: Whimbrel, Spotted Redshank.

Contact: Jonathan Smith, Tollesbury, Maldon, Essex CM9 8RJ. 01621 868 628.
e-mail: jonathans@essexwt.org.uk

OTHER SITES

Full details in previous editions, (year indicated in brackets).
A. Abbotts Hall Farm – Essex WT, 01621 862 960 (06).
B. Blue House Farm - Essex WT, 01621 862 960 (04).
C. Chigborough Lakes – Essex WT, 01621 862 960 (06).
D. Colne Point – Essex WT, 01621 862 960 (05).
E. Hainault Forest Country Park – 0208 500 7353 (04).
F. Leigh – Essex WT, 01621 862 960 (04).
G. Little Waltham Meadows – Essex WT, 01621 862 960 (04).
H. Phyllis Currie Nature Reserve – Essex WT, 01621 862 960 (04).
I. Wat Tyler Country Park – 01268 550 088 (04).

Gloucestershire

1. ASHLEWORTH HAM AND MEEREND THICKET

Gloucestershire Wildlife Trust.
Location: SO 830 265. Leave Gloucester N on A417; R at Hartpury and follow minor road through Ashleworth towards Hasfield.
Access: Access prohibited at all times but birds may be viewed from new hide in Meerend Thicket.
Facilities: Bird viewing hide and screen, interpretation panels.
Public transport: None.
Habitat: Low-lying grassland flood plain.
Key birds: *Winter*: Wildfowl (inc. 4,000 Wigeon, 1,500 Teal, Pintail, Goldeneye, Bewick's Swan), passage waders, Peregrine. *Summer*: Hobby.
Contact: Trust HQ, 01452 383 333.
e-mail: info@gloucestershirewildlifetrust.co.uk
www.gloucestershirewildlifetrust.co.uk

2. COOME HILL NATURE RESERVE

Gloucestershire Wildlife Trust.
Location: SO 887 272. On A38 between Gloucester and Tewkesbury, at traffic lights for A4019 to Cheltenham, take narrow lane opposite to reserve entrance at The Wharf.
Access: Permitted at all times but may be limited in winter due to flooding.
Facilities: Two bird hides and interpretation panels.
Public transport: Bus stop nearby on A38.
Habitat: Low-lying grassland, floodplain and canal.
Key birds: *Summer*: Little Egret, Lapwing, Redshank, Curlew, warblers. *Winter*: Little Grebe, Black-tailed Godwit, Snipe and Little Egret, Whooper and Bewick's Swan, Canada, Barnacle and Greylag Geese, Wigeon, Teal, Pintail, Shoveler.
Contact: Trust HQ, 01452 383 333.
e-mail: info@gloucestershirewildlifetrust.co.uk
www.gloucestershirewildlifetrust.co.uk

3. COTSWOLD WATER PARK

Cotswold Water Park Society.
Location: The CWP comprises 140 lakes in the Upper Thames Valley, between Cirencester and Swindon. Many of these lakes are accessible by the public using public rights of way. Start from Cotswold Water Park Gateway Visitor Centre (SU 072 971). The Visitor Centre is immediately on L after A419. For Millenium Visitor Centre at Keynes Country Park (SU 026 957) from A419, take B4696 towards Ashton Keynes. At staggered crossroads, go straight over, heading towards Somerford Keynes. Take next R turn to Circencester. The entrance to Keynes Country Park is the second entrance on the R.
Access: Cotswold Water Park is open all year round. The visitor centres are open every day except Christmas Day.
Facilities: Paths are flat but with stiles and footbridges. Many are wheelchair accessible. Toilets, refreshments, car parking and information available from the visitor centres. Hides available at Cleveland Lakes/Waterhay (lakes 68a and 68c), Shorncote Reed Bed (lakes 84/85), Cokes Pit (Lake 34) and Whelford Pools (Lake 111). Free copies of the CWP Leisure Guide are available from the visitor centres. These have maps showing the lake numbering. The guidebook *Wildlife in the Cotswold Water Park: Where to go and what to see* also available from centres.
Public transport: Bus: from Kemble, Cheltenham,

Cirencester and Swindon. Tel: 08457 090 899. Train: nearest station is four miles away at Kemble. Tel: 08457 484 950.
Habitat: Gravel extraction has created more than 1,000ha of standing open water or 140 lakes, plus other associated wetland habitats, creating one of the largest man-made wetlands in Europe.
Key birds: *Winter*: Common wildfowl, Smew, Red-crested Pochard, Merlin, Peregrine.
Summer: Breeding ducks, warblers, Nightingale, Hobby, Common Tern, Black-headed Gull colony, Reed Bunting, hirundines.
Contact: Cotswold Water Park Society, 01285 861 459; Fax.01285 860 186. e-mail: info@waterpark.org www.waterpark.org

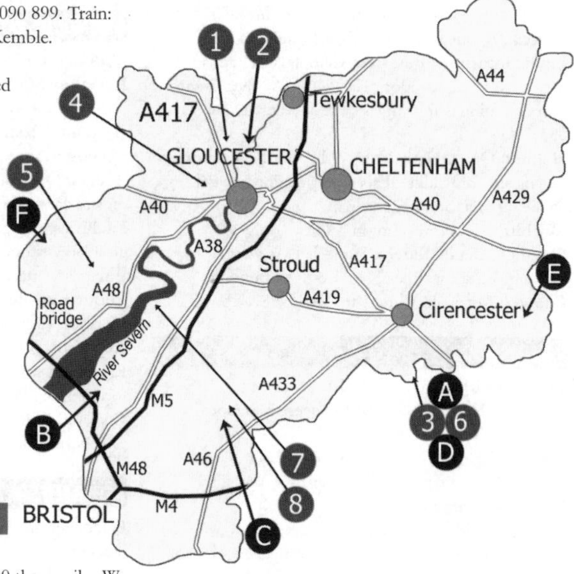

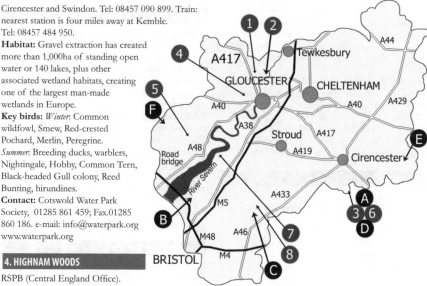

4. HIGHNAM WOODS

RSPB (Central England Office).
Location: SO 778 190. Signed on A40 three miles W of Gloucester.
Access: Open at all times, no permit required. The nature trails can be very muddy. Some limited wheelchair access. Dogs allowed on leads.
Facilities: One nature trail (approx 1.5 miles).
Public transport: Contact Glos. County Council public transport information line. Tel: 01452 425 543.
Habitat: Ancient woodland in the Severn Vale with areas of coppice and scrub.
Key birds: *Spring/summer*: The reserve has about 12 pairs of breeding Nightingales. Resident birds include all three woodpeckers, Buzzard and Sparrowhawk. Ravens are frequently seen. *Winter*: Feeding site near car park for woodland birds.
Contact: Barry Embling, Site Manager, The Puffins, Parkend, Lydney, Glos GL15 4JA. 01594 562 852. e-mail: barry.embling@rspb.org.uk

5. NAGSHEAD

RSPB (Central England Office).
Location: SO 097 085. In Forest of Dean, N of Lydney. Signed immediately W of Parkend village on the road to Coleford.
Access: Open at all times, no permit required. The reserve is hilly and there are some stiles on nature trails. Some limited wheelchair access. Dogs must be kept under close control.
Facilities: There are two nature trails (one mile and 2.25 miles). Information centre, with toilet facilities (including disabled), open at weekends mid-Apr to end Aug. Schools education programme available.
Public transport: Contact Glos. County Council public transport information line, 01452 425 543.
Habitat: Much of the reserve is 200-year-old oak plantations, grazed in some areas by sheep. The rest of the reserve is a mixture of open areas and conifer/mixed woodland.
Key birds: *Spring*: Pied Flycatcher, Wood Warbler, Redstart, warblers. *Winter*: Siskin, Crossbill in some years. *All year*: Buzzard, Raven, Hawfinch, all three woodpeckers.
Contact: Barry Embling, 01594 562 852. e-mail:barry.embling@rspb.org.uk

6. SHORNCOTE REEDBED (LAKES 84/85)

Cotswold Water Park Society.
Location: SU 026 957. Lakes 84/85 located adjacent to Keynes Country Park and most easily accessed from here. From A419, take B4696 towards Ashton Keynes. At the staggered crossroads, go straight over, heading towards Somerford Keynes. Take the next R turn to Circencester. The entrance to Keynes Country Park is the second entrance on the R.
Access: Open at all times to walkers. Seasonal opening hours - check website for details. Per person charges apply. Paths are uneven with footbridges. No disabled access.
Facilities: Toilets, refreshments, car parking and

information available from Keynes Country Park adjacent. A hide with log book is located on E shore.
Public transport: Bus: from Kemble, Cheltenham, Cirencester and Swindon. Tel: 08457 090 899. Train: nearest station is four miles away at Kemble. Tel: 08457 484 950.
Habitat: Only lakes in Cotswold Water Park restored specifically for wildlife. Lakes with reedbed, marsh, ditches, islands and loafing areas.
Key birds: *Winter*: Common wildfowl, Smew, Peregrine, Merlin, Bittern, Stonechat. *Summer*: Breeding ducks, warblers, Hobby, Reed Bunting.
Contact: Cotswold Water Park Society. See above.

7. SLIMBRIDGE

The Wildfowl & Wetlands Trust.
Location: SO 723 048. S of Gloucester. Signposted from M5 (exit 13 or 14).
Access: Open daily except Christmas Day, (9am-5.30pm, 5pm in winter). Group visits a speciality. Contact Bookings Officer 01453 891 900.
Facilities: Hides, observatory, observation tower, Hanson Discovery Centre, wildlife art gallery, tropical house, facilities for disabled, worldwide collection of wildfowl species.
Habitat: Reedbed, saltmarsh, freshwater pools, mudflats.
Key birds: Kingfisher, waders, raptors. *Winter*; Wildfowl esp. Bewick's Swans, White-fronted Geese, Wigeon, Teal.
Contact: Samantha Snow, Marketing Manager, WWT, Slimbridge, Gloucester GL2 7BT. 01453 891 900; (Fax) 01453 890 927.
e-mail: info.slimbridge@wwt.org.uk

8. SYMOND'S YAT

RSPB/Forest Enterprise.
Location: SO 563 160. Hill-top site on the edge of Forest of Dean, three miles N of Coleford on B4432, signposted from Forest Enterprise car park. Also signposted from A40, S of Ross-on-Wye.
Access: Open at all times. RSPB Information Officer on site daily, April to August..
Facilities: Car park, toilets with adapted facilities for disabled visitors, picnic area, drinks and light snacks. Environmental education programmes available.
Public transport: None.
Habitat: Cliff above the River Wye and woodland.
Key birds: *Summer*: Peregrine, Buzzard, Goshawk, Raven and woodland species. Telescope is set up daily to watch the Peregrines.
Contact: RSPB, The Puffins, Parkend, Lydney, Gloucestershire, GL15 4JA, 01594 562 852.

OTHER SITES

Full details in previous editions, (year indicated in brackets).
A. Cokes Pits LNR – www.waterpark.org (07).
B. Littleton Brick Pits – The Wildlife Centre, 01179 177 270 (04).
C. Lower Woods – Gloucs WT, 01452 383 333 (05).
D. Waterhay & Cleveland Lakes Reserve - www.waterpark.org (07).
E. Whelford Pools – Gloucs WT, 01452 383 333 (05).
F. Woorgreens Lake – Gloucs WT, 01452 383 333 (06).

Hampshire

1. BLASHFORD LAKES

Hampshire & Isle of Wight Wildlife Trust in partnership with Wessex Water, Bournemouth and West Hampshire Water and New Forest District Council.
Location: SU 153 080. From Ringwood take A338 for two miles towards Fordingbridge/Salisbury, pass Ivy Lane R and take next R to Moyles Court / Linwood at Ellingham Cross, into Ellingham Drove. The main car park for hides is first L (entrance shared with Hanson works) after 400 yards. For Education Centre turn R opposite (entrance shared with Wessex Water and water-ski club) and straight on through gate and bear R between wooden pillars. Parking is just inside pillars or in front of centre.
Access: A network of permissive paths run through the reserve which link to New Forest and Avon Valley Long Distance footpaths. These paths and a number of wildlife viewing screens are always open. The six hides and Centre are open daily (9am-4.30pm). The Centre is also used for school and other organised visits, please phone for further details. No dogs allowed on the reserve. The paths are fully wheelchair

accessible and kissing gates are RADAR key operated to allow passage of disability buggies.
Facilities: Parking, footpaths, six hides, viewing screens, toilets and information including recent sightings board. Coach parking by arrangement. Picnic tables available beside the centre when not being used by booked groups.
Public transport: A bus route runs along the A338 Ringwood to Salisbury/Fordingbridge road with stops just north of Ivy Lane, Ellingham Cross and Ibsley Church.
Habitat: Flooded gravel pits, areas of wet woodland, some of it ancient also dry grassland and lichen heath.
Key birds: *Winter*: Large number of over-wintering wildfowl, with species such as Tufted Duck, Pochard, Wigeon, Shoveler, Goosander and internationally important numbers of Gadwall. Also a large gull roost. *Spring/summer*: Breeding birds include Common Tern, Lapwing, Redshank, Oystercatcher, Kingfisher, Garden Warblers are especially common. *Autumn*: Waders on migration including Green and Common Sandpipers and Greenshank, also Hobby, Black Tern and passerines.
Other notable flora and fauna: Dragonflies (23 species recorded) including brown hawker, scarce chaser and large and small red-eyed damselfly. roe deer are regular, also present badgers, otters, foxes, reptiles include adders and grass snakes
Contact: Blashford Lakes Centre, Ellingham Drove, Ringwood, Hampshire BH24 3PJ. 01425 472 760; e mail: feedback@hwt.org.uk www.hwt.org.uk

2. FARLINGTON MARSHES

Hampshire & Isle of Wight Wildlife Trust.
Location: SU 685 045. E side of Portsmouth. Entrance of roundabout at junction of A2030 (Eastern Road) and A27, or from Harts Farm Way, Broadmarsh, Havant (S side of A27).
Access: Open at all times, no charge or permits, but donations welcome. Dogs on leads only. Wheelchair access via cycleway from E&W to building and stream viewpoint. Paths around site are mostly on level ground but the main path running along the sea wall can be uneven in places and muddy in wet weather. Groups – please book to avoid clash of dates.
Facilities: Information at entrance and in shelter area of building. No toilets.
Public transport: By bus: Several bus routes pass along the A2030 (Easter Road), close to the western entrance to the marsh. Contact First bus service on 023 8058 4321. By train: Hilsea station is one mile from reserve. Contact South West Trains on 0845 6000 650.
Habitat: Coastal grazing marsh with pools and reedbed within reserve. Views over intertidal mudflats/saltmarshes of Langstone Harbour.
Key birds: *Summer*: Breeding waders and wildfowl (including Lapwing, Redshank and Shelduck) also breeding Cetti's, Sedge and Reed Warbler, Bearded Tit. *Autumn to spring*: Waders and wildfowl, good numbers of migrating Yellow Wagtail among the cattle. *Winter*: Brent Goose, Wigeon, Pintail etc and waders (Dunlin, Grey Plover etc). On migration wide range of waders including rarities. Reedbeds with Bearded Tit, Water Rail etc, scrub areas attract small migrants (Redstart, Wryneck, warblers etc).
Contact: Mike Allen, Hampshire and Isle of Wight Wildlife Trust, Beechcroft House, Vicarage Lane, Curdridge, Hants SO32 2DP. 01489 774 400. www.hwt.org.uk - go to 'Reserves' and then 'news' for sightings, etc

3. FLEET POND LNR

Hart District Council.
Location: SY 85. Located in Fleet, W of Farnborough. From the B3013, head to Fleet Station. Park in the long-stay car park at Fleet Station. Parking also available in Chestnut Grove and Westover Road. Pond car park off B3013.

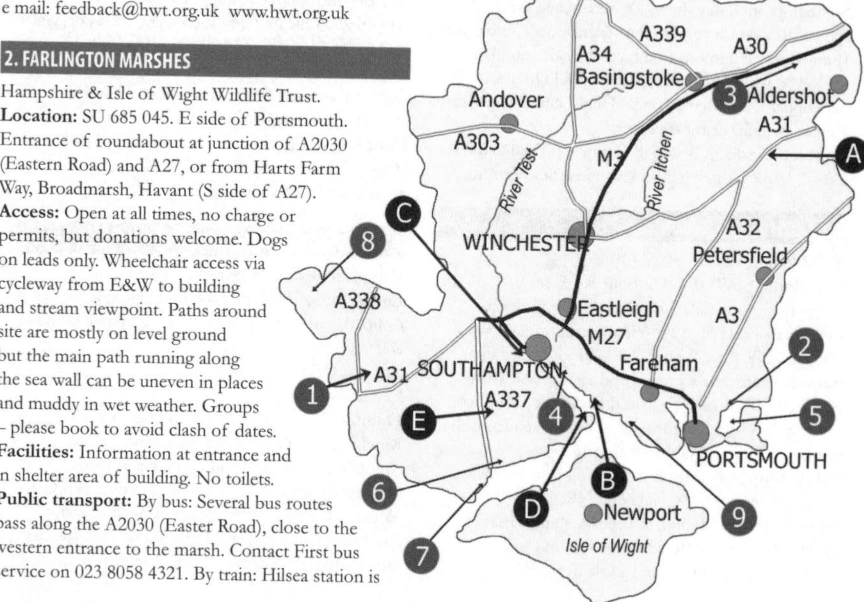

Access: Open all year.
Facilities: None.
Public transport: Fleet railway station lies N of site.
Habitat: Lake, reedbed, willow scrub, heathland.
Key birds: *Spring/autumn*: Migrant waders incl. Little Ringed Plover, Dunlin, Greenshank, Little Gull, Lesser Spotted Woodpecker, occasional Kittiwake, terns, Wood Lark, Sky Lark, occasional Ring Ouzel, Firecrest, Pied Flycatcher. *Summer*: Hobby, Common Tern, Tree Pipit, Occasional Red Kite and Osprey. *Winter*: Bittern, wildfowl, occasional Smew, Snipe, occasional Jack Snipe, Siskin, Redpoll.
Contact: Hart District Council, 01252 622 122.

4. HAMBLE COMMON AND COPSE

Eastleigh Borough Council (Countryside Service).
Location: SU 48 09. Hamble Common is reached via Copse Lane from the B3397 Hamble Lane, which links with A27 and M27 (junction B) at Windhover roundabout near Bursledon.
Access: Open all year.
Facilities: Car parks are linked to each other and the rest of the site by a good network of footpaths. Ground conditions good in summer, but in winter/after rain, stout waterproof footwear is advisable.
Public transport: None.
Habitat: Wet heathland, scrub, woodland, meadow, grassland overlookimg Southampton Water.
Key birds: *Winter*: Wildfowl and waders. On the Southampton Water shore, Oystercatcher, Grey Plover, Ringed Plover, Dunlin, Turnstone, Curlew and Brent Geese common. In the creek wader numbers are lower, with Redshank, Lapwing and Dunlin, occasional Greenshank, Teal, Mallard, Shelduck, Grey Heron, Kingfisher most years.
Contact: Eastleigh Borough Council, 023 8046 6 091.
e-mail: ivcp@eastleigh.gov.uk www.eastleigh.gov.uk

5. LANGSTONE HARBOUR

RSPB (South East England Office).
Location: SU 695 035. Harbour lies E of Portsmouth, one mile S of Havant. Car parks at Broadmarsh (SE of A27/A3(M) junction) and West Hayling LNR (first R on A2030 after Esso garage).
Access: Restricted access. Good views from West Hayling LNR, Broadmarsh and Farlington Marshes LNR (qv). Winter boat trips may be booked from the nearby Portsmouth Outdoor Centre.
Public transport: Mainline trains all stop at Havant. Local bus service to W Hayling LNR.
Habitat: Intertidal mud, saltmarsh, shingle islands.
Key birds: *Summer*: Breeding waders and seabirds inc. Mediterranean Gull and Little Tern. *Passage/winter*: Waterfowl, inc. Black-necked Grebes, c5,000 dark-bellied Brent Geese, Shelduck, Shoveler, Goldeneye and Red-breasted Merganser. Waders inc. Oystercatcher, Ringed and Grey Plover, Dunlin, Black and Bar-tailed Godwits and Greenshank. Peregrine, Merlin and Short-eared Owl.
Contact: Chris Cockburn (Warden), RSPB Langstone Harbour, Unit B3, Wren Centre, Emsworth PO10 7SU. 01243 378 784.
e-mail: chris.cockburn@rspb.org.uk

6. LYMINGTON REEDBEDS

Hampshire & Isle of Wight Wildlife Trust.
Location: SZ 324 965. From Lyndhurst in New Forest take A337 to Lymington. Turn L after railway bridge into Marsh Lane. Park in the lay-by next to allotments. The reserve entrance is on opposite side, to R of the house and over railway crossing. The footpath exits the reserve near the Old Ampress Works, leading to a minor road between the A337 and Boldre.
Access: Open all year. The best viewpoint over the reedbeds is from Bridge Road or from the Undershore leading from the B3054.
Facilities: None.
Public transport: Bus: at either end of the footpath through site, Marsh Lane and on the A337 (route 112). Five minutes walk from train station.
Habitat: One of largest reedbeds on S coast, fringed by alder and willow woodland.
Key birds: One of highest concentrations of Water Rail in the country; resident but most evident in winter. *Spring/summer*: Cetti's Warbler, Bearded Tit, Yellow Wagtail, Swallow, martins, Reed Warbler. *Passage*: Snipe, ducks. Otters are in the area.
Contact: Michael Boxall, Hampshire and Isle of Wight Wildlife Trust, 01489 774 400.
e-mail: feedback@hwt.org.uk www.hwt.org.uk

7. LYMINGTON-KEYHAVEN NNR

Hampshire County Council.
Location: SZ 315 920. S of Lymington along seawall footpath; car parks at Bath Road, Lymington and at Keyhaven Harbour.
Access: Open all year.
Facilities: None.
Habitat: Coastal marshland and lagoons.
Key birds: *Spring*: Passage waders (inc. Knot, Sanderling, Bar-tailed and Black-tailed Godwits, Whimbrel, Spotted Redshank), Pomarine and Great Skuas. Breeding Oystercatcher, Ringed Plover, Sandwich, Common and Little Terns. *Autumn*: Passage raptors, waders and passerines. *Winter*: Wildfowl

(inc. Brent Goose, Wigeon, Pintail, Red-breasted Merganser), waders (inc. Golden Plover), Little Egret, gulls.
Contact: Hampshire County Council, Mottisfont Court, High Street, Winchester, Hants SO23 8ZF.

8. MARTIN DOWN

Natural England (Wiltshire Team).
Location: SU 05 19. Nine miles SW of Salisbury. Car park on A354.
Access: Open access, organised groups should book in advance. Car park height barrier of 7ft 6 ins. Coaches only by prior arrangement. Hard flat track from A354 car park suitable for wheelchairs.
Facilities: Two car parks, interpretative boards.
Public transport: One bus Salisbury/Blandford. Call 01722 336 855 or visit www.wdbus.co.uk
Habitat: Chalk downland.
Key birds: *Spring/summer*: Grey Partridge, Turtle Dove, warblers, Nightingale. *Winter*: Occasional Merlin, Hen Harrier.
Contact: South Wiltshire NNR Office, Parsonage Down NNR, Cherry Lodge, Shrewton, Nr Salisbury, Wilts, 01980 620 485. www.naturalengland.org.uk email: wiltshire@naturalengland.org.uk

9. TITCHFIELD HAVEN

Hampshire County Council.
Location: SU 535 025. From A27 W of Fareham; public footpath follows derelict canal along W of reserve and road skirts S edge.
Access: Open Wed-Sun all year, plus Bank Hols, except Christmas and Boxing Days.
Facilities: Centre has information desk, toilets, tea room and shop. Guided tours (book in advance). Hides.
Public transport: None.
Habitat: Reedbeds, freshwater scrapes, wet grazing meadows.
Key birds: *Spring/summer*: Bearded Tit, waders (inc. Black-tailed Godwit, Ruff), wildfowl, Common Tern, breeding Cetti's Warbler, Water Rail. *Winter*: Bittern.
Contact: Barry Duffin, Titchfield Haven Visitor Centre, Cliff Road, Hill Head, Fareham, Hants PO14 3JT. 01329 662 145; (Fax) 01329 667 113.

OTHER SITES

Full details in previous editions, (year indicated in brackets).
A. Alice Holt Forest – Forest Enterprise, 01179 066 000 (04).
B. Hook-with-Warsash LNR – Titchfield Haven visitor centre, 01329 662 145 (06).
C. Lower Test – Hants WT, 02380 424 206 (06).
D. North Solent – Natural England, 012380 286 428 (04).
E. Roydon Woods – Hants WT, 01590 622 708 (04).

Herefordshire

HOLYWELL DINGLE

Hereford Nature Trust.
Location: SO 313 510, NE of Hay-on-Wye. Take A438 N then L on A4111. Park in lay-by on R, 1 mile N of Eardisley and take footpath to reserve.
Access: Open at all times. Some parts near the stream can be wet and muddy, so waterproof footwear is advised. The northern part of the reserve is very steep-sided in places, and there are precipitous drops into the stream-bed.
Facilities: Good network of marked paths and two footbridges crossing the stream.
Habitat: Narrow, steep-sided, wooded valley, mainly oak and ash. Fast-flowing freshwater stream.
Key birds: Good variety of woodland birds, including breeding Nuthatch, Pied Flycatcher, Marsh Tit, Treecreeper, Great Spotted Woodpecker, Chiffchaff, Rook and Blackcap.
Contact: Reserves Department, Herefordshire Nature Trust, Lower House Farm, Ledbury Road, Hereford HR1 1UT. 01432 356 872.
www.wildlifetrust.org.uk/hereford/reserves

LEA AND PAGETS WOOD

Hereford Nature Trust.
Location: SO 598 343, SE of Hereford. Take B4224 S towards Ross-on-Wye. Turn L on small road 0.25 mile S of Fownhope towards Woolhope. Footpath is on R after turning for Common Hill. Parking for two cars at top of the hill.

Access: Open at all times. Upper paths generally dry in spring and summer, but the low-lying main track can be very muddy and treacherous in places in winter. Take extra care in the vicinity of the old quarry in Church Wood. This is partly fenced off, but there are still unguarded near-vertical drops.
Facilities: Footpaths.
Habitat: Ancient broad-leaved woodland.
Key birds: Small breeding population of Pied Flycatchers in nest-boxes, good range of woodland species, including all three woodpeckers (though Lesser Spotted Woodpeckers have not been recorded for some years) and warblers including Blackcap, Willow Warbler, Chiffchaff and the occasional Wood Warbler. Also Nuthatch, Treecreeper, Marsh Tit, Jay. Buzzard, Tawny Owl and Sparrowhawk also seen.
Contact: Reserves Department, Herefordshire Nature Trust, 01432 356 872.
www.wildlifetrust.org.uk/hereford/reserves

LUGG MEADOW SSSI

Hereford Nature Trust.
Location: SO 539405, NE of Hereford. Take A438 from Hereford towards Ledbury. Near Lugwardine, park in lane on L adjacent to Lower House Farm, before crossing Lungwardine bridge.
Access: Access over Upper Lugg Meadow unrestricted but do not walk in the growing hay between late April and July. In winter, the whole area may be flooded to a depth of more than 1m. for long periods, and access becomes impossible or distinctly dangerous. Take care when walking near the river as there are vertical cliffs along its banks.
Facilities: Permissive path and footpath. Not suitable for wheelchairs.
Public transport: None.
Habitat: Ancient hay meadows, flooded in winter, river.
Key birds: *Spring*: Curlew, Sky Lark. *Passage*: Greenshank, Redshank, Black-tailed Godwit, Snipe, Lapwing and Common Sandpiper *Winter*: Roosting gulls, wildfowl, swans and geese, Peregrine, Merlin.
Contact: Reserves Department, Herefordshire Nature Trust, 01432 356 872.
www.wildlifetrust.org.uk/hereford/reserves

Hertfordshire

1. CASSIOBURY PARK

Welwyn & Hatfield Council.
Location: TL 090 970. Close to Watford town centre.
Access: Open all year.
Facilities: Car park, footpaths.
Public transport: Watford Metropolitan Underground station.
Habitat: Municipal park, wetland, river, alder/willow wood.
Key birds: *Spring/summer*: Kingfisher, Grey Wagtail. *Winter*: Snipe, Water Rail, occasional Bearded Tit.
Contact: Welwyn & Hatfield Council, Council Offices, The Campus, Welwyn Garden City, Herts AL8 6AE. 01707 357 000.
e-mail: council.services@welhat.gov.uk

2. LEMSFORD SPRINGS

Herts & Middlesex Wildlife Trust.
Location: TL 223 123. Lies 1.5 miles W of Welwyn Garden City town centre, off roundabout leading to Lemsford village on B197, W of A1(M).
Access: Access, via key, by arrangement with warden. Open at all times, unless work parties or group visits in progress. Keep to paths. Dogs on leads. Wheelchair access ramp to hide. Coaches welcome and room to park on road, but limit of 30 persons.
Facilities: Two hides, classroom, chemical toilet, paths and bridg e.
Public transport: Bus service to Valley Road, WGC & Lemsford Village No 366 (Centrebus-telephone Intalink 0870 608 2608). Nearest railway station Welwyn Garden City.
Habitat: Former water-cress beds, open shallow lagoons. Stretch of the River Lea, marsh, hedgerows. Nine acres.
Key birds: *Spring/summer*: Breeding warblers, Grey Wagtail, Kestrel. *Autumn/winter*: Green Sandpiper, Water Rail, Snipe, Siskin, occasional Jack Snipe. *All year*: Kingfisher, Grey Heron, Sparrowhawk.
Contact: Barry Trevis, 01707 335 517.
e-mail: info@hmwt.org
www.wildlifetrust.org.uk/herts

3. MAPLE LODGE NATURE RESERVE

Thames Water/Maple Lodge Conservation Society
Location: TQ 036 925. South of Ricksmanworth, close to village of Maple Cross. From M25 (Jt 17) turn

left at traffic lights by The Cross pub. Drive down Maple Lodge Close and park in social club car park.
Access: Restricted to members of MLCS – combination locks on entrance gates. Visits by non-members and groups can be arranged in advance. Site can be boggy – please keep to designated paths.
Facilities: Information centre, toilets. Eight bird hides – two wheelchair-friendly. Winter feeding station.
Habitat: A man-made wetland habitat formed from two gravel pits and a sludge settlement area. Mixed broadleaf plantation on eastern side.
Key birds: Wildfowl throughout year, numbers building in winter. All three woodpeckers, plus variety of finches, thrushes and woodland species. Nesting species include Kingfisher, Tawny Owl, migrant warblers. Green, Common and Wood Sandpipers on passage.
Other notable flora and fauna: 170 species of moth recorded, plus many butterflies and aquatic insects. 125 species of wildflower recorded.
Contact: For membership of MLCS or to arrange visits, contact chairman Mrs Gwyneth Bellis on 01923 230 277.

4. RYE MEADS

RSPB/Hertfordshire & Middlesex Wildlife Trust.
Location: TL 387 099. Take Hoddesdon turn off A10 and follow brown duck signs. Near Rye House railway station.
Access: Open every day 10am-5pm (or dusk if earlier), except Christmas Day and Boxing Day.
Facilities: Disabled access and toilets. Drinks machine, staffed reception, classrooms, picnic area, car park, bird feeding area. Nature trails, hides. RSPB reserve has close-circuit TV on Kingfisher and Common Terns in summer.
Public transport: Rail (Rye House) 55 metres, bus (310) stops 600 metres from entrance.
Habitat: Marsh, willow scrub, pools, scrapes, lagoons and reedbed.
Key birds: *Summer*: Breeding Tufted Duck, Gadwall, Common Tern, Kestrel, Kingfisher, nine species of warblers. *Winter*: Bittern, Shoveler, Water Rail, Teal, Snipe, Jack Snipe, Redpoll and Siskin.
Contact: RSPB Rye Meads Visitor Centre, Rye Road, Stanstead Abbotts, Herts SG12 8JS. 01992 708 383; (Fax) 01992 708 389.

5. STOCKER'S LAKE

Herts & Middlesex Wildlife Trust.
Location: TQ 044 931. Rickmansworth, off A412 into Springwell Lane (TQ043932) L after bridge, or via Bury Lake Aquadrome (parking).
Access: Open all year.
Facilities: None.
Public transport: Within 20 min walk of Rickmansworth tube station.
Habitat: Mature flooded gravel pit with islands.
Key birds: 50 species breed; over 200 recorded. Heronry. *Summer*: Breeding Pochard, Gadwall, Common Tern. Large numbers of migrants. *Winter*: Duck (inc. Goldeneye and nationally significant numbers of Shoveler).
Contact: Trust HQ, 01727 858 901. e-mail: info@hmwt.org www.wildlifetrust.org.uk/herts

6. TRING RESERVOIRS

All four reservoirs – British Waterways in conjunction with Herts & Middlesex Wildlife Trust and Friends of Tring Res. WTW lagoon – Thames Water/FOTR.
Location: Wilstone Reservoir SP90 51 34. Other reservoirs SP 92 01 35. WTW Lagoon SP 92 31 34

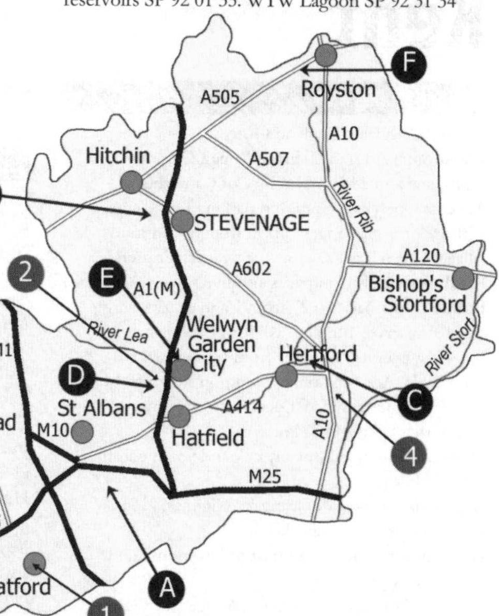

adjacent to Marsworth Reservoir. Reservoirs 1.5 miles due N of Tring, all accessible from B489 which crosses A41 Aston Clinton By-pass, NB exit from by-pass only Southbound, entry only Northbound.
Access: *Reservoirs* – open at all times. All group visits need to be cleared with British Waterways. *WTW Lagoon*: open at all times by permit from FOTR. Coaches can only drop off and pick up, for advice contact FOTR. Wilstone Reservoir has restricted height access of 2.1 metres.
Facilities: Café and public house adjacent to Startops Reservoir car park, safe parking for cycles. Also disabled trail from here. Wilstone Reservoir: Public house about 0.5 mile away in village and cafe about 0.25 mile from car park at Farm Shop. Hides with disabled access at Startops/Marsworth Reservoir & WTW Lagoon. Also other hides.
Public transport: Buses from Aylesbury & Tring including a weekend service, tel. 0870 6082 608. Tring Station is 2.5 miles away via canal towpath.
Habitat: Four reservoirs with surrounding woodland, scrub and meadows. Two of the reservoirs with extensive reedbeds. WTW Lagoon with islands and dragonfly scrape, surrounding hedgerows and scrub.
Key birds: *Spring/summer*: Breeding warblers, regular Hobby, occasional Black Tern, Marsh Harrier, Osprey. *Autumn*: Passage waders and wildfowl. *Winter*: Gull roost, large wildfowl flocks, bunting roosts, Bittern.
Contact: Herts & Middsx Wildlife Trust: see Directory entry, FOTR: see Peter Hearn in Bucks BTO entry, www.fotr.org.uk, British Waterways, Ground Floor, Witangate House, 500-600 Witan Gate, Milton Keynes MK9 1BW 01908 302 500, www.waterscape.com
e-mail:enquiries.southeast@britishwaterways.co.uk

OTHER SITES

Full details in previous editions, (year indicated in brackets).
A. Broad Colney Lakes – Herts & Middx WT, 01727 858 901 (04).
B. Hill End Pit – Herts & Middx WT, 01727 858 901 (04).
C. The Meads – Herts & Middx WT, 01727 858 901 (04).
D. Sherrards Park Wood – Welwyn & Hatfield Council, 01707 357 000 (04).
E. Stanborough Reed Marsh – Herts & Middx WT, 01727 858 901 (06).
F. Therfield Heath LNR – Herts & Middx WT, 01727 858 901 (04).

Kent

1. BLEAN WOODS NNR

RSPB (South East England Office).
Location: TR 126 592. From Rough Common (off A290, one and a half miles NW of Canterbury).
Access: Open 8am-9pm. No parking for coaches – please drop passengers off in Rough Common village. Green Trail suitable for wheelchair users.
Facilities: Public footpaths and five waymarked trails.
Public transport: No 27 from Canterbury hourly, stops at reserve entrance (ask for Lovell Road). No 4/4A every 20 minutes from Canterbury to Whitstable. Ask for Rough Common Road, 500m walk from site entrance. Local bus company Stagecoach 0870 243 3711.
Habitat: Woodland (mainly oak and sweet chestnut), relics of heath.
Key birds: *Summer*: Nightingale, Nightjar. *All year*: three species of woodpecker.
Other notable flora and fauna: Dormouse and heath fritillary.
Contact: Michael Walter, Site Manager, 11 Garden Close, Rough Common, Canterbury, Kent CT2 9BP. 01227 455 972.

2. CLIFFE POOLS

RSPB (South-East office)
Location: TQ 722 757. On S bank of River Thames, N of Rochester. Take A289 off the A2 at Strood and follow B2000 to reserve. See RSPB website for more detailed directions.
Access: Free admission at all times, but donations welcome. Group bookings welcome. Monthly guided walks available. Dogs only on public footpaths.
Facilities: Six viewing points. Public rights of way encircle reserve and bisect it.
Public transport: Nearest bus stop at Six Bells pub in Cliffe.
Habitat: A mix of saline lagoons, freshwater pools, grassland, saltmarsh and scrub.
Key birds: Massed flocks of waders in winter, plus a wide range of wildfowl. A great variety of passage birds in spring and autumn. Breeding species include

NATURE RESERVES - ENGLAND

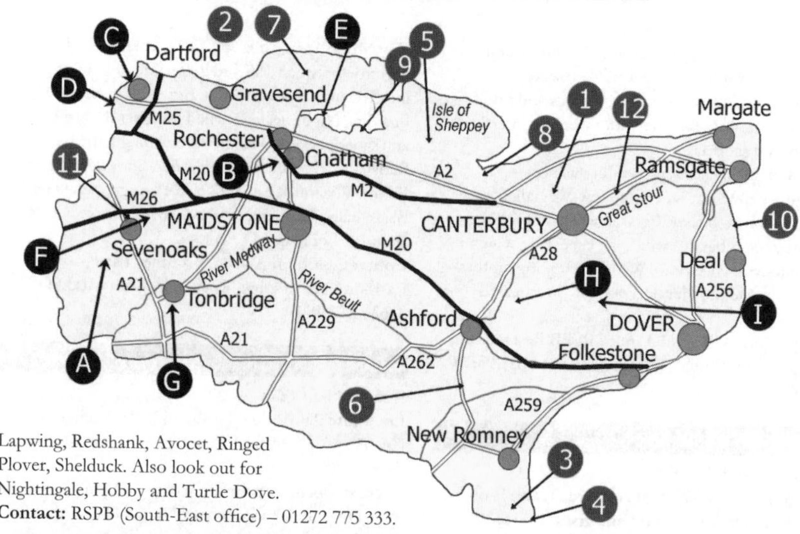

Lapwing, Redshank, Avocet, Ringed Plover, Shelduck. Also look out for Nightingale, Hobby and Turtle Dove.
Contact: RSPB (South-East office) – 01272 775 333.

3. DUNGENESS

RSPB (South East England Office).
Location: TR 063 196. SE of Lydd.
Access: Open daily (9am-9pm) or sunset when earlier. Visitor centre open (10am-5pm, or 4pm Nov-Feb). Parties over 12 by prior arrangement. Closed Dec 25 & 26.
Facilities: Visitor centre, toilets (including disabled access), seven hides, viewing screen, two nature trails, wheelchair access to visitor centre and four hides. Fully equipped classroom/meeting room.
Public transport: Limited service. Bus 11 from Ashford stops at reserve entrance on request – one mile walk to visitor centre. Contact reserve for details.
Habitat: Shingle, flooded gravel pits, sallow scrub, reedbed, wet grassland.
Key birds: *Resident*: Bearded Tit. *Winter*: Bittern, Wildfowl (including Wigeon, Goldeneye, Goosander, Smew), divers and grebes. Migrant waders, landfall for passerines. *Summer*: Breeding Lapwing, Redshank, wildfowl, gulls, Cetti's Warbler.
Contact: Christine Hawkins/Bob Gomes, Boulderwall Farm, Dungeness Road, Lydd, Romney Marsh, Kent TN29 9PN. 01797 320 588; (Fax) 01797 321 962. e-mail: dungeness@rspb.org.uk

4. DUNGENESS BIRD OBSERVATORY

Dungeness Bird Observatory Trust.
Location: TR 085 173. Three miles SE of Lydd. Turn south off Dungeness Road at TR 087 185 and continue to end of road.
Access: Observatory open throughout the year.
Facilities: Accommodation available. Bring own sleeping bag/sheets and toiletries. Shared facilities including fully-equipped kitchen.
Public transport: Bus service between Rye and Folkestone, numbers 11, 12, 711, 712. Alight at the Pilot Inn, Lydd-on-Sea. Tel: 01227 472 082.
Habitat: Shingle promontory with scrub and gravel pits. RSPB reserve nearby.
Key birds: Breeding birds include Wheatear and Black Redstart and seabirds on RSPB Reserve. Important migration site.
Contact: David Walker, Dungeness Bird Observatory, 11 RNSSS, Dungeness, Kent TN29 9NA. 01797 321 309.
e-mail dungeness.obs@tinyonline.co.uk
www.dungenessbirdobs.org.uk

5. ELMLEY MARSHES

RSPB (South East England Office).
Location: TQ 93 86 80. Isle of Sheppey signposted from A249, one mile beyond old Kingsferry Bridge. Reserve car park is two miles from the main road.
Access: Use old bridge road – access road is one mile from bridge. Open every day except Tue, Christmas and Boxing days. (9am-9pm or dusk if earlier). No charge to RSPB members. Dogs are not allowed on the reserve. Less able may drive closer to the hides.
Facilities: Five hides. Disabled access to Wellmarsh hide. No visitor centre. Toilets located in car park 1.25 miles from hides.
Public transport: Swale Halt, a request stop is nearest

railway station on Sittingbourne to Sheerness line. From there it is a three mile walk to reserve
Habitat: Coastal grazing marsh, ditches and pools alongside the Swale Estuary with extensive intertidal mudflats and saltmarsh
Key birds: *Spring/summer*: Breeding waders – Redshank, Lapwing, Avocet, Yellow Wagtail, passage waders, Hobby. *Autumn*: Passage waders. *Winter*: Spectacular numbers of wildfowl, especially Wigeon and White-fronted Goose. Waders. Hunting raptors – Peregrine, Merlin, Hen Harrier and Short-eared Owl.
Contact: Barry O'Dowd, Elmley RSPB Reserve, Kingshill Farm, Elmley, Sheerness, Kent ME12 3RW. 01795 665 969.

6. HAM STREET WOODS NNR

Natural England (Kent Team).
Location: TR 003 337. S of Ashford. Travel E on A2067 from Hamstreet, car park first L at green.
Access: Open at all times. Keep to paths. One easy-access trail suitable for wheelchairs.
Facilities: Three way-marked trails.
Public transport: Stagecoach bus stops 700m from reserve.
Habitat: Damp oak woodland, coppice/standards.
Key birds: Over 90 species recorded. Woodcock, Great and Lesser Spotted Woodpeckers, Nightingale, Redstart, warblers, Hawfinch; Hoopoe regular summer visitor.
Contact: Stephen Etherington, Natural England, Coldharbour Farm, Wye, Ashford, Kent TN25 5DB. 07767 321 053 (mobile).

7. NORTHWARD HILL

RSPB (South East England Office).
Location: TQ 780 765. Adjacent to High Halstow, off A228, approx six miles N of Rochester.
Access: Open all year, free access, trails in public area of wood joining Saxon Shoreway link to grazing marsh. Dogs allowed in public area on leads. Trails often steep and not suitable for wheelchair users.
Facilities: New trail takes visitors to viewpoint overlooking heronry.Three nature trails in the wood and one joining with long distance footpath. Toilets at village hall. New car park at Bromhey Farm (Marshland car park) is signposted from High Halstow village. Information and public toilet in this car park.
Public transport: Buses to village of High Halstow. Contact Arriva buses (01634 283 600) for timetable details.
Habitat: Ancient and scrub woodland (approximately 130 acres), grazing marsh (approximately 350 acres).
Key birds: *Spring/summer*: Wood holds UK's largest heronry (between 150 and 200 pairs most years), inc growing colony of Little Egrets (50 pairs 2007), breeding Nightingale, Turtle Dove, scrub warblers and woodpeckers. Marshes – breeding Lapwing, Redshank, Avocet, Marsh Harrier, Shoveler, Pochard. *Winter*: Wigeon, Teal, Shoveler. Passage waders (ie Black-tailed Godwit), raptors, Tree Sparrow, Corn Bunting. Long-eared Owl roost.
Contact: Gordon Allison, Bromhey Farm, Eastborough, Cooling, Rochester, Kent ME3 8DS. 01634 222 480.

8. OARE MARSHES LNR

Kent Wildlife Trust.
Location: TR 01 36 48 (car park). Two miles N of Faversham. From A2 follow signs to Oare and Harty Ferry.
Access: Open at all times. Access along marked paths only. Dogs under strict control to avoid disturbance to birds and livestock.
Facilities: Three hides. Roadside viewpoint of East Hide accessible to wheelchairs.Those with pneumatic tyres can reach seawall path and hide. Small car park, restricted turning space, not suitable for coaches.
Public transport: Bus to Oare Village one mile from reserve. Arriva service (Mon-Sat), Jaycrest (Sun) - call Traveline on 0870 608 2608. Train: Faversham (two miles distance).
Habitat: Grazing marsh, mudflats/estuary.
Key birds: *All year*: Waders and wildfowl. *Winter*: Merlin, Peregrine. Divers, grebes and sea ducks on Swale. *Spring/summer*: Avocet, Garganey, Green, Wood and Curlew Sandpipers, Little Stint, Black-tailed Godwit, Little Tern, Marsh Harrier.
Contact: Kent Wildlife Trust, 01622 662 012. e-mail: info@kentwildlife.org.uk www.kentwildlife.org.uk

9. RIVERSIDE COUNTRY PARK

Medway Council.
Location: TQ 808 683. From Rochester, take the A2 E into Gillingham and turn L onto the A289. After one mile, turn R onto the B2004 at Grange. After one mile, the visitor centre is on the L.
Access: Open all year, free access to all paths from 8.30am-4.30pm (winter) or 8.30am-dusk (summer).
Facilities: Visitor Centre with restaurant and toilets open every day except Christmas, Boxing and New Year's Days (no parking on these days except New Year's Day) from 10am-5pm summer (4pm winter). Large car park and smaller one at Rainham Dock. Car park locked at dusk. Check times on arrival. Coach parking available.

Public transport: Bus: contact Arriva tel: 08706 082 608. Train: nearest stations at Rainham and Gillingham. Cycle racks at visitor centre and a Sustrans cycle route.
Habitat: Mudflats, saltmarsh, ponds, reedbeds, grassland and scrub.
Key birds: *Winter*: Dunlin, Redshank, Grey Plover, Avocet, Brent Goose, Teal, Pintail, Wigeon, Shelduck, Peregrine, Hen Harrier, thrushes, Mediterranean Gull, Water Rail, Rock Pipit, Little Egret and Red-breasted Merganser. *Summer*: Whitethroat, Cetti's Warbler, Nightingale, Turtle Dove.
Contact: Riverside Country Park, Lower Rainham Road, Gillingham, Kent, ME7 2XH. 01634 337 432. e-mail: riversidecp@medway.gov.uk

10. SANDWICH BAY BIRD OBSERVATORY

Sandwich Bay Bird Observatory Trust.
Location: TR 355 575. 2.5 miles from Sandwich, five miles from Deal. A256 to Sandwich from Dover or Ramsgate. Follow signs to Sandwich Station and then Sandwich Bay.
Access: Open daily. Disabled access.
Facilities: New Field Study Centre. Visitor centre, toilets, refreshments, hostel-type accommodation, plus self-contained flat.
Public transport: Sandwich train station two miles from Observatory.
Habitat: Coastal, dune land, farmland, marsh, two small scrapes.
Key birds: *Spring/ autumn passage*: Good variety of migrants and waders, specially Corn Bunting. Annual Golden Oriole. *Winter*: Golden Plover.
Contact: The Secretary, Sandwich Bay Bird Observatory, Guildford Road, Sandwich Bay, Sandwich, Kent CT13 9PF. 01304 617 341. e-mail: sbbot@talk21.com www.sbbo.co.uk

11. SEVENOAKS WILDLIFE RESERVE

Kent Wildlife Trust/Lafarge plc. .
Location: TQ 519 568. From A25 at Bradbourne Vale Road, immediately N of Sevenoaks.
Access: Reserve open daily from dawn to dusk. Parking available. Access by car for disabled visitors.
Facilities: Nature trail, hides. Visitor centre open Weds, Sat, Sun and Bank Hols (excl Christmas Day & New Year period), 10am-5pm or dusk.
Public transport: 15 minutes walk from Bat & Ball station, 20 minutes from Sevenoaks station.
Habitat: Flooded gravel pits, reedbed and woodland.
Key birds: Breeding Little Ringed Plover, waterbirds and Lesser Spotted Woodpecker. Wintering wildfowl, passage waders, woodland birds.
Contact: David King, Tadorna, Bradbourne Vale Road, Sevenoaks, Kent TN13 3DH. 01732 456 407. e-mail: dave.king@kentwildlife.org.uk

12. STODMARSH NNR

Natural England (Kent Team).
Location: TR 222 618. Lies alongside River Stour and A28, five miles NE of Canterbury.
Access: Open at all times. Keep to reserve paths. No dogs allowed.
Facilities: Fully accessible toilets are available at the Stodmarsh entrance car park. Five hides (one fully accessible), easy access nature trail, footpaths and information panels. Car park, picnic area and toilets adjoining the Grove Ferry entrance with easily accessible path, viewing mound and two hides.
Public transport: There is a regular Stagecoach bus service from Canterbury to Margate/Ramsgate. Alight at Upstreet for Grove Ferry. Hourly on Sun.
Habitat: Open water, reedbeds, wet meadows, dry meadows, woodland.
Key birds: *Spring/ summer*: Breeding Bearded Tit, Cetti's Warbler, Garganey, Reed, Sedge and Willow Warblers, Nightingale. Migrant Black Tern, Hobby, Osprey, Little Egret. *Winter*: Wildfowl, Hen Harrier, Bittern.
Contact: David Feast, Natural England, Coldharbour Farm, Wye, Ashford, Kent TN25 5DB. 07767 321 058 (mobile).

OTHER SITES

Full details in previous editions, (year indicated in brackets).
A. Bough Beech Reservoir – Kent WT, 01622 662 012 (04).
B. Burham Marshes – Kent WT, 01622 662 012 (04).
C. Danson Park LNR – Bexley Council, 0208 303 7777 (04).
D. Footscray Meadows LNR – Bexley Council, 0208 303 7777 (04).
E. Nor Marsh – Gordon Allison (RSPB), 01634 222 480 (07).
F. Oldbury Hill & Styant's Wood – National Trust, 01372 453 401 (04).
G. Tudeley Woods – RSPB, 01273 775 333.
H. Wye NNR – James Plunkett, Natural England, 07767 321 057 (07).
1. Yockletts Bank – Kent WT, 01622 662 012 (04).

Lancashire

1. HEYSHAM NATURE RESERVE & BIRD OBSERVATORY

The Wildlife Trust for Lancashire, Manchester and North Merseyside in conjunction with British Energy Estates.
Location: Main reserve is at SD 404 596 W of Lancaster. Take A683 to Heysham port. Turn L at traffic lights by Duke of Rothesay pub, then first R after 300m.
Access: Gate to reserve car park usually open 9.30am-6pm (longer in summer and shorter in winter). Pedestrian access at all times. Dogs on lead. Limited disabled access.
Facilities: Hide overlooking Power Station outfalls. Map giving access details at the reserve car park. No manned visitor centre or toilet access, but someone usually in reserve office, next to the main car park, in the morning. Latest sightings board can be viewed through the window if office closed.
Public transport: Train services connect with nearby Isle of Man ferry. Plenty of buses to Lancaster from various Heysham sites within walking distance (ask for nearest stop to the harbour).
Habitat: Varied: wetland, acid grassland, alkaline grassland, foreshore.
Key birds: Passerine migrants in the correct conditions. Good passage of seabirds in spring, especially Arctic Tern. Storm Petrel and Leach's Petrel during strong onshore (SW-WWNW) winds in midsummer and autumn respectively. Good variety of breeding birds (e.g. eight species of warbler on the reserve itself). Two-three scarce land-birds each year, most frequent being Yellow-browed Warbler. Notable area for dragonflies.
Contact: Rueben Neville, Reserve Warden, The Wildlife Trust, The Barn, Berkeley Drive, Bamber Bridge, Preston, PR5 6BY. 07979 652 138.
Annual report from Leighton Moss RSPB shop.

2. LEIGHTON MOSS

RSPB (Northern England Region).
Location: SD 478 750. Four miles NW of Carnforth. Signposted from A6 N of Carnforth.
Access: Reserve open daily 9am-dusk. Visitor centre open daily 9.30am-5pm (9.30am-4.30pm Nov-Jan inclusive), except Christmas Day. No charge to RSPB members or those who arrive by public transport or bike. Dogs allowed on causeway only. Groups and coaches welcome - please book in advance.
Facilities: Visitor centre, shop, tea-room and toilets. Nature trails and five hides (four have wheelchair access), plus two hides at saltmarsh pools.
Public transport: Silverdale train station 150 metres from reserve. Tel: 08457 484 950.
Habitat: Reedbed, shallow meres and woodland. saltmarsh pool approx 1 mile.
Key birds: *All year*: Bittern, Bearded Tit, Water Rail, Pochard and Shoveler. *Summer*: Marsh Harrier, Reed and Sedge Warblers. Avocet at saltmarsh pools.
Contact: Robin Horner, RSPB Leighton Moss Nature Reserve, Myers Farm, Silverdale, Carnforth, Lancashire LA5 0SW. 01524 701 601.
e-mail: leighton.moss@rspb.org.uk

3. MARTIN MERE

The Wildfowl & Wetlands Trust.
Location: SD 428 145. Six miles N of Ormskirk via Burscough Bridge (A59), 20 miles from Liverpool and Preston.
Access: Opening times: 9.30am-5.00pm (Nov-Feb), 9.30am-5.30pm (rest of year). Special dawn and evening events. Guide dogs only allowed. Admission charge. No charge for members. Fully accessible to disabled, all hides suitable for wheelchairs. Coach park available. Special rates for coach parties.
Facilities: Visitor centre with toilets, gift shop, restaurant, education centre, play area, nature reserve and nature trails, hides, waterfowl collection and sustainable garden. Provision for disabled visitors.
Public transport: Bus service to WWT Martin Mere from Ormskirk. Train to Burscough Bridge or New Lane Stations (both 1.5 miles from reserve). For bus times contact Traveline 0870 608 2608.
Habitat: Open water, wet grassland, moss, copses, reedbed, parkland.
Key birds: *Winter*: Whooper and Bewick's Swans, Pink-footed Goose, various duck, Ruff, Black-tailed Godwit, Peregrine, Hen Harrier, Tree Sparrow. *Spring*: Ruff, Shelduck, Little Ringed and Ringed Plover, Lapwing, Redshank. *Summer*: Marsh Harrier, Garganey, hirundines, Tree Sparrow. Breeding Avocets, Lapwing, Redshank, Shelduck. *Autumn*: Pink-footed Goose, waders on passage.
Contact: Senior Operations Manager, WWT Martin Mere, Fish Lane, Burscough, Lancs L40 0TA. 01704 895 181. e-mail: info.martinmere@wwt.org.uk www.wwt.org.uk

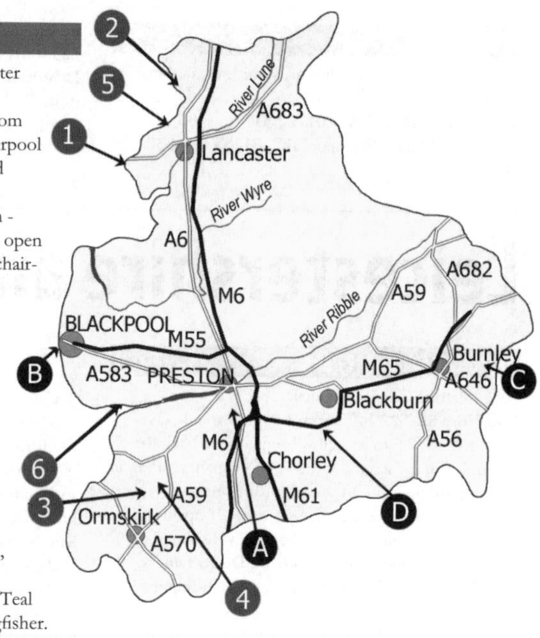

4. MERE SANDS WOOD

The Wildlife Trust for Lancashire, Manchester and North Merseyside.
Location: SD 44 71 57. 12 miles by road from Southport, 0.5 miles off A59 Preston – Liverpool road, in Rufford along B5246 (Holmeswood Road).
Access: Visitor centre open 9.30am-4.30pm - closed Fridays and Christmas Day. Car park open until 8pm in summer. Three miles of wheelchair-accessible footpaths. All hides accessible to wheelchairs.
Facilities: Visitor centre with toilets (disabled), six viewing hides, three trails, exhibition room, latest sightings board. Feeding stations. Booking essential for two motorised buggies.
Public transport: Bus: Southport-Chorley 347 stops in Rufford, 0.5 mile walk. Train: Preston-Ormskirk train stops at Rufford station, one mile walk.
Habitat: Freshwater lakes, mixed woodland, sandy grassland/heath. 105h.
Key birds: *Winter*: Regionally important for Teal and Gadwall, good range of waterfowl, Kingfisher. Feeding stations attract Tree Sparrow, Bullfinch, Reed Bunting, Water Rail. *Woodland*: Treecreeper, Nuthatch. *Summer*: Kingfisher. *Passage*: Most years, Osprey, Crossbill, Green Sandpiper, Greenshank.
Other notable flora and fauna: 18 species of dragonfly recorded annually.
Contact: Kim Neal, Warden, Mere Sands Wood Nature Reserve, Holmeswood Road, Rufford, Ormskirk, Lancs L40 1TG. 01704 821 809. e-mail: meresandswood@lancswt.org.uk www.wildlifetrust.org/lancashire

5. MORECAMBE BAY (HEST BANK)

RSPB (Northern England Region).
Location: SD 468 667. Two miles N of Morecambe at Hest Bank.
Access: Open at all times. Do not venture onto saltmarsh or intertidal area, there are dangerous channels and quicksands.
Facilities: Viewpoint at car park.
Public transport: No 5 bus runs between Carnforth and Morecambe. Tel: 0870 608 2608.
Habitat: Saltmarsh, estuary.
Key birds: *Winter*: Wildfowl (Pintail, Shelduck, Wigeon) and waders – important high tide roost for Oystercatcher, Curlew, Redshank, Dunlin, Bar-tailed Godwit.
Contact: Robin Horner, Leighton Moss & Morecambe Bay RSPB Reserves, Myers Farm, Silverdale, Carnforth, Lancashire LA5 0SW. 01524 701 601. e-mail: leighton.moss@rspb.org.uk www.rspb.org.uk

6. RIBBLE ESTUARY

Natural England (Cheshire to Lancashire team).
Location: SD 380 240. W of Preston.
Access: Open at all times.
Facilities: No formal visiting facilities.
Public transport: None.
Habitat: Saltmarsh, mudflats.
Key birds: High water wader roosts (of Knot, Dunlin, Black-tailed Godwit, Oystercatcher and Grey Plover) are best viewed from Southport, Marshside, Lytham and St Annes. Pink-footed Geese and wintering swans are present in large numbers from Oct-Feb on Banks Marsh and along River Douglas respectively. The large flocks of Wigeon, for which the site is renowned, can be seen on high tides from Marshside but feed on saltmarsh areas at night. Good numbers of raptors also present in winter.
Contact: Site Manager, Natural England, Ribble Estuary NNR, Old Hollow, Marsh Road, Banks, Southport PR9 8DU. 01704 225 624.

OTHER SITES

Full details in previous editions, (year indicated in brackets).
A. Cuerden Valley Park – 01722 317 234 (06).
B. Marton Mere – Blackpool BC, 01253 830 830 (04).
C. Upper Coldwell Valley – Lancs WT, 01772 324 129 (04).
D. Withnell Fold LNR – Lancs CC, 01722 534 709 (05).

Leicestershire and Rutland

BEACON HILL COUNTRY PARK

Leicestershire County Council.
Location: SK 522 149. From Loughborough, take A512 SW for 2.5 miles. Turn L onto Breakback Road and follow it for 2.5 miles through Nanpantan. Park in the car park on the L in Woodhouse Lane.
Access: Open all year from 8am-dusk. If opening times are different, these will be clearly displayed at the park. A permissive path from Deans Lane to Woodhouse Lane is occasionally closed during the year. Please check first.
Facilities: Two pay and display car parks, easy-to-follow, waymarked tracks and woodland paths. Several climbs to hill tops. Rocky outcrops slippery after rain. Information boards. Toilets at lower car park, The Outwoods car park and Woodhouse Eves. Wheelchair access along park paths but no access to summit. Refreshments at Bull's Head, Woodhouse Eaves.
Public transport: Bus: No 123 Leicester to Shepshed calls at Woodhouse Eaves. Tel: 0870 608 2608. Train: from Loughborough and Leicester.
Habitat: Forest, one of the oldest geological outcrops in England and the second highest point in Leicestershire.
Key birds: *All year*: Treecreeper, Nuthatch, Lesser Spotted and Green Woodpeckers, Great and Coal Tits, Little Owl, wagtails. *Summer*: Pied Flycatcher, Whitethroat, Blackcap, Whinchat, Garden Warbler, Stonechat.
Contact: Beacon Hill Country Park, Beacon Hill Estate Office, Broombriggs Farm, Beacon Road, Woodhouse Eaves, Loughborough, Leics., LE12 8SR. 01509 890 048.

EYEBROOK RESERVOIR

Corby & District Water Co.
Location: SP 853 964. Reservoir built 1940. S of Uppingham, from unclassified road W of A6003 at Stoke Dry.
Access: Access to 150 acres private grounds granted to members of Leics and Rutland Ornithological Society and Rutland Nat Hist Soc. Organised groups need written permission (from Corby Water Co).
Facilities: SSSI since 1955. Good viewing from public roads. Trout fishery season Apr-Oct.
Public transport: None.
Habitat: Open water, plantations and pasture.
Key birds: *Summer*: Good populations of breeding birds, sightings of Ospreys and Red Kite. Passage waders and Black Tern. *Winter*: Wildfowl (inc. Goldeneye, Goosander, Smew) and waders.
Contact: Corby (Northants) & District Water Co., Fishing lodge 01536 770 264.
www.eyebrook.com or www.eyebrook.org.uk

RUTLAND WATER

Leics and Rutland Wildlife Trust. .
Location: SK 866 6760 72. 1. Egleton Reserve: from Egleton village off A6003 S of Oakham. Hosts British Birdwatching Fair every August. 2. Lyndon Reserve: south shore E of Manton village off A6003 S of Oakham.
Access: 1. Open daily 9am-5pm, (4pm Nov to Jan). 2. Open winter (Sat, Sun 10am-5pm), Summer daily (9am-5pm). Day permits available for both.
Facilities: 1: Anglian Water Birdwatching Centre, now enlarged. Toilets and disabled access to 11 hides, conference facilities. 2: Interpretive centre now upgraded with new toilets, including disabled, new paths, use of a mobility scooter and new interpretive material. Winter 2007 covers climate change and the impact to UK wildlife. Marked nature trail leaflet.
Public transport: None.
Habitat: Reservoir, lagoons, scrapes, woods, meadows, plantations.
Key birds: *Spring/ autumn*: Outstanding wader passage. Also harriers, owls, passerine flocks, terns (Black, Arctic, breeding Common, occasional Little and Sandwich). *Winter*: Wildfowl (inc Goldeneye, Smew,

Goosander, rare grebes, all divers), Ruff. *Summer*: Breeding Ospreys on Lyndon reserve.
Contact: Tim Appleton, Fishponds Cottage, Stamford Road, Oakham, Rutland LE15 8AB. 01572 770 651; (Fax) 01572 755 931; e-mail awbc@rutlandwater.org.uk; www.rutlandwater.org.uk www.ospreys.org.uk www.birdfair.org.uk.

SENCE VALLEY FOREST PARK

Forestry Commission
Location: SK 400 115. Within The National Forest. Ten miles NW of Leicester and two miles SW of Coalville, between Ibstock and Ravenstone. The car park is signed from A447 N of Ibstock.
Access: Open all year. Car park open 8.30am-dusk (precise times on noticeboard). Lower car park (2.2m height barrier) gives easy access to wheelchair-friendly surfaced paths. Week's notice required for coach or minibuses visits.
Facilities: Two car parks, toilets (including disabled and baby-changing facilities), information and recent sightings boards, hide, surfaced trails.
Public transport: None.
Habitat: New forest (native broadleaf, mixed and pine), rough grassland, wildflower meadow, pools, wader scrape, river.
Key birds: *Spring/summer*: Artificial Sand Martin nesting wall, Wheatear, Whinchat, Redstart, Common and Green Sandpiper, Ringed and Little Ringed Plovers, Redshank. Dunlin and Greenshank frequent, possible Wood Sandpiper. Reed Bunting, Meadow Pipit, Sky Lark, Linnet, Yellow Wagtail. Possible Quail. Kestrel and Barn Owl seen occasionally. *Winter*: Stonechat, Redpoll, Short-eared Owl, Goosander and Wigeon possible.
Contact: Forestry Commission, Lady Hill, Birches Valley, Rugeley, Staffs WS15 2UQ. 01889 586 593. website: www.forestry.gov.uk

OTHER SITES

Full details in previous editions, (year indicated in brackets).
Burbage Common – Hinckley Borough Council, 01455 238 141 (04).

Lincolnshire

1. FAR INGS

Lincolnshire Wildlife Trust.
Location: TA 011 229 and TA 023 230. Off Far Ings Lane, W of Barton-on-Humber, the last turn-off before the Humber Bridge.
Access: Open all year. No dogs. Limited disabled access.
Facilities: Toilets, visitor centre open some weekends and weekdays – not all week. Hides and paths.
Habitat: Chain of flooded clay pits and reedbeds.
Key birds: *Summer*: Marsh Harrier, Bittern, Bearded Tit, Water Rail. *Winter*: Wildfowl (Mallard, Teal, Gadwall, Pochard, Tufted and Ruddy Ducks).
Contact: Lionel Grooby, Far Ings Visitor Centre, Far Ings Road, Barton on Humber DN18 5RG. 01652 634 507. e-mail: farings@lincstrust.co.uk

2. FRAMPTON MARSH

RSPB (East Anglia Office).
Location: TR 36 43 85. Four miles SE of Boston. From A16 follow signs to Frampton then Frampton Marsh.
Access: Open at all times. Free. Coaches by prior arrangement.
Facilities: Footpaths, bench, car park, bicycle rack. Free information leaflets available (please contact the office), guided walks programme.
Habitat: Saltmarsh.
Key birds: *Summer*: Breeding Redshank, passage waders (inc Greenshank, Ruff and Black-tailed Godwit) and Hobby. *Winter*: Hen Harrier, Short-eared Owl, Merlin, dark-bellied Brent Goose, Twite, Golden Plover.
Contact: John Badley, RSPB Lincolnshire Wash Office, 61a Horseshoe Lane, Kirton, Boston, Lincs PE20 1LW. 01205 724 678.
e-mail: john.badley@rspb.org.uk

3. FREISTON SHORE

RSPB (Eastern England Office).
Location: TF 39 74 24. Four miles E of Boston. From A52 at Haltoft End follow signs to Freiston Shore.
Access: Open at all times, free. Coaches by prior arrangement.
Facilities: Footpaths, two car parks, bird hide. Free information leaflets available on site, guided walks programme. Bicycle rack.

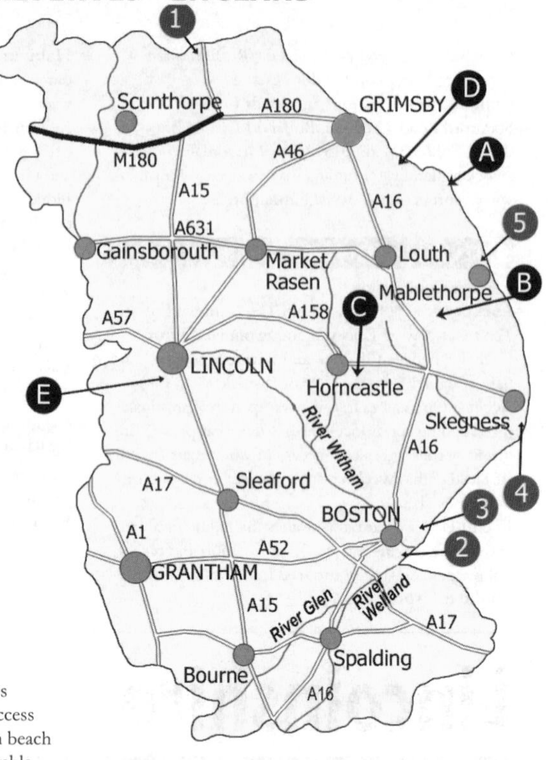

Public transport: None.
Habitat: Saltmarsh, saline lagoon, mudflats.
Key birds: *Summer*: Breeding waders including Avocets, Ringed Plovers and Oystercatchers, Corn Bunting and Tree Sparrow. *Winter*: Twite, dark-bellied Brent Goose, wildfowl, waders, birds of prey including Short-eared Owl and Hen Harrier. *Passage*: Waders, including Curlew Sandpiper and Little Stint. *Autumn*: Occasional seabirds including Arctic and Great Skuas.
Contact: John Badley, RSPB Lincolnshire Wash Office, 61a Horseshoe Lane, Kirton, Boston, Lincs PE20 1LW. 01205 724 678. e-mail: john.badley@rspb.org.uk www.rspb.org.uk

4. GIBRALTAR POINT NNR & BIRD OBSERVATORY

Lincolnshire Wildlife Trust.
Location: TF 556 580. Three miles S of Skegness on the N edge of The Wash. Signposted from Skegness town centre.
Access: Reserve open dawn-dusk all year. Charges for car parking. Free admission to reserve, visitor centre and toilets. Some access restrictions to sensitive sites at S end, open access to N. Dogs on leads at all times – no dogs on beach during summer. Visitor centre and toilets suitable for wheelchairs, as well as network of surfaced foot paths. Bird observatory and four hides suitable for wheelchairs. Day visit groups must be booked in advance. Access for coaches. Contact The Wash Study Centre for residential or day visits.
Facilities: Site also location of Wash Study Centre and Bird Observatory. Field centre is an ideal base for birdwatching/natural history groups in spring, summer and autumn. Visitor centre, gift shop and cafe. Toilets open daily. Network of footpaths bisect all major habitats. Public hides overlook freshwater and brackish lagoons. Wash viewpoint overlooks saltmarsh and mudflats.
Public transport: Bus service from Skegness runs occasionally but summer service only. Otherwise taxi/car from Skegness. Cycle route from Skegness.
Habitat: Sand dune grassland and scrub, saltmarshes and mudflats, freshwater marsh and lagoons.
Key birds: Large migration visible during spring and autumn passage – hirundines, chats, pipits, larks, thrushes and occasional rarities. Large numbers of waterfowl including internationally important populations of non-breeding waders. Sept-May impressive wader roosts on high tides. *Summer*: Little Tern and good assemblage of breeding warblers. *Winter*: Shore Lark, raptors, waders and wildfowl.
Contact: Kev Wilson, (Site Manager), Sykes Farm, Gibraltar Point Nature Reserve, Gibraltar Road, Skegness, Lincs PE24 4SU. 01754 898 057. e-mail: lincstrust@gibpoint.freeserve.co.uk www.lincstrust.org.uk

5. SALTFLEETBY-THEDDLETHORPE DUNES

Natural England (East Midlands Team).
Location: TF 46 59 24 - TF 49 08 83. Approx two miles N of Mablethorpe. All the following car parks may be accessed from the A1031: Crook Bank, Brickyard Lane, Churchill Lane, Rimac, Sea View.
Access: Open all year at all times. Keep dogs under close control. Easy access half mile trail suitable for wheelchair users starts adjacent to Rimac car park. Includes pond-viewing and saltmarsh-viewing platforms.
Facilities: Toilets, including wheelchair suitability at Rimac car park. May to end of Sept events programme.
Public transport: Grayscroft coaches (01507 473

236) and Lincolnshire Roadcar (01522 532 424) run services past Rimac entrance (Louth to Mablethorpe service). Lincs Roadcar can connect with trains at Lincoln. Applebys Coaches (01507 357 900) Grimsby to Saltfleet bus connects with Grimsby train service.
Habitat: 13th Century dunes, freshwater marsh, new dune ridge with large areas of sea buckthorn, saltmarsh, shingle ridge and foreshore.
Key birds: *Summer*: Breeding birds in scrub include Nightingale, Grasshopper Warbler, Whitethroat, Lesser Whitethroat, Redpoll. *Winter*: Large flocks of Brent Goose, Shelduck, Teal and Wigeon. Wintering Short-eared Owl, Hen Harrier. Migrant birds in scrub and waders on Paradise scrape.
Contact: Site Manager, Natural England Eastern Area NNRs, Roads Farmhouse, Frampton Roads, Frampton, Boston, Lincs PE20 1AY. 01205 723 614. email: simon.cooter@naturalengland.org.uk www.naturalengland.org.uk

OTHER SITES

Full details in previous editions, (year indicated in brackets).
A. Donna Nook – Lincs WT, 01507 526 667 (06).
B. Rigsby Wood – Lincs WT, 01507 526 667 (05).
C. Snipe Dales – Lincs WT, 01507 526 667 (05).
D. Tetney Marshes – RSPB, 0191 281 3366 (06).
E. Whisby Nature Park – Phil Porter, 01522 500 676 (07).

London, Greater

BEDFONT LAKES COUNTRY PARK

Ecology and Countryside Parks Service.
Location: TQ 080 728. OS map sheet 176 (west London). 0.5 miles from Ashford, Middx, 0.5 miles S of A30, Clockhouse Roundabout, on B3003 (Clockhouse Lane).
Access: Open (7.30am-9pm or dusk, whichever is earlier), all days except Christmas Day. Disabled friendly. Dogs on leads. Main nature reserve only open Sun (2pm-4pm). Keyholder membership available.
Facilities: Toilets, information centre, several hides, nature trail, free parking, up-to-date information.
Public transport: Train to Feltham and Ashford. Bus – H26 and 116 from Hounslow.
Habitat: Lakes, wildflower meadows, woodland, scrub.
Key birds: *Winter*: Water Rail, Bittern, Smew and other wildfowl, Meadow Pipit. *Summer*: Common Tern, Willow, Garden, Reed and Sedge Warblers, Whitethroat, Lesser Whitethroat, hirundines, Hobby, Blackcap, Chiffchaff, Sky Lark. *Passage*: Wheatear, Wood Warbler, Spotted Flycatcher, Ring Ouzel, Redstart, Yellow Wagtail.
Other notable flora and fauna: 140 plant species, wasp spider, butterflies and dragonflies
Contact: Paul Morgan (Ecology Ranger), BLCP, Clockhouse Lane, Bedfont, MiddxTW14 8QA. 01784 423 556; (Fax): 423 451.
e-mail: bedfont_lakes_lnr@hotmail.com

CHASE (THE) LNR

London Wildlife Trust.
Location: TQ 515 860. Lies in the Dagenham Corridor, an area of green belt between the London Boroughs of Barking & Dagenham and Havering.
Access: Open throughout the year and at all times. Reserve not suitable for wheelchair access. Eastbrookend Country Park which borders The Chase LNR has surfaced footpaths for wheelchair use.
Facilities: Millennium visitor centre, toilets, ample car parking, Timberland Trail walk.
Public transport: Rail: Dagenham East (District Line) 15 minute walk. Bus: 174 from Romford five minute walk.
Habitat: Shallow wetlands, reedbeds, horse-grazed pasture, scrub and wetland. These harbour an impressive range of animals and plants including the nationally rare black poplar tree. A haven for birds, with approx 190 different species recorded.
Key birds: *Summer*: Breeding Reed Warbler, Lapwing, Water Rail, Lesser Whitethroat and Little Ringed Plover, Kingfisher, Reed Bunting. *Winter*: Significant numbers of Teal, Shoveler, Redwing, Fieldfare and Snipe dominate the scene. *Spring/autumn migration*: Yellow Wagtail, Wheatear, Ruff, Wood Sandpiper, Sand Martin, Ring Ouzel, Black Redstart and Hobby regularly seen.
Contact: The Millennium Centre, The Chase, Off Dagenham Road, Rush Green, Romford, Essex RM7 0SS. 02085 938 096. e-mail: lwtchase@cix.co.uk www.wildlifetrust.org.uk/london/

SYDENHAM HILL WOOD

London Wildlife Trust.
Location: TQ 335 722. SE London, SE26, between Forest Hill and Crystal Palace, just off South Circular (A205).
Access: Open at all times, no permits required. Some steep slopes – wheelchair access not possible.
Facilities: Nature trail, no toilets.
Public transport: Train – Sydenham Hill, Forest Hill. Bus nos 363, 202, 356, 185, 312, 176, P4. Call Transport For London on 02075 657 299.
Habitat: Oak and hornbeam woodland, small pond, meadow and glades.
Key birds: Resident: Kestrel, Sparrowhawk, Tawny Owl, all three woodpeckers, Treecreeper, Nuthatch, Song Thrush. *Summer*: Chiffchaff, Blackcap. *Winter*: Redwing, Fieldfare.
Contact: The Warden, London Wildlife Trust, Horniman Museum, 100 London Road, London SE23 3PQ. 02086 995 698. e-mail: lwtsydenham@cix.co.uk www.wildlondon.org.uk

LONDON WETLAND CENTRE

The Wildfowl & Wetlands Trust.
Location: TQ 228 770. Less than 1 mile from South Circular (A205) at Roehampton. In London, Zone 2/3, one mile from Hammersmith.
Access: Winter (9.30am-5pm: last admission 4pm), summer (9.30am-6pm: last admission 5pm). Charge for admission.
Facilities: Visitor centre, hides, nature trails, discovery centre and children's adventure area, restaurant (hot and cold food), cinema, shop, observatory centre, seven hides (all wheelchair accessible), three interpretative buildings.
Public transport: Train: Barnes. Tube: Hammersmith then Duckbus 283 (comes into centre). Bus from Hammersmith – 283, 33, 72, 209. Bus from Richmond 33.
Habitat: Main lake, reedbeds, wader scrape, mudflats, open water lakes, grazing marsh.
Key birds: *Winter*: Nationally important numbers of wintering waterfowl, including Gadwall and Shoveler. Important numbers of wetland breeding birds, including grebes, swans, a range of duck species such as Pochard, plus Lapwing, Little Ringed Plover, Redshank, warblers, Reed Bunting and Bittern.
Contact: The Receptionist, London Wetland Centre, Queen Elizabeth Walk, Barnes, London SW13 9WT. 020 8409 4400. e-mail: info.london@wwt.org.uk www.wwt.org.uk

OTHER SITES

Full details in previous editions, (year indicated in brackets).
Battersea Park – London WT, 0207 261 0447 (04).
Bramley Bank – London WT, 0207 261 0447 (06).
Camley Street Natural Park – London WT, 0207 261 0447 (06).
Ripple Nature Reserve – London WT, 0207 261 0447 (05).

Manchester, Greater

1. AUDENSHAW RESERVOIRS

United Utilities, Bottoms Office.
Location: NW Water SJ915965. Access and parking on Audenshaw Road B6390 at N end of site.
Access: No disabled access.
Facilities: Hide (contact R Travis on 0161 330 2607). Permit (free) from D Tomes, UU Bottoms Office, Woodhead Road, Tintwistle, Glossop SK13 1HS.
Public transport: None.
Habitat: Reservoir.
Key birds: Major migration point; *Winter*: Notable gull roost inc. regular Mediterranean Gull; large Goosander roost; many rarities.

2. ETHEROW COUNTRY PARK

Stockport Metropolitan Borough Council.
Location: SJ 965 908. B6104 into Compstall near Romiley, Stockport.
Access: Open at all times; permit required for conservation area. Keep to paths.
Facilities: Reserve area has SSSI status. Hide, nature trail, visitor centre, scooters for disabled.
Public transport: None.
Habitat: River Etherow, woodlands, marshy area.
Key birds: Sparrowhawk, Buzzard, Dipper, all three woodpeckers, Pied Flycatcher, warblers. *Winter*: Brambling, Siskin, Water Rail. Frequent sightings of Merlin and Raven over hills.

Contact: John Rowland, Etherow Country Park, Compstall, Stockport, Cheshire SK6 5JD. 01614 276 937; (Fax) 01614 273 643. e-mail: parks@stockport.gov.uk

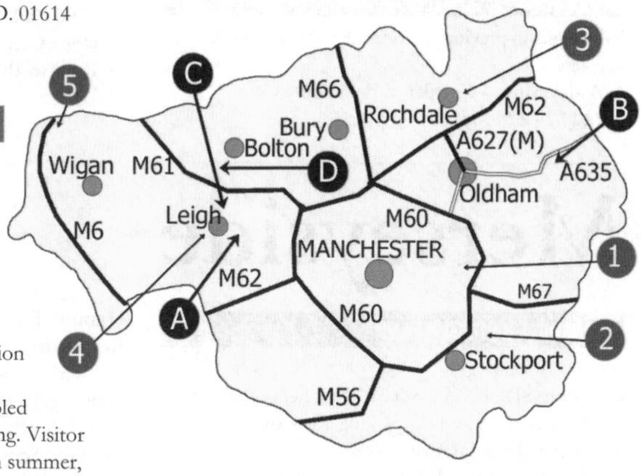

3. HOLLINGWORTH LAKE

Hollingworth Lake – Rochdale MBC.
Location: SD 939 153 (visitor centre). Four miles NE of Rochdale, signed from A58 Halifax Road and J21 of M62 – B6225 to Littleborough.
Access: Access open to lake and surroundings at all times.
Facilities: Cafes, hide, trails and education service, car parks, coach park by prior arrangement. Free wheelchair hire, disabled toilets and baby changing facilities, fishing. Visitor centre open 10.30am-6pm (Mon-Sun) in summer, 11am-4pm (Mon-Fri), 10.30am-5pm (Sat & Sun) in winter.
Public transport: Bus Nos 452, 450. Train to Littleborough or Smithy Bridge.
Habitat: Lake (116 acres, includes 20 acre nature reserve), woodland, streams, marsh, willow scrub.
Key birds: *All year*: Great Crested Grebe, Kingfisher, Lapwing, Little Owl, Bullfinch, Cormorant. Occasional Peregrine, Sedge Warbler, Water Rail, Snipe. *Spring/ autumn*: Passage waders, wildfowl, Kittiwake. *Summer*: Reed Bunting, Dipper, Common Sandpiper, Curlew, Oystercatcher, Black Tern, 'Commic' Tern, Grey Partridge, Blackcap. *Winter*: Goosander, Goldeneye, Siskin, Redpoll, Golden Plover.
Contact: The Ranger, Hollingworth Lake Visitor Centre, Rakewood Road, Littleborough, OL15 0AQ. 01706 373 421. www.rochdale.gov.uk

4. PENNINGTON FLASH COUNTRY PARK

Wigan Leisure and Culture Trust
Location: SJ 640 990. One mile from Leigh town centre. Main entrance on A572 (St Helens Road).
Access: Park is signposted from A580 (East Lancs Road) and is permanently open. Four largest hides, toilets and information point open 9am-dusk (except Christmas Day). Main paths flat and suitable for disabled. Coach parking available if booked in advance.
Facilities: Toilets including disabled and information point. Total of seven bird hides. Site leaflet available and Rangers based on site. Group visits welcome, guided tours or a site introduction can be arranged subject to staff availability.
Public transport: Only 1 mile from Leigh bus station. Several services stop on St Helens Road near entrance to park. Contact GMPTE 0161 228 7811.
Habitat: Lowland lake, ponds and scrapes, fringed with reeds, rough grassland, scrub and young woodland.
Key birds: Waterfowl all year, waders mainly passage spring and autumn (14-plus species). Breeding Common Tern and Little Ringed Plover. Feeding station attracts Willow Tit and Bullfinch all year.
Contact: Peter Alker, Pennington Flash Country Park, St Helens Road, Leigh WN7 3PA. 01942 605 253 (Also (Fax) number). e-mail: pfcp@wlct.org

5. WIGAN FLASHES

Lancashire Wildlife Trust/Wigan Council.
Location: SD 580 035. One mile from J25 of M6.
Access: Free access, open at all times. Areas suitable for wheelchairs but some motorcycle barriers (gates can be opened by reserve manager for large groups). Paths being upgraded. Access for coaches - contact reserve manager for details.
Facilities: Six hide screens.
Public transport: 610 bus (Hawkley Hall Circular). Local timetable info - call 0161 228 7811.
Habitat: Wetland with reedbed.
Key birds: Black Tern on migration. *Summer*: Nationally important for Reed Warbler and breeding Common Tern. Willow Tit, Grasshopper Warbler, Kingfisher. *Winter*: Wildfowl, especially diving duck and Gadwall. Bittern (especially winter).
Contact: Mark Champion, Lancashire Wildlife Trust. Highfield Grange Community Centre, Highfield Grange, Wigan, Lancs WN3 6SU. 01942 233 976. e-mail: wiganflashes@lancswt.org.uk

OTHER SITES

Full details in previous editions, (year indicated in brackets).

A. Astley Moss – Cuerden Park Wildlife Centre, 01722 324 129 (04).

B. Dovestones Reservoir – Peak District NP, 01629 816 200 (06).

C. Hope Carr – 01942 269 027.

D. Rumworth Lodge – Lancs WT, 01722 924 729 (04).

Merseyside

1. AINSDALE & BIRKDALE LNR

Sefton Council.

Location: SD 300 115. SD 310 138. Leave the A565 just N of Formby and car parking areas are off the unnumbered coastal road.

Access: Track from Ainsdale or Southport along the shore. Wheelchair access across boardwalks at Ainsdale Sands Lake Nature Trail and the Queen's Jubilee Nature Trail, opposite Weld Road.

Facilities: Ainsdale Visitor Centre open summer and toilets (Easter-Oct).

Public transport: Ainsdale and Southport stations 20 minute walk. Hillside Station is a 30 minute walk across the Birkdale Sandhills to beach.

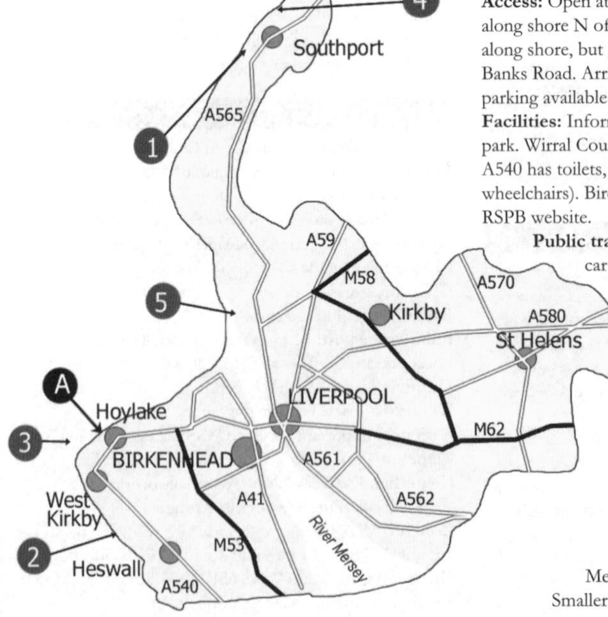

Habitat: Foreshore, dune scrub and pine woodland.

Key birds: *Spring/summer*: Grasshopper Warbler, Chiffchaff, waders. *Winter*: Blackcap, Stonechat, Redwing, Fieldfare, waders and wildfowl. *All year*: Sky Lark, Grey Partridge.

Contact: Sefton Council, Southport Town Hall, Lord Street, Southport, PR8 1DA, www.sefton.gov.uk

2. DEE ESTUARY

Metropolitan Borough of Wirral.

Location: SJ 255 815. Leave A540 Chester to Hoylake road at Heswall and head downhill (one mile) to the free car park at the shore end of Banks Road. Heswall is 30 minutes from South Liverpool and Chester by car.

Access: Open at all times. Best viewpoint 600 yards along shore N of Banks Road. No disabled access along shore, but good birdwatching from bottom of Banks Road. Arrive 2.5 hours before high tide. Coach parking available.

Facilities: Information board. No toilets in car park. Wirral Country Park Centre three miles N off A540 has toilets, hide, café, kiosk (all accessible to wheelchairs). Birdwatching events programme on RSPB website.

Public transport: Bus service to Banks Road car park from Heswall bus station, or bus to Irby village then walk one mile. Contact Mersey Travel (tel 0151 236 7676).

Habitat: Saltmarsh and mudflats.

Key birds: *Autumn/winter*: Large passage and winter wader roosts – Redshank, Curlew, Black-tailed Godwit, Oystercatcher, Golden Plover, Knot, Shelduck, Teal, Red-breasted Merganser, Peregrine, Merlin, Hen Harrier, Short-eared Owl. Smaller numbers of Pintail, Wigeon, Bar-

tailed Godwit, Greenshank, Spotted Redshank, Grey and Ringed Plovers, Whimbrel, Curlew Sandpiper, Little Stint, occasional Scaup and Little Egret.
Contact: The Senior Ranger, Wirral Country Park Centre, Station Road, Thustaston, Wirral, Merseyside CH61 0HN. 01516 484 371/3884.
e-mail: wirralcountrypark@wirral.gov.uk
www.wirral.gov.uk/er

3. HILBRE ISLAND LNR

Wirral Country Park Centre (Metropolitan Borough of Wirral).
Location: SJ 184 880. Three tidal islands in the mouth of the Dee Estuary. Park in West Kirby which is on the A540 Chester-to-Hoylake road – 30 minutes from Liverpool, 45 minutes from Chester. Follow the brown Marine Lake signs to Dee Lane pay and display car park. Coach parking available at West Kirby but please apply for permit to visit island well in advance as numbers limited.
Access: Two mile walk across the sands from Dee Lane slipway. No disabled access. Do not cross either way within 3.5 hours of high water – tide times and suggested safe route on noticeboard at slipway. Prior booking and permit needed for parties of five or more – maximum of 50. Book early.
Facilities: Toilets at Marine Lake and Hilbre (primitive!). Permits, leaflets and tide times from Wirral Country Park Centre. Hilbre Bird Observatory.
Public transport: Bus and train station (from Liverpool) within 0.5 mile of Dee Lane slipway. Contact Mersey Travel, tel 0151 236 7676.
Habitat: Sandflats, rocky shore and open sea.
Key birds: *Late summer/autumn*: Seabird passage – Gannets, terns, skuas, shearwaters and after NW gales good numbers of Leach's Petrel. *Winter*: Wader roosts at high tide, Purple Sandpiper, Turnstone, sea ducks, divers, grebes. Passage migrants.
Contact: The Senior Ranger, Wirral Country Park Centre, 01516 484 371/3884.
e-mail: wirralcountrypark@wirral.gov.uk

4. MARSHSIDE

RSPB (North England Office).
Location: SD 355 202. On south shore of Ribble Estuary, one mile north of Southport centre on Marine Drive.
Access: Open 8.30am-5pm all year. Toilets. No dogs please. Coach parties please book in advance. No charges but donations welcomed. Park in Sefton Council car park along Marine Drive.
Facilities: Two hides and trails accessible to wheelchairs. Two viewing screens and a viewing platform.
Public transport: Bus service to Elswick Road/ Marshside Road half-hourly, bus No 44, from Lord Street. Contact Traveline (0870 608 2608).
Habitat: Coastal grazing marsh and lagoons.
Key birds: *Winter*: Pink-footed Goose, wildfowl, waders, raptors. *Spring*: Breeding waders, inc. Avocet and wildfowl, Garganey, migrants. *Autumn*: Migrants. *All year*: Black-tailed Godwit.
Contact: Graham Clarkson, Warden, RSPB, 24 Hoghton Street, Southport PR9 0PA. 01704 536 378.
e-mail: graham.clarkson@rspb.org.uk

5. SEAFORTH NATURE RESERVE

The Wildlife Trust for Lancashire, Manchester and North Merseyside.
Location: SJ 315 970. Five miles from Liverpool city centre. From M57/M58 take A5036 to docks.
Access: Only organised groups which pre-book are now allowed access. Groups should contact the reserve office (see below) at least seven days in advance of their planned trip. Coaches welcome.
Facilities: Toilets when visitor centre open, three hides.
Public transport: Train to Waterloo or Seaforth stations from Liverpool. Buses to dock gates from Liverpool.
Habitat: Saltwater and freshwater lagoons, scrub grassland.
Key birds: Little Gull on passage (Apr) plus Roseate, Little and Black Terns. Breeding and passage Common Tern (Apr-Sept) plus Roseate, Little and Black Terns on passage. Passage and winter waders and gulls. Passage passerines, especially White Wagtail, pipits and Wheatear.
Contact: Steve White, Seaforth Nature Reserve, Port of Liverpool, L21 1JD. 0151 9203 769.
e-mail: swhite@lancswt.org.uk

OTHER SITES

Full details in previous editions, (year indicated in brackets).
A. Red Rocks Marsh – Cheshire WT, 01270 610 180 (05).

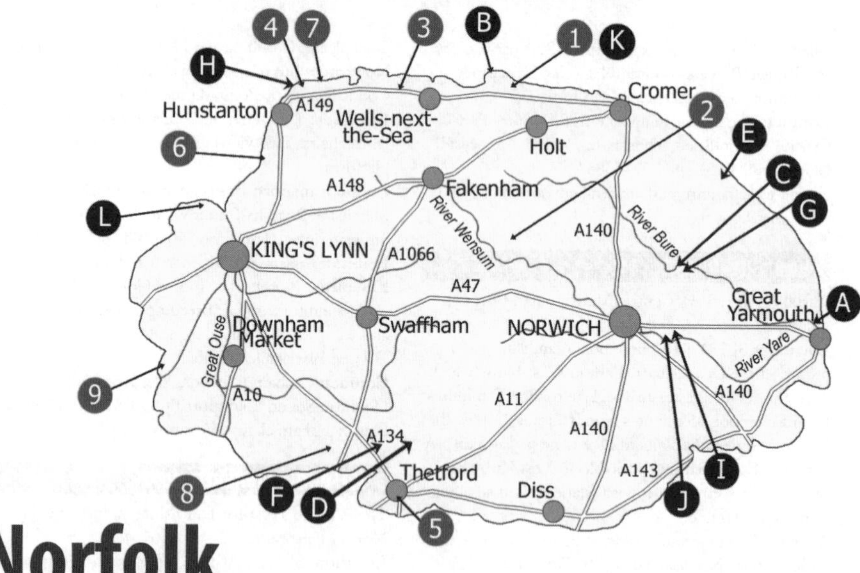

Norfolk

1. NWT CLEY MARSHES

Norfolk Wildlife Trust.

Location: TG 054 441. NWT Cley Marshes is situated four miles N of Holt on A149 coast road, half a mile E of Cley-next-the-Sea. Visitor centre and car park on inland side of road.

Access: Open all year round, except Christmas Day. Visitor centre open Apr-Oct (10am-5pm daily), Nov-early Dec (10am-4pm Wed-Sun). Cost: adults £3.75, children under 16 free. NWT members free. Out of season, obtain permit from Watcher's Cottage, 400m along coast road towards Cley village.

Facilities: Brand new environmentally-friendly visitor centre incorporates an observation area, interactive interpretation including a remote controllable wildlife camera, a café, and sales area. Four hides (with excellent wheelchair access) provide birdwatching within metres of the pools where the birds congregate. Audio trail. Wildlife Detective Bumbags for children are free to hire. Boardwalk and information boards. Reserve leaflet.

Public transport: Coasthopper bus service stops outside, every two hours. Connections for train and bus services at Sheringham. Special discounts to visitors arriving by bus. Call Norfolk County Bus Information Line on 01603 223 800 for info.

Habitat: Reedbeds, salt and freshwater marshes, scrapes and shingle ridge with international reputation as one of the finest birdwatching sites in Britain.

Key birds: Bittern, Avocet, Marsh Harrier, Spoonbill, Bearded Tit and large numbers of wildfowl, including Wigeon, Teal, Pintail and Brent Goose. Migrating waders such as Ruff and Temminck's Stint. Many rarities.

Contact: NWT, Bewick House, 22 Thorpe Road, Norwich Norfolk NR1 1RY. 01603 625 540. e-mail admin@norfolkwildlifetrust.org.uk www.wildlifetrust.org.uk.Norfolk

2. NWT FOXLEY WOOD

Norfolk Wildlife Trust.

Location: TG 049 229. Foxley Wood is situated 12 miles NW of Norwich on A1067, signposted at Foxley village from main road.

Access: Open all year, (10am-5pm). Closed Thursdays.

Facilities: Trails, car park, no toilets, groups welcome.

Public transport: Bus – Norwich to Fakenham services stop at Foxley War Memorial approximately 15 minutes' walk. Sanders Coaches Sun service.

Habitat: Norfolk's largest ancient woodland.

Key birds: Woodland birds including Great Spotted and Green Woodpeckers, Woodcock, Blackcap, Garden Warbler. White admiral butterfles.

Other notable flora and fauna: Rich woodland flora including early purple orchids, wood anemone, wood sorrell and bluebells.

Contact: Trust HQ, 01603 625 540.
e-mail admin@norfolkwildlifetrust.org.uk
www.norfolkwildlifetrust.org.uk

3. HOLKHAM

Natural England (Norfolk Team).
Location: TF 890 450. From Holkham village turn N off A149 down Lady Ann's Drive; parking.
Access: Access unrestricted, but keep to paths and off grazing marshes and farmland.
Facilities: Two hides. Disabled access.
Public transport: Bus Norbic Norfolk bus information line 0845 3006 116.
Habitat: Sandflats, dunes, marshes, pinewoods.
Key birds: *Passage*: Migrants. *Winter*: Wildfowl, inc. Brent, Pink-footed and White-fronted Geese. *Summer*: Breeding Little Tern.
Contact: R Harold, Hill Farm Offices, Main Road, Holkham, Wells-next-the-Sea, NR23 1AB. 01328 711 183; (Fax) 01328 711 893.

4. HOLME BIRD OBSERVATORY

Norfolk Ornithologists' Association (NOA).
Location: TF 717 450. E of Hunstanton, signposted from A149. Access from Broadwater Road, Holme. The reserve and visitors centre are beyond the White House at the end of the track.
Access: Reserve open daily to members dawn to dusk; non-members (9am-5pm) by permit from the Observatory. Please keep dogs on leads in the reserve. Parties by prior arrangement.
Facilities: Accredited Bird Observatory operating 12 months of the year for bird ringing, MV moth trapping and other scientific monitoring. Visitor centre, car park and several hides (seawatch hide reserved for NOA members), together with access to beach and coastal path.
Public transport: Coastal bus service runs from Hunstanton to Sheringham roughly every 30 mins but is seasonal and times may vary. Phone Norfolk Green Bus, 01553 776 980.
Habitat: In ten acres of diverse habitat: sand dunes, Corsican pines, scrub and reed-fringed lagoon make this a migration hotspot.
Key birds: Species list over 320. Ringed species over 150. Recent rarities have included Red Kite, Common Crane, Red-backed Shrike, Osprey, Pallas', Yellow-browed, Greenish and Barred Warblers.
Contact: Jed Andrews, Holme Bird Observatory, Broadwater Road, Holme, Hunstanton, Norfolk PE36 6LQ. 01485 525 406. e-mail: info@noa.org.uk
www.noa.org.uk

5. NUNNERY LAKES

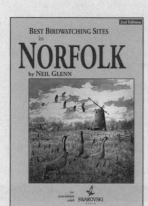

British Trust for Ornithology.
Location: TL 873 815. On the S edge of Thetford, adjacent to the BTO's headquarters at The Nunnery, off Nun's Bridges Road. Main access point is about 60 yards upriver of Nun's Bridges car park (TL 874 825) on the opposite side of the River Little Ouse.
Access: Open during daylight hours. No permits required on permissive paths; BTO authorisation needed to gain access to rest of reserve. Keep dogs

on leads at all times. Pre-booked coaches can park in grounds. Call Reception in advance to arrange wheelchair access to the lakes and hide.
Facilities: Waymarked paths with information panels, bird hide. No toilets or visitor centre. Enquiries welcome at BTO Reception (01842 750 050) during office hours.
Public transport: Various bus services to Thetford Bus Terminal, off Bridge Street (about a ten minute walk to site alongside river). Thetford Railway Station – Station Road (about 20 minutes' walk across town to the reserve).
Habitat: Flood meadows, flooded gravel pits, woodland, grass heath.
Key birds: *Spring*: Passage waders, Little Ringed Plover, Wheatear. *Summer*: Hobby, breeding Oystercatcher and Lapwing, Sky Lark, warblers. *Winter*: Water Rail, Snipe, Goosander, Gadwall, Siskin, Lesser Redpoll, Hawfinch. *All year*: Kingfisher, Grey Wagtail, Nuthatch, Willow Tit.
Contact: Chris Gregory, The British Trust for Ornithology, The Nunnery, Thetford, Norfolk IP24 2PU. 01842 750 050. e-mail: chris.gregory@bto.org www.bto.org

6. SNETTISHAM

RSPB (East Anglia Office).
Location: TF 630 310. Car park two miles along Beach Road, signposted off A149 King's Lynn to Hunstanton, opposite Snettisham village.
Access: Open at all times. Dogs to be kept on leads. Two hides are suitable for wheelchairs. Disabled access is across a private road. Please phone office number for permit and directions. Coaches welcome, but please book in advance as a height barrier needs to be removed.
Facilities: Four birdwatching hides, connected by reserve footpath. No toilets on site.
Public transport: Nearest over two miles away.
Habitat: Intertidal mudflats, saltmarsh, shingle beach, brackish lagoons, and unimproved grassland/scrub. Best visited on a high tide.
Key birds: *Autumn/winter/spring*: Waders (particularly Knot, Bar and Black-tailed Godwits, Dunlin, Grey Plover), wildfowl (particularly Pink-footed and Brent Geese, Wigeon, Gadwall, Goldeneye), Peregrine, Hen Harrier, Merlin, owls. Migrants in season. *Summer*: Breeding Mediterranean Gull (records from last three years), Ringed Plover, Redshank, Avocet, Common Tern. Marsh Harrier regular.
Contact: Jim Scott, RSPB, Barn A, Home Farm Barns, Common Road, Snettisham, King's Lynn, Norfolk PE31 7PD. 01485 542 689.

7. TITCHWELL MARSH

RSPB (East Anglia Office).
Location: TF 749 436. E of Hunstanton, off A149.
Access: Wheelchairs available free of charge. All paths and trails suitable for wheelchairs. Reserve and hides open at all times. Coach parking available but pre-booking essential.
Facilities: Visitor centre, shop with large selection of binoculars, telescopes and books, open every day 9.30am to 5pm (Nov 5 - Feb 10, 9.30 to 4pm). Tearoom open from 9.30am to 4.30pm every day (Nov 5 - Feb 10, 9.30 to 4pm). Visitor centre and tearoom closed on Christmas Day and Boxing Day.
Public transport: Phone Traveline East Anglia on 0870 608 2608.
Habitat: Reedbed, brackish & freshwater pools, saltmarsh, dunes, shingle.
Key birds: *Spring/summer*: Nesting Avocet, Bearded Tit, Water Rail, Marsh Harrier, Bittern, Reed and Sedge Warblers. *Autumn*: Knot and other waders. *Winter*: Brent Geese, Goldeneye, Common Scoter, Eider, Hen Harrier roost, Snow Bunting and Shore Lark on beach.
Contact: Centre Manager, Titchwell Marsh Reserve, King's Lynn, Norfolk PE31 8BB. Tel/Fax 01485 210 779.

8. NWT WEETING HEATH

Norfolk Wildlife Trust.
Location: TL 756 881. Weeting Heath is signposted from the Weeting-Hockwold road, two miles W of Weeting near to Brandon in Suffolk. Nature reserve can be reached via B1112 at Hockwold or B1106 at Weeting.
Access: Open daily from Apr-Sep. Cost: adults £2.50, children free. NWT members free. Disabled access to visitor centre and hides.
Facilities: Visitor centre open daily Apr-Aug, birdwatching hides, wildlife gift shop, refreshments, toilets, coach parking, car park, groups welcome (book first).
Public transport: Train services to Brandon and bus connections (limited) from Brandon High Street.
Habitat: Breckland, grass heath.
Key birds: Stone Curlew, migrant passerines, Wood Lark.
Contact: Bev Nichols, Norfolk Wildlife Trust, 01603 625 540. e-mail: BevN@norfolkwildlifetrust.org.uk www.wildlifetrust.org.uk/Norfolk

9. WELNEY

The Wildfowl & Wetlands Trust.
Location: TL 546 944. Ten miles N of Ely,

signposted from A10 and A1101.
Access: Open daily (10am-5pm) except Christmas Day. Free admission to WWT members, otherwise £3.50 (adult), £2.75 (senior), £2 (child).
Facilities: Visitor centre, cafe open 10am-4pm daily. Large, heated observatory, plus six other birdwatching hides. Provision for disabled visitors.
Public transport: Poor. Train to Littleport (6 miles away), but from there, taxi is only option. Excellent cycling country!
Habitat: 1,000 acres of washland reserve, spring damp meadows, winter wildfowl marsh.
Key birds: *Winter*: Bewick's Swan, Whooper Swan, winter wildfowl. *Spring*: Breeding/migrant waders, warblers.
Contact: The Warden, WWT, Hundred Foot Bank, Welney, Nr Wisbech PE14 9TN. 01353 860 711.
e-mail: welney@wwt.org.uk www.wwt.org.uk

OTHER SITES

Full details in previous editions, (year indicated in brackets).

A. Berney Marshes – RSPB, 01603 661 662 (05).
B. Blakeney Point – John Sizer, National Trust, 01263 740 241 (07).
C. Cockshoot Broad – Norfolk WT, 01603 625 540 (05).
D. East Wretham Heath – Norfolk WT, 01603 625 540 (06).
E. Hickling Broad – Norfolk WT, 01603 625 540 (06).
F. Lynford Arboretum – Forest Enterprise, 01832 810 271 (06).
G. Ranworth Broad – Norfolk WT, 01603 625 540 (04).
H. Redwell Marsh – Jed Andrews (NOA), 01485 525 406 (06).
I. Strumpshaw Fen – Tim Strudwick (RSPB), 01603 715 191 (06).
J Surlingham Church Marsh – Tim Strudwick (RSPB), 01603 715 191 (04).
K Walsey Hills – Jed Andrews (NOA), 01485 525 406 (05).
L The Wash NNR – Natural England site manager, 01205 723 614 (07).

Northamptonshire

1. CLIFFORD HILL GRAVEL PITS

Location: SP 781 595. Take the A428 Bedford Road from Northampton town centre E to A45 roundabout. Go straight over and turn L to park by the Courtyard Hotel.
Access: Open all year. Shooting may take place Tues.
Facilities: Car park, toilets.
Public transport: None.
Habitat: Reservoir, river, grassland.
Key birds: *Spring*: Wheatear, Sand Martin, Yellow Wagtail. *Winter*: Excellent for wintering wildfowl inc Goosander, Pintail, Red-crested Pochard and Smew. Geese, Golden Plover, Green Sandpiper, Redshank, thrushes. *All year*: Meadow Pipit, Reed Bunting, Grey Wagtail, Redpoll, Linnet, Green Woodpecker.

2. DAVENTRY RESERVOIR COUNTRY PARK

Daventry District Council .
Location: SP 577 642. Signposted from B4036 Daventry to Welton road.
Access: Open at all times.
Facilities: Toilets, cafe, visitor centre. No hides.
Public transport: None.
Habitat: Open water, wetlands, reed, meadows, woodland.
Key birds: *Autumn*: Passage waders inc. Dunlin, Ruff, Greenshank, Green Sandpiper; nesting Common Tern, Arctic and sometimes Black Tern on passage; gull roost; rare species inc. Pacific Swift, Baird's Sandpiper, Wilson's Phalarope, Sabine's Gull, Honey Buzzard. Over 180 species recorded; 60 have bred.
Contact: Dewi Morris, Daventry Country Park, Daventry District Council, Contracts House, High March, Daventry NN11 4HB. 01327 300 001;
e-mail: countrysideservices@daventrydc.gov.uk.

3. PITSFORD RESERVOIR

Beds, Cambs, Northants and Peterborough Wildlife Trust.
Location: SP 787 702. Five miles N of Northampton. On A43 take turn to Holcot and Brixworth. On A508 take turn to Brixworth and Holcot.
Access: Lodge open mid-Mar to mid-Nov from 8am-dusk. Winter opening times variable, check in

advance. Permits for reserve available from Lodge on daily or annual basis. Reserve open to permit holders 365 days a year. No dogs. Disabled access from Lodge to first hide.
Facilities: Toilets available in Lodge, 15 miles of paths, eight bird hides, car parking.
Public transport: None.
Habitat: Open water (up to 120 ha), marginal vegetation and reed grasses, wet woodland, grassland and mixed woodland (40 ha).
Key birds: 150 species in 2004. *Summer*: Breeding warblers, terns, Hobby, Tree Sparrow. *Autumn*: Waders only if water levels suitable. *Winter*: Wildfowl, feeding station with Tree Sparrow and Corn Bunting.
Contact: Dave Francis, Pitsford Water Lodge, Brixworth Road, Holcot, Northampton NN6 9SJ. 01604 780 148. e-mail: pitsford@cix.compulink.co.uk

4. SHORT WOOD

Beds, Cambs, Northants and Peterborough Wildlife Trust.
Location: TL 015 913. Via bridle path from minor road between Glapthorn and Southwick, NW of Oundle. Park on roadside verge.
Access: Open all year.
Facilities: None.
Public transport: Not known.
Habitat: Primary and secondary mixed woodland (oak, ash, field maple, hazel), coppiced.
Key birds: Woodcock, Marsh Tit, warblers, Redpoll.
Contact: Trust HQ, Northants Wildlife Trust, Ling House, Billing Lings, Northampton NN3 8BE. 01604 405 285; (Fax) 01604 784 835. www.wildlifebcnp.org e-mail: northamptonshire@wildlifebcnp.org

5. SUMMER LEYS LNR

Northamptonshire County Council.
Location: SP 886 634. Three miles from Wellingborough, accessible from A45 and A509, situated on Great Doddington to Wollaston Road.
Access: Open 24 hours a day, 365 days a year, no permits required. Dogs welcome but must be kept on leads at all times. 40 space car park, small tarmaced circular route suitable for wheelchairs.
Facilities: Three hides, one feeding station. No toilets, nearest are at Irchester Country Park on A509 towards Wellingborough.
Public transport: Nearest main station is Wellingborough. No direct bus service, though buses run regularly to Great Doddington and Wollaston, both about a mile away. Tel: 01604 670 060 (24 hrs) for copies of timetables.
Habitat: Scrape, two ponds, lake, scrub, grassland, hedgerow.
Key birds: Hobby, Lapwing, Golden Plover, Ruff, Gadwall, Garganey, Pintail, Shelduck, Shoveler, Little Ringed Plover, Tree Sparrow, Redshank, Green Sandpiper, Oystercatcher, Black-headed Gull colony, terns.
Contact: Chris Haines, Countryside Service, Northamptonshire Council, PO Box 163, County Hall, Northampton NN1 1AX. 01604 237 227. e-mail: countryside@northamptonshire.gov.uk

6. THRAPSTON GRAVEL PITS & TITCHMARSH LNR

Beds, Cambs, Northants and Peterborough Wildlife Trust/Natural England.
Location: TL 008 804.
Access: Public footpath from layby on A605 N of Thrapston. Car park at Aldwincle, W of A605 at Thorpe Waterville.
Facilities: Six hides.
Public transport: Bus service to Thrapston.

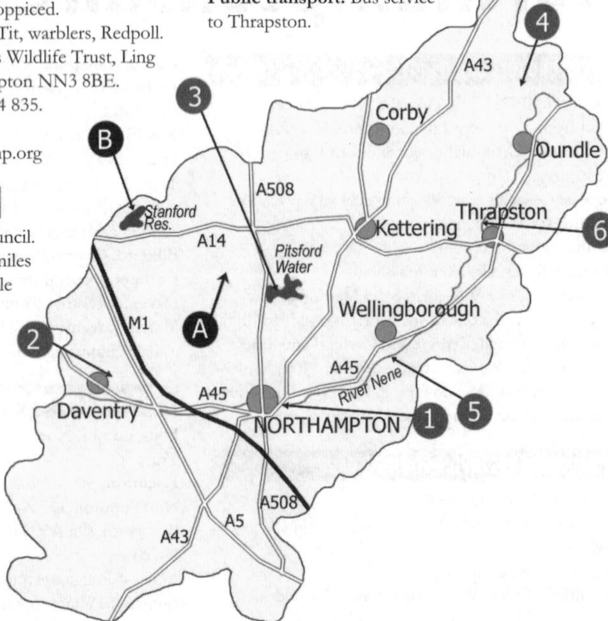

Habitat: Alder/birch/willow wood; old duck decoy, series of water-filled gravel pits.
Key birds: *Summer*: Breeding Grey Heron (no access to Heronry), Common Tern, Little Ringed Plover; warblers. Migrants, inc. Red-necked and Slavonian Grebes, Bittern and Marsh Harrier recorded.
Contact: Trust HQ, 01604 405 285; (Fax) 01604 784 835. e-mail:northamptonshire@wildlifebcnp.org www.wildlifebcnp.org

OTHER SITES

Full details in previous editions, (year indicated in brackets).
A. Hollowell Reservoir – Anglian Water, 01480 323 000 (06).
B. Stanford Reservoir – BCN & P Wildlife Trust, 01604 405 285 (07).

Northumberland

1. ARNOLD RESERVE, CRASTER

Northumberland Wildlife Trust.
Location: NU255197. Lies NE of Alnwick and SW of Craster village.
Access: Public footpath from car park in disused quarry.
Facilities: Information centre (not NWT) open in summer. Interpretation boards.Toilets (incl disabled) and picnic site in quarry car park. Easy going access along path through site. Coach parking in adjacent public car park.
Public transport: Arriva Northumberland nos. 401, 500, 501.
Habitat: Semi-natural woodland and scrub near coast.
Key birds: Good site for migrant passerines to rest and feed. Interesting visitors can inc. Bluethroat, Red-breasted Flycatcher, Barred and Icterine Warblers, Wryneck; moulting site for Lesser Redpoll. Breeding warblers in summer.
Contact: Trust HQ, Northumberland Wildlife Trust, The Garden House, St Nicholas Park, Jubilee Road, Newcastle upon Tyne, NE3 3XT. 01912 846 884; (Fax) 01912 846 794; e-mail: mail@northwt.org.uk www.nwt.org.uk

2. BOLAM LAKE COUNTRY PARK

Northumberland County Council.
Location: NZ 08 81. 4.8km N of main Jedburgh Road (A696), 27km NW of Newcastle. Signed along a minor road from Belsay.
Access: Open all year, small parking fee. Good access around lake for wheelchairs. Coach parking only at Low House Wood and West Wood car parks.
Facilities: Car parks, leaflets from visitor centre in the main car park.
Public transport: None.
Habitat: Parkland, lake, carr, conifers, woodland.
Key birds: *Spring/ summer*: Ruddy Duck, Woodcock, Common Sandpiper, Sand Martin, House Martin, Redstart, warblers inc Grasshopper, Garden, Wood and Willow, possible flycatchers, waders. *Winter*: Whooper Swan, Greylag and Canada Geese, Wigeon,

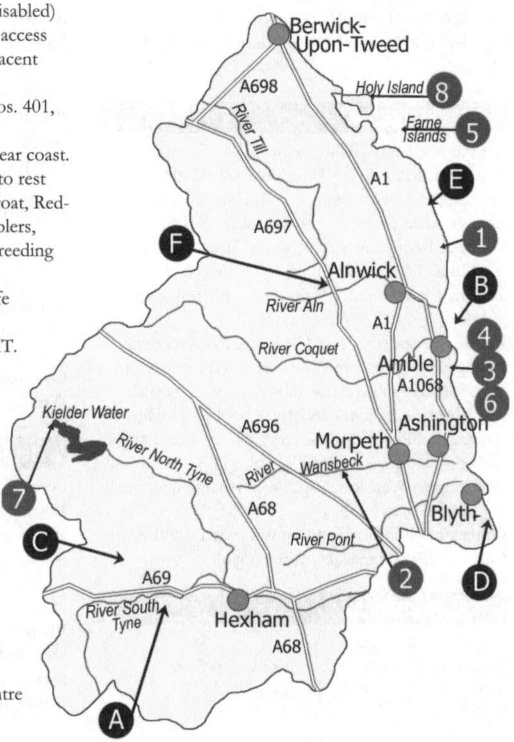

Pintail, Goosander, Water Rail, Woodcock, thrushes, Siskin, Redpoll. *All year*: possible Grey Partridge, Green and Great Spotted Woodpeckers, Goldcrest, tits, Treecreeper, Nuthatch, Bullfinch.
Contact: Northumberland County Council, County Hall, Morpeth NE61 2EF. 01661 881 234.

3. DRURIDGE POOLS - CRESSWELL POND

Northumberland Wildlife Trust.
Location: 1. Druridge Pools NZ 272 965.
2. Cresswell Pond NZ 283 945. Half mile N of Cresswell.
Access: Day permits for both reserves. Wheelchair users can view northern part of Cresswell Pond from public footpath or roadside.
Facilities: 1. Three hides. 2. Hide.
Public transport: None.
Habitat: 1. Deep lake and wet meadows with pools behind dunes. 2. Shallow brackish lagoon behind dunes fringed by saltmarsh and reedbed, some mudflats.
Key birds: 1. Especially good in spring. Winter and breeding wildfowl; passage and breeding waders.
2. Good for waders, esp. on passage.
Contact: Jim Martin, Hauxley Nature Reserve, Low Hauxley, Amble, Morpeth, Northumberland. 01665 711 578.

4. EAST CHEVINGTON

Northumberland Wildlife Trust.
Location: NZ 265 985. Overlooking Druridge Bay, off A 1068 between High Hauxley and Cresswell.
Access: Main access from overlow car park at Druridge Bay Country Park (signed from main road).
Facilities: Four public hides, café, toilets and information at Country Park. ID boards for coastal plants.
Public transport: Arriva 420 and 423 bus services.
Habitat: Ponds and reedbeds created from former open cast coal mine. Areas of scrub and grassland.
Key birds: Large numbers of wildfowl, including Greylag and Pinkfooted Geese in winter. Breeding Sky Lark, Stonechat , Reed Bunting, plus Reed, Sedge and Grasshopper Warblers. Capable of attracting rarities at any time of year.
Other notable flora and fauna: Coastal wildflowers.
Contact: E-mail: mail@northwt.org.uk

5. FARNE ISLANDS

The National Trust.
Location: NU 230 370. Access by boat from Seahouses Harbour. Access from A1.
Access: Apr, Aug-Sept: Inner Farne and Staple 10.30am-6pm (majority of boats land at Inner Farne when conditions are calm). May-Jul: Staple Island 10.30am-1.30pm, Inner Farne: 1.30pm-5pm. Disabled access possible on Inner Farne, telephone Property Manager for details. Dogs allowed on boats – not on islands.
Facilities: Toilets on Inner Farne.
Public transport: Nearest rail stations at Alnmouth and Berwick.
Habitat: Maritime islands – between 15-28 depending on state of tide.
Key birds: 18 species of seabirds/waders, four species of tern (including Roseate), 55,000-plus pairs of Puffin, 1,200 Eider, Rock Pipit, Pied Wagtail etc.
Contact: John Walton, 8 St Aidans, Seahouses, Northumberland NE68 7SR. 01665 720 651.

6. HAUXLEY

Northumberland Wildlife Trust
Location: NU 285 023. South of Amble.
Access: Day permit required. Access through High Hauxley village. Site is signposted off A1068.
Facilities: Reception hide open daily from 10am-5pm (summer) or 10am-3pm (winter) and five public hides. Toilets and information.
Public transport: Arriva 420 and 423 bus services.
Habitat: Ponds created from former opencast coal mine. Areas of woodland and grassland.
Key birds: Roseate Terns sometimes join commoner species in late summer. Waders and migrants on passage. *Winter*: Bewick's Swan, Shoveler, Lapwing and Purple Sandpiper.
Other notable flora and fauna: A variety of invertebrates, including butterflies, dragonflies and amphibians such as great crested newt.
Contact: Northumberland WT – 0191 284 6884. E-mail: mail@northwt.org.uk

7. KIELDER FOREST

Forestry Commission
Location: NY 632 934. Kielder Castle is situated at N end of Kielder Water, NW of Bellingham.
Access: Forest open all year. Toll charge on 12 mile forest drive. Visitor centre has limited opening in winter.
Facilities: Visitor centre, exhibition, toilets, shop, access for disabled, licensed café. Local facilities include youth hostel, camp site, pub and garage.
Public transport: Bus: 814, 815, 816 from

Hexham and seasonal service 714 from Newcastle.
Habitat: Commercial woodland, mixed and broadleaved trees.
Key birds: *Spring/summer*: Goshawk, Chiffchaff, Willow Warbler, Redstart, Siskin. *Winter*: Crossbill.
Resident: Jay, Dipper, Great Spotted Woodpecker, Tawny Owl, Song Thrush, Goldcrest.
Other notable flora and fauna: Impressive display of northern marsh orchids at entrance to Kielder Castle.
Contact: Forestry Commission, 01434 220 242. e-mail: richard.gilchrist@forestry.gsi.gov.uk

8. LINDISFARNE NNR

Natural England (Northumbria Team).
Location: NU 090 430. Island access lies two miles E of A1 at Beal, eight miles S of Berwick-on-Tweed.
Access: Open all hours. Some restricted access (refuges). Coach parking available on Holy Island.
Facilities: Toilets, visitor centre in village. Hide on island (new hide with disabled access at Fenham-le-Moor). Self-guided trail on island.
Public transport: Irregular bus service to Holy Island, mainly in summer. Main bus route follows mainland boundary of site north-south.
Habitat: Dunes, sand and mudflats.
Key birds: *Passage and winter*: Wildfowl and waders, including pale-bellied Brent Goose, Long-tailed Duck and Whooper Swan. Rare migrants.
Contact: Phil Davey, Site Manager, Beal Station, Berwick-on-Tweed, TD15 2PB. 01289 381 470.

OTHER SITES

Full details in previous editions, (year indicated in brackets).
A. Briarwood Banks – Northumberland WT, 01912 846 884 (05).
B. Cocquet Island – RSPB, 01912 813 366 (04).
C. Grindon Lough – Northumberland WT, 01912 846 884 (04).
D. Holywell Pond – Northumberland WT, 01912 846 884 (04).
E. Newton Pool – National Trust, 01670 774 691 (06).
F. Thrunton Wood – 01904 696 300 (04).

Nottinghamshire

1. ATTENBOROUGH GRAVEL PITS

Nottinghamshire Wildlife Trust.
Location: SK 523 343. On A6005, seven miles SW of Nottingham alongside River Trent. Signposted from main road.
Access: Open at all times. Dogs on leads (guide dogs only in visitor centre). Paths suitable for disabled access. Coaches welcome by prior appointment.
Facilities: Education and visitor centre with café and shop, all accessible to wheelchair users. Nature trail (leaflet from Notts WT), one hide.
Public transport: Railway station at Attenborough – reserve is five mins walk away, visitor centre a further 10 minutes. Rainbow 5 bus service between Nottingham Broadmarsh and Derby bus station runs regularly throughout day. Alight at Chilwell Retail Park and walk 500m along Barton Lane.
Habitat: Disused, flooded gravel workings with associated marginal and wetland vegetation.
Key birds: *Spring/summer*: Breeding Common Tern (40-plus pairs), Reed Warbler, Black Tern regular (bred once). *Winter*: Wildfowl (including Bittern), Grey Heron colony, adjacent Cormorant roost.
Contact: Attenborough Nature Centre, Barton Lane, Attenborough, Nottingham NG9 6DY. 01159 721 777. www.attenboroughnaturecentre.co.uk
e-mail: enquiries@attenboroughnaturecentre.co.uk

2. BESTHORPE NATURE RESERVE

Nottinghamshire Wildlife Trust.
Location: SK 817 640 and SK813 646 (access points). Take A1133 N of Newark. Turn into Trent Lane S of Besthorpe village, reserve entrances second turn on L and R turn at end of lane (at River Trent).
Access: Open access to two hides (one with disabled access from car park at present). No access to SSSI meadows. Limited access to areas grazed with sheep. Dogs on leads.
Facilities: No toilets (pubs etc in Besthorpe village), two hides, paths, nature trail (northern part).
Public transport: Buses (numbers 22, 67, 68, 6, S7L) run by Marshalls, Lincs, Road Car and Travel Wright along A1133 to Besthorpe village (0.75 mile away). Tel: 0115 924 0000 or 01777 710 550 for information.
Habitat: Gravel pit with islands, SSSI neutral grasslands, hedges, reedbed, etc.

Key birds: *Spring/summer*: Breeding Grey Heron, Cormorant, Little Ringed Plover, Kingfisher, Grasshopper Warbler. *Winter*: Large numbers of ducks (Pochard, Tufted Duck, Pintail, Wigeon) and Peregrine.
Contact: Trust HQ, 01159 588 242.
e-mail: info@nottswt.co.uk
www.wildlifetrust.org.uk/nottinghamshire

3. BUNNY OLD WOOD WEST

Nottinghamshire Wildlife Trust.
Location: Limited parking off the A60 at SK 579 283. Please do not obstruct access. Further footpath access is at SK 584 293 off Wysall Lane.
Access: Open all year. No coach parking available.
Facilities: None
Public transport: None.
Habitat: Mixed woodland.
Key birds: *All year*: Usual woodland species, all three woodpeckers, Tawny and Little Owls. *Spring/summer*: Usual visitors, including Blackcap. Possible Brambling and Hawfinch. Also good for butterflies.
Contact: Trust HQ, 01159 588 242.
e-mail: info@nottswt.co.uk
www.wildlifetrust.org.uk/nottinghamshire

4. COLWICK COUNTRY PARK

Nottingham City Council.
Location: SK 610 395. Off A612 three miles E of Nottingham city centre.
Access: Open at all times, but no vehicle access after dusk or before 7am.
Facilities: Nature trails. Sightings log book in Fishing Lodge.
Public transport: Call park office for advice
Habitat: Lakes, pools, woodlands, grasslands, new plantations, River Trent.
Key birds: *Summer*: Warblers, Hobby, Common Tern (15+ pairs). *Winter*: Wildfowl and gulls. Passage migrants.
Contact: Head Ranger, The Fishing Lodge, Colwick Country Park, River Road, Colwick, Nottingham NG4 2DW. 01159 870 785.
www.colwick2000.freeserve.co.uk

5. LOUND GRAVEL PITS

Tarmac, Hanson, Nottinghamshire Wildlife Trust.
Location: SK 690 856. Two miles N of Retford off A638 adjacent to Sutton and Lound villages.
Access: Open at all times. Use public rights of way only (use OS Map Sheet No 120 - 1:50,000 Landranger Series).

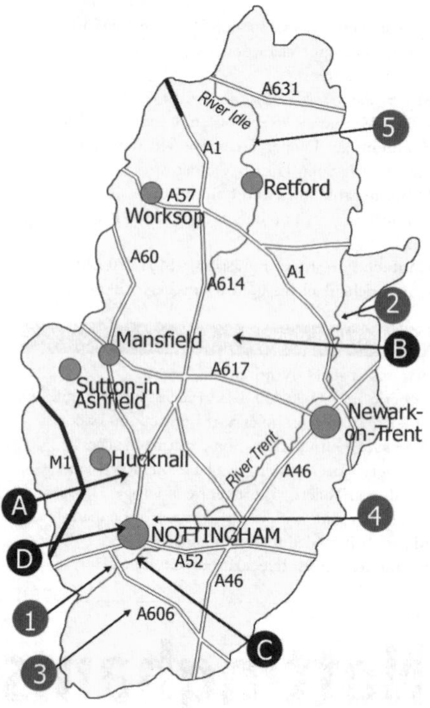

Facilities: Public viewing platform/screen off Chainbridge lane (overlooking Chainbridge NR Scrape).
Public transport: Buses from Bawtry (Church Street), Retford bus station and Worksop (Hardy Street) on services 27/27A/83/83A/84 to Lound Village crossroads (Chainbridge Lane).
Habitat: Working sand and gravel quarries, restored gravel workings, woodland, reedbeds, fishing ponds, river valley, in-filled and disused fly ash tanks, farmland, scrub, willow plantations, open water.
Key birds: Over 235 species recorded. *Summer*: Gulls, terns, wildfowl and waders. Passage waders, terns, passerines and raptors. *Winter*: Wildfowl, gulls, raptors. Rarities have inc. Ring-billed Gull, Caspian, White-winged Black, Gull-billed and Whiskered Terns, Manx Shearwater, Lesser Scaup, Green-winged and Blue-winged Teal, Richard's Pipit, Baird's, Pectoral and Buff-breasted Sandpiper, Long-billed Dowitcher, Killdeer, Spoonbill, Bluethroat, Nightingale, Snow Bunting, Shore Lark, Great Skua.
Contact: Lound Bird Club, Gary Hobson (Secretary),

23 Milne Road, Bircotes, Doncaster, South Yorks DN11 8AL. 01302 743 654.
e-mail: loundbirdclub@tiscali.co.uk
www.loundbirdclub.piczo.com

OTHER SITES

Full details in previous editions, (year indicated in brackets).

A. Bestwood Country Park – Nottingham CC, 01159 823 823 (05).
B. Dukes Wood – Notts WT, 01159 588 242 (04).
C. Wilwell Farm – Notts WT, 01159 588 242 (04).
D. Wollaton Park – Wollaton Hall, 01159 153 920 (06).

Oxfordshire

1. ASTON ROWANT NNR

Natural England (Thames and Chilterns).
Location: SU 731 966. From the M40 Lewknor interchange at J6, travel NE for a short distance and turn R onto A40. After 1.5 miles at the top of the hill, turn R and R again into a narrow, metalled lane. Drive to car park, which is signposted from the A40.
Access: Open all year. Some wheelchair access, please contact site manager for more information.
Facilities: On-site parking, easy access path to viewpoint, seats, interpretation panels.
Public transport: Regular bus services to Stokenchurch, 2km S of reserve. Red Rose Travel bus goes to Aston Rowant village (call 01296 747 926).
Habitat: Chalk grassland, chalk scrub, beech woodland.
Key birds: *Spring/summer*: Blackcap, warblers, Turtle Dove, Tree Pipit. *Winter*: Possible Short-eared Owl, Brambling, Siskin, winter thrushes. *Passage*: Whinchat, Wheatear, Ring Ouzel. *All year*: Red Kite, Buzzard, Sparrowhawk, Woodcock, Little and Tawny Owls, Green and Great Spotted Woodpeckers, Sky Lark, Meadow Pipit, Marsh Tit.
Other notable flora and fauna: Rich chalk grassland flora, including Chiltern gentian clustered bellflower, frog, bee pyramidal and fragrant orchids. Good range of less common butterflies.
Contact: Aston Rowant Reserve Office, Aston Hill, Lewknor, Watlington OX49 5SG. 01844 351 833. www.naturalengland.org.uk

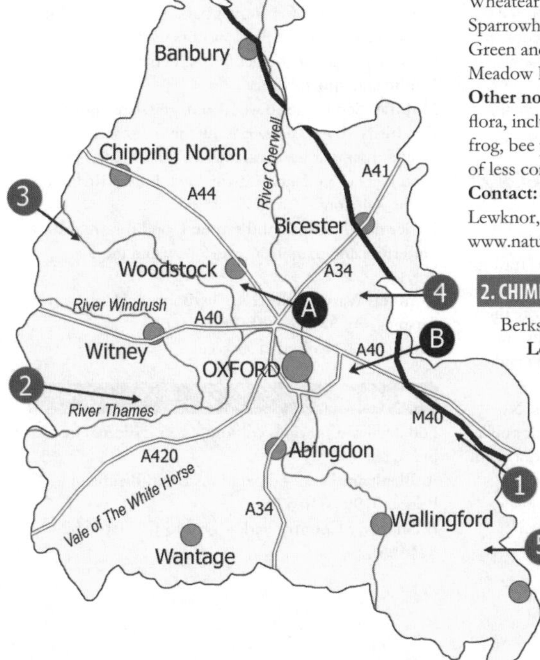

2. CHIMNEY MEADOWS

Berks, Bucks & Oxon Wildlife Trust.
Location: SP 353 014. Take A4095 from Witney to Bampton or A420 from Oxford to Buckland. The reserve is on an unclassified road between Bampton and Buckland. Head N from Tadpole Bridge, turn R after half mile. Go 1.25 miles E and turn R towards Chimney. Car park is on L at first bend – do not drive beyond it into hamlet.
Access: Open all year but limited access. Dogs on leads to avoid disturbance to breeding and wintering waders. Leaflets

available from dispenser at car park.
Facilities: Car park, two hides, leaflets.
Public transport: None.
Habitat: Six meadows next to the River Thames and 500 acres of recently-acquired farmland with meadows and wet grassland.
Key birds: *Spring/summer*: Whitethroat, Willow Warbler, Chiffchaff, Sedge Warbler. Curlew, Redshank. *Winter*: Waders, Snipe, Short-eared Owl.
Contact: BBOWT, Chimney Meadows Nature Reserve, Chimney, Nr Bampton, Oxford OX18 2EH, 01865 775 476.

3. FOXHOLES RESERVE

Berks, Bucks & Oxon Wildlife Trust.
Location: SP 254 206. Head N out of Burford on the A424 towards Stow-on-theWold. Take third turning on R. Head NE on unclassified road to Bruern for 3.5km. Just before reaching Bruern, turn L along track following Cocksmoor Copse. After 750m, park in car park on R just before some farm buildings.
Access: Open all year. Please keep to the paths.
Facilities: Car park, footpaths. Can be very muddy in winter.
Public transport: None.
Habitat: River, woodland, wet meadow.
Key birds: *Spring/summer*: Nightingale, Yellow Wagtail, possible Redstart, Wood Warbler, Spotted Flycatcher. *Winter*: Redwing, Fieldfare, Woodcock. *All year*: Little Owl, all three woodpeckers, possible Hawfinch.
Contact: BBOWT, The Lodge, 1 Armstrong Road, Littlemore, Oxford OX4 4XT. 01865 77 5476.

4. OTMOOR NATURE RESERVE

RSPB (Central England Office).
Location: SP 570 126. Car park seven miles NE of Oxford city centre. From B4027, take turn to Horton-cum-Studley, then first L to Beckley. After 0.67 miles at the bottom of a short hill turn R (before the Abingdon Arms public house). After 200 yards, turn L into Otmoor Lane. Reserve car park is at the end of the lane (approx one mile).
Access: Open dawn-dusk. No permits or fees. No dogs allowed on the reserve visitor trail (except public rights of way). In wet conditions, the visitor route can be muddy and wellingtons are essential.
Facilities: Limited. Small car park with cycle racks, visitor trail (3 mile round trip) and two screened viewpoints. The reserve is not accessible by coach and is unsuitable for large groups.
Public transport: None.
Habitat: Wet grassland, reedbed and open water.
Key birds: *Summer*: Breeding birds include Cetti's and Grasshopper Warblers, Lapwing, Redshank, Curlew, Snipe, Yellow Wagtail, Shoveler, Gadwall, Pochard, Tufted Duck, Little and Great Crested Grebes. Hobby breeds locally. *Winter*: Wigeon, Teal, Shoveler, Pintail, Gadwall, Pochard, Tufted Duck, Lapwing, Golden Plover, Hen Harrier, Peregrine, Merlin. *Autumn and spring passage*: Marsh Harrier, Short-eared Owl, Greenshank, Green Sandpiper, Common Sandpiper, Spotted Redshank and occasional Black Tern.
Contact: RSPB , c/o Folly Farm, Common Road, Bexley OX3 9YR. 01865 351 163. www.rspb.org.uk

5. WARBURG RESERVE, THE

Berks, Bucks & Oxon Wildlife Trust.
Location: SU 720 879. Leave Henley-on-Thames NW on A4130. Turn R at the end of the Fair Mile onto B480. L fork in Middle Assendon. After 1 mile, follow road round to R at grassy triangle, then on for 1 mile. Car park is on R.
Access: Open all year – visitor centre opens 9am-5pm. Please keep dogs on a lead. In some areas, only guide dogs allowed.
Facilities: Visitor Centre, car park, hide with disabled access, nature trail, leaflets. Visitors with disabilities and groups should contact the warden before visits.
Public transport: None.
Habitat: Scrub, mixed woodland, grassland, ponds.
Key birds: *Spring/summer*: Whitethroat, Lesser Whitethroat. *All year*: Sparrowhawk, Red Kite, Treecreeper, Nuthatch, Tawny Owl. *Winter*: Redpoll, Siskin, sometimes Crossbill, Woodcock.
Other notable flora and fauna: Good for orchids, butterflies and mammals (roe, fallow and muntjac deer).
Contact: Warburg Reserve, Bix Bottom, Henley-on-Thames, Oxfordshire, 01491 642 001.
e-mail: bbowtwarburg@cix.co.uk

OTHER SITES

Full details in previous editions, (year indicated in brackets).
A. Blenheim Park – Operations Dept, Blenheim Palace, 01993 810 570 (07).
B. Shotover Country Park – Oxford CC, 01865 249 811 (06).

Shropshire

1. BUSHMOOR COPPICE

Shropshire Wildlife Trust
Location: SO 430 880. Head S from Church Stretton and take first R off A49 signed Bushmoor.
Access: Park in Busmoor village and follow track leading from right-angled bend. Follow green lane to gate and carry onto wood along field margin.
Facilities: None.
Public transport: No information available.
Habitat: Small mixed woodland and scrub.
Key birds: *Spring/summer:* Migrant warblers and flycatchers, plus common woodland species.
Other notable flora and fauna: Golden saxifrage, bluebells and yellow archangel. Dormouse.
Contact: Shropshire WT – 01743 284 280.

2. CHELMARSH BIRD RESERVE

South Staffordshire Water/Shropshire Wildlife Trust.
Location: SO 726 881. Reservoir lies next to the reservoir, 6km south of Bridgnorth, off the B4555. From Chelmarsh village head S towards Highley. Turn L at Sutton and L at the T-junction. From the car park, walk to the other end of the reservoir to the hides.
Access: Open all year. No public car park at Dinney Farm.
Facilities: Car park.
Public transport: None.
Habitat: Reservoir, wader scrape, reedbed.
Key birds: *Winter:* Wildfowl, inc Pintail, Smew, geese, swans, Water Rail. Large gull roost on reservoir. *Spring/summer:* Reed and Sedge Warblers, Reed Bunting. *Passage:* Possible Osprey.
Contact: Shropshire Wildlife Trust, 193 Abbey Foregate, Shrewsbury SY2 6AH. 01743 284 280 Fax 01743 284 281.

3. CLUNTON COPPICE

Shropshire Wildlife Trust.
Location: SO 343 806. From Craven Arms, take B4368 to Clunton village, go straight over bridge and up the hill to small car park just before reserve sign.
Access: Open at all times. Access along road and public rights of way only.
Facilities: Limited parking in small quarry entrance on R, or opposite The Crown pub.
Public transport: Not known.
Habitat: Sessile oak coppice. Good for ferns, mosses and fungi.
Key birds: Buzzard and Raven regular. *Spring/summer:* Wide range of woodland birds, inc. Redstart, Wood Warbler and Pied Flycatcher, Woodcock.
Contact: Trust HQ, 01743 284 280.
e-mail: shropshirewt@cix.co.uk

4. EARL'S HILL

Shropshire Wildlife Trust
Location: SJ 409 048. Near Minsterley, SW of Shrewsbury. Turn off A488 at Pontesford along lane by Rea Valley Tractors. Park in Forestry Commisson car park 700 yards further on.
Access: Follow green route for easier walking. Purple route leads to summit. Park in lane leading to reserve but do not block FC vehicles.
Facilities: None.
Public transport: No information available.
Habitat: Steep-sided volcanic hill, scree slopes and crags, topped by Iron Age fort. Ancient woodland on eastern slopes.
Key birds: *Spring:* Migrants species such as Redstart, Pied Flycatcher and warblers. Dipper and Grey

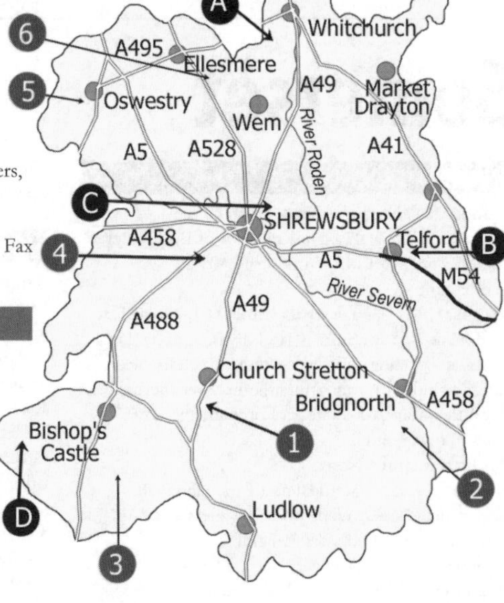

Wagtail on stream. Green Woodpecker common on open grassland.
Other notable flora and fauna: More than 30 species of butterfly recorded, plus many wildflowers. Yellow meadow ant.
Contact: Shropshire WT – 01743 284 280.

5. LLYNCLYS COMMON

Shropshire Wildlife Trust.
Location: SJ 273 237. SSW of Oswestry. Park in layby on A495 at SJ277242, opposite Dolgoch and walk up Turner's Lane.
Access: Open at all times.
Facilities: None.
Public transport: None.
Habitat: Old mixed limestone sward with some woodland and scrub, small pond.
Key birds: Sparrowhawk, Green Woodpecker, Goldcrest, large warbler population. Occasional Peregrine, Buzzard. Eight species of orchid.
Contact: Shropshire Wildlife Trust, 193 Abbey Foregate, Shrewsbury, Shropshire SY2 6AH. 01743 284 280. e-mail: shropshirewt@cix.co.uk www.shropshirewildlifetrust.org.uk

6. WOOD LANE

Shropshire Wildlife Trust.
Location: SJ 421 331. Turn off A528 at Spurnhill, 1 mile SE of Ellesmere. Car park is .75 miles down on R.
Access: Open at all times. Apply to Trust for permit to use hides. Reserve accessible to people of all abilities.
Facilities: Car parks clearly signed. Hides (access by permit).
Public transport: None.
Habitat: Gravel pit restored by Tudor Griffiths.
Key birds: *Summer*: Breeding Sand Martin, Lapwing, Little Ringed Plover and Tree Sparrow. Osprey platforms erected to tempt over-flying birds. Popular staging post for waders (inc. Redshank, Greenshank, Ruff, Dunlin, Little Stint, Green and Wood Sandpiper). *Winter*: Lapwing and Curlew.
Other notable flora and fauna: Hay meadow plants.
Contact: Shropshire Wildlife Trust, 01743 284 280. e-mail: shropshirewt@cix.co.uk

OTHER SITES

Full details in previous editions, (year indicated in brackets).
A. Fenn's Whixall & Bettisfield Mosses NNR – Natural England, 01948 880 362 (06).
B. Granville Nature Reserve – Salop WT, 01743 284 280 (04).
C. Monkmoor Pool – Salop WT, 01743 284 280 (05).
D. Rhos Fiddle – Salop WT, 01743 284 280 (04).

Somerset

1. BRIDGWATER BAY NNR

Natural England (Somerset & Dorset Team).
Location: ST 270 470. Nine miles N of Bridgwater. Take J23 or 24 off M5. Turn N off A39 at Cannington.
Access: Hides open every day except Christmas Day. Permits needed for Steart Island (by boat only). Dogs on leads – grazing animals/nesting birds. Disabled access to hides by arrangement, other areas accessible.
Facilities: Car park at Steart. Footpath approx 0.5 miles to tower and hides.
Public transport: None.
Habitat: Estuary, intertidal mudflats, saltmarsh.
Key birds: *All year*: Wildfowl and waders, birds of prey. *Spring/autumn*: Passage migrants.
Contact: The Site Manager, Natural England (Somerset and Dorset Team), Roughmoor, Bishop's Hull, Taunton, Somerset, TA1 5AA. 01823 283 211. www.naturalengland.org.uk

2. CHEW VALLEY LAKE

Avon Wildlife Trust, Bristol Water Plc.
Location: ST 570 600. Reservoir (partly a Trust reserve) between Chew Stoke and West Harptree, crossed by A368 and B3114, nine miles S of Bristol.
Access: Permit for access to hides (five at Chew, two at Blagdon). Best roadside viewing from causeways at Herriott's Bridge (nature reserve) and Herons Green Bay. Day, half-year and year permits from Bristol Water, Recreation Department, Woodford Lodge, Chew Stoke, Bristol BS18 8SH. Tel/Fax 01275 332339. Parking for coaches available.
Facilities: Hides.
Public transport: Travel line, 0870 6082 608.

Habitat: Reservoir.
Key birds: *Autumn/winter*: Concentrations of wildfowl (inc. Bewick's Swan, Goldeneye, Smew, Ruddy Duck), gull roost (inc. regular Mediterranean, occasional Ring-billed). Migrant waders and terns (inc. Black). Recent rarities inc. Blue-winged Teal, Spoonbill, Alpine Swift, Citrine Wagtail, Little Bunting, Ring-necked Duck, Kumlien's Gull.
Contact: Avon Wildlife Trust HQ or Bristol Water Recreation Dept, Woodford Lodge, Chew Stoke, Bristol, BS40 8XH. 01275 332 339.
e-mail: mail@avonwildlifetrust.org.uk
www.avonwildlifetrust.org.uk

3. GREYLAKE

RSPB (West Sedgemoor office)
Location: ST 399 346. Off A361 Taunton to Glastonbury road between Othery and Greinton.
Access: Open all year, dawn to dusk, free admission. No dogs, apart from guide-dogs. Wheelchair users can access a 700 metre-long boardwalk and viewing hide.
Facilities: Surfaced nature trail, interpretive signs. No toilets on site.
Public transport: No information available.
Habitat: A large wet grassland reserve bought by RSPB in 2003. Formerly arable farmland.
Key birds: *Spring/summer*: Breeding Snipe, Lapwing, Sky Lark, Yellow Wagtail, Kingfisher. Grey Heron, Little Egret. *Autumn*: Large Starling roost, Green Sandpiper, waders on passage. *Winter*: Wildfowl, waders, Peregrine.
Other notable flora and fauna: Roe deer, water vole, otter, dragonflies including four-spotted chaser.
Contact: RSPB West Sedgemoor office – 01458 252 805.

4. HAM WALL

RSPB (West Sedgemoor office)
Location: ST 449 397. W of Glastonbury. From A39 turn N in Ashcott and follow road onto the moor. After three miles pass Church Farm Horticultural building. Shortly after, at metal bridge, reserve is opposite side of road to Shapwick Heath NNR.
Access: Open all year. Dogs only on public footpaths and disused railway line. Wheelchair users can access viewing areas from main track. Other rougher tracks cover 3.8 miles.
Facilities: Two open-air viewing platforms, four roofed viewing screens. Part-time education officer available for school visits.
Habitat: Newly-created 200-plus hectare wetland, including region's largest reedbed.
Key birds: *Spring/summer*: Cetti's Warbler, Water Rail. Bittern, warblers, Hobby, Barn Owl. *Autumn*: Migrant thrushes, Lesser Redpoll, Siskin, Kingfisher, Bearded Tit. *Winter*: Millions of Starlings roost, plus large flocks of ducks, Bittern, Little Egret, Peregrine, Merlin, Short-eared Owl.
Other notable flora and fauna: Otter, water vole, dragonflies, butterflies.
Contact: RSPB West Sedgemoor office, 01458 252 805.

5. HORNER WOOD NATURE RESERVE

National Trust
Location: SS 897 454. From Minehead, take A39 W to a minor road 0.8km E of Porlock signed to Horner. Park in village car park.
Access: Open all year. Car parking in Horner village, extensive footpath system.
Facilities: Tea-room and toilets. Walks leaflets available from Holnicote Estate office and Porlock visitor centre. Interpretation boards in car parks.
Public transport: Bus: Porlock.
Habitat: Oak woodland, moorland.
Key birds: *Spring/summer*: Wood Warbler, Pied Flycatcher, Redstart, Stonechat, Whinchat, Tree Pipit,

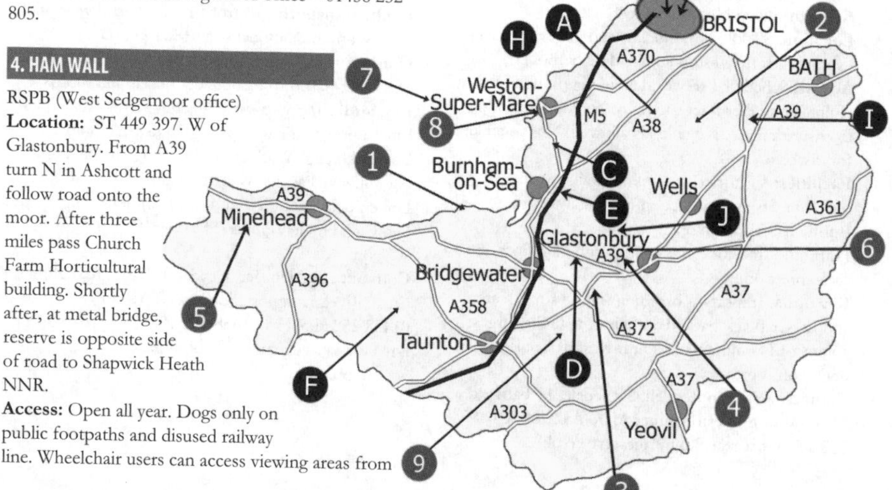

Dartford Warbler possible. *All year*: Dipper, Grey Wagtail, woodpeckers, Buzzard, Sparrowhawk.
Other notable flora and fauna: Silver-washed fritillary in July.
Contact: National Trust, Holnicote Estate, Selworthy, Minehead, Somerset TA24 8TJ. 01643 862 452. e-mail: holnicote@nationaltrust.org.uk www.nationaltrust.org.uk

6. SHAPWICK HEATH NNR

Natural England (Somerset & Dorset Team).
Location: ST 426 415. Situated between Shapwick and Westhay, near Glastonbury. The nearest car park is 400 metres away at the Peat Moors centre, south of Westhay.
Access: Open all year. Disabled access to displays, hides. No dogs.
Facilities: Network of paths, hides, elevated boardwalk. Toilets, leaflets and refreshments available at the Peat Moors centre.
Public transport: None.
Habitat: Traditionally managed herb-rich grassland, ferny wet woodland, fen, scrub, ditches, open water, reedswamp and reedbed.
Key birds: *All year*: Ducks and waders. *Summer*: Hobby, Cuckoo, Cetti's Warbler. *Winter*: Starling roost.
Contact: The Manager, Natural England (Somerset and Dorset Team), Roughmoor, Bishop's Hull, Taunton, Somerset, TA1 5AA. 01458 860 120. email: somerset@naturalengland.org.uk

7. STEEP HOLM ISLAND

Kenneth Allsop Memorial Trust.
Location: ST 229 607. Small island in Severn River, five miles from Weston-super-Mare harbour.
Access: Scheduled service depending on tides, via Knightstone Pier ferry. Advance booking necessary to ensure a place. No animals allowed. Not suitable for disabled.
Facilities: Visitor centre, toilets, trails, basic refreshments and sales counter, postal service.
Public transport: None.
Habitat: Limestone grassland, scrub, rare flora, small sycamore wood.
Key birds: Important breeding station for Greater and Lesser Black-backed and Herring Gulls, largest colony of Cormorants in south-west of England. On migration routes.
Contact: Mrs Joan Rendell, Stonedale, 11 Fairfield Close, Milton, Weston-super-Mare BS22 8EA. 01934 632 307. www.steepholm.freeserve.co.uk

8. WALBOROUGH LNR

Avon Wildlife Trust.
Location: ST 315 579. On S edge of Weston-super-Mare at mouth of River Axe.
Access: Access from Uphill boatyard. Special access trail suitable for less able visitors. Parking for coach available.
Facilities: None.
Public transport: Travel line, 0870 6082 608.
Habitat: Limestone grassland, scrub, saltmarsh, estuary.
Key birds: The Axe Estuary holds good numbers of migrant and wintering wildfowl (inc. Teal, Shelduck) and waders (inc. Black-tailed Godwit, Lapwing, Golden Plover, Dunlin, Redshank). Other migrants inc. Little Stint, Curlew Sandpiper, Ruff. Little Egret occurs each year, mostly in late summer.
Contact: Avon Wildlife Trust, 01179 177 270; e-mail: mail@avonwildlifetrust.org.uk www.avonwildlifetrust.org.uk

9. WEST SEDGEMOOR

RSPB (South West England Office).
Location: ST 361 238. Entrance down by-road off A378 Taunton-Langport road, one mile E of Fivehead.
Access: Access at all times to woodland car park and heronry hide. Coach parking in lay-by across main road. Heronry hide and part of the woodland trail are wheelchair accessible.
Facilities: Heronry hide, two nature trails: Woodland Trail and Scarp trail (link to public footpaths), disabled parking area.
Public transport: Bus from Taunton to Fivehead. First Southern National Ltd 01823 272 033.
Habitat: Semi-natural ancient oak woodland and wet grassland. Part of the Somerset Levels and Moors.
Key birds: *Spring/summer*: Breeding Grey Heron, Little Egret, Curlew, Lapwing, Redshank, Snipe, Buzzard, Sedge Warbler, Yellow Wagtail, Sky Lark, Nightingale. Passage Whimbrel and Hobby. *Winter*: Large flocks of waders and wildfowl (including Lapwing, Golden Plover, Shoveler, Pintail, Teal and Wigeon).
Contact: Site Manager, Dewlands Farm, Redhill, Curry Rivel, Langport, Somerset TA10 0PH. 01458 252 805, Fax 01458 252 184. e-mail: west.sedgemoor@rspb.org.uk www.rspb.org.uk

OTHER SITES

Full details in previous editions, (year indicated in brackets).

A. Blagdon Lake – Bristol Waterworks, 01275 332 339 (07).

B. Brandon Hill Nature Park – Avon WT, 01179 177 270 (06).

C. Brean Down – National Trust, 01934 844 518 (07).

D. Catcott Lows – National Trust, 01934 844 518 (04).

E. Hankridge Farm – Somerset WT, 01823 652 400 (04).

F. Langford Heathfield – Somerset WT, 01823 652 400 (07).

G. Leigh Woods – National Trust, 01936 429 336 (06).

H. Puxton Moor – Avon WT, 01179 177 270 (04).

I. Stephen's Vale – Avon WT, 01179 177 270 (04).

J. Westhay Moor NNR – Somerset WT, 01823 652 400 (04).

K. Willsbridge Mill – Avon WT, 01179 177 270 (05).

Staffordshire

1. BELVIDE RESERVOIR

British Waterways Board and West Midland Bird Club.

Location: SJ865102. Near Brewood, 7 miles NW of Wolverhampton.

Access: Access only by permit from the West Midland Bird Club.

Facilities: Hides.

Public transport: Bus to Kiddermore Green – eight minute walk. Traveline – 0870 6082608.

Habitat: Canal feeder reservoir with marshy margins and gravel islands.

Key birds: Important breeding, moulting and wintering ground for wildfowl), including Ruddy Duck, Goldeneye and Goosander), passage terns and waders. Night roost for gulls.

Contact: Barbara Oakley, 147 Worlds End Lane, Quinton, Birmingham B32 1JX; e-mail: permits@westmidlandbirdclub.com www.westmidlandbirdclub.com/belvide

2. BLITHFIELD RESERVOIR

South Staffs Waterworks Co.

Location: SK 058 237. View from causeway on B5013 (Rugeley/Uttoxeter).

Access: Access to reservoir and hides by permit from West Midland Bird Club.

Facilities: None.

Public transport: None.

Habitat: Large reservoir.

Key birds: *Winter*: Good populations of wildfowl (inc. Bewick's Swan, Goosander, Goldeneye, Ruddy Duck), large gull roost (can inc. Glaucous, Iceland). Passage terns (Common, Arctic, Black) and waders, esp. in autumn (Little Stint, Curlew Sandpiper, Spotted Redshank regular).

Contact: Barbara Oakley, 147 Worlds End Lane, Quinton, Birmingham B32 1JX; e-mail: permits@westmidlandbirdclub.com

3. BRANSTON WATER PARK

East Staffordshire Borough Council.

Location: SK 217 207. Follow brown tourist sign from A38 N. No access from A38 S - head to the Barton-under-Needwood exit and return N. The park is 0.5 miles S of A5121 Burton-upon-Trent exit.

Access: Open all year, flat wheelchair accessible stoned path, all round the lake.

Facilities: Disabled toilets, picnic area (some wheelchair accessible tables), modern children's play area.

Public transport: Contact ESBC Tourist information 01283 508 111.

Habitat: Reedbed, willow carr woodland, scrub, meadow area.

Key birds: *Spring/summer*: Reed Warbler, Cuckoo, Reed Bunting. Important roost for Swallow and Sand Martin. *Winter*: Waders, Little Ringed Plover occasionally, Pied Wagtail roost.

Contact: East Staffordshire Borough Council, Midland Grain Warehouse, Derby Street, Burton-on-Trent, Staffordshire DE14 2JJ. 01283 508 657; Fax 01283 508 571.

4. COOMBES VALLEY

RSPB (North West England Office).

Location: SK 005 530. Four miles from Leek along A523 between Leek and Ashbourne and 0.5 miles down unclassified road – signposted.

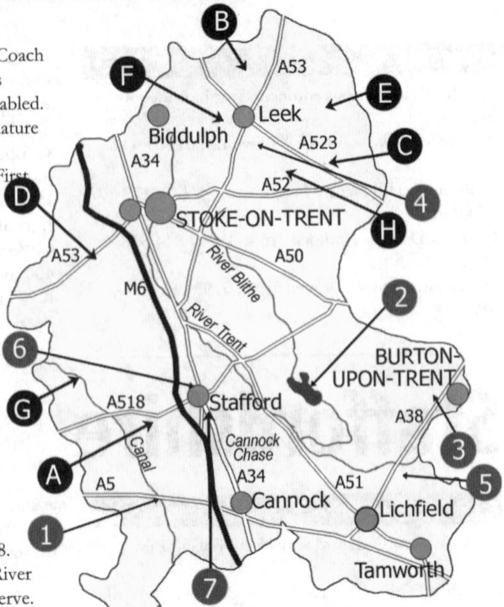

Access: Open daily – no charge. Free parking. Coach groups welcome by prior arrangement. No dogs allowed. Most of the trails are unsuitable for disabled.
Facilities: Visitor centre, toilets, two miles of nature trail, one hide.
Public transport: Contact local bus company First PMT on 01782 207 999.
Habitat: Sessile oak woodland, unimproved pasture and meadow.
Key birds: *Spring*: Pied Flycatcher, Redstart, Wood Warbler. Jan-Mar: Displaying birds of prey.
Contact: Jarrod Sneyd, Six Oaks Farm, Bradnop, Leek, Staffs ST13 7EU. 01538 384 017. www.rspb.org.uk

5. CROXALL LAKES

Staffordshire Wildlife Trust.
Location: SK 188 139. From Rugeley follow the A513 passing through Kings Bromley and Alrewas. Continue along this road over the A38. After approx one mile, you will pass over the River Tame, which forms the W boundary of the reserve. The entrance to the reserve is the second track on L.
Access: Open all year. Gravel track to the N of the reserve.
Facilities: Interpretation boards, two bird hides, parking and access to be improved.
Public transport: None.
Habitat: Two lakes, wader scrapes, pools, floodplain grassland.
Key birds: *Winter*: Teal, Wigeon, Smew. *Spring/summer*: Breeding Lapwing, Redshank, Little Ringed Plover, Oystercatcher.
Contact: Trust HQ, 01889 880 100.
e-mail: info@staffs-wildlife.org.uk
www.staffs-wildlife.org.uk

6. DOXEY MARSHES

Staffordshire Wildlife Trust.
Location: SJ 903 250. In Stafford. Parking 0.25 miles off M6 J14/A513 Eccleshall Road or walk from town centre.
Access: Open at all times. Dogs on leads. Disabled access being improved. Coach and car parking off Wooton Drive.
Facilities: One hide, three viewing platforms, two are accessible to wheelchairs.
Public transport: Walk from town centre via Sainsbury's.
Habitat: Marsh, pools, reedbeds, hedgerows, reed sweet-grass swamp.
Key birds: *Spring/summer*: Breeding Snipe, Lapwing, Redshank, Little Ringed Plover, Oystercatcher, warblers, buntings, Sky Lark, Water Rail. *Winter*: Snipe, wildfowl, thrushes, Short-eared Owl. Passage waders, vagrants.
Other notable flora and fauna: Otter, noctule bat, musk beetle.
Contact: Trust HQ, 01889 880 100.
e-mail: info@staffs-wildlife.org.uk

7. RADFORD MEADOWS

Staffordshire Wildlife Trust.
Location: SJ 938 216. South of Radford Bridge on A34, Stafford and alongside Staffs & Worcs Canal.
Access: View reserve from canal towpath only (access from A34 between bridge and BMW garage or via Hazelstrine Lane (over canal bridge). On-site visits restricted to special events only. No formal carpark.
Facilities: Trust intends to erect information boards along towpath.
Public transport: Site is close to National Cycle Network routes (www.sustrans.co.uk).
Habitat: 104 acres of lowland wet grassland, forming part of River Penk floodplain.
Key birds: Largest heronry in county (more than 20 pairs of Grey Heron). Breeding Sky Lark, Lapwing, Snipe and Reed Bunting. *Winter*: Wildfowl, Kingfisher, Buzzard.
Other notable flora and fauna: Several veteran black poplar trees.

Contact: Staffordshire Wildlife Trust – 01889 880 100. Leaflet about birding the Trent Valley available on request.

OTHER SITES

Full details in previous editions, (year indicated in brackets).

A. Allimore Green Common – Staffs WT, 01889 880 100 (05).

B. Black Brook – Staffs WT, 01889 880 100 (06).

C. Brown End Quarry – Staffs WT, 01889 880 100 (06).

D. Burnt Wood – Staffs WT, 01889 880 100 (06).

E. Castern Wood – Staffs WT, 01889 880 100 (04).

F. Longsdon Woods – Staffs Moorland District Council, 01538 483 577 (06).

G. Loynton Moss – Staffs WT, 01889 880 100 (05).

H. Swineholes Wood – Staffs WT, 01889 880 100 (05).

Suffolk

1. CASTLE MARSHES

Suffolk Wildlife Trust.

Location: TM 471 904. Head E on the A146 from Beccles to Lowestoft. Take the first L turn after Three Horseshoes pub. Continue on the minor road which bends round to the R. Carry straight on - the road bends to the R again. The car park is on the L just after White Gables house.

Access: Public right of way. Unsuitable for wheelchairs. Stiles where path leaves the reserve. Unmanned level crossing is gated.

Facilities: None.

Public transport: Bus: nearest bus route is on the A146 Lowestoft to Beccles road. Tel: 0845 958 3358. Train: Beccles and Oulton Broad South on the Ipswich to Lowestoft line.

Habitat: Grazing marshes, riverbank.

Key birds: *Spring/summer*: Marsh Harrier, Cetti's Warbler, occasional Grasshopper Warbler. *Winter*: Hen Harrier, wildfowl, Snipe.

Contact: Suffolk Wildlife Trust, Brooke House, Ashbocking, Ipswich, IP6 9JY. 01473 890 089. e-mail: info@suffolkwildlifetrust.org www.suffolkwildlifetrust.org

2. DINGLE MARSHES, DUNWICH

Suffolk Wildlife Trust/RSPB.

Location: TM 48 07 20. Eight miles from Saxmundham. Follow brown signs from A12 to Minsmere and continue to Dunwich. Forest carpark (hide) – TM 467 710. Beach carpark – TM 479 707. The reserve forms part of the Suffolk Coast NNR.

Access: Open at all times. Access via public rights of way and permissive path along beach. Dogs on lead please. Coaches can park on beach car park.

Facilities: Toilets at beach car park, Dunwich. Hide in Dunwich Forest overlooking reedbed, accessed via Forest car park. Circular trail waymarked from car park.

Public transport: Via Coastlink, Dial a ride service to Dingle 01728 833 546 links to buses and trains.

Habitat: Grazing marsh, reedbed, shingle beach and saline lagoons

Key birds: *All year*: In reedbed, Bittern, Marsh Harrier, Bearded Tit. *Winter*: Hen harrier, White-fronted Goose, Wigeon, Snipe, Teal on grazing marsh. *Summer*: Lapwing, Avocet, Snipe, Black-tailed Godwit, Hobby. Good for passage waders.

Contact: Alan Miller, Suffolk Wildlife Trust, 9 Valley Terrace, Valley Road, Leiston, Suffolk IP16 4AP. 01728 833 405. e-mail: alanm@keme.co.uk

3. HAVERGATE ISLAND

RSPB (East Anglia Office).

Location: TM 425 496. Part of the Orfordness-Havergate Island NNR on the Alde/Ore estuary. Orford is 17km NE of Woodbridge, signposted off the A12.

Access: Open Apr-Aug (1st & 3rd weekends and every Thu), Sep-Mar (1st Sat every month). Book in advance through Minsmere RSPB visitor centre, tel 01728 648 281. Park in Orford at the large pay and display car park next to the quay.

Facilities: Toilets, picnic area, five birdwatching hides, viewing platform, visitor trail (approx 2km).

Public transport: Orford served by local buses (route 160). For timetable info call 0870 608 2608. Bus stop is 0.25 miles from quay. Boat trips from Orford (one mile)

Habitat: Shallow brackish water, lagoons with islands, saltmarsh, shingle beaches.

Key birds: *Summer*: Breeding gulls, terns, Avocet, Redshank and Oystercatcher. *Winter*: Wildfowl and waders.
Contact: RSPB Havergate Reserves, 01394 450 732.

4. LACKFORD LAKES NATURE RESERVE

Suffolk Wildlife Trust.
Location: TL 803 708. Via track off N side of A1101 (Bury St Edmunds to Mildenhall road), between Lackford and Flempton. Five miles from Bury.
Access: Visitor centre open winter (10am-4pm), summer (10am-5pm) Wed to Sun, (closed Mon and Tues). Tea and coffee facilities, toilets.
Facilities: Visitor centre with viewing area upstairs. Tea and coffee facilities, toilets. Eight hides. Coaches should pre-book.
Public transport: Bus to Lackford village (Bury St Edmunds to Mildenhall service) – walk from church.
Habitat: Restored gravel pit with open water, lagoons, islands, willow scrub.
Key birds: *Winter*: Bittern, Water Rail, Bearded Tit. Large gull roost. Wide range of waders and wildfowl (inc. Goosander, Pochard, Tufted Duck, Shoveler). *Spring/ autumn*: Migrants, inc. raptors. Breeding Shelduck, Little Ringed Plover and reedbed warblers.
Contact: Lackford Lakes Visitor Centre, Lackford, Bury St Edmunds, Suffolk IP28 6HX. 01284 728 706. www.suffolkwildlifetrust.org
e-mail: lackford@suffolkwildlifetrust.org

5. LAKENHEATH FEN

RSPB (East Anglian office)
Location: TL722 864. W of Thetford, straddling the Norfolk/Suffolk border. From A11, head N on B1112 to Lakenheath and then two miles further. Entrance is 200 metres after level crossing.
Access: Open all year, dawn to dusk. Group bookings welcome. Guided walks available. Visitor centre accessible to wheelchair users.
Facilities: Visitor centre with toilets (inc disabled). Two trails and four open viewpoints. Picnic area. No height restriction at car park.
Public transport: Brecks Bus is available Monday-Friday and can be used to reach the reserve from Brandon and Thetford. To book, phone Brecks Bus on 01842 816 170 by noon the weekday before travel.
Habitat: Poplar woodland, plus extensive reedbeds, open water and marsh.
Key birds: Country's most reliable site for Golden Oriole. Also look for regular Marsh Harrier, Bearded Tit, Hobby and breeding reedbed warblers. Listen for booming Bitterns. *Winter*: Wildfowl species.
Contact: RSPB (East Anglia office) – 01603 661 662.

6. LANDGUARD BIRD OBSERVATORY

English Heritage
Location: TM 283 317. Road S of Felixstowe to Landguard Nature Reserve and Fort.

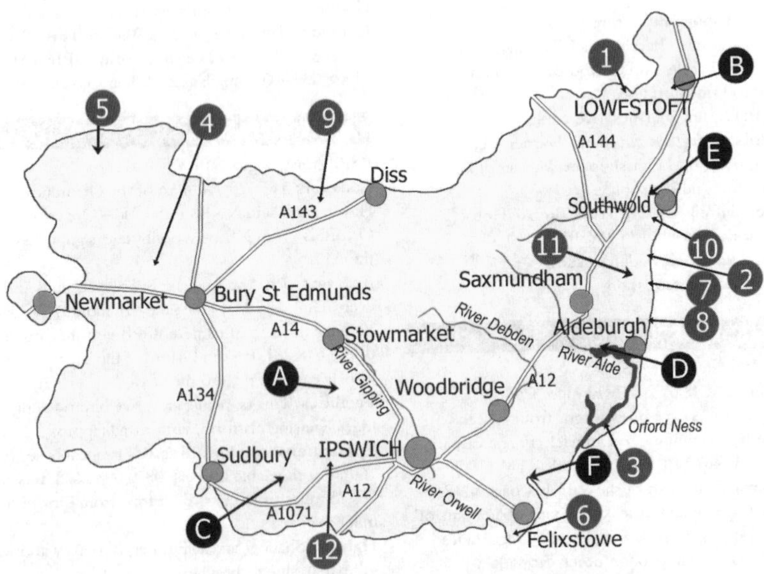

Access: Visiting by appointment.
Facilities: Migration watch point and ringing station.
Public transport: Call for advice.
Habitat: Close grazed turf, raised banks with holm oak, tamarisk, etc.
Key birds: Unusual species and common migrants. Seabirds.
Contact: The Warden, Landguard Bird Observatory, View Point Road, Felixstowe, Suffolk IP11 3TW. 01394 673 782. e.mail: landguardbo@yahoo.co.uk www.lbo.co.uk

7. MINSMERE

RSPB (Eastern England Regional Office)
Location: TM 452 680. Six miles NE of Saxmundham. From A12 head for Westleton, N of Yoxford. Access from Westleton (follow the brown tourist signs).
Access: Open every day, except Christmas Day and Boxing Day (9am-9pm or dusk if earlier). Visitor centre open 9am-5pm (9am-4pm Nov-Jan). Tea-room 10.30am-4.30pm (10am-4pm Nov-Jan). Free to RSPB members, otherwise £5 adults, £1.50 children, £3 concession. Max two coaches per day (not Bank Holiday weekends) by appointment only. Site partially accessible to wheelchairs.
Facilities: Toilets, visitor centre, hides, nature trails, family activity packs.
Public transport: Train to Saxmundham then Coastlink (book in advance on 01728 833 526).
Habitat: Woodland, wetland (reedbed and grazing marsh), heathland, dunes and beach, farmland (arable conversion to heath), coastal lagoons, 'the scrape'.
Key birds: *Summer*: Hobby, Avocet, Spotted Redshank, Redstart, Nightingale, Nightjar, Mediterranean Gull, terns. *Winter*: Wigeon, Teal, White-fronted Goose, Bewick's Swan, Hen Harrier, Starling roost. *Autumn/spring*: Passage migrants, waders etc. *All year*: Marsh Harrier, Bearded Tit, Bittern, Cetti's and Dartford Warblers, red deer.
Contact: RSPB Minsmere Nature Reserve, Saxmundham, Suffolk IP17 3BY. 01728 648 281. e-mail: minsmere@rspb.org.uk www.rspb.org.uk

8. NORTH WARREN & ALDRINGHAM WALKS

RSPB (East Anglia Office).
Location: TM 468 575. Directly N of Aldeburgh on Suffolk coast. Use signposted main car park on beach.
Access: Open at all times. Please keep dogs under close control. Beach area suitable for disabled. Three spaces at Thorpeness Beach pay and display car park. On a first-come first-served basis only.
Facilities: Three nature trails, leaflet available from TIC Aldeburgh or Minsmere RSPB. Toilets in Aldeburgh and Thorpeness.
Public transport: Bus service to Aldeburgh. First Eastern Counties (08456 020 121).
Habitat: Grazing marsh, lowland heath, reedbed, woodland.
Key birds: *Winter*: White-fronted Goose, Tundra Bean Goose, Wigeon, Shoveler, Teal, Gadwall, Pintail, Snow Bunting. *Spring/summer*: Breeding Bittern, Marsh Harrier, Hobby, Nightjar, Wood Lark, Nightingale, Dartford Warbler.
Contact: Dave Thurlow, 1 Ness House Cottages, Sizewell, Leiston, Suffolk IP16 4UB. 01728 832 719. e-mail: dave.thurlow@rspb.org.uk

9. REDGRAVE AND LOPHAM FENS

Suffolk Wildlife Trust.
Location: TM 05 07 97. Five miles from Diss, signposted and easily accessed from A1066 and A143 roads.
Access: Open all year, dogs strictly on short leads only. Visitor centre open all year at weekends & sometimes during the week in school holidays: call for details on 01379 688 333.
Facilities: Visitor centre with coffee shop, toilets, including disabled toilets, car park with coach space. Bike parking area, wheelchair access to visitor centre and viewing platform/short boardwalk. Other general circular trails (not wheelchair accessible).
Public transport: Buses and trains to Diss town – Simonds coaches to local villages of Redgrave and South Lopham from Diss.
Habitat: Calcareous fen, wet acid heath, scrub and woodland
Key birds: *All year*: Water Rail, Snipe, Teal, Shelduck, Gadwall, Woodcock, Sparrowhawk, Kestrel, Great Spotted, Lesser Spotted and Green Woodpeckers, Tawny, Little and Barn Owls, Reed Bunting, Bearded Tit, Willow Tit, Linnet. *Summer*: Reed, Sedge and Grasshopper Warblers, Willow Warbler, Whitethroat, Hobby plus large Swallow and Starling roosts. *Winter/occasionals on passage*: Marsh Harrier, Greenshank, Green Sandpiper, Shoveler, Pintail, Garganey, Jack Snipe, Bittern, Little Ringed Plover, Oystercatcher.
Contact: Andrew Excell, Redgrave and Lopham Fens, Low Common Road, South Lopham, Diss, Norfolk IP22 2HX. 01379 687 618. e-mail: redgrave@suffolkwildlifetrust.org

10. WALBERSWICK

Natural England (Suffolk Team).
Location: TM 475 733. Good views from B1387 and from lane running W from Walberswick towards

Westwood Lodge; elsewhere keep to public footpaths or shingle beach.
Access: Parties and coach parking by prior arrangement.
Facilities: Hide on S side of Blyth estuary, E of A12.
Public transport: Call for advice.
Habitat: Tidal estuary, fen, freshwater marsh and reedbeds, heath, mixed woodland, carr.
Key birds: *Spring/summer*: Marsh Harrier, Bearded Tit, Water Rail, Bittern, Nightjar. *Passage/winter*: Wildfowl, waders and raptors.
Contact: The Warden, Natural England, Regent House, 110 Northgate Street, Bury St Edmunds IP33 1HP. 01502 676 171.

11. WESTLETON HEATH NNR

Natural England (Suffolk team)
Location: Lies either side of Dunwich-Westleton minor road, E of A12.
Access: Open all year - please keep dogs on leads between March-August breeding season.
Facilities: Car park next to minor road.
Public transport: Train station in Darsham, 5 km to W, served by One Railway. First Group bus services on A12 (also 5km distance).
Habitat: Lowland heath with heather-burning regime.
Key birds: Breeding Tree Pipit, Stonechat, Dartford Warbler and Nightjar on open heathland, Nightingale in woods.
Other notable flora and fauna: Silver-sudded blue and white admiral butterflies, solitary bees and wasps, adder.
Contact: Suffolk Natural England, 01284 762 218. E-mail: enquiries. east@naturalengland.org.uk

12. WOLVES WOOD RESERVE

RSPB (East Anglia Office).
Location: Two miles E of Hadleigh on the A1071 to Ipswich.
Access: Open all year. Wellington boots advisable between Sept-May. Unsuitable for wheelchairs. Donations welcome.
Facilities: Car park for 15 cars (no coaches), group bookings, guided walks, no dogs except guide dogs.
Public transport: Bus: Hadleigh (two miles). Train: nearest station Ipswich.
Habitat: Ancient woodland.
Key birds: *Spring/summer*: Nightingale, usual woodland species.
Contact: Mark Nowers, Warden, RSPB, Unit 13, Court Farm, Stutton Road, Brantham, Manningtree, Essex CO11 1PW. 01473 328 006.
e-mail: mark.nowers@rspb.org.uk www.rspb.org.uk

OTHER SITES

Full details in previous editions, (year indicated in brackets).
A. Bonny Wood – Suffolk WT, 01473 890 089 (06).
B. Carlton Marshes – Steve Melton (SWT), 01502 589 970 (O6).
C. Groton Wood LNR – Suffolk WT, 01473 890 089 (04).
D. Hazelwood Marshes – Suffolk WT, 01473 890 089 (06).
E. Hen Reedbed – Suffolk WT, 01473 890 089 (04).
F. Trimley Marshes – Suffolk WT, 01473 890 089 (05).

Surrey

1. FRENSHAM COMMON AND CP

Waverley BC and National Trust .
Location: SU 855 405. Common lies on either side of A287 between Farnham and Hindhead.
Access: Open at all times. Car park (locked 9pm-9am). Keep to paths.
Facilities: Information rooms, toilets and refreshment kiosk at Great Pond.
Public transport: Call Trust for advice.
Habitat: Dry and humid heath, woodland, two large ponds, reedbeds.
Key birds: *Summer*: Dartford Warbler, Wood Lark, Hobby, Nightjar, Stonechat. *Winter*: Wildfowl (inc. occasional Smew), Bittern, Great Grey Shrike.
Contact: Steve Webster, Rangers Office, Bacon Lane, Churt, Surrey GU10 2QB. 01252 792 416.

2. LIGHTWATER COUNTRY PARK

Surreyheath Council
Location: SU 921 622. From J3 of M3, take the A322 and follow brown Country Park signs. From the Guildford Road in Lightwater, turn into The Avenue. Entrance to the park is at the bottom of the road.
Access: Open all year dawn-dusk.
Facilities: Car park, visitor centre open most days

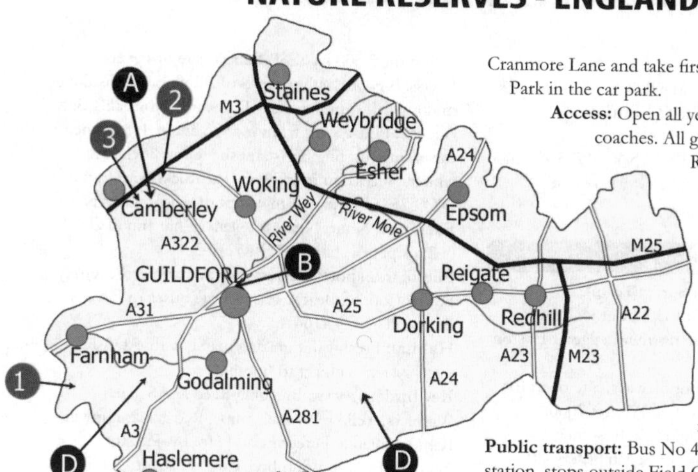

during summer, toilets, leaflets.
Public transport: Train: Bagshot two miles. Tel 08457 484950. Bus: No 34 from Woking, Guildford and Camberley. Tel: 08706 082608.
Habitat: Reclaimed gravel quarries. Heath, woodland, bog.
Key birds: *Summer*: Dartford Warbler, Stonechat, Wood Lark, Tree Pipit, Hobby, Nightjar, all three woodpeckers. *Autumn*: Ring Ouzel, Crossbill, Siskin, Fieldfare, Redwing, possible Woodcock.
Contact: Surreyheath Council, Surrey Heath House, Knoll Road, Camberley, Surrey GU15 3HD. 01276 707 100. www.surreycc.gov.uk

3. ROWHILL COPSE LNR

Waverley Borough Council/Rowhill Nature Reserve Society.
Location: SU 853 497. In either direction from Farnham or Farnborough along A325 towards Aldershot. At a mini-roundabout, turn down Cranmore Lane and take first R after central bollards. Park in the car park.
Access: Open all year. Not suitable for coaches. All groups must book with RNRS secretary. A small wheelchair-friendly trail from Parkland Grove, Weybourne, off B3100.
Facilities: Footpaths around the site, visitor centre open Sunday afternoons, Blackwater Valley long-distance path runs through site.
Public transport: Bus No 4 from Aldershot bus station, stops outside Field Centre. Aldershot railway station is 1.5 miles from reserve.
Habitat: Heathland, alder carr, ponds.
Key birds: *All year*: All three woodpeckers, Grey Heron, Kingfisher.
Other notable flora and fauna: Holly blue and purple hairstreak butterflies.
Contact: Rowhill Nature Reserve Society, Field Centre, Cranmere Lane, Aldershot HampshireGU11 3BD. 01252 319 749.Secretary MK Spink, 01252 371 442.

OTHER SITES

Full details in previous editions, (year indicated in brackets).
A. Brentmoor Heath LNR – Surrey WT, 01483 795 440 (04).
B. Riverside Park, Guildford – Guildford Borough Council, 01483 444 715 (06).
C. Thursley Common – Natural England, 01428 685 878.
D. Wallis Wood LNR – Surrey WT, 01483 795 440 (04).

Sussex, East

1. FORE WOOD

RSPB (South East England Office).
Location: TQ 758 123. From the A2100 (Battle/Hastings) take lane to Crowhurst at Crowhurst Park Caravan Park. Park at Crowhurst village hall and walk up Forewood Lane for 500 yards. Look for the finger post on L and follow the public footpath across farmland to reserve entrance.
Access: Open all year apart from Christmas Day. No disabled facilities. No dogs. No coaches.
Facilities: Two nature trails.
Public transport: Station at Crowhurst, about 0.5 mile walk. Charing Cross/Hastings line. No buses within one mile.
Habitat: Semi-natural ancient woodland.

Key birds: Three species woodpecker, Nuthatch, Treecreeper, Sparrowhawk, Marsh Tit. *Spring/summer*: Blackcap, Nightingale, Spotted Flycatcher.
Contact: Martin Allison, 12 The Grove, Crowborough, East Sussex TN6 1NY. 01273 775 333 (South East Regional Office). www.rspb.org.uk e-mail: martin.allison@rspb.org.uk

2. LULLINGTON HEATH

Natural England (Sussex & Surrey Team).
Location: TQ 525 026. W of Eastbourne, between Jevington and Litlington, on northern edge of Friston Forest.
Access: Via footpaths and bridleways. Site open for access on foot as defined by CROW Act 2000.
Facilities: None. Nearest toilets/refreshmenst at pubs in Jevington, Litlington or Seven Sisters CP, 2km to S.
Public transport: Nearest bus stop is Seven Sisters Country Park. Phone Brighton & Hove services on 01273 886 200 or visit: www.buses.co.uk/bustimes/
Habitat: Grazed chalk downland and heath, with mixed scrub and gorse.
Key birds: *Summer*: Breeding Nightingale, Turtle Dove, Nightjar and diverse range of grassland/scrub-nesting species.Passage migrants include Wheatear, Redstart, Ring Ouzel. *Winter*: Raptors (inc. Hen Harrier), Woodcock.
Contact: The Site Manager, East Sussex Natural England, 01273 476 595; www.natural-england.org.uk. e-mail sussex.surrey@natural-england.org.uk

3. PEVENSEY LEVELS

Natural England (Sussex & Surrey Team).
Location: TQ 665 054. A small reserve of 12 fields, within the 3,500 ha SSSI/Ramsar site of Pevensey Levels. NE of Eastbourne. S of A259, one mile along minor road from Pevensey E towards Norman's Bay.
Access: Please view from road to avoid disturbance to summer nesting birds and sheltering flocks in winter. Access on foot allowed at Rockhouse Bank (TQ 675 057) - panoramic view of whole reserve.
Facilities: None. Nearest toilets at Star Inn (TQ 687 062) or petrol station (TQ 652 052).
Public transport: Nearest railway stations: Pevensey Bay or Cooden Beach. Eastbourne buses to Pevensey Bay - call 01323 416416.
Habitat: Freshwater grazing marsh with extensive ditch system, subject to flooding.
Key birds: *Summer*: Breeding Reed and Sedge Warblers, Yellow Wagtail, Snipe, Redshank, Lapwing. Raptors include Peregrine and Hobby. Passage migrants include Whimbrel, Curlew, Brent Geese. *Winter*: Flocks of wildfowl and waders, Short-eared Owl, Merlin and other raptors.
Contact: The Site Manager, East Sussex Natural England, 01273 476 595; www.natural-england.org.uk. e-mail sussex.surrey@natural-england.org.uk

4. RYE HARBOUR

Rye Harbour Local Nature Reserve Management Committee.
Location: TQ 941 188. One mile from Rye off A259 signed Rye Harbour. From J10 of M20 take A2070 until it joins A259.
Access: Open at all times by footpaths. Organised groups please book.
Facilities: Car park in Rye Harbour village. Information kiosk in car park. Shop, 2 pubs, Toilets and disabled facilities near car park, four hides (wheelchair access, two with induction sound loop fitted), information centre open most days (10am-4pm) by volunteers.
Public transport: Train (tel: 08457 484 950), bus (tel: 0870 608 2608), Rye tourist information (tel: 01797 226 696).
Habitat: Sea, sand, shingle, pits and grassland.
Key birds: *Spring*: Passage waders, especially roosting Whimbrel. *Summer*: Breeding terns, waders, Wheatear, Yellow Wagtail. *Winter*: Wildfowl, Water Rail, Bittern, Smew.
Contact: Barry Yates (Manager), 2 Watch Cottages, Winchelsea, East Sussex TN36 4LU. 01797 223 862.

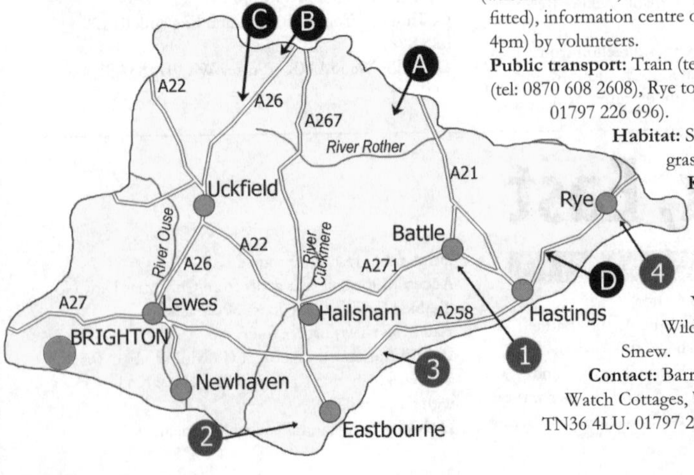

e-mail: yates@clara.net www.wildrye.info
see also www.rxwildlife.org.uk for latest sightings in area.

OTHER SITES

Full details in previous editions, (year indicated in brackets).

A. **Bewl Water** – Sussex WT, 01273 492 630 (06).
B. **Edridge Rocks Reserve** – Sussex WT, 01273 492 630 (04).
C. **Old Lodge** – Sussex WT, 01273 492 630 (05).
D. **Pett Pools** – Sussex WT, 01273 492 630 (04).

Sussex, West

1. ARUNDEL

The Wildfowl & Wetlands Trust.
Location: TQ 020 081. Clearly signposted from Arundel, just N of A27.
Access: Summer (9.30am-5.30pm) winter (9.30am-4.30pm). Closed Christmas Day. Approx 1.5 miles of level footpaths, suitable for wheelchairs. No dogs except guide dogs.
Facilities: Visitor centre, restaurant, shop, hides, picnic area, seasonal nature trails. Eye of The Wind Wildlife Gallery. Corporate hire facilities.
Public transport: Arundel station, 15-20 minute walk. Tel: 01903 882 131.
Habitat: Lakes, wader scrapes, reedbed.
Key birds: *Summer*: Nesting Redshank, Lapwing, Oystercatcher, Common Tern, Sedge, Reed and Cetti's Warblers, Peregrine, Hobby. *Winter*: Teal, Wigeon, Reed Bunting, Water Rail, Cetti's Warbler and occasionally roosting Bewick's Swan.
Contact: James Sharpe, Mill Road, Arundel, West Sussex BN18 9PB. 01903 883 355. www.wwt.org.uk e-mail: info.arundel@wwt.org.uk

2. PAGHAM HARBOUR

West Sussex County Council.
Location: SZ 857 966. Five miles S of Chichester on B2145 towards Selsey.
Access: Open at all times, dogs must be on leads, disabled trail with accessible hide. All groups and coach parties must book in advance.
Facilities: Visitor centre open at weekends (10am-4pm), toilets (including disabled), three hides, one nature trail.
Public transport: Bus stop by visitor centre.
Habitat: Intertidal saltmarsh, shingle beaches, lagoons and farmland.
Key birds: *Spring*: Passage migrants. *Autumn*: Passage waders, other migrants. *Winter*: Brent Goose, Slavonian Grebe, wildfowl. *All year*: Little Egret.
Contact: Sarah Patton, Pagham Harbour LNR, Selsey Road, Sidlesham, Chichester, West Sussex PO20 7NE. 01243 641 508. e-mail: pagham.nr@westsussex.gov.uk

3. PULBOROUGH BROOKS

RSPB (South East England Office).
Location: TQ 054 170. Signposted on A283 between Pulborough (via A29) and Storrington (via A24). Two miles SE of Pulborough.
Access: Open daily. Visitor centre 9.30am-5pm (tea-room 4.30pm), closed Christmas Day and Boxing Day. Nature trail and hides (9am-9pm or sunset), closed Christmas Day. Admission fee for nature trail (free to RSPB members). No dogs. All four hides accessible to wheelchair users, though strong helper is needed.
Facilities: Visitor centre (incl RSPB shop, tea room with

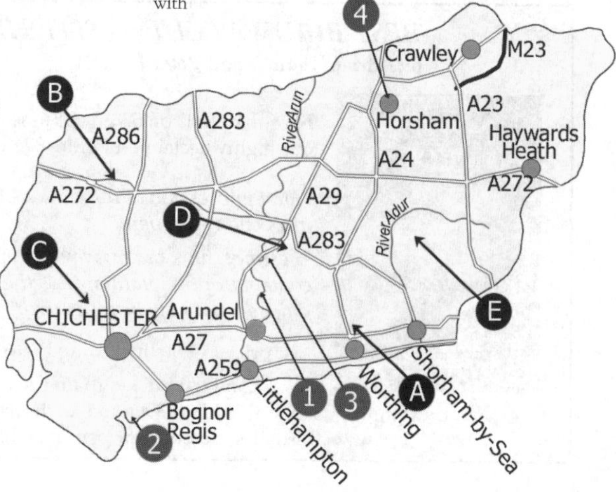

terrace, displays, toilets). Nature trail, four hides and additional viewpoints. Large car park including coach area. Play and picnic areas. An electric buggy is available for free hire, for use on trail.
Public transport: Two miles from Pulborough train station. Connecting bus service regularly passes reserve entrance (not Suns). Compass Travel (01903 690 025). Cycle stands.
Habitat: Lowland wet grassland (wet meadows and ditches). Hedgerows and woodland.
Key birds: *Winter*: Wintering waterbirds, Bewick's Swan. *Spring*: Breeding wading birds and songbirds (incl Lapwing and Nightingale). *Summer*: Butterflies and dragonflies, warblers. *Autumn*: Passage wading birds, Redstart, Whinchat.
Contact: The administrator, Pulborough Brooks Nature Reserve, Upperton's Barn, Wiggonholt, Pulborough, West Sussex RH20 2EL. 01798 875 851. e-mail: pulborough.brooks@rspb.org.uk

4. WARNHAM NATURE RESERVE

Horsham District Council.
Location: TQ 167 324. One mile from Horsham town centre, just off A24 'Robin Hood' roundabout on B2237.
Access: Open every day all year and Bank Hols (10am-6pm or dusk). Day permits - adults 50p, children free. Annual permits also available. No dogs or cycling allowed. Good wheelchair access over most of the Reserve.
Facilities: Visitor centre and café open weekends, bank holidays, school holidays and every day from July to September (11am-4pm). Ample car park – coaches by request. Toilets (including disabled), two hides, reserve leaflets, millpond nature trail, bird feeding station, boardwalks, benches and hardstanding paths.
Public transport: From Horsham Railway Station it is a mile walk along Hurst Road, with a R turn onto Warnham Road. Buses from 'CarFax' in Horsham Centre stop within 150 yards of the reserve. Travel line, 0870 608 2608.
Habitat: 17 acre millpond, reedbeds, marsh, meadow and woodland (deciduous and coniferous).
Key birds: *Summer*: Breeding Common Tern, Kingfisher, woodpeckers, Mandarin Duck, Little Owl, Marsh Tit, Goldcrest, hirundines, Hobby, warblers including Cetti's. *Winter*: Cormorant, gulls, Little Grebe, Water Rail, Brambling, Siskin, Lesser Redpoll, thrushes and wildfowl. *Passage*: Waders, pipits, terns and Sand Martin. Extensive invertebrate interest, including 31 species of butterfly and 23 dragonfly species.
Contact: Sam Bayley, Countryside Warden, Leisure Services, Park House Lodge, North Street, Horsham, W Sussex RH12 1RL. 01403 256 890. e-mail: sam.bayley@horsham.gov.uk www.horshamdistrictcountryside.org

OTHER SITES

Full details in previous editions, (year indicated in brackets).
A. Adur Estuary – RSPB 01273 775 333 (04).
B. Iping & Stedham Commons – Sussex WT, 01273 492 630 (05).
C. Kingley Vale – Natural England, 01243 575 353 (06).
D. Waltham Brooks – Sussex WT, 01273 492 630 (04).
E. Woods Mill – Sussex WT, 01273 492 630 (04).

Tyne & Wear

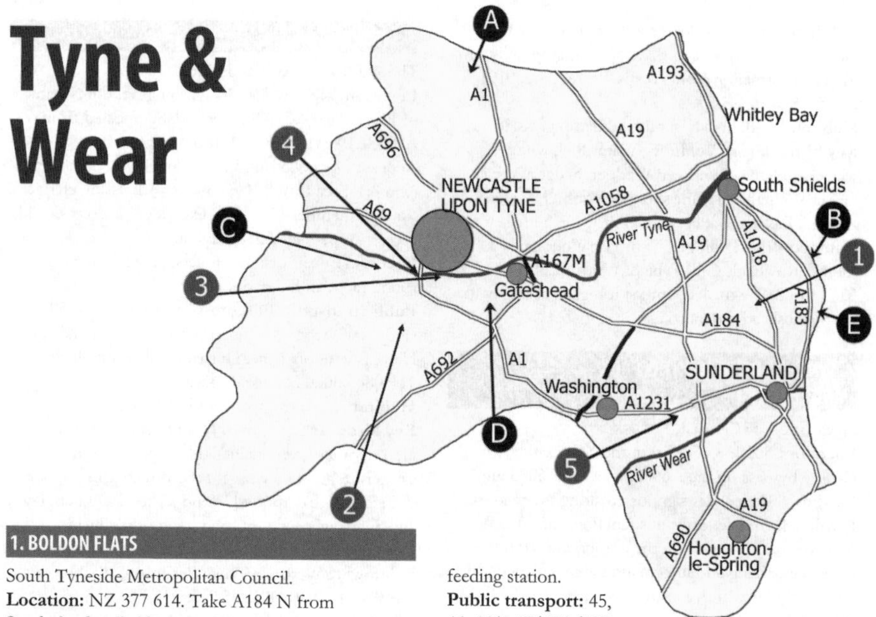

1. BOLDON FLATS

South Tyneside Metropolitan Council.

Location: NZ 377 614. Take A184 N from Sunderland to Boldon.

Access: View from Moor Lane on minor road NE of East Boldon station towards Whitburn. Limited lay-by parking.

Facilities: None.

Public transport: East Boldon Metro Station approx. 800 metres from site. 0191 203 3333, e-mail: metro.communications@nexus.org.uk

Habitat: Meadows, part SSSI, managed flood in winter, pond, ditches.

Key birds: *Passage/winter*: Wildfowl and waders. Gull roost may inc. Mediterranean, Glaucous, Iceland; Merlin fairly regular.

Contact: Countryside Officer, South Tyneside Metropolitan Council, Town Hall, Westoe Road, South Shields, Tyne & Wear NE33 2RL. 01914 271 717; Fax 01914 550 208. www.southtyneside.info

2. DERWENT WALK COUNTRY PARK

Gateshead Council.

Location: NZ 178 604. Along River Derwent, four miles SW of Newcastle and Gateshead. Several car parks along A694.

Access: Site open all times. Thornley visitor centre open weekends and Bank Holidays (12-5pm). Keys for hides available from Thornley Woodlands Centre. Swalwell visitor centre open daily (9am-5pm).

Facilities: Toilets at Thornley and Swalwell visitor centres. Hides at Far Pasture Ponds and Thornley feeding station.

Public transport: 45, 46, 46A, 47/47A/47B buses from Newcastle/Gateshead to Swalwell/Rowlands Gill. Bus stop Thornley Woodlands Centre. (Regular bus service from Newcastle). Information from Nexus Travel Information, 0919 203 3333, www.nexus.org.uk

Habitat: Mixed woodland, river, ponds, meadows.

Key birds: *Summer*: Red Kite, Grashopper Warbler, Lesser Whitethroat, Kingfisher, Dipper, Great Spotted and Green Woodpeckers, Blackcap, Garden Warbler, Nuthatch. *Winter*: Teal, Tufted Duck, Brambling, Marsh Tit, Bullfinch, Great Spotted Woodpecker, Nuthatch, Goosander, Kingfisher.

Contact: Trevor Weston, Thornley Woodlands Centre, Rowlands Gill, Tyne & Wear NE39 1AU. 01207 545 212. e-mail: countryside@gateshead.gov.uk www.gatesheadbirders.co.uk www.gateshead.gov.uk

3. SHIBDON POND

Gateshead Council.

Location: NZ 192 628. E of Blaydon, S of Scotswood Bridge, close to A1. Car park at Blaydon swimming baths. Open access from B6317 (Shibdon Road).

Access: Open at all times. Disabled access to hide. Key for hide available from Thornley Woodlands Centre (£2).

Facilities: Hide in SW corner of pond. Free leaflet available.

Public transport: At least six buses per hour from Newcastle/Gateshead to Blaydon (bus stop Shibdon Road). Information from Nexus Travel Line (0191 232 5325).
Habitat: Pond, marsh, scrub and damp grassland.
Key birds: *Winter*: Wildfowl, Water Rail, white-winged gulls. *Summer*: Reed Warbler, Sedge Warbler, Lesser Whitethroat, Grasshopper Warbler, Water Rail. *Autumn*: Passage waders and wildfowl, Kingfisher.
Contact: Brian Pollinger, Thornley Woodlands Centre, Rowlands Gill, Tyne & Wear NE39 1AU. 1209 545 212. e-mail: countryside@gateshead.gov.uk www.gatesheadbirders.co.uk

4. TYNE RIVERSIDE COUNTRY PARK AND THE REIGH

Newcastle City Council
Location: NZ 158 658. From the Newcastle to Carlisle by-pass on the A69(T) take the A6085 into Newburn. The park is signposted along the road to Blaydon. 0.25 miles after this junction, turn due W (the Newburn Hotel is on the corner) and after 0.5 miles the parking and information area is signed just beyond the Newburn Leisure Centre.
Access: Open all year.
Facilities: Car park. Leaflets and walk details available.
Habitat: River, pond with reed and willow stands, mixed woodland, open grassland.
Key birds: *Spring/summer*: Swift, Swallow, Whitethroat, Lesser Whitethroat. *Winter*: Sparrowhawk, Kingfisher, Little Grebe, finches, Siskin, Fieldfare, Redwing, Goosander. *All year*: Grey Partridge, Green and Great Spotted Woodpecker, Bullfinch, Yellowhammer.
Contact: Newcastle City Council, The Riverside Country Park, Newburn, Newcastle upon Tyne NE15 8BW.

5. WASHINGTON

The Wildfowl & Wetlands Trust.
Location: NZ 331 566. In Washington. On N bank of River Wear, W of Sunderland. Signposted from A195, A19, A1231 and A182.
Access: Open 9.30am-5pm (summer), 9.30am-4pm (winter). Free to WWT members. Admission charge for non-members. No dogs except guide dogs. Good access for people with disabilities.
Facilities: Visitor centre, toilets, parent and baby room, range of hides. Shop and café.
Public transport: Buses to Waterview Park (250 yards walk) from Washington, from Sunderland, Newcastle-upon-Tyne, Durham and South Shields. Tel: 0845 6060 260 for details.
Habitat: Wetlands, woodland and meadows.
Key birds: *Spring/summer*: Nesting colony of Grey Heron, other breeders include Common Tern, Oystercatcher, Lapwing. *Winter*: Bird-feeding station visited by Great Spotted Woodpecker, Bullfinch, Jay and Sparrowhawk. Goldeneye and other ducks.
Contact: Dean Heward, (Conservation Manager), Wildfowl & Wetlands Trust, Pottinson, Washington NE38 8LE. 01914 165 454 ext 231.
e-mail: dean.heward@wwt.org.uk www.wwt.org.uk

OTHER SITES

Full details in previous editions, (year indicated in brackets).
A. Big Waters – Wildlife Trust, 01912 846 884 (04).
B. Marsden Bay – National Trust, 01915 293 161 (05).
C. Ryton Willows – Andrew McLay (Gateshead Council), 01208 545 212 (07).
D. Wallsend Swallow Pond – Wildlife Trust, 01912 846 884 (04).
E. Whitburn Bird Observatory – Peter Bell (Durham Bird Club), 01915 294 941 (06).

Warwickshire

1. ALVECOTE POOLS

Warwickshire Wildlife Trust.
Location: SK 253 034. Located alongside River Anker E of Tamworth. Access via Robey's Lane (off B5000) just past Alvecote Priory car park. Also along towpath via Pooley Hall visitor centre, also number of points along towpath.
Access: Some parts of extensive path system are accessible to wheelchair-users. Parking Alvecote Priory car park.
Facilities: Nature trail.
Public transport: Within walking distance of the Alvecote village bus stop.
Habitat: Marsh, pools (open and reedbeds) and woodland.

NATURE RESERVES - ENGLAND

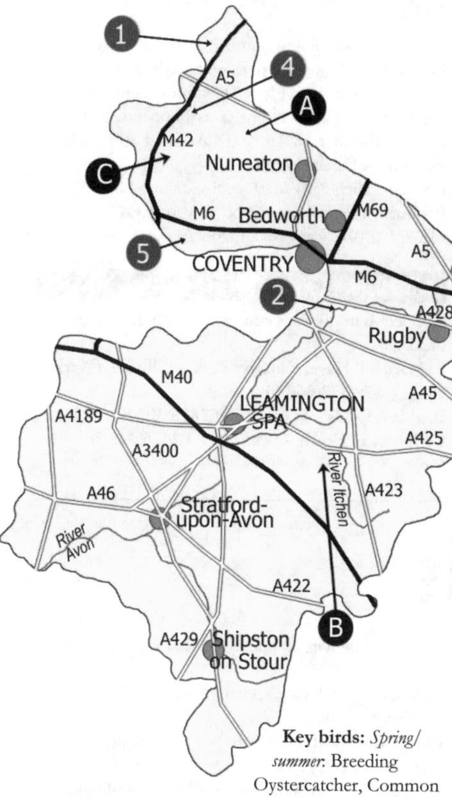

Key birds: *Spring/summer*: Breeding Oystercatcher, Common Tern and Little Ringed Plover. Common species include Great Crested Grebe, Tufted Duck and Snipe. Important for wintering, passage and breeding wetland birds.
Contact: Reserves Team, Brandon Marsh Nature Centre, Brandon Lane, Brandon, Coventry CV3 3GW. 02476 302 912. e-mail: reserves@warkswt.cix.co.uk www.warwickshire-wildlife-trust.org.uk

2. BRANDON MARSH

Warwickshire Wildlife Trust.
Location: SP 386 762. Three miles SE of Coventry, 200 yards SE of A45/A46 junction (Tollbar End). Turn E off A45 into Brandon Lane. Reserve entrance 1.25 miles on R.
Access: Open weekdays (9am-4.30pm), weekends (10am-4pm). Entrance charge currently £2.50 (free to Wildlife Trust members). Wheelchair access to nature trail and Wright hide. No dogs. Parking for 2 coaches.
Facilities: Visitor centre, toilets, tea-room (open daily 10am-3pm weekdays, 10am-4pm weekends), nature trail, seven hides.
Public transport: Bus service from Coventry to Tollbar End then 1.25 mile walk. Tel Travel West Midlands 02476 817 032 for bus times.
Habitat: Ten pools, together with marsh, reedbeds, willow carr, scrub and small mixed woodland in 260 acres, designated SSSI in 1972.
Key birds: *Spring/summer*: Garden and Grasshopper Warblers, Whitethroat, Lesser Whitethroat, Hobby, Little Ringed Plover, Whinchat, Wheatear. *Autumn/winter*: Bittern (last two winters), Dunlin, Ruff, Snipe, Greenshank, Green and Common Sandpipers, Wigeon, Shoveler, Pochard, Goldeneye, Siskin, Redpoll. *All year*: Cetti's Warbler, Kingfisher, Water Rail, Gadwall, Little Grebe, Buzzard.
Contact: Ken Bond, Hon. Sec. Brandon Marsh Voluntary Conservation Team, 54 Wiclif Way, Stockingford, Nuneaton, Warwickshire CV10 8NF. 02476 328 785.

3. KINGSBURY WATER PARK

Warwickshire County Council.
Location: SP 203 960. Signposted 'Water Park' from J9 M42, A4097 NE of Birmingham.
Access: Open all year except Christmas Day.
Facilities: Four hides, two with wheelchair access. Miles of flat surfaced footpaths, free loan scheme for mobility scooters. Cafes, Information Centre with gift shop.
Public transport: Call for advice.
Habitat: Open water; numerous small pools, some with gravel islands; gravel pits; silt beds with reedmace, reed, willow and alder; rough areas and grassland.
Key birds: *Summer*: Breeding warblers (nine species), Little Ringed Plover, Great Crested and Little Grebes. Shoveler, Shelduck and a thriving Common Tern colony. Passage waders (esp. spring). *Winter*: Wildfowl, Short-eared Owl.
Contact: Kingsbury Water Park, Bodymoor Heath Lane, Sutton Coldfield, West Midlands B76 0DY. 01827 872 660; e-mail parks@warwickshire.gov.uk www.warwickshire.gov.uk/countryside.

4. MARSH LANE NATURE RESERVE

Packington Estate Enterprises Limited.
Location: SP 217 804. Equidistant between Birmingham and Coventry, both approx 7-8 miles away. Off A452 between A45 and Balsall Common, S of B4102/A452 junction. Turn R into Marsh Lane and immediately R onto Old Kenilworth Road (now a public footpath), to locked gate. Key required for access.

Access: Only guide dogs allowed. Site suitable for disabled. Access by day or year permit only. Contact reserve for membership rates: day permit adult £3.50, OAP £3, children (under 16) £2.50 obtained from Golf Professional Shop, Stonebridge Golf Centre, Somers Road, off Hampton Lane, Meriden, (tel 01676 522 442), four minutes' car journey from site. Open Mon-Sun (7am-7pm). Golf Centre open to non-members for drinks and meals. £33 deposit required for key. Readily accessible for coaches.
Facilities: No toilets or visitor centre. Four hides and hard tracks between hides. Car park behind locked gates.
Public transport: Hampton-in-Arden railway station within walking distance on footpath loop. Bus no 194 stops at N end of Old Kenilworth Road, one mile from reserve gate.
Habitat: Two large pools with islands, three small areas of woodland, five acre field set aside for arable growth for finches and buntings as winter feed.
Key birds: 177 species. *Summer*: Breeding birds include Little Ringed Plover, Common Tern, most species of warbler including Grasshopper. Good passage of waders in Apr, May, Aug and Sept. Hobby and Buzzard breed locally.
Contact: Nicholas P Barlow, Packington Hall, Packington Park, Meriden, Nr Coventry CV7 7HF. 01676 522 020. www.packingtonestate.net

OTHER SITES

Full details in previous editions, (year indicated in brackets).
A. Hartshill Hayes Country Park – Sally Silk (Warks CC), 01827 872 660 (07).
B. Ufton Fields – Warks WT, 02476 302 912 (04).
C. Whitacre Heath – Warks WT, 02476 328 785 (06).

West Midlands

1. LICKEY HILLS COUNTRY PARK

Birmingham County Council.
Location: Eleven miles SW of Birmingham City Centre.
Access: Open all year, (10am-7pm in summer; 10am-4.30pm in winter). Land-Rover tours can be arranged for less able visitors.
Facilities: Car park, visitor centre with wheelchair pathway with viewing gallery, picnic site, toilets, café, shop.
Public transport: Bus: West Midlands 62 Rednal (20 mins walk to visitor centre. Rail: Barnt Green (25 mins walk through woods to the centre).
Habitat: Hills covered with mixed deciduous woodland, conifer plantations and heathland.
Key birds: *Spring/summer*: Warblers, Tree Pipit, Redstart. *Winter*: Redwing, Fieldfare. *All year*: common woodland species.
Contact: The Visitor Centre, Lickey Hills Country Park, Warren Lane, Rednal, Birmingham, B45 8ER, 01214 477 106.
e-mail: lickey.hills@birmingham.gov.uk

2. ROUGH WOOD CHASE

Walsall MBC
Location: SJ 987 012. From M6 (Jt 10) head for Willenhall and A462. Turn right into Bloxwich Road North and right again into Hunts Lane. Park by site entrance.
Access: Open all year. Circular nature trail.
Facilities: None.
Public transport: WMT bus 341 from Walsall.
Habitat: 70 acres of oakwood, significant for West Midlands. Also meadows, ponds, marshes and scrubland.
Key birds: Great Crested and Little Grebes on pools. Breeding Jay and Sparrowhawk. Common woodland species all year and warblers in summer.
Other notable flora and fauna: Great crested and smooth newts, water vole, various dragonfly species, purple hairstreak, brimstone and small heath butterflies.
Contact: Walsall Metropolitan Borough Council Ranger Service (Darlaston office) – 0121 568 6114. Website: www.walsall.gov.uk

3. SANDWELL VALLEY 1

Metropolitan Borough Council.
Location: SP 012 918 & SP 028 992.
Access: Access and car park from Dagger Lane or Forge Lane, West Bromwich.
Facilities: Mainly public open space.
Public transport: Call for advice.
Habitat: Nature reserve, lakes, woods and farmland.
Key birds: *Summer*: Breeding Lapwing, Little Ringed

Plover, Sparrowhawk. Great Spotted and Green Woodpeckers, Tawny Owl, Reed Warbler. Passage waders.
Contact: Senior Ranger, Sandwell Valley Country Park, Salters Lane, West Bromwich, W Midlands B71 4BG. 01215 530 220 or 2147.

4. SANDWELL VALLEY 2

RSPB
Location: SP 035 928. Great Barr, Birmingham. Follow signs S from M6 J7 via A34. Take R at 1st junction onto A4041. Take 4th L onto Hamstead Road (B4167), then R at 1st mini roundabout onto Tanhouse Avenue.
Access: 800 metres of paths accessible to assisted and powered wheelchairs with some gradients (please ring centre for further information), centre fully accessible.
Facilities: Visitor Centre and car park (open Tue-Fri 9am-5pm, Sat-Sun 10am-5pm. Closes at dusk in winter), with viewing area, small shop and hot drinks, four viewing screens, one hide. Phone centre for details on coach parking.
Public transport: Bus: 16 from Corporation Street (Stand CJ), Birmingham City Centre (ask for Tanhouse Avenue). Train: Hamstead Station, then 16 bus for one mile towards West Bromwich from Hamstead (ask for Tanhouse Avenue).
Habitat: Open water, wet grassland, reedbed, dry grassland and scrub.
Key birds: *Summer*: Lapwing, Little-Ringed Plover, Reed Warbler, Whitethroat, Sedge Warbler, Willow Tit. *Passage*: Sandpipers, Yellow Wagtail, chats, Common Tern. *Winter*: Water Rail, Snipe, Jack Snipe, Goosander, Bullfinch, woodpeckers and wildfowl.
Contact: Lee Copplestone, 20 Tanhouse Avenue, Great Barr, Birmingham B43 5AG. 0121 3577 395.

OTHER SITES

Full details in previous editions, (year indicated in brackets).
A. Smestow Valley LNR – Wolverhampton Leisure Services, 01902 556 556 (04).
B. Swan Pool/The Swag – Walsall Country Services, 01922 650 000 (04).

Wiltshire

1. FYFIELD DOWNS NNR

Natural England (Wiltshire team).
Location: On the Marlborough Downs. From the A345 at N end of Marlborough a minor road signed Broad Hinton, bisects the downs, dipping steeply at Hackpen Hill to the A361 just before Broad Hinton. From Hackpen Hill walk S to Fyfield Down.
Access: Open all year but avoid the racing gallops. Keep dogs on leads.
Facilities: Car park.
Public transport: None.
Habitat: Downs.
Key birds: *Spring*: Ring Ouzel possible on passage, Wheatear, Cuckoo, Redstart, common warblers. *Summer*: possible Quail. *Winter*: Occasional Hen Harrier, possible Merlin, Golden Plover, Short-eared Owl, thrushes. *All year*: Sparrowhawk, Buzzard, Kestrel, partridges, Green and Great Spotted Woodpeckers, Goldfinch, Corn Bunting.
Contact: Natural England (Wiltshire team), 01380 726 344. email: wiltshire@naturalengland.org.uk

2. LANGFORD LAKES

Wiltshire Wildlife Trust.
Location: SU 037 370. Nr Steeple Langford, S of A36, approx eight miles W of Salisbury. In the centre of the village, turn S into Duck Street, signposted Hanging Langford. Langford Lakes is the first turning on the L just after a small bridge across the River Wylye.
Access: Opened to the public in Sept 2002. Main gates opening the during the day - ample parking. Advance notice required for coaches. No dogs allowed on this reserve.
Facilities: Four hides, all accessible to wheelchairs. Cycle stands provided (250m from Wiltshire Cycleway between Great Wishford and Hanging Langford).
Public transport: Nearest bus stop 500m - X4 Service between Salisbury and Warminster.
Habitat: Three former gravel pits, with newly created islands and developing reed fringes. 12 ha (29 acres) of open water; also wet woodland, scrub, chalk river.
Key birds: *Summer*: Breeding Coot, Moorhen, Mallard

Tufted Duck, Pochard, Gadwall, Little Grebe, Great Crested Grebe. Also Kingfisher, Common Sandpiper, Grey Wagtail, warblers (8 species). *Winter*: wildfowl, sometimes also Wigeon, Shoveler, Teal, Water Rail, Little Egret, Bittern. *Passage*: Sand Martin, Green Sandpiper, waders, Black Tern.
Contact: Wiltshire Wildlife Trust, Langford Lakes, Duck Street, Steeple Langford, Salisbury, Wiltshire SP3 4NH. 01722 790 770. www.wiltshirewildlife.org e-mail: admin@wiltshirewildlife.org

3. SAVERNAKE FOREST

Savernake Estate Trustees.
Location: From Marlborough the A4 Hungerford road runs along the N side of the forest. Two pillars mark the Forest Hill entrance, 1.5 miles E of the A346/A4 junction. The Grand Avenue leads straight through the middle of the woodland to join a minor road from Stibb Green on the A346 N of Burbage to the A4 W of Froxfield.
Access: Privately owned but open all year to public.
Facilities: Car park, picnic site at NW end by A346. Fenced-off areas should not be entered unless there is a footpath.
Public transport: None.
Habitat: Ancient woodland, with one of the largest collections of veteran trees in Britain.
Key birds: *Spring/summer*: Garden Warbler, Blackcap, Willow Warbler, Chiffchaff, Wood Warbler, Redstart, occasional Nightingale, Tree Pipit, Spotted Flycatcher. *Winter*: finch flocks possibly inc Siskin Redpoll, Brambling. All year: Sparrowhawk, Buzzard, Woodcock, owls, all three woodpeckers, Marsh, Tit, Willow Tit, Jay and other woodland birds.
Contact: Forest Enterprise, Postern Hill Lodge, Marlborough, SN8 4ND. 01672 512 520.

OTHER SITES

Full details in previous editions, (year indicated in brackets).
Jones Mill Nature Reserve – Wilts WT, 01722 790 770 (05).
Swillbrook Lakes – Wilts WT, 01722 790 770 (04).

Worcestershire

1. MONKWOOD NATURE RESERVE

Worcestershire Wildlife Trust.
Location: SO 804 607. Five miles NW of Worcester. From A443 Worcester to Holt Heath road, take any of the minor roads N of Hallow (Monkwood Green) to Sinton Green. At village green, turn to Monkwood by New Inn pub. After about a mile there is a car park on R.
Access: Open daily excluding Christmas Day. Stoned bridleway. Other paths grass, difficult to negotiate when wet. Coach parking only by request.
Facilities: Two nature trails.
Public transport: First Midland Red - tel 0870 608 2608 for timetable info.
Habitat: Ancient woodland.
Key birds: *Spring/summer*: Garden Warbler, Lesser Whitethroat, Cuckoo, Blackcap, Woodcock. *All year*: Tawny Owl, Sparrowhawk, Jay.
Other notable flora and fauna: Good for butterflies, especially wood white.
Contact: Trust HQ, 01905 754 919.
e-mail: enquiries@ worcestershirewildlifetrust.org
www.worcswildlifetrust.co.uk

2. TIDDESLEY WOOD

Worcestershire Wildlife Trust.
Location: SO 929 462. Take the A44 from Pershore to Worcester. Turn L towards Besford and Croome near town boundary just before the summit of the hill. Entrance is on L after about 0.75 miles.
Access: Open all year except Christmas Day. Cycles and horses only allowed on the bridleway. Please keep dogs fully under control. Military firing range at the SW corner of wood, so do not enter the area marked by red flags. The NE plot is private property and visitors should not enter the area. Main ride stoned, with some potholes. Small pathways difficult if wet. Coach parking by appointment.
Facilities: Information board. May find numbered posts around the reserve which were described in an old leaflet. Circular trail around small pathways.
Public transport: First Midland Red services (see above).
Habitat: Ancient woodland, conifers.
Key birds: *Spring*: Chiffchaff, Blackcap, Cuckoo, occasional Nightingale. *All year*: Crossbill, Coal Tit, Goldcrest, Sparrowhawk, Willow Tit, Marsh Tit.

Winter: Redwing, Fieldfare.
Contact: Trust HQ, 01905 754 919.
e-mail: enquiries@
worcestershirewildlifetrust.org
www.worcswildlifetrust.co.uk

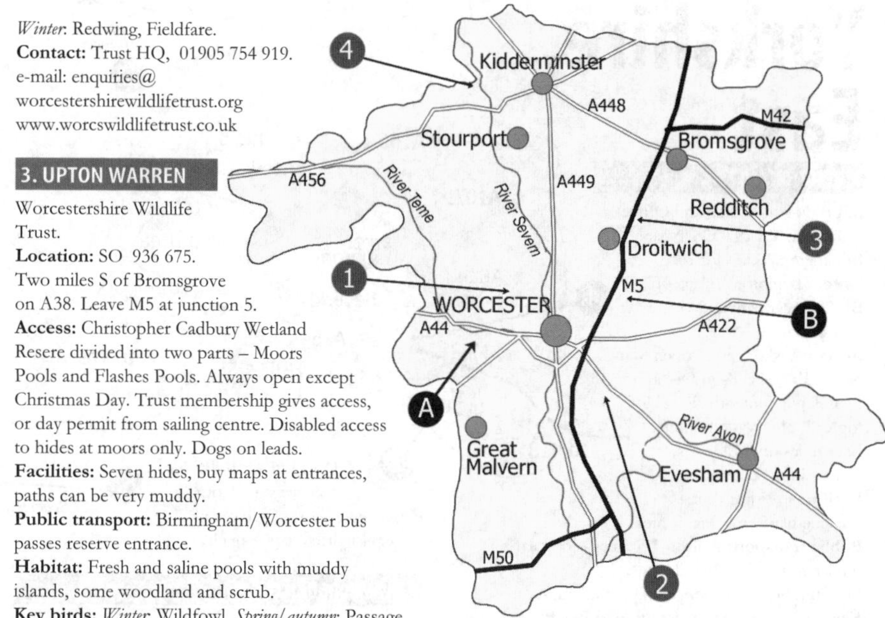

3. UPTON WARREN

Worcestershire Wildlife Trust.
Location: SO 936 675. Two miles S of Bromsgrove on A38. Leave M5 at junction 5.
Access: Christopher Cadbury Wetland Resere divided into two parts – Moors Pools and Flashes Pools. Always open except Christmas Day. Trust membership gives access, or day permit from sailing centre. Disabled access to hides at moors only. Dogs on leads.
Facilities: Seven hides, buy maps at entrances, paths can be very muddy.
Public transport: Birmingham/Worcester bus passes reserve entrance.
Habitat: Fresh and saline pools with muddy islands, some woodland and scrub.
Key birds: *Winter*: Wildfowl. *Spring/ autumn*: Passage waders, Common Tern, Cetti's Warbler, Oystercatcher and Little Ringed Plover, Avocet, many breeding warblers and a good track record of rarities.
Other notable flora and fauna: Saltmarsh plants, dragonflies.
Contact: A F Jacobs, 3 The Beeches, Upton Warren, Bromsgrove, Worcs B61 7EL. 01527 861 370.

4. WYRE FOREST

Natural England/Worcs Wildlife Trust.
Location: SO 750 760. Half a mile NW of Bewdley (on the A456) and four and a half miles W of Kidderminster.
Access: Observe reserve signs and keep to paths. Forestry Commission visitor centre at Callow Hill. Fred Dale Reserve is reached by footpath W of B4194 (parking at SO 776 763).
Facilities: Toilet and refreshment facilities at Wyre Forest Visitor Centre (near the Discovery Centre) at Callow Hill. Several waymarked trails in the Forest (some suitable for wheelchair users) as well as regular guided walks, also family cycle routes through the reserve. The Visitor Centre and Discovery Centre provide facilities for disabled visitors.
Public transport: The nearest train station is in Bewdley, served by the Severn Valley Railway (01299 403 816) although seasonal and sometimes infrequent, service. Also Central Trains to Kidderminster (0121 634 2040) and local bus services between Bewdley and Kidderminster.
Habitat: Oak forest, conifer areas, birch heath, lowland grassland, stream.
Key birds: Breeding birds include Redstart, Pied Flycatcher, Wood Warbler, Buzzard and Raven, with Dipper, Grey Wagtail and Kingfisher found on the larger streams.
Other notable flora and fauna: Mammals found in the reserve include, fallow, roe and muntjac deer, polecats, otters and mink. Yellow neck mice, dormice, voles and water shrews are also found. Several bat species including pipistrelle and Daubenton's. The site supports an important invertebrate population that includes England's largest colony of pearl-bordered fritillary butterflies.
Contact: Tim Dixon, Natural England, Block B, Government Buildings, Whittington Road, Worcester, WR5 2LQ. 01905 763 355; e-mail: herefordshire.worcestershire@naturalengland.org.uk.

OTHER SITES

Full details in previous editions, (year indicated in brackets).
A. Knapp & Papermill – Worcs Wildlife Trust, 01905 754 919 (05).
B. Trench Wood – Worcs Wildlife Trust, 01905 754 919 (07).

Yorkshire, East

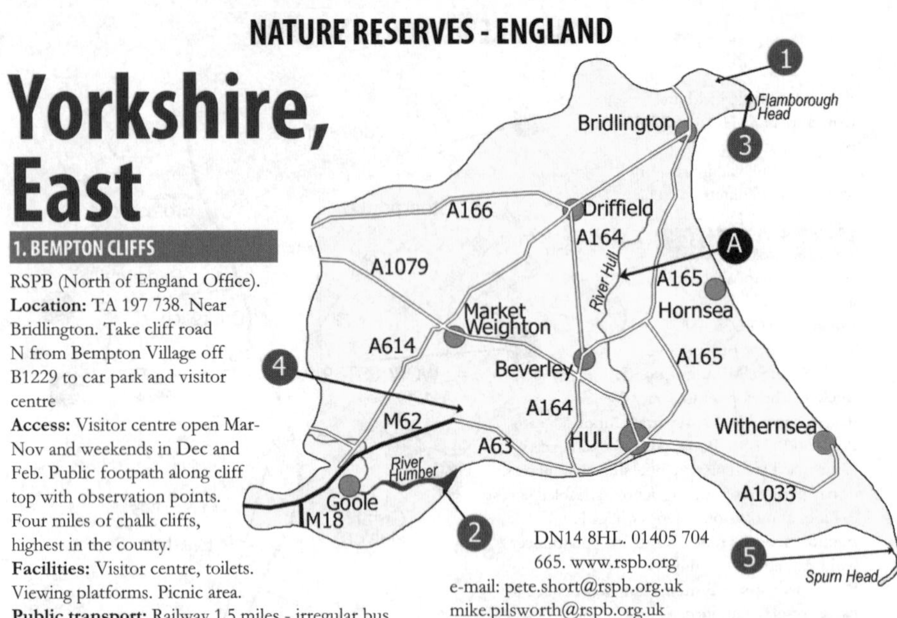

1. BEMPTON CLIFFS

RSPB (North of England Office).
Location: TA 197 738. Near Bridlington. Take cliff road N from Bempton Village off B1229 to car park and visitor centre
Access: Visitor centre open Mar-Nov and weekends in Dec and Feb. Public footpath along cliff top with observation points. Four miles of chalk cliffs, highest in the county.
Facilities: Visitor centre, toilets. Viewing platforms. Picnic area.
Public transport: Railway 1.5 miles - irregular bus service to village 1.25 miles.
Habitat: Seabird nesting cliffs, farmland, scrub.
Key birds: Best to visit May to mid-July for eg Puffin, Gannet (only colony on English mainland), Fulmar, Kittiwake; also nesting Tree Sparrow, Corn Bunting; good migration watchpoint for skuas, shearwaters and terns.
Contact: Site Manager, RSPB Visitor Centre, Cliff Lane, Bempton, Bridlington, E Yorks YO15 1JF. 01262 851 179.

2. BLACKTOFT SANDS

RSPB (North of England Office).
Location: SE 843 232. Eight miles E of Goole on minor road between Ousefleet and Adlingfleet.
Access: Open 9am-9pm or dusk if earlier. RSPB members free, £3 permit for non-members, £2 concessionary, £1 children, £6 family.
Facilities: Car park, toilets, visitor centre, six hides, footpaths suitable for wheelchairs.
Public transport: Goole/Scunthorpe bus (Sweynes' Coaches stops outside reserve entrance).Bus timetable on main RSPB website (see Blacktoft Reserve details).
Habitat: Reedbed, saline lagoons, lowland wet grassland, willow scrub.
Key birds: *Summer*: Breeding Avocet, Marsh Harrier, Bittern, Bearded Tit, passage waders (exceptional list inc many rarities). *Winter*: Hen Harrier, Merlin, Peregrine, wildfowl.
Contact: Pete Short (Warden) & Mike Pilsworth (Asst Warden), Hillcrest, Whitgift, Nr Goole, E Yorks DN14 8HL. 01405 704 665. www.rspb.org
e-mail: pete.short@rspb.org.uk
mike.pilsworth@rspb.org.uk

3. FLAMBOROUGH CLIFFS

Yorkshire Wildlife Trust
Location: TA 240 722. The reserve is part of the Flamborough headland approx 4 miles NE of Bridlington. From Bridlington take B1255 to Flamborough and follow the signs for the North Landing.
Access: Open all year. Public pay and display car park at North Landing gives access to both parts of the reserve. Paths not suitable for wheelchairs.
Facilities: Car park (pay and display), trails, refreshments available at café at North Landing (open Apr-Oct 10am-5pm), toilets.
Public transport: Flamborough is served by buses from Bridlington and Bempton. Phone 01482 222 222 for details.
Habitat: Coastal cliffs, rough grassland and scrub, farmland.
Key birds: *Summer*: Puffin, Guillemot, Razorbill, Kittiwake, Shag, Fulmar, Sky Lark, Meadow Pipit, Linnet, Whitethroat, Yellowhammer, Tree Sparrow, occasional Corn Bunting. *Passage migrants*: Fieldfare, Redwing and occasional rarities such as Wryneck and Red-backed Shrike.
Contact: Trust HQ, 01904 659 570.
e-mail: info@ywt.org.uk www.ywt.org.uk

4. NORTH CAVE WETLANDS

Yorkshire Wildlife Trust
Location: SE 887 328. At NW of North Cave

village, approx 10 miles W of Hull. From junction 28 of M62, follow signs to North Cave on B1230. In village, turn L and follow road to next crossroads where you go L, then take next L onto Dryham Lane. Alternatively, from N, follow minor road direct from Market Weighton. After the turning for Hotham, take the next R (Dryham Lane), which is one mile further down the road.
Access: Open all year with car parking on Dryham Lane. Some of the footpaths are suitable for all abilities.
Facilities: Three bird-viewing hides, two accessible to wheelchair users. Nearest toilet and refreshment facilities in North Cave, one mile away,
Public transport: Buses serve North Cave from Hull and Goole: telephone 01482 222 222 for details.
Habitat: Six former gravel pits have been converted into various lagoons for wetland birds, including one reedbed. There are also grasslands, scrub and hedgerows.
Key birds: More than 150 different species have been recorded including Great Crested Grebe, Gadwall, Pochard, Sparrowhawk, Avocet, Ringed Plover, Golden Plover, Dunlin, Ruff, Redshank, Green Sandpiper, Common Sandpiper and Tree Sparrow.
Contact: Trust HQ, 01904 659 570.
e-mail: info@ywt.org.uk www.ywt.org.uk

5. SPURN POINT NNR

Yorkshire Wildlife Trust.
Location: Entrance Gate TA 417 151. 26 miles from Hull. Take A1033 from Hull to Patrington then B1445 from Patrington to Easington and unclassed roads on to Kilnsea and Spurn Head.
Access: Normally open at all times. Vehicle admission fee (at present £3). No charge for pedestrians. No dogs allowed under any circumstances, not even in cars. Coaches by permit only (must be in advance).
Facilities: Centre open weekends, Bank Holidays, school holidays. Three hides. Cafe at point open weekends Apr to Oct 10am to 5pm. Public toilets in Blue Bell car park.
Public transport: Nearest bus service is at Easington (3.5 miles away).
Habitat: Sand dunes with marram and sea buckthorn scrub. Mudflats around Humber Estuary.
Key birds: *Spring*: Many migrants on passage and often rare birds such as Red-backed Shrike, Bluethroat etc. *Autumn*: Passage migrants and rarities such as Wryneck, Pallas's Warbler. *Winter*: Waders and Brent Goose.
Other notable flora and fauna: Unique habitats and geographical position make Spurn the most important site in Yorkshire for butterflies and moths (25 species recorded).
Contact: Spurn Reserves Officer, Spurn NNR, Blue Bell, Kilnsea, Hull HU12 0UB.
e-mail: spurnywt@ukonline.co.uk

OTHER SITES

Full details in previous editions, (year indicated in brackets).
A. Tophill Low Nature Reserve – Peter Izzard, 01377 270 690 (05).

Yorkshire, North

1. COATHAM MARSH

Tees Valley Wildlife Trust.
Location: NZ 585 250. Located on W edge of Redcar. Access from minor road to Warrenby from A1085/A1042.
Access: Reserve is open throughout daylight hours. Please keep to permissive footpaths only.
Facilities: Two hides. Key required for one of these – available to Tees Valley Wildlife Trust members for £10 deposit. No toilets or visitor centre.
Public transport: Very frequent bus service between Middlesbrough and Redcar. Nearest stops are in Coatham 0.25 mile from reserve (Arriva tel 0870 6082 608). Redcar Central Station one mile from site. Frequent trains from Middlesbrough and Darlington.
Habitat: Freshwater wetlands, lakes, reedbeds.
Key birds: *Spring/ autumn*: Wader passage (including Wood Sandpiper and Greenshank). *Summer*: Passerines (including Sedge Warbler, Yellow Wagtail). *Winter*: Ducks (including Smew). *Occasional rarities*: Water Rail, Great White Egret, Avocet, Bearded Tit and Bittern.
Contact: Steve Ashton, Tees Valley Wildlife Trust, Bellamy Pavilion, Margrove Heritage Centre, Margrove Park, Boosbeck, Saltburn-by-the-Sea, TS12 3B2. 01287 636 382; Fax 01287 636 383;
e-mail: info@teeswildlife.org www.teeswildlife.org

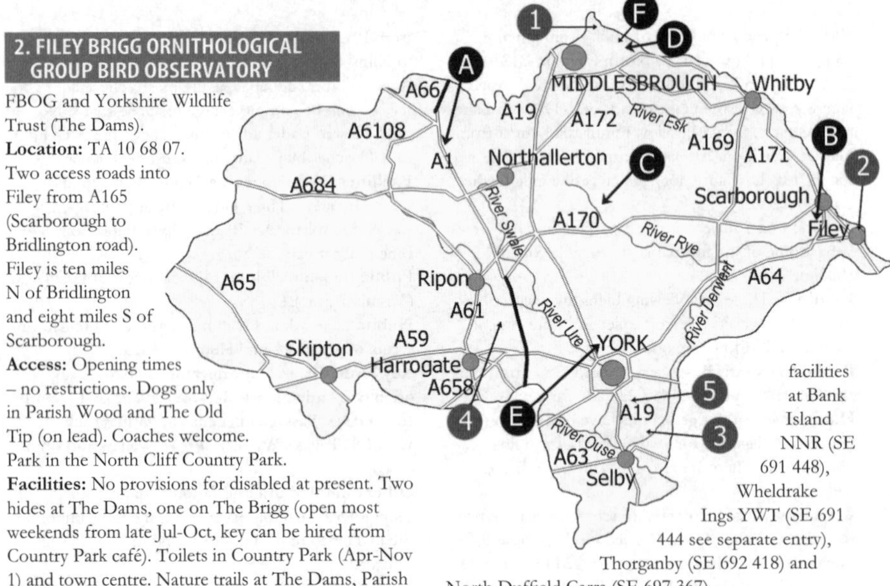

2. FILEY BRIGG ORNITHOLOGICAL GROUP BIRD OBSERVATORY

FBOG and Yorkshire Wildlife Trust (The Dams).

Location: TA 10 68 07. Two access roads into Filey from A165 (Scarborough to Bridlington road). Filey is ten miles N of Bridlington and eight miles S of Scarborough.

Access: Opening times – no restrictions. Dogs only in Parish Wood and The Old Tip (on lead). Coaches welcome. Park in the North Cliff Country Park.

Facilities: No provisions for disabled at present. Two hides at The Dams, one on The Brigg (open most weekends from late Jul-Oct, key can be hired from Country Park café). Toilets in Country Park (Apr-Nov 1) and town centre. Nature trails at The Dams, Parish Wood/Old Tip. Cliff top walk for seabirds along Cleveland Way.

Public transport: All areas within a mile of Filey railway station. Trains into Filey tel. 08457 484 950; buses into Filey tel. 01723 503 020

Habitat: The Dams – two freshwater lakes, fringed with some tree cover and small reedbeds. Parish Wood – a newly planted wood which leads to the Old Tip, the latter has been fenced (for stock and crop strips) though there is a public trail. Carr Naze has a pond and can produce newly arrived migrants.

Key birds: The Dams: Breeding and wintering water birds, breeding Sedge Warbler, Reed Warbler and Tree Sparrow. The Tip: important for breeding Sky Lark, Meadow Pipit, common warblers and Grey Partridge. *Winter*: Buntings, including Lapland. Seawatch Hide: Jul-Oct. All four skuas, shearwaters, terns. *Winter*: Divers and grebes. Totem Pole Field: A new project should encourage breeding species and wintering larks, buntings etc. Many sub-rare/rare migrants possible at all sites.

Contact: Craig Thomas, Recorder, 16 Scarborough Road, Filey, N Yorks YO14 9NU. 01723 513 055. e-mail: recorder@fbog.co.uk www.fbog.co.uk

3. LOWER DERWENT VALLEY

Natural England (Yorkshire and Humber Region).

Location: Six miles SE of York, stretching 12 miles S along the River Derwent from Newton-on-Derwent to Wressle and along the Pocklington Canal. Visitor facilities at Bank Island NNR (SE 691 448), Wheldrake Ings YWT (SE 691 444 see separate entry), Thorganby (SE 692 418) and North Duffield Carrs (SE 697 367).

Access: Open all year. No dogs. Disabled access at North Duffield Carrs.

Facilities: Bank Island - two hides, viewing tower. Wheldrake Ings - four hides. Thorganby - viewing platform. North Duffield Carrs - two hides and wheelchair access. Car parks at all sites, height restriction of 2.1m at Bank Island and North Duffield Carrs. Bicycle stands in car parks at Bank Island and North Duffield Carrs.

Public transport: Bus from York/Selby – contact First (01904 622 992).

Habitat: Hay meadow and pasture, swamp, open water and alder/willow woodland.

Key birds: *Spring/summer*: Breeding wildfowl and waders, incl. Garganey, Snipe and Ruff. Barn Owl and warblers. *Winter/spring*: 20,000-plus waterfowl including Whooper Swan, wild geese, Teal and Wigeon. Large gull roost, incl. white-winged gulls. Also passage waders, incl. Whimbrel.

Contact: Peter Roworth, Site Manager, Natural England, Genesis 1, University Road, Heslington, York YO10 5ZQ. 01904 435 500.
e-mail: york@naturalengland.org.uk
www.naturalengland.org.uk
Pocklington Canal: www.pocklington.gov.uk/pcas
Wheldrake Ings: www.yorkshire-wildlife-trust.org.uk

4. STAVELEY NATURE RESERVE

Yorkshire Wildlife Trust

Location: SE 365 634. The reserve is just N of

Staveley village and lies 3 miles SW of Boroughbridge.
Access: Open all year. Public footpath runs through reserve. Limited car parking. Park near village green opposite phone box. Walk along Minskip Road for 150 yards past Spellow Crescent on the R. Turn L between the bungalow and Ceres House into unmarked lane. At the end of the lane bear R through a kissing gate onto the reserve.
Facilities: An information panel overlooks the main lagoon. Keys for locked bird hide available from the reserve chairman for a small fee.
Public transport: Staveley is served by bus. Telephone: 01423 537 300.
Habitat: Shallow lagoon edged with reedswamp, fen and flower-rich grassland with scrub and pasture. Ponds and small area of woodland.
Key birds: *Spring/summer*: Breeding Reed, Sedge, Garden and Grasshopper Warblers and Reed Bunting. *Winter*: Wildfowl are attracted to the main lagoon. Jack Snipe and Short-eared Owl frequently seen.
Contact: Bob Evison (reserve chairman), Yorkshire Wildlife Trust, 1 St George's Place, York, YO24 1GN. 01904 659 570 or 01423 865 342 Bob Evison. e-mail: info@ywt.org.uk www.ywt.org.uk

5. WHELDRAKE INGS

Yorkshire Wildlife Trust.
Location: From York ring-road head S onto A19 Selby road. After one mile turn L, signed Wheldrake and Thorganby. Continue through Wheldrake towards Thorganby. After a sharp R bend, turn L after 0.5 miles onto an unsigned tarmac track. Look for two stone gateposts with pointed tops. Car park is about 0.25 miles down the track. To reach the reserve, cross the bridge over river and turn R over a stile.
Access: Open all year. Please keep to the riverside path. From Apr-Sep.
Facilities: Car park, four hides.
Habitat: Water meadows, river, scrub, open water.
Key birds: *Spring/summer*: Duck species, Grey Partridge, Turtle Dove, some waders, Spotted Flycatcher, warblers. *Winter*: Occasional divers and scarce grebes. wildfowl inc. Pintail, Pochard, Goshawk, Hen Harrier, Water Rail, Short-eared Owl, thrushes, good mix of other birds.
Contact: Yorkshire Wildlife Trust, 01904 659 570. e-mail: info@ywt.org.uk www.ywt.org.uk

OTHER SITES

Full details in previous editions, (year indicated in brackets).
A. Bolton-on-Swale Lake – Yorks WT, 01904 659 570 (04).
B. Burton Riggs LNR – Yorks WT, 01904 659 570 (04).
C. Duncombe Park NNR – Estate Office, 01439 770 213 (04).
D. Huntcliff – Tees Valley WT, 01642 759 900 (06).
E. Moorlands Wood – Yorks WT, 01904 659 570 (06).
F. Saltburn Gill – Bill Ashton-Wickett, Tees Valley WT, 01287 636 382 (07).

Yorkshire, South & West

1. BRETTON COUNTRY PARK AND SCULPTURE PARK/OXLEY BANK WOOD

Yorkshire Wildlife Trust/Wakefield MDC.
Location: SE 295 125. Fifteen miles S of Leeds and N of Sheffield. Leave motorway at J38. Take A637 Huddersfield road to the N. After 0.5 miles Park entrance is on L. Can also park in Sculpture Park's car park, which is first L off A637 in West Bretton.
Access: Open all year. Permit required for the Yorkshire Wildlife Trust area.
Facilities: Car park, visitor centre, information leaflets. **Public transport:** None.
Habitat: Landscaped park, mature woodland, two lakes.
Key birds: *Spring/summer*: Cuckoo, warblers, Spotted Flycatcher, Sand Martin, Swallow. *Winter*: Fieldfare, Redwing, Brambling, Redpoll, Siskin, Hawfinch. *All year*: Kingfisher, all three woodpeckers, Little and Tawny Owls, Linnet, Bullfinch, Yellowhammer, usual woodland birds.
Contact: Yorkshire Wildlife Trust, 01904 659 570. e-mail: info@ywt.org.uk www.ywt.org.uk

2. FAIRBURN INGS

RSPB (North West England Office).
Location: SE 452 277. 12.5 miles from Leeds, six miles from Pontefract, 3.5 miles from Castleford situated next to A1 at Fairburn turn-off.
Access: Reserve and hides open every day (9am-dusk). Centre with shop open weekdays and weekends

(9am-5pm) and Bank Holidays. Hot and cold drinks available. Dogs on leads at all times. Boardwalk leading to Pickup Pool and feeding station and paths to centre wheelchair-friendly.
Facilities: Reserve hides: three open at all times with one locked at dusk. Toilets open when centre open or 9am-5pm. Disabled access to toilets. All nature trails follow public paths and are open at all times.
Public transport: Nearest train stations are Castleford or Pontefract. Buses approx every hour from Pontefract and Tadcaster. Infrequent from Castleford and Selby.
Habitat: Open water due to mining subsidence, wet grassland, marsh and willow scrub, reclaimed colliery spoil heaps.
Key birds: *Winter*: A herd of Whooper Swan usually roost. Normally up to five Smew including male, Wigeon, Gadwall, Goosander, Goldeney. *Spring*: Osprey, Wheatear, Little Gull and five species of tern pass through. *Summer*: Breeding birds include Reed and Sedge Warblers, Shoveler, Gadwall, Cormorant.
Contact: Fairburn Ings Visitor Centre, Newton Lane, Fairburn, Castleford WF10 2BH. 01977 603 796.

3. HARDCASTLE CRAGS

National Trust.
Location: From Halifax, follow A646 W for five miles to Hebden Bridge and pick up National Trust signs in town centre to the A6033 Keighley Road. Follow this for 0.75 miles. Turn L at the National Trust sign to the car parks. Alternate pay-and-display car park at Clough Hole, Widdop Road, on R above Gibson Mill.
Access: Open all year. NT car park charges: £2.50 up to 3 hours, £3 all day weekdays, £4 at weekends and bank holidays. No charge for NT members and disabled badge holders.
Facilities: 2 small pay car parks, cycle racks and several way-marked trails. Gibson Mill has toilets, café, exhibitions. Not connected to any mains services, in extreme conditions the mill may be closed for health and safety reasons.
Public transport: Good public transport links. Trains to Hebden Bridge from Manchester or Leeds every 30 minutes. Call 08457 484 950. Weekday buses every 30 minutes to Keighley Road, then 1 mile walk to Midghole. Summer weekend bus 906 Widdop-Hardcastle Crags leaves Hebden Bridge rail station every 90 minutes 9.20am-6.05pm. Tel: 0113 245 7676.
Habitat: Wooded valleys, ravines, streams, hay meadows and moorland edge.
Key birds: *Spring/summer*: Cuckoo, Redstart, Lesser Whitethroat, Garden Warbler, Blackcap, Wood Warbler, Chiffchaff, Spotted Flycatcher, Pied Flycatcher, Curlew, Lapwing, Meadow Pipit. *All year*: Sparrowhawk, Kestrel, Green and Greater Spotted Woodpeckers, Tawny Owl, Barn Owl, Little Owl, Jay, Coal Tit and other woodland species.
Contact: National Trust. 01422 844 518.

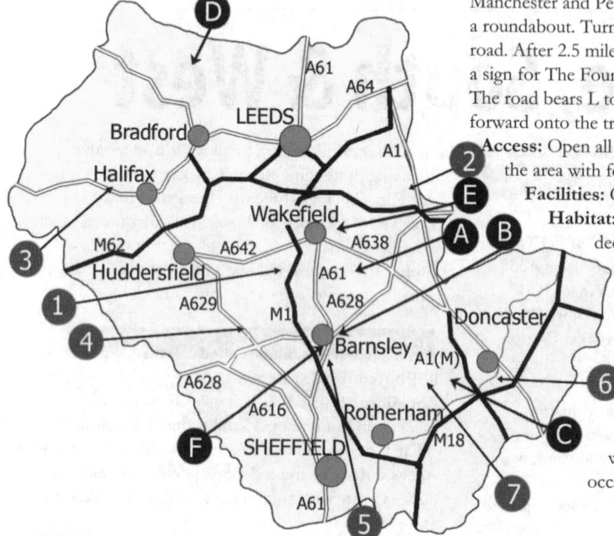

4. INGBIRCHWORTH RESERVOIR

Yorkshire Water.
Location: Leave the M1 at J37 and take the A628 to Manchester and Penistone. After five miles you reach a roundabout. Turn R onto the A629 Huddersfield road. After 2.5 miles you reach Ingbirchworth. At a sign for The Fountain Inn, turn L. Pass a pub. The road bears L to cross the dam, proceed straight forward onto the track leading to the car park.
Access: Open all year. One of the few reservoirs in the area with footpath access.
Facilities: Car park, picnic tables.
Habitat: Reservoir, small strip of deciduous woodland.
Key birds: *Spring/summer*: Whinchat, warblers, woodland birds, House Martin. *Spring/autumn passage*: Little Ringed Plover, Ringed Plover, Dotterel, waders, Common Tern, Arctic Tern, Black Tern, Yellow Wagtail, Wheatear. *Winter*: wildfowl, Golden Plover, waders, occasional rare gull such as Iceland

or Glaucous, Grey Wagtail, Fieldfare, Redwing, Brambling, Redpoll.
Contact: Yorkshire Water, PO Box 52, Bradford BD3 7YD.

5. OLD MOOR

RSPB North West Office.
Location: SE 422 011. From M1 J36, then A6195. From A1 J37, then A635 and A6195 – follow brown signs.
Access: Open Apr 1-Oct 31 (Wed-Sun 9am-5pm), Nov 1-Mar 31 (Wed/Thu-Sat/Sun 10am-4pm). Members free. Non-member adults – £2.50. Concessions – £2.
Facilities: Toilets (including disabled), large visitor centre and shop, five superb hides. All sites including hides fully accessible for disabled.
Public transport: Buses – information from South Yorkshire Passenger Transport 01709 589 200.
Habitat: Lakes and flood meadows, wader scrape and reedbeds.
Key birds: *Winter*: Large numbers of wildfowl. *Summer*: Breeding waders and wildfowl. Rare vagrants recorded annually.
Contact: The Warden, RSPB Old Moor, Old Moor Lane, Wombwell, Barnsley, South Yorkshire S73 0YF. 01226 751 593 Fax: 01226 341 078. www.rspb.org.uk

6. POTTERIC CARR

Yorkshire Wildlife Trust.
Location: SE 589 007. From M18 junction 3 take A6182 (Doncaster) and at first roundabout take third exit; entrance and car park are on R after 50m.
Access: Access by permit only. Parties must obtain prior permission.
Facilities: Field Centre (hot and cold drinks, snacks and meals, toilet) open 9.30am-4pm Thursdays to Sundays all year round. Bank Holiday Mondays open, also Tues 9.30am-1.30pm. Approx 12 km of footpaths including 8km suitable for disabled unaided. Twelve new/refurbished hides, 10 suitable for wheelchairs. See website for more details and events programme.
Public transport: Buses from Doncaster to new B&Q store travel within easy reach of entrance.
Habitat: Reed fen, subsidence ponds, artificial pools, grassland, woodland.
Key birds: 96 species have bred. Nesting waterfowl (inc. Shoveler, Gadwall, Pochard), Water Rail, Kingfisher, all three woodpeckers, Lesser Whitethroat, Reed and Sedge Warblers, Willow Tit. *Passage/winter*: Bittern, Marsh Harrier, Black Tern, waders, wildfowl.
Other notable flora and fauna: 20 species of dragonfly recorded, 28 species of butterfly including purple hairstreak and dingy skipper, palmate and great crested newt.
Contact: For further contact information, visit www.potteric-carr.org.uk.

7. SPROTBOROUGH FLASH RESERVE AND THE DON GORGE

Yorkshire Wildlife Trust.
Location: From A1, follow A630 to Rotherham 4.8km W of Doncaster. After 0.8km, turn R at traffic lights to Sprotborough. After approx 1.6km the road drops down the slopes of the Gorse. Cross a bridge over river, then another over a canal, turn immediately L. Park in a small roadside parking area 45m on L beside canal. Walk along canal bank, past The Boat Inn to reserve entrance approx 90m further on.
Access: Open all year.
Facilities: Three hides, footpaths.
Public transport: River bus from Doncaster in summer months.
Habitat: River, reed, gorge, woodland.
Key birds: *Summer*: Turtle Dove, Cuckoo, hirundines, Lesser Whitethroat, Whitethroat, Garden Warbler, Blackcap, Chiffchaff, Willow Warbler, Spotted Flycatcher. *Spring/autumn passage*: Little Ringed Plover, Dunlin, Greenshank, Green Sandpiper, waders, Yellow Wagtail. *Winter/all year*: Wildfowl, Water Rail, Snipe, Little Owl, Tawny Owl, all three woodpeckers, thrushes, Siskin, possible Corn Bunting.
Contact: Yorkshire Wildlife Trust, 01904 659 570. e-mail: info@ywt.org.uk www.ywt.org.uk

OTHER SITES

Full details in previous editions, (year indicated in brackets).
A. Anglers Country Park – Wakefield MBC, 01924 302 600 (04).
B. Carlton Marsh – Barnsley MBC, 01226 772 142 (04).
C. Denaby Ings – Yorks WT, 01904 659 570 (06).
D. Denso Marston – Andrew Clarke, 01274 582 266 (04).
E. Pugneys Country Park – Wakefield MBC, 01924 302 600 (04).
F. Worsborough Country Park – Worsborough Mill, 01226 774 527 (04).

SCOTLAND

Border Counties

Borders

1. BEMERSYDE MOSS

Scottish Wildlife Trust.
Location: NT 614 340. 7.9 miles E of Melrose on minor road, between Melrose and Smailholm.
Access: Open all year.
Facilities: Hide with parking nearby and disabled access.
Public transport: None.
Habitat: Shallow loch and marsh.
Key birds: *Summer*: Grasshopper Warbler. *Winter*: Wildfowl, waders on migration, raptors.
Contact: SWT headquarters, 0131 312 7765.

2. DUNS CASTLE

Scottish Wildlife Trust.
Location: NT 778 550. Located N of the centre of Duns (W of Berwick upon Tweed).
Access: Access from Castle Street or at N end of reserve from B6365.
Facilities: None
Public transport: None.
Habitat: Loch and woodland.
Key birds: Woodland birds, waterfowl.

Other notable flora and fauna: Occasional otter.
Contact: SWT headquarters, 132 312 7765.

3. GUNKNOWE LOCH AND PARK

Borders Council.
Location: NT 523 51. 3.2km from Galashiels on the A6091. Park at Gunknowe Loch.
Access: Open all year. Surfaced paths suitable for wheelchair use.
Facilities: Car park, paths.
Public transport: Tweedbank is on the Melrose to Peebles bus route.
Habitat: River, parkland, scrub, woodland.
Key birds: *Spring/summer*: Grey Wagtail, Kingfisher, Sand Martin, Blackcap, Sedge and Grasshopper Warblers. *Passage*: Yellow Wagtail, Whinchat, Wheatear. *Winter*: Thrushes, Brambling, Wigeon, Tufted Duck, Pochard, Goldeneye. *All year*: Great Spotted and Green Woodpeckers, Redpoll, Goosander, possible Marsh Tit.
Contact: Countryside Ranger Service, Harestanes,Ancrum,Jedburgh,TD8 6UQ. 01835 830 281; Fax: 01835 830 717. www.scotborders.gov.uk

4. ST ABB'S HEAD

National Trust for Scotland.
Location: NT 914 693. Lies five miles N of Eyemouth. Follow A1107 from A1.
Access: Reserve open all year. Keep dogs under control. Viewpoint at Starney accessible for disabled visitors. Coach parking at Northfield Farm by prior arrangement.
Facilities: Visitor centre and toilets open daily Apr-Oct.
Public transport: Nearest rail station is Berwick-upon-Tweed. Bus service from Berwick, tel 018907 81533.
Habitat: Cliffs, coastal grasslands and freshwater loch.
Key birds: Apr-Aug: Seabird colonies with large numbers of Kittiwake, auks, Shag, Fulmar, migrants. Apr-May and Sept-Oct: Good autumn seawatching.
Contact: Kevin Rideout, Rangers Cottage, Northfield, St Abbs, Borders TD14 5QF. 01890 771 443.
e-mail: krideout@nts.org.uk www.nts.org.uk

5. THE HIRSEL

The Estate Office, The Hirsel.
Location: NT 827 403. Signed off the A69 on the outskirts of Coldstream.
Access: Open all year. Private estate so please stick to the public paths.
Facilities: Car parks, visitor centre, leaflets, trails.
Public transport: Bus: Coldstream, Kelso, Berwick-upon-Tweed, Edinburgh.
Habitat: Freshwater loch, reeds, woods.
Key birds: *Spring/summer*: Redstart, Garden Warbler, Blackcap, flycatchers, possible Water Rail, wildfowl. *Autumn*: Wildfowl, Goosander, possible Green Sandpiper. *Winter*: Whooper Swan, Pink-footed Goose, Wigeon, Goldeneye, Pochard, occasional Smew, Scaup, Slavonian Grebe.
Contact: The Estate Office, The Hirsel, Coldstream TD12 4LF. 01890 882 834.

OTHER SITES

Full details in previous editions, (year indicated in brackets).
A. Pease Dean – Scottish WT, 01313 127 765 (05).
B. Yetholm Loch – Scottish WT, 01313 127 765 (04).

Dumfries & Galloway

6. CAERLAVEROCK

The Wildfowl & Wetlands Trust.
Location: NY 051 656. From Dumfries take B725 towards Bankend.
Access: Open daily except Christmas Day.
Facilities: 20 hides, heated observatory, four towers, Salcot Merse Observatory, sheltered picnic area. Self-catering accommodation and camping facilities. Nature trails in summer. Old Granary visitor building with fair-trade coffee shop serving light meals and snacks; natural history bookshop; binoculars & telescopes for sale. Theatre/conference room. Binoculars for hire. Parking for coaches.
Public transport: Bus 371 from Dumfries stops 30 mins walk from reserve. Stagecoach 01387 253 496.
Habitat: Saltmarsh, grassland.
Key birds: *Winter*: Wildfowl esp. Barnacle Geese (max 25,000) and Whooper Swan.
Contact: The Wildfowl & Wetlands Trust, Eastpark Farm, Caerlaverock, Dumfries DG1 4RS. 01387 770 200.

7. KEN/DEE MARSHES

RSPB (South & West Scotland Office).
Location: NX 699 684. Six miles from Castle Douglas – good views from A762 and A713 roads to New Galloway.
Access: From car park at entrance to farm Mains of Duchrae. Open during daylight hours. No dogs.
Facilities: Hides, nature trails. Three miles of trails

available, nearer parking for elderly and disabled, but phone warden first. Part of Red Kite trail.
Public transport: None.
Habitat: Marshes, woodlands, open water.
Key birds: *All year*: Mallard, Grey Heron, Buzzard. *Spring/summer*: Pied Flycatcher, Redstart, Tree Pipit, Sedge Warbler. *Winter*: Greenland White-fronted and Greylag Geese, birds of prey (Hen Harrier, Peregrine, Merlin, Red Kite).
Contact: Paul Collin, Gairland, Old Edinburgh Road, Minnigaff, Newton Stewart DG8 6PL. 01671 402 861.

8. MERSEHEAD

RSPB (South & West Scotland Office).
Location: NX 925 560. From Dalbeattie, take B793 or A710 SE to Caulkerbush.
Access: Open at all times.
Facilities: Hide, nature trails, information centre and toilets. **Public transport:** None.
Habitat: Wet grassland, arable farmland, saltmarsh, inter-tidal mudflats.
Key birds: *Winter*: Up to 9,500 Barnacle Geese, 4,000 Teal, 2,000 Wigeon, 1,000 Pintail, waders (inc. Dunlin, Knot, Oystercatcher). *Summer*: Breeding birds include Lapwing, Redshank, Sky Lark.
Contact: Eric Nielson, Mersehead, Southwick, Mersehead, Dumfries DG2 8AH. 01387 780 298.

9. MULL OF GALLOWAY

RSPB (South & West Scotland Office).
Location: NX 156 304. Most southerly tip of Scotland – five miles from village of Drummore, S of Stranraer.
Access: Open at all times. Access suitable for disabled. Disabled parking by centre. Centre open summer only (Apr-Oct).
Facilities: Visitor centre, toilets, nature trails, CCTV on cliffs. **Public transport:** None.
Habitat: Sea cliffs, coastal heath.
Key birds: *Spring/summer*: Guillemot, Razorbill, Kittiwake, Black Guillemot, Puffin, Fulmar, Raven, Wheatear, Rock Pipit, Twite. Migrating Manx Shearwater. *All year*: Peregrine.
Contact: Paul Collin, Gairland, Old Edinburgh Road, Minnigaff, Newton Stewart DG8 6PL. 01671 402 851.

10. WIGTOWN BAY LNR

Dumfries & Galloway Council.
Location: NX 465 545. Between Wigtown and Creetown, S of Newton Stewart. It is the largest LNR in Britain at 2,845 ha. The A75 runs along E side with A714 S to Wigtown and B7004 providing superb views of the LNR.
Access: Open at all times. The hide is disabled friendly. Main accesses: Roadside lay-bys on A75 near Creetown and parking at Martyr's Stake and Wigtown Harbour. All suitable for coaches. The visitor facility in Wigtown County Building has full disabled access, including lift and toilets.
Facilities: A hide at Wigtown Harbour with views over the River Bladnoch, saltmarsh and fresh water wetland has disabled access from harbour car park. Walks and interpretation in this area. Visitor room in Wigtown County Buildings has interpretation facilities and a commanding view of the bay. CCTV of Ospreys breeding in Galloway during summer and wetland birds in winter. Open Mon-Sat (10am-5pm, later some days). Sun (2pm-5pm).
Public transport: Travel Information Line 08457 090 510 (local rate 9am-5pm Mon-Fri). Bus No 415 for Wigtown and W side. Bus No 431 or 500 X75 for Creetown and E side.
Habitat: Estuary with extensive saltmarsh/merse and mudflats with developed fresh water wetland at Wigtown Harbour.
Key birds: *Winter*: Internationally important for Pink-footed Goose, nationally important for Curlew,

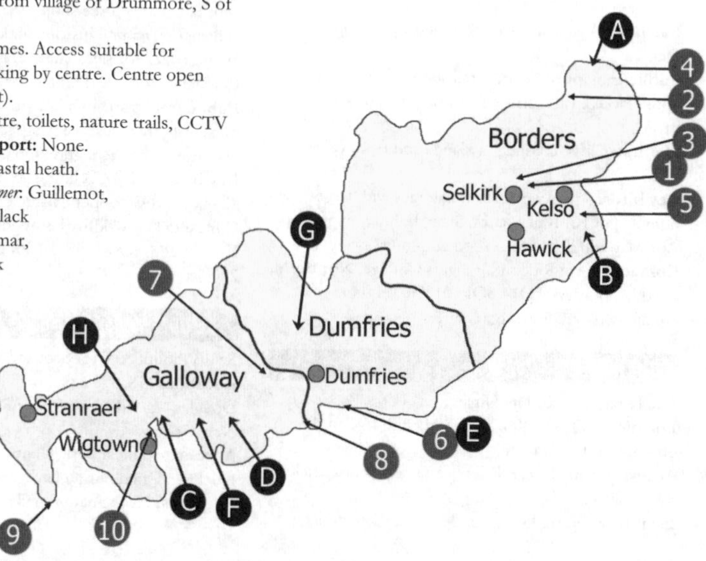

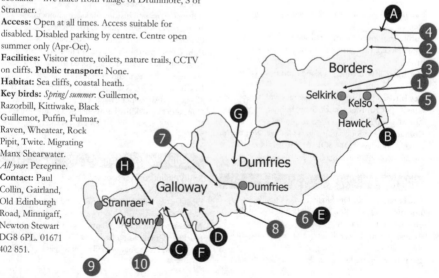

Whooper Swan and Pintail, with major gull roost and other migratory coastal birds. *Summer*: Breeding waders and duck.
Contact: Elizabeth Tindal, County Buildings, Wigtown, Dumfries & Galloway DG8 9JH. 01988 402 401, mobile 07702 212 728.
e-mail: Elizabeth.Tindal@dumgal.gov.uk
www.dgcommunity.net/wbln

OTHER SITES

Full details in previous editions, (year indicated in brackets).

C. Black Craig Wood – Scottish WT, 01313 127 765 (05).
D. Carstramon Wood – Scottish WT, 01313 127 765 (04).
E. Caerlaverock NNR – Scottish Natural Heritage, 01387 770 275 (05).
F. Cairnsmore of Fleet NNR – SNH, 01557 814 435 (05).
G. Stenhouse Wood – Scottish WT, 01313 127 765 (04).
H. Wood of Cree – RSPB, 01671 402 861 (04).

Central Scotland

Argyll

1. COLL RSPB RESERVE

RSPB (South & West Scotland Office).
Location: NM 168 561. By ferry from Oban. Take the B8070 W from Arinagour for five miles. Turn R at Arileod. Continue for about one mile. Park at end of the road. Reception point at Totronald.
Access: Open all year. Please avoid walking through fields and crops.
Facilities: Car park, information bothy at Totronald, guided walks in summer. Corn Crake viewing bench.
Public transport: None.
Habitat: Sand dunes, beaches, machair grassland, moorland, farmland.
Key birds: *Spring/summer*: Corn Crake, Redshank, Lapwing, Snipe. *Winter*: Barnacle and Greenland White-fronted Geese.
Contact: RSPB Coll Nature Reserve, Totronald, Isle of Coll, Argyll, PA78 6TB, 01879 230 30.

2. LOCH GRUINART, ISLAY

RSPB Scotland (South & West Scotland Office).
Location: Sea loch on N coast, seven miles NW from Bridgend.
Access: Hide open all hours, visitor centre open (10am-5pm), disabled access to hide, toilets. Assistance required for wheelchair users.Coach parking at visitor centre only. No dogs.
Facilities: Toilets, visitor centre, hide, trail.
Public transport: None.
Habitat: Lowland wet grasslands, moorland.
Key birds: Oct-Apr: Barnacle and Greenland White-fronted Goose. May-Aug: Corn Crake. Sept-Nov: Migrating wading birds.
Contact: Liz Hathaway, RSPB Scotland, Bushmills Cottage, Gruinart, Isle of Islay PA44 7PP. 01496 850 505. e-mail: loch.gruinart@rspb.org.uk
www.rspb.org.uk/scotland

3. MACHRIHANISH SEABIRD OBSERVATORY

Eddie Maguire and John McGlynn.
Location: NR 628 209. Southwest Kintyre, Argyll. Six miles W of Campbeltown on A83, then B843.
Access: Daily April-Oct. Wheelchair access. Dogs welcome. Parking for three cars. Digiscoping facilities include electricity and monitor.
Facilities: Seawatching hide, toilets in nearby village.
Public transport: Regular buses from Campbeltown (West Coast Motors, tel 01586 552 319).
Habitat: Marine, rocky shore and upland habitats.
Key birds: *Summer*: Golden Eagle, Peregrine, Storm Petrel and Twite. *Autumn*: Passage seabirds and waders. On-shore gales often produce inshore movements of Leach's Petrel and other scarce seabirds, including Balearic Shearwater, Sabine's Gull and Grey Phalarope. *Winter*: Great Northern Diver.
Contact: Eddie Maguire, Seabird & Wildlife Observatory, Lossit Park, Machrihanish, SW Kintyre, Argyll PA28 6PZ. 07919 660 292.
www.machrihanishbirds.org.uk

4. THE OA, ISLAY

RSPB Scotland
Location: NR 282 423. Six miles SW of Port Ellen, Islay.
Access: Open all year.
Facilities: Car park and waymarked trail. No toilets or other facilities. Two guided walks per month (May to September).

Public transport: None.
Habitat: Open moorland, freshwater loch, seacliffs, coastal grassland and heath.
Key birds: Breeding Golden Eagle, Red-throated Diver, Peregrine, Hen Harrier, Chough waders and farmland birds. *Winter*: Greenland White-fronted Goose and winter thrushes.
Contact: Angus Keys, RSPB Scotland, Kinnabus Farm, The Oa, Port Ellen PA42 7AU. 01496 300 118. E-mail: angus.keys@rspb.org.uk

OTHER SITES

Full details in previous editions, (year indicated in brackets).
A. Knapdale Reserve – Scottish WT (West), 01313 127 765 (04).

Ayrshire

5. AYR GORGE WOODLANDS

Scottish Wildlife Trust.
Location: NS 457 249. From Ayr take A719 NE for about three miles to A768. Go straight over the roundabout onto B473 and continue to Failford. Park in the lay-by in village.
Access: Open all year. Access by path along east bank of River Ayr.
Facilities: Footpaths, interpretation boards, leaflets and information board. Parking.
Public transport: Bus from Ayr to Machline.
Habitat: Woodland.
Key birds: Woodland and riverside birds.
Contact: SWT headquarters, 0131 312 7765.

OTHER SITES

Full details in previous editions, (year indicated in brackets).
B. Culzean Castle & Country Park – National Trust, 0131 243 9300 (06).
C. Dalmellington Moss – Scottish WT, 0131 312 7765 (04).
D. Garnock Floods – Scottish WT, 01313 127 765 (07).

Clyde

6. FALLS OF CLYDE

Scottish Wildlife Trust.
Location: NS 88 34 14. Approx one mile S of Lanark. Directions from Glasgow – travel S on M74 until J7 then along A72, following signs for Lanark and New Lanark.
Access: Open during daylight hours all year. Disabled access limited.
Facilities: Visitor centre open 11am-5pm Mar-Dec, 12-4pm Jan-Feb. Toilets and cafeteria on site. Seasonal viewing facility for Peregrines. Numerous walkways and ranger service offers comprehensive guided walks programme.
Public transport: Scotrail trains run to Lanark (0845 7484 950). Local bus service from Lanark to New Lanark.
Habitat: River Clyde gorge, waterfalls, mixed woodland and broadleaved riparian gorge, meadow, pond.
Key birds: More than 100 species of bird recorded on the reserve, including unrivalled views of breeding Peregrine. Others include Tawny Owl, Kingfisher, Dipper, Great Spotted Woodpecker, Spotted Flycatcher and Goosander.
Contact: Miss Lindsay Cook, The Falls of Clyde Reserve & Visitor Centre, New Lanark, South Lanark ML11 9DB. 01555 665 262.
e-mail: fallsofclyde@swt.co.uk
www.swt.org.uk

7. LOCHWINNOCH

RSPB (South & West Scotland Office).
Location: NS 358 582. 18 miles SW of Glasgow, adjacent to A760.
Access: Open every day except Christmas and Boxing Day, Jan 1 and Jan 2. (10am-5pm).
Facilities: Special facilities for schools and disabled. Refreshments available. Visitor centre, hides.
Public transport: Rail station adjacent, bus services nearby.
Habitat: Shallow lochs, marsh, mixed woodland.
Key birds: *Winter*: Wildfowl (esp. Whooper Swan, Wigeon, Goosander, Goldeneye). Occasional passage migrants inc. Whimbrel, Greenshank. *Summer*: Breeding Great Crested Grebe, Water Rail, Sedge and Grasshopper Warblers, Reed Bunting.
Contact: RSPB Nature Centre, Largs Road, Lochwinnoch, Renfrewshire PA12 4JF. 01505 842 663; Fax 01505 843 026;
e-mail lochwinnoch@rspb.org.uk.

OTHER SITES

Full details in previous editions, (year indicated in brackets).
E. Barons Haugh – RSPB, 01413 310 993 (04).
F. Knockshinnock Lagoons – Scottish WT, 01313 127 765 (07).

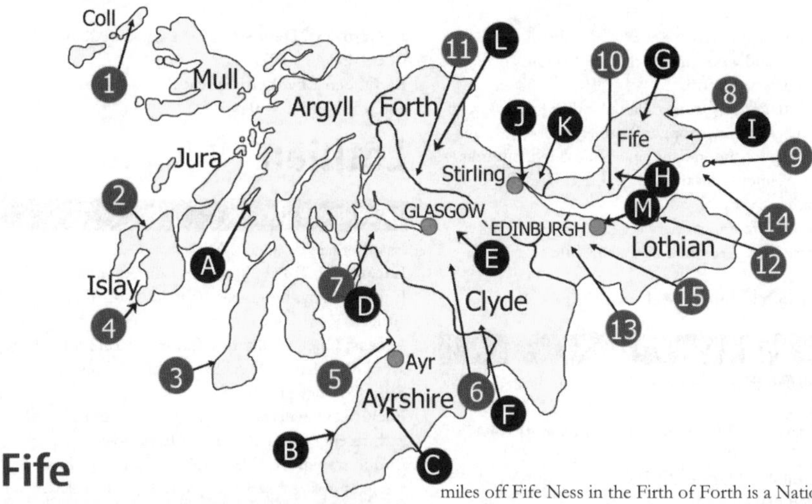

Fife

8. EDEN ESTUARY

Fife Council.

Location: NO 470 195. The reserve can be accessed from Guardbridge, St Andrews (one mile) on A91, and from Leuchars via Tentsmuir Forest off A919 (four miles).

Access: The Eden Estuary Centre is open (9am-5pm) every day except Christmas Day, New Year's Day and the day of the Leuchars airshow. Reserve is open all year, but a permit (from Ranger Service) is required to access the N shore. Limited coach access and coach charge if using Kinshaldy car park.

Facilities: Visitor centre at Guardbridge. Information panels at Outhead. Hide at Balgove Bay (key from Ranger Service).

Public transport: Leuchars train station. Regular buses Cupar-Dundee-St Andrews. Tel: 01334 474238.

Habitat: Saltmarsh, river, tidal flats, sand dunes.

Key birds: *Winter*: Main interest is wildfowl and waders, best place in Scotland to see Black-tailed Godwit. Other species include Grey Plover, Shelduck, Bar-tailed Godwit. Offshore Common and Velvet Scoter occur and Surf Scoter is regularly seen. Peregrine, Merlin and Short-eared Owl occur in winter.

Contact: Les Hatton, Fife Ranger Service, Craigtown Country Park, St Andrews, Fife KY16 8NX. 01334 473 047/07985 707 593 (mobile).
e-mail: refrs@craigtoun.freserve.co.uk

9. ISLE OF MAY NNR

Scottish Natural Heritage.

Location: NT 655 995. This small island lying six miles off Fife Ness in the Firth of Forth is a National Nature Reserve.

Access: Boats run from Anstruther and North Berwick. Contact SNH for details 01334 654038. Keep to paths. Fishing boat from Anstruther arranged for those using Observatory accommodation. Delays are possible, both arriving and leaving, because of weather.

Facilities: No dogs; no camping; no fires. Prior permission required if scientific work or filming is to be carried out.

Public transport: Regular bus service to Anstruther and North Berwick harbour.

Habitat: Sea cliffs, rocky shoreline.

Key birds: Early *Summer*: Breeding auks and terns, Kittiwake, Shag, Eider, Fulmar. Over 68,000 pairs of Puffins. *Autumn/spring*: Weather-related migrations include rarities each year.

Contact: For Observatory accomodation: David Thorne, Craigurd House, Blyth Bridge, West Linton, Peeblesshire EH46 7AH. For all other enquiries: SNH, 46 Crossgate, Cupar, Fife Ky15 5HS.

10. LOCHORE MEADOWS COUNTRY PARK

Fife Ranger Service.

Location: NT165 958. Exit the M90 at J4. Drive E past Kelty on the A909. Turn L onto the B996 Cowdenbeath-Kinross road after one mile and take the 1st R to a car park.

Access: Open all year. Coach parking available at Main Centre car park.

Facilities: Café, play park, car park, hide in nature reserve. Suitable for wheelchairs.

Public transport: Bus: from Cowdenbeath/ Dunfermline to Kelty.

Habitat: Nature reserve at W end of Loch Ore, meadows and woodland, reclaimed from former coalmining wasteland..
Key birds: *Spring/summer*: Pintail, other ducks, Green Woodpecker, Grasshopper Warbler, Wood Warbler, Whinchat, Common Sandpiper, Redshank, hirundines. *Winter*: Whooper Swan, Redwing, Fieldfare, Redpoll, Siskin.
Contact: Fife Ranger Service, Lochore Meadows Country Park, Crosshill, Lochgelly, Fife KY5 8BA. 01592 414 300.
e-mail: info.Lochore-Meadows@fife.gov.uk

OTHER SITES

Full details in previous editions, (year indicated in brackets).
G . Cameron Reservoir – Sheila Taylor, 01334 475 541 (04)
H. Cullaloe Nature Reserve – Scottish WT, 01313 127 765 (04).
I. Kilminning Coast – Scottish WT, 01313 127 765 (07).

Forth

11. INVERSNAID

RSPB (South & West Scotland Office).
Location: NN 337 088. On E side of Loch Lomond. Via B829 W from Aberfoyle, then along minor road to car park by Inversnaid Hotel.
Access: Open all year.
Facilities: New car park and trail at Garrison Farm (NN 348 095).
Public transport: None.
Habitat: Deciduous woodland rises to craggy ridge and moorland.
Key birds: *Summer*: Breeding Black Grouse, Snipe, Wheatear and Twite. Grey Wagtail, Dipper, Wood Warbler, Redstart, Pied Flycatcher, Tree Pipit. The loch is on a migration route, especially for wildfowl and waders.
Other notable flora and fauna: Small pearl bordered fritillary on nature trail at Inversaid. Wilsons and Tunbridge filmy ferns on boulders through woodland.
Contact: RSPB South & West Scotland Office, 10 Park Quadrant, Glasgow, G3 6BS. 01413 310 993.

OTHER SITES

Full details in previous editions, (year indicated in brackets).
J. Cambus Pools – Scottish WT, 01313 127 765 (04).
K. Gartmorn Dam – Clackmannanshire Rangers, 01259 452 409 (07).
L. Queen Elizabeth Forest Park – Forest enterprise 01313 340 303.

Lothian

12. ABERLADY BAY

East Lothian Council (LNR).
Location: NT 472 806. From Edinburgh take A198 E to Aberlady. Reserve is 1.5 miles E of Aberlady village.
Access: Open at all times. Please stay on footpaths to avoid disturbance. Disabled access from reserve car park. No dogs please.
Facilities: Small car park and toilets. Notice board with recent sightings at end of footbridge.
Public transport: Edinburgh to N Berwick bus service stops at reserve (request), service no 124. Railway 4 miles away at Longniddry.
Habitat: Tidal mudflats, saltmarsh, freshwater marsh, dune grassland, scrub, open sea.
Key birds: *Summer*: Breeding birds include Shelduck, Eider, Reed Bunting and up to eight species of warbler. Passage waders inc. Green, Wood and Curlew Sandpipers, Little Stint, Greenshank, Whimbrel, Black-tailed Godwit. *Winter*: Divers (esp. Red-throated), Red-necked and Slavonian Grebes and geese (large numbers of Pink-footed roost); sea-ducks, waders.
Contact: John Harrison, Reserve Warden, Landscape & Countryside Management, East Lothian Council, Council Buildings, East Lothian EH41 3HA. 01875 870 588. email: jharrison@eastlothian.gov.uk www.aberlady.org

13. ALMONDELL AND CALDERWOOD CP

West Lothian Council.
Location: NT 091 697 – north entrance, the closest to the visitor centre – signposted off A89, two miles S of Broxburn.
Access: Open all year. Parking available at N entrance. S entrance at East Calder. Mid Calder and Oakbank on A71 (furthest from visitor centre). Disabled car park at visitor centre. Coach parking available with prior notice.
Facilities: Car park, picnic area,hot and cold drinks, toilets, pushchair access, partial access for wheelchairs, visitor centre (open every day), gift shop, countryside ranger service.
Public transport: None.
Habitat: Woodland, river.

Key birds: *Spring/summer*: Woodcock, Tawny Owl, Grasshopper Warbler, Yellowhammer, Blackcap, Garden Warbler. *Winter*: Goldcrest, Redpoll, Willow Tit. *All year*: Dipper, Grey Wagtail, Sparrowhawk.
Contact: Head Ranger, Almondell and Calderwood Country ParkVisitor Centre, Broxburn, West Lothian, EH52 5PE, 01506 882 254. www.beecraigs.com
e-mail: almondell&calderwood@westlothian.gov.uk

14. BASS ROCK

Location: NT 602 873. Island in Firth of Forth, lying E of North Berwick.
Access: Private property. Regular daily sailings from N Berwick around Rock; local boatman has owner's permission to land individuals or parties by prior arrangement. For details contact 01620 892 838 or The Scottish Seabird Centre 01620 890 202; www.seabird.org
Facilities: None.
Habitat: Sea cliffs.
Key birds: The spectacular cliffs hold a large Gannet colony, (up to 9,000 pairs), plus auks, Kittiwake, Shag and Fulmer.

15. GLADHOUSE RESERVOIR LNR

Scottish Water.
Location: NT 295 535. S of Edinburgh off the A703.
Access: Open all year although there is no access to the reservoir itself. Most viewing can be done from the road (telescope required).
Facilities: Small car park on north side. Not suitable for coaches.
Habitat: Reservoir, grassland, farmland.
Key birds: *Spring/summer*: Oystercatcher, Lapwing, Curlew. Possible Black Grouse. *Winter*: Geese, including Pinkfeet, Twite, Brambling, Hen Harrier.
Contact: Scottish Water, PO Box 8855, Edinburgh, EH10 6YQ, 084 6 018 855.
e-mail: customer.service@scottishwater.co.uk
www.scottishwater.co.cuk

OTHER SITES

Full details in previous editions, (year indicated in brackets).
M. Bawsinch & Duddingston Loch – Scottish WT, 01313 127 765 (04).

Eastern Scotland

Angus And Dundee

1. LOCH OF KINNORDY

RSPB (East Scotland).
Location: NO 351 539. Car park on B951 one mile W of Kirriemuir. Perth 45 minutes drive, Dundee 30 minutes drive, Aberdeen one hour drive.
Access: Open dawn-dusk. Disabled access to two hides via short trails.
Facilities: Three birdwatching hides.
Public transport: Nearest centre is Kirriemuir.
Habitat: Freshwater loch, fen, carr, marsh.
Key birds: *Spring/summer*: Osprey, Black-headed Gull. *Winter*: Wildfowl including Goosander, Goldeneye and Whooper Swan.
Contact: Alan Leitch, RSPB, 1 Atholl Crescent, Perth PH1 5NG. 01738 639 783. www.rspb.org
e-mail: alan.leitch@rspb.org

2. LOCH OF LINTRATHEN

Scottish Wildlife Trust.
Location: H 278 550. Seven miles W of Kirriemuir. Take B951 and choose circular route on unclassified roads round loch.
Access: Public hide planned but to date, Scottish Wildlife Trust hide (members' permit system only). Good viewing points from several places along unclassified roads.
Facilities: Parking
Public transport: None.
Habitat: Oligatrophic/mesotrophic loch. Surrounded by mainly coniferous woodland.
Key birds: *Summer*: Osprey. *Winter*: Greylag Goose, Goosander, Whooper Swan, Wigeon, Teal.
Contact: Rick Goater, SWT, Annat House, South Anag, Ferryden, Montrose, Angus DD10 9UT. 01674 676 555. e-mail: swtnero@cix.co.uk

3. MONTROSE BASIN

Scottish Wildlife Trust on behalf of Angus Council.
Location: NO 690 580 – centre of basin. NO 702 565 – Wildlife SWT Centre on A92. 1.5 miles from centre of Montrose.
Access: Apr 1-Oct 31 (10.30am-5pm). Nov 1-Mar 31, (10.30am-4pm).
Facilities: Visitor centre, shop, vending machine,

toilets, disabled access to centre, two hides on western half of reserve.
Public transport: Train 1.5 miles in Montrose. Buses same as above.
Habitat: Estuary, saltmarsh, reedbeds, farmland.
Key birds: Pink-footed Goose – up to 35,000 arrive Oct. Wintering wildfowl and waders. Breeding Eider Ducks.
Contact: Karen van Eeden, Scottish Wildlife Trust, Montrose Basin Wildlife Centre, Rossie Braes, Montrose DD10 9TJ. 01674 676 336. www.swt.org.uk e-mail: montrosebasin@swt.org.uk

OTHER SITES

Full details in previous editions, (year indicated in brackets).
A. Balgavies Loch – Montrose Basin Centre, 01674 676 336 (04).
B. Seaton Cliffs – Scottish WT, 01313 127 765 (07).

Moray & Nairn

4. CULBIN SANDS

RSPB (North Scotland Office).
Location: NH 900 580. Approx ½ mile from Nairn. Access to parking at East Beach car park, signed off A96.
Access: Open at all times. Path to reserve suitable for all abilities.
Facilities: Toilets at car park. Track along dunes and saltmarsh.
Public transport: Buses stop in Nairn, half mile W of site. Train station in Nairn three-quarters mile W of reserve.
Habitat: Saltmarsh, sandflats, dunes.
Key birds: *Winter*: Flocks of Common Scoter, Long-tailed Duck, Knot, Bar-tailed Godwit, Red-breasted Merganser. Raptors like Peregrine, Merlin and Hen Harrier attracted by wader flocks. Roosting geese. *Summer*: Breeding Ringed Plover, Oystercatcher.
Contact: RSPB North Scotland Office, Etive House, Beechwood Park, Inverness IV2 3BW. 01463 715 000. e-mail: nsro@rspb.org.uk www.rspb.org.uk

5. SPEY BAY

Scottish Wildlife Trust.
Location: NJ 335 657. Eight miles NE of Elgin. From Elgin take A96 and B9015 to Kingston. Reserve is immediately E of village. Car parks at Kingston and Tugnet.
Access: Open all year.
Facilities: Car park, information board.
Public transport: None.
Habitat: Shingle, rivermouth and coastal habitats.
Key birds: *Summer*: Osprey, waders, wildfowl. *Winter*: Seaduck and divers offshore, esp. Long-tailed Duck, Common and Velvet Scoters, Red-throated Diver.
Contact: SWT headquarters. 0131 312 7765.

6. TROUP HEAD

RSPB (East Scotland)
Location: NJ 825 672. Lies between Banff and Fraserburgh overlooking the Moray Firth. Turn off B9031, 1.5miles E of Gardenstown and follow informal paths to clifftop from Northfield Farm.
Access: Unrestricted, but not suitable for wheelchair users. Boat trips available from Banff and Macduff – Puffin Cruises (www.puffincruises.com or call 01542 832 560) and North58 (www.north58.co.uk or call 01261 819 900).
Facilities: Informal car park 920 yards from entrance.
Habitat: Sea cliffs and coastal grassland.

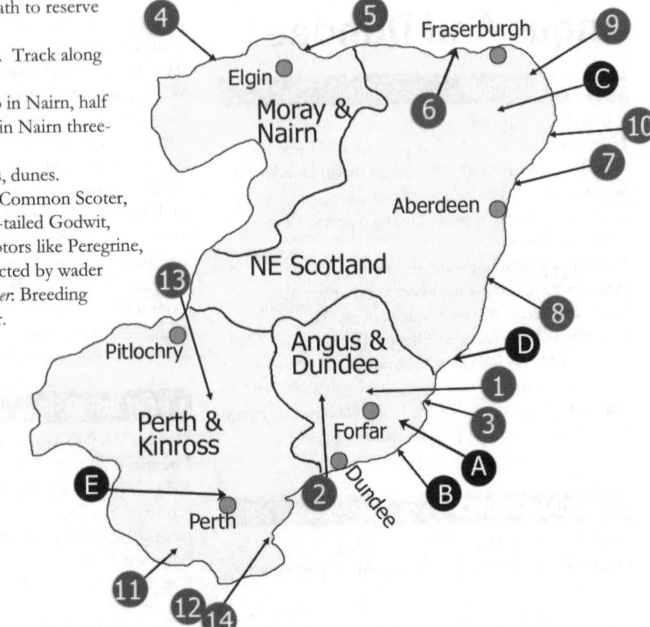

Key birds: Scotland's only mainland Gannet colony, plus Fulmar, Kittiwake and auks.
Other notable flora and fauna: Minke whale, bottle-nosed dolphin, porpoise, grey and common seals regularly seen offshore.
Contact: The warden, Starnafin, Crimond, Fraserbugh AB43 8QN. Tel: 01346 532 017. E-mail: troup@rspb.org.uk

NE Scotland

7. FORVIE NNR

Scottish Natural Heritage.
Location: NK 034 289.
Access: Dogs on leads only. Reserve open at all times but ternery closed Apr 1-end of Aug annually. Stevenson Forvie Centre open every day (Apr-Sept) and, when staff are available, outside those months. Wheelchair access to the centre.
Facilities: Interpretive display and toilets in Stevenson Forvie Centre. Bird hide, waymarked trail. Space is available for coach parking at the Stevenson Forvie Centre or at Waterside Car Park.
Public transport: Bluebird No 263 to Cruden Bay. Ask for the Newburgh or Collieston Crossroads stop. Tel: 01224 591 381.
Habitat: Estuary, dunes, coastal heath.
Key birds: *Spring/ summer*: Eider and terns nesting. *Winter*: Waders and wildfowl on estuary.
Contact: Annabel Drysdale (Reserve Manager), Scottish Natural Heritage, 01358 751 330. www.snh.org.uk

8. FOWLSHEUGH

RSPB (East Scotland).
Location: NO 879 80. Cliff top path N from Crawton, signposted from A92, three miles S of Stonehaven.
Access: Unrestricted. Not suitable for wheelchair users. Boat trips (May-Jul) from Stonehaven Harbour.
Facilities: Car park with 12 spaces, 200 yards from reserve.
Public transport: Request bus stop (Stonehaven to Johnshaven route). Mile walk to reserve entrance.
Habitat: Sea cliffs.
Key birds: Spectacular seabird colony, mainlyFulmar, Kittiwake and auks.
Other notable flora and fauna: Grey and common seals, Bottle-nosed dolphins seen regularly.
Contact: The Warden, Starnafin, Crimond, Fraserburgh AB43 8QN. 01346 532 017. e-mail: strathbeg@rspb.org.uk www.rspb.org.uk

9. LOCH OF STRATHBEG

RSPB (East Scotland).
Location: NK 057 581. Near Crimond on the A90, nine miles S of Fraserburgh.
Access: Starnafin visitor centre and Tower Pool hide open dawn-dusk. Loch hides, access restricted to 8am-4pm daily. Visitor centre now fully accessible to wheelchairs and disabled visitors. Access to certain parts of reserve liable to change at short notice - check at visitor centre. Please book coaches in advance.
Facilities: Visitor centre and observation room at Starnafin, four hides. Tower Pool hide accessible via 1,000 metre footpath from Starnafin.Three hides overlooking Loch accessed via MOD airfield). Toilets (with disabled access), car parking.
Public transport: Access to whole of reserve difficult without a vehicle. Stagecoach bus service between Fraserburgh and Peterhead stops at Crimond, just over one mile from visitor centre. Call 01779 470 077 for timetable info.
Habitat: Dune loch with surrounding marshes, reedbeds, grasslands, dunes and agricultural land.
Key birds: *Winter*: Internationally important numbers of Whooper Swan, Pink-footed and Barnacle Geese, large numbers of winter duck including Smew. *Spring/ summer*: Waders, Black-headed Gull, Common Tern, Water Rail, farmland birds including Corn Bunting. *Spring/ autumn*: Spoonbill, Little Egret, Marsh Harrier, passage waders including Black-tailed Godwit.
Contact: RSPB Warden, RSPB Loch of Strathbeg, 01346 532 017. e-mail: strathbeg@rspb.org.uk

10. LONGHAVEN CLIFFS

Scottish Wildlife Trust.
Location: NK 116 394. 3.8 miles S of Peterhead. Take A952 S from Peterhead and then A975 to Bullers of Buchan (gorge).
Access: Access from car park at Blackhills quarry or Bullers of Buchan.
Facilities: Leaflet available. Parking.
Habitat: Rugged red granite cliffs and cliff-top vegetation.
Key birds: May-July: Nine species of breeding seabird, including Kittiwake, Shag, Guillemot, Razorbill, Puffin.
Contact: SWT headquarters 0131 312 7765.

OTHER SITES

Full details in previous editions, (year indicated in brackets).
C. Haddo Country Park – Aberdeenshire Council, 01658 726 414 (07).
D. St Cyrus – SNH, 01674 830 736 (04).

Perth & Kinross

11. DOUNE PONDS

Stirling Council.
Location: NN 726 019. Take the A820 Dunblane road E from the junction with the A84 Callander-Stirling road. Turn L onto Moray Street just before Doune Church.
Access: Open all year.
Facilities: Information board, nature trail, hides. Wheelchair access to both hides. Leaflet from local tourist information offices, local library.
Public transport: Bus: from Stirling and Callander to Doune. Traveline 0870 608 2608.
Habitat: Pools, scrape, plantations, birch woodlands.
Key birds: *All year*: Grey Heron, Buzzard, Snipe, Goldcrest, Siskin, Red Kite. *Spring/summer*: Common Sandpiper, Whitethroat, warblers.
Contact: Stirling Council Countryside Ranger Service, Viewforth, Stirling FK8 2ET. 0845 2777 000.

12. LOCH LEVEN NNR

SNH, Loch Leven Laboratory.
Location: NO 150 010. Head S from Perth and leave M90 at exit 6, Kinross.
Access: Traditional shoreline access areas at three stretches of shoreline. New local access guidance is in place at the site. See www.snh.org.uk for details or pick up leaflet locally. New paths are in place between Kinross and Burleigh Sands.
Facilities: Hides and paths along the west shore. Café and toilets at Kinross harbout. Observation room, café, shop and toilets at Vane Farm.
Public transport: Bus from Perth or Edinburgh to Kinross.
Habitat: Lowland loch with islands.
Key birds: *Winter*: Flocks of geese (more than 20,000 Pinkfeet), huge numbers of the full range of ducks, Whooper Swan. *Summer*: Greatest concentration of inland breeding ducks in Britain (10 species), Ospreys and grebes. *Passage*: Waders (Golden Plover flocks up to 500).
Contact: Paul Brooks, SNH, Loch Leven Laboratory, The Pier, Kinross KY13 8UF. 01577 864 439. www.snh.org.uk

13. LOCH OF THE LOWES

Scottish Wildlife Trust.
Location: NO 042 435. Sixteen miles N of Perth, two miles NE of Dunkeld – just off A923 (signposted).
Access: Visitor centre open Apr-Sept inclusive (10am-5pm). Observation hide open all year – daylight hours. No dogs allowed. Full access for wheelchairs.
Facilities: Visitor centre with toilets, observation hide.
Public transport: Railway station – Birnam/Dunkeld – three miles from reserve. Bus from Dunkeld – two miles from reserve.
Habitat: Freshwater loch with fringing woodland.
Key birds: Breeding Ospreys (Apr-end Aug). Nest in view, 200 metres from hide. Wildfowl and woodland birds. Greylag roost (Oct-Mar).
Contact: Peter Ferns, (Manager), Scottish Wildlife Trust, Loch of the Lowes, Visitor Centre, Dunkeld, Perthshire PH8 0HH. 01350 727 337.

14. VANE FARM NNR

RSPB (East Scotland).
Location: NT 160 993. By Loch Leven. Take exit 5 from M90 onto B9097.
Access: Open daily (10am-5pm) except Christmas Day, Boxing Day, Jan 1 and Jan 2. Cost £3 adults, £2 concessions, 50p children, £6 family. Free to members. No dogs except guide dogs. Disabled access to shop, coffee shop, observation room and toilets. Coach parking available for up to two coaches. Free car parking.
Facilities: Shop, coffee shop and observation room overlooking Loch Leven and the reserve. There is a 1.25 mile hill trail through woodland and moorland. Wetland trail with three observation hides. Toilets, including disabled.
Public transport: Nearest train station Cowdenbeath (nine miles away). Nearest bus station Kinross at Green Hotel (five miles away).
Habitat: Wet grassland and flooded areas by Loch Leven. Arable farmland. Native woodland and heath moorland.
Key birds: *Spring/summer*: Breeding and passage waders (including Lapwing, Redshank, Snipe, Curlew). Farmland birds (including Sky Lark and Yellowhammer). *Winter*: Whooper Swan, Bewick's Swan, Pink-footed Goose.
Contact: Uwe Stoneman, Business Manager, Vane Farm Nature Centre, Kinross, Tayside KY13 9LX. 01577 862 355. e-mail: vanefarm@rspb.co.uk

OTHER SITES

Full details in previous editions, (year indicated in brackets).
E. Quarrymill Woodland Park – Gannochy Trust, 01738 633 890 (04).

Highlands & Islands

Highland & Caithness

1. ABERNETHY FOREST RESERVE – LOCH GARTEN

RSPB (North Scotland Office).
Location: NH 981 184. 2.5 miles from Boat of Garten, eight miles from Aviemore. Off B970, follow 'RSPB Ospreys' road signs (between Apr - Aug only).
Access: Osprey Centre open daily 10am-6pm (Apr to end Aug). Disabled access. No dogs (guide dogs only). No charge to RSPB members. Non-members: adults £3, senior citizens £2, children 50p.
Facilities: Osprey Centre overlooking nesting Ospreys, toilets, optics and CCTV live pictures.
Public transport: Bus service to Boat of Garten from Aviemore, 2.5 mile footpath to Osprey Centre. Steam railway to Boat of Garten from Aviemore.
Habitat: Caledonian pine wood.
Key birds: Ospreys nesting from Apr to Aug, Crested Tit, Crossbill, red squirrel. Possible views of lekking Capercaillies from the hide, Apr to mid-May.
Contact: R W Thaxton, RSPB, Forest Lodge, Nethybridge, Inverness-shire PH25 3EF. 01479 821 894.

2. BEN MOR COIGACH

Scottish Wildlife Trust.
Location: NC 075 065. 10 miles N of Ullapool, W of A835.
Access: Access at several points from minor road off A835 to Achiltibuie.
Facilities: Parking.
Public transport: None.
Habitat: Loch, bog, mountain and moorland.
Key birds: Upland birds, inc. Ptarmigan, Raven, Ring Ouzel, Golden Plover, Twite. *Winter:* Grazing Barnacle Goose.
Contact: SWT headquarters, 0131 312 7765.

3. CAIRNGORM NNR

SNH (East Highland Area).
Location: NJ 010 010. Largest NNR in Britain, SE of Aviemore.
Access: Unrestricted but contact local landowners during deer culling season.
Facilities: Visitor centre open all year.
Public transport: Call tourist office for advice.
Habitat: Mountain, moorland, pine woodland and lochs.
Key birds: Goosander, Crested Tit, Siskin, Redstart, Crossbill, Capercaillie, Black Grouse, Ptarmigan, Dotterel, Golden Eagle.
Contact: SNH, Achantoul, Aviemore, Inverness-shire PH22 1QD. 01479 810 477; Fax 01479 811 363. website: www.snh.org.uk

4. FORSINARD

RSPB (North Scotland).
Location: NC 890 425. 30 miles SW of Thurso on A897. Turn off at Helmsdale from S (24 miles) or A836 at Melvich from N coast road (14 miles).
Access: Open at all times, but few birds Sept-Feb. Contact visitor centre during breeding season (mid-Apr to end Jun) and during deerstalking season (Jul 1-Feb 15) for advice. Families welcome. Self-guided trail open all year, no dogs, not suitable for wheelchairs.
Facilities: Visitor centre open Apr 1-Oct (9am-5.30pm), seven days per week. Static and AV displays. Wheelchair access to centre and toilet. Guided walks Tue and Thu, May-Aug. Hotel and B&B nearby.
Public transport: Train from Inverness and Thurso (08457 484 950) – RSPB visitor centre in Forsinard Station building.
Habitat: Blanket bog, upland hill farm.
Key birds: Red-throated Diver, Golden Plover, Greenshank, Dunlin, Hen Harrier, Merlin, Short-eared Owl.
Contact: RSPB, Forsinard Flows Reserve, 01641 571 225. e-mail: forsinard@rspb.org.uk www.rspb.org.uk

5. INSH MARSHES

RSPB (North Scotland Office).
Location: NN 775 999. In Spey Valley, two miles NE of Kingussie on B970 minor road.
Access: Open at all times. No disabled access. Coach parking available along access road to car park.
Facilities: Information viewpoint, two hides, three nature trails. Not suitable for disabled. No toilets.
Public transport: Nearest rail station Kingussie (two miles).
Habitat: Marshes, woodland, river, open water.
Key birds: *Spring/summer:* Waders (Lapwing, Curlew,

Redshank, Snipe), wildfowl (including Goldeneye and Wigeon), Wood Warbler, Redstart, Tree Pipit. *Winter*: Hen Harrier, Whooper Swan, other wildfowl.
Contact: Pete Moore, Ivy Cottage, Insh, Kingussie, Inverness-shire PH21 1NT. 01540 661 518.
e-mail: pete.moore@rspb.org.uk
www.visitkincraig.com

6. ISLE OF EIGG

Scottish Wildlife Trust.
Location: NM 38 48. Small island S of Skye, reached by ferry from Maillaig or Arisaig (approx 12 miles).
Access: Ferries seven days per week (weather permitting) during summer. Four days per week (weather permitting) Sept-Apr. Coach parties would need to transfer to ferries for visit to Eigg. Please contact ferry companies prior to trip.
Facilities: Pier centre – shops/Post Office, tea-room, craftshop, toilets.
Public transport: Train service from Glasgow, via Arisaig to Mallaig. Caledonian MacBrayne Ferries NE from Mallaig (tel: 01687 462403), MV Sheerwater from Arisaig (tel: 01678 450 224).
Habitat: Moorland (leading to sgurr pitchstone ridge), wood and scrub, hay fields, shoreline. Marsh and bog.
Key birds: *All-year*: Red-throated Diver, Golden Eagle, Buzzard, Raven. *Summer*: Manx Shearwater, Arctic Tern, various warblers, Twite, etc.
Contact: John Chester, Millers Cottage, Isle of Eigg, Small Isles PH42 4RL. 01687 482 477.
www.isleofeigg.org

7. RSPB NIGG BAY

RSPB Scotland
Location: NE of Dingwall on Cromarty Firth. From A9 take B9175 in direction of Nigg village.
Access: Open all year.
Facilities: One wheelchair-friendly bird hide.
Public transport: Call Stagecoach on 01463 239 292 for information on closest service.
Habitat: Extensive mudflats, saltmarsh and wet grassland.
Key birds: Large numbers of wildfowl, inc Wigeon and Pink-footed Geese, plus waders such as Bar-tailed Godwit, Knot and Dunlin feed and roost on site from October to March, Lapwing and Redshank nest in grassland areas in summer.
Contact: RSPB Scotland – 01463 715 000.

OTHER SITES

Full details in previous editions, (year indicated in brackets).

A. Beinn Eighe – SNH, 01445 760 254 (05).
C. Fairy Glen – RSPB, 01463 715 000 (04).
D. Glenborrodale – RSPB, 01463 715 000 (04).
E. Handa – Scottish WT, 01463 714 746; boatman, 01971 502 347 (05).
F. Isle of Rum – SNH (Rum office), 01687 462 026 (05).
G. Loch Fleet – Scottish WT, 01313 127 765 (05).
H. Loch Ruthven – RSPB, 01463 715 000 (04).
I. Rahoy Hills – Scottish WT, 01313 127 765 (05).
J. Udale Bay – RSPB, 01463 715 000 (04).

Orkney

8. BIRSAY MOORS

RSPB (East Scotland).
Location: Access to hide at Burgar Hill (HY 344 257), signposted from A966 at Evie. Birsay Moors viewed from layby on B9057 NW of Dounby (HY 347 245).
Access: Open access all year round.
Facilities: One hide at Burgar Hill very good for watching breeding Red-throated Divers Apr to Aug. Wheelchair access.
Public transport: Orkney Coaches. Service within 0.5 mile of reserve. Tel: 01856 877 500.
Habitat: Diverse example of Orkney moorland - wet and dry heath, bog, mire, scrub and some farmland.
Key birds: *Spring/summer*: Nesting Hen Harrier, Merlin, Great and Arctic Skuas, Short-eared Owl, Golden Plover, Curlew, Red-throated Diver. *Winter*: Hen Harrier roost.
Contact: The Warden, 12/14 North End Road, Stromness, Orkney KW16 3AG. 01856 850 176.
e-mail: orkney@rspb.org.uk www.rspb.co.uk

9. COPINSAY

RSPB (East Scotland).
Location: HY 610 010. Access by private boat or hire boat from mainland Orkney.
Access: Open all year round.
Facilities: House on island open to visitors, but no facilities. No toilets or hides.
Public transport: None.
Habitat: Sea cliffs, farmland.
Key birds: *Summer*: Stunning seabird-cliffs with breeding Kittiwake, Guillemot, Black Guillemot, Puffin, Razorbill, Shag, Fulmar, Rock Dove, Eider, Twite, Raven and Greater Black-backed Gull. Passage migrants esp. during periods of E winds.
Contact: The Warden, 12/14 North End Road,

Stromness, Orkney KW16 3AG. 01856 850 176.
e-mail: orkney@rspb.org.uk
www.rspb.co.uk
S Foubisher (boatman) 01856 741 252 - cannot sail if wind is in the east.

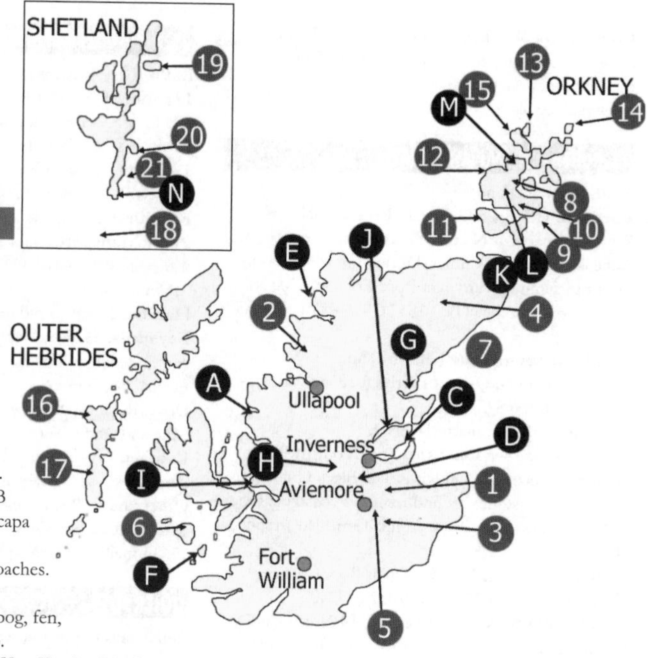

10. HOBBISTER

RSPB (East Scotland).
Location: HY 396 070 or HY 381 068. Near Kirkwall.
Access: Open access between A964 and the sea. Dogs on leads please.
Facilities: A council-maintained footpath to Waulkmill Bay, two car parks. New circular walk from RSPB car park along cliff top and Scapa Flow.
Public transport: Orkney Coaches. Tel: 01856 877 500.
Habitat: Orkney moorland, bog, fen, saltmarsh, coastal cliffs, scrub.
Key birds: *Summer*: Breeding Hen Harrier, Merlin, Short-eared Owl, Red Grouse, Red-throated Diver, Eider, Merganser, Black Guillemot. Wildfowl and waders at Waulkmill Bay. *Autumn/winter*: Waulkmill for sea ducks, divers, auks and grebes (Long-tailed Duck, Red-throated, Black-throated and Great Northern Divers, Slavonian Grebe).
Contact: The Warden, 12/14 North End Road, Stromness, Orkney KW16 3AG. 01856 850 176.
e-mail: orkney@rspb.org.uk
www.rspb.co.uk

11. HOY

RSPB (East Scotland).
Location: HY 210 025. Located in NW of Hoy, a large island S of mainland Orkney. Car ferry from Houten to Lyness.
Access: Open all year round. Keep dogs on lead. Not suitable for wheelchairs – rough terrain.
Facilities: Toilet facilities at Moaness Pier and at Rackwick. Nature trail – circular route from Moaness Pier to Old Man of Hoy via Old Rackwick Post Road. Leaflets available from 2003.
Public transport: Foot passenger ferry service from Stromness to Moaness Pier. Minibus taxis
Habitat: Coastal heath, moorland, fellfield, woodland and cliffs.
Key birds: *Spring/summer*: Red-throated Diver, Merlin, Peregrine, Golden Plover, Dunlin, Great Skua, Arctic Skua, Short-eared Owl, Guillemot, Razorbill, Puffin, Fulmar, Kittiwake, Stonechat, Wheatear. *Autumn/winter*: Redwing, Fieldfare, Snow Bunting. Migration species: Whimbrel, Brambling, plus almost anything is possible.
Contact: The Warden,Ley House, Hoy, Orkney KW16 3NJ. 01856 791 298.
e-mail: orkney@rspb.org.uk www.rspb.org.uk

12. MARWICK HEAD

RSPB (East Scotland).
Location: HY 229 242. On W coast of mainland Orkney, near Dounby. Path N from Marwick Bay, or from council car park at Cumlaquoy at HY 232 252.
Access: Open all year. Rough terrain not suitable for wheelchairs.
Facilities: Cliff top path.
Public transport: Orkney Coaches (01856 877 500), 1 mile.
Habitat: Rocky bay, sandstone cliffs. Beach path good place for great yellow bumble bee in Aug.
Key birds: May-Jul best. Huge numbers of Kittiwakes and auks, inc. Puffins, also nesting Fulmar, Rock Dove, Raven, Rock Pipit.

Contact: The Warden, 12/14 North End Road, Stromness, Orkney KW16 3AG. 01856 850 176. e-mail: orkney@rspb.org.uk www.rspb.co.uk

13. NORTH HILL, PAPA WESTRAY

RSPB (East Scotland).
Location: HY 496 538. Small island lying NE of Westray, reserve at N end of island's main road.
Access: Access at all times. During breeding season report to summer warden at Rose Cottage, 650 yards S of reserve entrance (Tel 01857 644240.) or use trail guide.
Facilities: Nature trails, hide/info hut.
Public transport: Orkney Ferries (01856 872044), Loganair (01856 872494).
Habitat: Sea cliffs, maritime heath.
Key birds: *Summer*: Close views of colony of Puffin, Guillemot, Razorbill and Kittiwake. Black Guillemot nest under flagstones around reserve's coastline. One of UK's largest colonies of Arctic Tern, also Arctic Skua.
Contact: Apr-Aug, The Warden at Rose Cottage, Papay Westray DW17 2BU. 01857 644240. Sep-May, RSPB Orkney Office, 12/14 North End Road, Stromness, Orkney KW16 3AG. 01856 850 176. e-mail: orkney@rspb.org.uk www.rspb.co.uk

14. NORTH RONALDSAY BIRD OBSERVATORY

Location: HY 64 52. 35 miles from Kirkwall, Orkney mainland.
Access: Open all year except Christmas.
Facilities: Three star guest house and hostel accommodation, restaurant, cafe, fully licenced, croft walk.
Public transport: Daily subsidised flights from Kirkwall (Loganair 01856 872 494). Once weekly ferry from Kirkwall (Fri or Sat), some Sun sailings in summer (Orkney Ferries Ltd 01856 872 044).
Habitat: Crofting island with a number of eutrophic and oligotrophic wetlands. Coastline has both sandy bays and rocky shore. Walled gardens concentrate passerines.
Key birds: Prime migration site in *Spring/Autumn* including regular BBRC species. Wide variety of breeding seabirds, wildfowl and waders. *Winter*: Waders and wildfowl include Whooper Swan and hard weather movements occur.
Contact: Alison Duncan, North Ronaldsay Bird Observatory, Twingness, North Ronaldsay, Orkney KW17 2BE. 01857 633 200.
e-mail: alison@nrbo.prestel.co.uk www.nrbo.f2s.com

15. NOUP CLIFFS, WESTRAY

RSPB (East Scotland).
Location: HY 392 499. Westray lies NE of Mainland and Rousay. From Pierowall take minor road to Noup Farm (HY 492 488) then track NW to lighthouse. Track not suitable for coaches. Rough terrain.
Access: No dogs, even on a lead.
Facilities: Trail guide leaflet and information board.
Public transport: Flights from Kirkwall daily (Loganair 01856 872 494). Daily ferry (Orkney Ferries 01856 872 044).
Habitat: 2.5km of old red sandstone cliff.
Key birds: *Summer*: May-Jul best. Huge seabird colony with breeding Kittiwake, Guillemot, Razorbill, Fulmar, Puffin and Gannet. Also breeding Shag, Raven, Rock Dove, Rock Pipit. Adjacent to reserve breeding Arctic Skua and Arctic Tern.
Contact: In Summer - RSPB Warden, Rose Cottage, Papa Westray, Orkney, KW17 2BU. 01857 644 240. Other times - RSPB Orkney Office, 12/14 North End Road, Stromness, Orkney KW16 3AG. 01856 850 176. e-mail: orkney@rspb.org.uk www.rspb.co.uk

OTHER SITES

Full details in previous editions, (year indicated in brackets).
K. Brodgar – RSPB warden, 01856 850 176 (06).
L. Cottasgarth & Rendell Moss – RSPB warden, 01856 850 176 (04).
M. Trumland, Rousay – The warden 01856 821 395 (04).

Outer Hebrides

16. BALRANALD

RSPB (North Scotland Office).
Location: NF 705 707. From Skye take ferry to Lochmaddy, North Uist. Drive W on A867 for 20 miles to reserve. Turn off main road three miles NW of Bayhead at signpost to Houghharry.
Access: Open at all times, no charge. Dogs on leads. Disabled access.
Facilities: Visitor Centre and toilets – disabled access. Marked nature trail.
Public transport: Bus service (tel 01876 560 244).
Habitat: Freshwater loch, machair, coast and croft lands.
Key birds: *Summer*: Corncrake, Corn Bunting, Lapwing, Oystercatcher, Dunlin, Ringed Plover, Redshank, Snipe. *Winter*: Twite, Greylag Goose,

Wigeon, Teal Shoveler. *Passage*: Barnacle Goose, Pomarine Skua, Long-tailed Skua.
Contact: Jamie Boyle, 9 Grenitote, Isle of North Uist, H56 5BP. 01876 560 287.
e-mail: james.boyle3@btinternet.com

17. LOCH DRUIDIBEG NNR

SNH (Western Isles Area).
Location: NF 782 378. Reserve of 1,577 ha on South Uist.
Access: Open all year. Several tracks and one walk covering a range of habitats – most not suitable for wheelchair use. Stout footwear essential. Observe National Access Code in all areas with livestock. View of E part of reserve from public roads but parking and turning areas for coaches is limited.
Facilities: None.
Public transport: Regular bus service stops at reserve. Hebridean Coaches 01870 620 345, MacDonald Coaches 01870 620 288. Large print timetable - call 01851 709 592.
Habitat: Range of freshwater lochs and marshes, machair, coast and moorland.
Key birds: *Summer*: Breeding waders, Corn Crake, wildfowl, terns and raptors. *Spring and autumn*: Migrant waders and wildfowl. *Winter*: Waders, wildfowl and raptors.
Contact: SNH Area Officer, tilligarry, South Uist, HS8 5RS. 01870 620 238; Fax 01870 620 350.
www.nnr-scotland.org.uk

Shetland

18. FAIR ISLE BIRD OBSERVATORY

Fair Isle Bird Observatory.
Location: HZ 2172.
Access: Open from end Apr-end Oct. Free to roam everywhere except one croft (Lower Leogh).
Facilities: Public toilets at Airstrip and Stackhoull Stores (shop). Accommodation at Fair Isle Bird Observatory (phone/e-mail: for brochure/details). Guests can be involved in observatory work and get to see birds in the hand. Slide shows, guided walks through Ranger Service.
Public transport: Tue, Thurs, Sat – ferry (12 passengers) from Grutness, Shetland. Tel: Jimmy or Florrie Stout 01595 760 222. Mon, Wed, Fri, Sat – air (7 seater) from Tingwall, Shetland. Tel: Loganair 01595 840 246.
Habitat: Heather moor and lowland pasture/crofting land. Cliffs.
Key birds: Large breeding seabird colonies (auks, Gannet, Arctic Tern, Kittiwake, Shag, Arctic Skua and Great Skua). Many common and rare migrants Apr/May/early Jun, late Aug-Nov.
Contact: Deryk Shaw (Warden), Hollie Shaw (Administrator), Fair Isle Bird Observatory, Fair Isle, Shetland ZE2 9JU. 01595 760 258.
e-mail: fairisle.birdobs@zetnet.co.uk
www.fairislebirdobs.co.uk

19. FETLAR

RSPB (East Scotland).
Location: HU 603 917. Lies E of Yell. Take car ferry from Gutcher, N Yell. Booking advised. Tel: 01957 722 259.
Access: Part of RSPB reserve (Vord Hill) closed mid-May-end Jul. Entry during this period is only by arrangement with warden.
Facilities: Hide at Mires of Funzie. Displays etc at interpretive centre, Houbie. Toilets at ferry terminal, shop and interpretive centre.
Public transport: None.
Habitat: Serpentine heath, rough hill lane, upland mire.
Key birds: *Summer*: Breeding Red-throated Diver, Eider, Shag, Whimbrel, Golden Plover, Dunlin, skuas, Manx Shearwater, Storm Petrel. Red-necked Phalarope on Loch of Funzie (HU 655 899) viewed from road or RSPB hide overlooking Mires of Funzie.
Contact: RSPB North Isles Officer, Bealance, Fetlar, Shetland ZE2 9DJ. Tel/Fax: 01957 733 246.
e-mail: malcolm.smith@rspb.org.uk

20. ISLE OF NOSS NNR

Scottish Natural Heritage (Shetland Office).
Location: HU 531 410. Take car ferry to Bressay from Lerwick and follow signs for Noss. Park at end of road and walk to shore (600 yards) where inflatable ferry (passenger only) to island will collect you (if red flag is flying, island is closed due to sea conditions). Freephone 0800 107 7818 for daily ferry information.
Access: Access (Tue, Wed, Fri, Sat, Sun) 10am-5pm, May-late Aug. Access by zodiac inflatable. No dogs allowed on ferry. Steep rough track down to ferry. Groups or anyone requiring asistance to board ferry should contact SNH as far in advance as possible.
Facilities: Visitor centre, toilets. Bike rack/car park on Bressay side. Parking for small coaches.
Public transport: None. Post bus available, phone Royal Mail on 01595 820 200. Cycle hire in Lerwick.
Habitat: Dune grassland, moorland, blanket bog, sea cliffs.
Key birds: *Spring/summer*: Fulmar, Shag, Gannet, Arctic Tern, Kittiwake, Great Black-backed Gull,

Great Skua, Arctic Skua, Guillemot, Razorbill, Puffin, Black Guillemot, Eider.
Contact: Simon Smith, Scottish Natural Heritage, Stewart Building, Alexandra Wharf, Lerwick, Shetland ZE1 0LL. 01595 693 345.
e-mail: northern_isles@snh.gov.uk

21. MOUSA

RSPB (Shetland Office).
Location: HU 460 240. Small uninhabited island east of Sandwick in South Mainland of Shetland.
Access: By ferry from Leebitton Pier, Sandwick, Shetland – mid-Apr–mid-Sept.
Facilities: The Mousa Broch is the best preserved Iron Age tower in the world (World Heritage Site).
Public transport: Buses run to Sandwick from Lerwick. Details of ferry available from Tom Jamieson (01950 431 367) or his web site (www.mousaboattrips.co.uk).
Habitat: A small uninhabited island with maritime grassland and a small area of shell sand.
Key birds: *Summer*: Storm Petrels can be seen on the special night trips run by Tom Jamieson. Arctic Tern, Arctic and Great Skuas, Black Guillemot and Puffin.
Contact: Tom Jamieson, Pytaslee, Leebitton, Sandwick, Shetland ZE2 9HP. 01950 431 367.

OTHER SITES

Full details in previous editions, (year indicated in brackets).
N. Sumburgh Head – RSPB Shetland, 01950 460 800 (07).

CHANNEL ISLANDS

COLIN McCATHIE RESERVE

La Société Guernesiaise.
Location: Perry's Island Guide (page 6 B5).
Access: Open at all times.
Facilities: Hide on road to Vale Church must be used.
Public transport: Hourly bus service 7/7A (island circular), tel: 01481 720 210.
Habitat: Brackish tidal pond, reed fringes.
Key birds: Passage waders. *Summer*: Breeding Reed Warbler, Moorhen, Coot. *Winter*: Wildfowl, Water Rail, Little Egret, Snipe, Kingfisher.
Contact: Vic Froome, La Cloture, Courtil de Bas Lane, St Sampson's, Guernsey GY2 4XJ. 01481 254 841. www.societe.org.gg

LA CLAIRE MARE

La Société Guernesiaise.
Location: *Perry's Island Guide* (page 12 C5).
Access: Open at all times.
Facilities: Hide down concrete track off the Rue de la Rocque Road then footpath to second hide.
Public transport: Hourly bus service 7/7A (island circular), tel: 01481 720 210.
Habitat: Reedbeds, pasture, willow thickets, scrape.
Key birds: Passage waders and passerines. *Summer*: Breeding Reed Warbler, Moorhen, Coot, Kestrel. *Winter*: Wildfowl, Water Rail, Snipe, Kingfisher.
Contact: Vic Froome, La Cloture, Courtil de Bas Lane, St Sampson's, Guernsey GY2 4XJ. 01481 254 841. www.societe.org.gg

PLEINMONT

La Société Guernesiaise.
Location: Perry's Island Guide Page 32 B3.
Access: Open at all times.
Facilities: Public footpath around reserve.
Public transport: Hourly bus service 7/7A (island circular) 0.5 miles from Imperial Hotel, tel 01481 720 210.
Habitat: Cliff-top headland of scrub, remnant heathland and small fields.
Key birds: Passage passerines. *Summer*: Breeding Shag, Fulmar, gulls, Dartford Warbler, Whitethroat, Stonechat and Linnet.
Contact: Vic Froome, La Cloture, Courtil Le Bas Lane, St Sampson's, Guernsey GY2 4XT. 01481 254 841. www.societe.org.gg

WALES

East Wales

1. ELAN VALLEY

Dwr Cymru /Welsh Water & Elan Valley Trust.
Location: SN 928 646 (visitor centre). Three miles SW of Rhayader, off B4518.
Access: Mostly open access.
Facilities: Visitor centre and toilets (open mid Mar-end Oct), nature trails all year and hide at SN 905 617.
Public transport: Post bus from Rhayader and Llandrindod Wells.
Habitat: 45,000 acres of moorland, woodland, river and reservoir.
Key birds: *Spring/summer*: Birds of prey, upland birds including Golden Plover and Dunlin. Woodland birds include Redstart and Pied Flycatcher.
Contact: Pete Jennings, Rangers Office, Elan Valley Visitor Centre, Rhayader, Powys LD6 5HP. 01597 810 880. e-mail: pete@elanvalley.org.uk
www.elanvalley.org.uk

2. GILFACH

Radnorshire Wildlife Trust.
Location: SN 952 714. Two miles NW from Rhayader/Rhaeadr-Gwy. Take minor road to St Harmon from A470 at Marteg Bridge.
Access: Open every day, all year.
Facilities: Visitor centre opening times may vary – contact Trust for details.
Public transport: None.
Habitat: Upland hill farm, river, oak woods, meadows, hill-land.
Key birds: *Spring/summer*: Pied Flycatcher, Redstart. *All year*: Dipper, Red Kite.
Contact: Gilfach, St Harmon, Rhaeadr-Gwy, Powys LD6 5LF. 01597 823 298.
e-mail: info@radnorshirewildlifetrust.org.uk
www.radnorshirewildlifetrust.org.uk

3. GLASLYN, PLYNLIMON

Montgomeryshire Wildlife Trust.
Location: SN 826 941. Nine miles SE of Machynlleth. Off minor road between the B4518 near Staylittle and the A489 at Machynlleth. Go down the track for about a mile to the car park.
Access: Open at all times – dogs on lead at all times.
Facilities: Footpath.
Public transport: None.
Habitat: Heather moorland and upland lake.
Key birds: Red Grouse, Short-eared Owl, Meadow Pipit, Sky Lark, Wheatear and Ring Ouzel, Red Kite, Merlin, Peregrine. Goldeneye – occasional.
Contact: Montgomeryshire Wildlife Trust, Collot House, 20 Severn Street, Welshpool, Powys SY21 7AD. 01938 555 654.
e-mail: info@montwt.co.uk
www.wildlifetrust.org.uk/montgomeryshire
www.montwt.co.uk

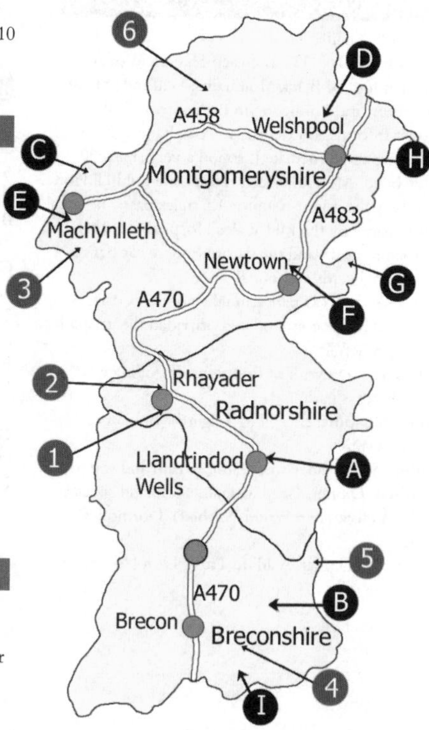

NATURE RESERVES - WALES

4. LLANGORSE LAKE

Privately owned.
Location: Head NW on the A40 between Brecon and Crickhowell, turn off at Bwlich onto the B4560. A minor road from Cathedine leads to the S shore. Access to the N shore is at Llangorse village.
Access: Open all year. A footpath from the parking area near Llangorse only goes along the W and S shore to Llagasty-Talyllyn.
Facilities: None.
Public transport: Train from Cardiff to Merthyr Tydfil then bus to Brecon. Only one post bus per day to Llangorse.
Habitat: The second largest natural lake in Wales.
Key birds: *Winter*: Wildfowl, Cormorants, Snipe, Jack Snipe, occasional Bittern. *Passage*: Oystercatcher, Ringed Plover, Dunlin, Black-tailed Godwit, Whimbrel, Greenshank, Green Sandpiper, Little Gull, terns.
Contact: Trust HQ, 01874 625 708.

5. PWLL-Y-WRACH

Brecknock Wildlife Trust.
Location: SO 165 327. Between Hay-on-Wye and Brecon at foot of Black Mountains. Half mile SE of Talgarth. At the T-junction in the centre of Talgarth (Tourist Information Centre on your R) turn R and take an almost immediate L round a very sharp 90 degree bend. After 20m turn L opposite the Bell Hotel and follow the minor road for 1.5 miles past The Prya Centre (formerly the Mid Wales Hospital) on the L. The road narrows and the nature reserve car park is a few hundred yards on your R.
Access: A small car park can take about six cars. A coach could be accommodated provided the car park is not already full.
Facilities: A network of footpaths, including a disabled access path.
Public transport: Bus 39 to Talgarth (Brecon to Hay-on-Wye).
Habitat: Steep valley woodland, stream and waterfall.
Key birds: Dipper, Grey Wagtail, woodland species (inc. Pied Flycatcher, Wood Warbler). Dormouse colony.
Contact: Brecknock Wildlife Trust, Lion House, Bethel Square, Brecon, Powys LD3 7AY. 01874 625 708. e-mail: info@brecknockwt@cix.co.uk www.brecknockwildlifetrust.org.uk

6. VYRNWY (LAKE)

RSPB (North Wales Office).
Location: SJ 020 193. Located WSW of Oswestry. Nearest village is Llanfyllin on A490. Take B4393 to lake.
Access: Reserve open all year. Visitor centre open Apr-Dec (10.30am-4.30pm), Dec-Apr weekends only (10.30am-4.30pm).
Facilities: Toilets, visitor centre, hides, nature trails, coffee shop, RSPB shop, craft workshops.
Public transport: Nothing closer than train and bus at Welshpool (25 miles away).
Habitat: Heather moorland, woodland, meadows, rocky streams and large reservoir.
Key birds: Dipper, Kingfisher, Pied Flycatcher, Wood Warbler, Redstart, Peregrine and Buzzard.
Contact: Jo Morris, Centre Manager, RSPB Lake Vyrnwy Reserve, Bryn Awel, Llanwddyn, Oswestry, Salop SY10 0LZ. 01691 870 278.
e-mail: lake.vyrnwy@rspb.org.uk

OTHER SITES

Full details in previous editions, (year indicated in brackets).
A. Bailey Einon LNR – Radnor WT, 01597 823 298 (05).
B. Brechfa Pool – Brecknock WT, 01874 625 708 (06).
C. Bwlchcoediog – Mr and Mrs Faith, 01650 531 329 (07).
D. Coed Pendugwm – Montgomery WT, 01938 555 654 (05)
E. Cors Dyfi – Montgomery WT, 01938 555 654 (06).
F. Pwll Penarth – Montgomery WT, 01938 555 654 (06).
G. Roundton Hill – Montgomery WT, 01938 555 654 (07).
H. Severn Farm Pond – Montgomery WT, 01938 555 654 (07).
I. Talybont Reservoir – Welsh Water (06).

North Wales

1. BARDSEY BIRD OBSERVATORY

Bardsey Bird Observatory.
Location: SH 11 21. Private 444 acre island. Two minute boat journey from Aberdaron.
Access: Mar-Nov. No dogs. Visitor accommodation in 150-year-old farmhouse (two single, two double, two x four dorms). To stay at the Observatory contact Alicia Normand (tel 01758 760 667, e-mail bookings@bbfo.org.uk). Day visitors by Bardsey Ferries (01758 730 326).
Facilities: Public toilets available for day visitors. Three hides, one on small bay, two seawatching.
Public transport: Trains from Birmingham to Pwllheli. Tel: 0345 484 950. Arriva bus from Bangor to Pwllheli. Tel: 0870 6082 608.
Habitat: Sea-birds cliffs viewable from boat only. Farm and scrubland, Spruce plantation, willow copses and gorse-covered hillside.
Key birds: *All year*: Chough, Peregrine. *Spring/summer*: Manx Shearwaters 16,000 pairs, other seabirds. Migrant warblers, chats, Redstart, thrushes. *Autumn*: Many rarities including Eye-browed Thrush, Lanceolated Warbler, American Robin, Yellowthroat, Scarlet Tanager.
Contact: Steven Stansfield, Cristin, Ynys Enlli (Bardsey), off Aberaron, via Pwllheil, Gwynedd LL53 8DE. 07855 264 151. e-mail: warden@bbfo.org.uk www.bbfo.org.uk

2. CONNAHS QUAY POWER STATION NATURE RESERVE

Deeside Naturalists' Society and E.ON UK.
Location: SJ 275 715. From England: Take A550 from Liverpool/N Wirral or A5117 from Ellesmere Port/M56, follow road to Queensferry. 200 metres after junction of A550 and A5117, turn L at A548 and follow signs to Flint. Cross Dee Bridge and turn off dual carriageway at B5129, signed Connah's Key. Turn R under A548 then L, following signs to power station. From Flint: Take A548 towards Connah's Quay/Queensferry. After 2.5 miles, take B5129 (Connah's Quay exit). Turn L following signs to power station. From Connah's Quay: Take B5129 towards Flint. Go under A548, turn L following signs to power station.
Access: Advance permit required (group bookings only). Wheelchair access. Public welcome on open days - see website for details.
Facilities: Field studies centre, five hides.
Public transport: Contact Arriva Cymru on 01745 343 492.
Habitat: Saltmarsh, mudflats, grassland scrub, open water, wetland meadow.
Key birds: *Summer*: Small roosts of non-breeding estuarine birds. *Winter*: High water roosts of waders and wildfowl including, Black-tailed Godwit, Oystercatcher, Redshank, Spotted Redshank, Curlew, Lapwing, Teal, Pintail and Wigeon.
Contact: Secretary, Deeside Naturalist's Society, 21 Woodlands Court, Hawarden, Deeside, Flintshire CH5 3NB. 01224 537 440.
email: deenaturalists@btinternet.com
www.deesidenaturalists.org.uk

3. CONWY

RSPB (North Wales Office).
Location: SH 799 771. On E bank of Conwy Estuary. Access from A55 at exit signed to Conwy and Deganwy.
Access: Open daily (10am-5pm) or dusk if earlier. Closed for Christmas Day. Ample parking for coaches.
Facilities: Visitor centre, toilets including disabled. One hide, accessible to wheelchairs. Trails firm and level, though a little rough in places. Two further hides accessible to pedestrians. Shop/coffee shop with views over lagoon.
Public transport: Train service to Llandudno Junction. Bus service to Tesco supermarket, Llandudno Junction. Tel: 08706 082 608. For BWS Conwy timetables, call 01492 575 412.
Habitat: Open water, islands, reedbeds, grassland, estuary.
Key birds: *Spring/summer*: Breeding Reed and Sedge Warblers, Lapwing, Redshank, Little Ringed Plover, Sky Lark, Reed Bunting and rarities. *Autumn*: Passage waders, spectacular Starling roost and rarities. *Winter*: Kingfisher, Goldeneye, Water Rail, Red-breasted Merganser, wildfowl.
Contact: Conwy RSPB Nature Reserve, Llandudno Junction, Conwy, North Wales LL31 9XZ. 01492 584 091.

4. LLYN CEFNI

Welsh Water/United Utilities.
Location: SH 440 775. A reservoir located two miles

NW of Llangefni, in central Anglesey. Follow B5111 or B5109 from the village.
Access: Open at all times. Dogs allowed except in sanctuary area. Good wheelchair access most of southern (Langefni) side. New cycle/foot and wheelchair path being constructed between Llangefni Dingle and Llyn Cefni - due for completion in 2007. Coach parking at Rhosmeich car park/picnic site (SH 451 783).
Facilities: Picnic site, hide, information boards.
Public transport: Bus 32, 4 (44 Sun only, 52 Tue and Thu only). Tel 0870 608 2608 for information.
Habitat: Large area of open water, reedy bays, coniferous woodland, carr, scrub.
Key birds: *Summer*: Sedge, Whitethroat and Grasshopper Warblers, Buzzard, Tawny Owl, Little Grebe, Gadwall, Shoveler. *Winter*: Waterfowl (Whooper Swan, Goldeneye), Crossbill, Redpoll, Siskin, Redwing. *All year*: Stonechat, Treecreeper, Song Thrush.
Contact: Jim Clark, Llyn Alaw, Llantrisant, Holyhead LL65 4TW. 01407 730 762.

5. MORFA HARLECH NNR

Countryside Council for Wales.
Location: SH 574 317. On the A496 Harlech road.
Access: Open all year.
Facilities: Car park. Disabled parking bays and three coach parking spaces.
Public transport: The site is served by both bus and train. Train stations are at Harlech and Ty gwyn (Ty Gwyn is near the saltmarsh wintering birds.) Contact Arriva for details (0844 8004 411).
Habitat: Shingle (no shingle at Harlech), coast, marsh, dunes. Also forestry plantation, grassland, swamp.
Key birds: *Spring/summer*: Whitethroat, Spotted Flycatcher, Grasshopper Warbler, migrants. *Passage*: Waders, Manx Shearwater, ducks. *Winter*: Divers, Whooper Swan, Wigeon, Teal, Pintail, Scaup, Common Scoter, Hen Harrier, Merlin, Peregrine, Short-eared Owl, Little Egret, Water Pipit, Snow Bunting, Twite. *All year/breeding*: Redshank, Lapwing, Ringed Plover, Snipe, Curlew, Shelduck, Oystercatcher, Stonechat, Whinchat, Wheatear, Linnet, Reed Bunting, Sedge Warbler. Also - Red-breasted Merganser, Kestrel, gulls.
Other notable flora and fauna: Sand lizard, otter, water vole.
Contact: Countryside Council for Wales North West Wales, Maes y Ffynnon, Ffordd, Bangor, Gwynedd, LL57 2DN, 0845 1306 229.
e-mail: enquiries@ccw.gov.uk www.ccw.gov.uk

6. POINT OF AYR

RSPB (Dee Estuary Office).
Location: SJ 140 840. At mouth of the Dee Estuary. Three miles E of Prestatyn. Access from A548 coast road to Talacre village. Park at end of Station Road.
Access: Open at all times.
Facilities: Car park, public hide overlooking saltmarsh and mudflats. No visitor centre. Toilets in Talacre village. Group bookings, guided walks and events. Track is 10min walk (1km).
Public transport: Bus – Prestatyn (Arriva 11, 11A/ Crossville). Rail – Prestatyn.
Habitat: Intertidal mud/sand, saltmarsh, shingle.
Key birds: *Spring/summer*: Breeding Sky Lark, Meadow Pipit, Reed Bunting. *Late summer*: Pre-migratory roost of Sandwich and Common Terns. *Autumn*: Passage waders. *Winter*: Roosting waterfowl (eg Shelduck, Pintail), Oystercatcher, Curlew, Redshank, Merlin, Peregrine, Short-eared Owl. Rarities have occurred.
Contact: Colin E Wells, Burton Point Farm, Station Road, Burton, Nr Neston, Cheshire CH64 5SB. 0151 3367 681. e-mail: colin.wells@rspb.org.uk

7. SOUTH STACK CLIFFS

RSPB (North Wales Office).
Location: RSPB Car Park SH 211 818, Ellins Tower information centre SH 206 820. Follow A55 to W end in Holyhead, proceed straight on at roundabout, continue straight on through traffic lights. After another 1/2 mile turn L and follow the Brown Tourist signs for RSPB Ynys Lawd/South Stack.
Access: RSPB car park with disabled parking, 'Access for all' track leading to a viewing area overlooking the lighthouse adjacent to Ellins Tower Visitor centre. Access to Ellins Tower gained via staircase. Access to other areas of the reserve an extensive network of paths, some of which are steep and uneven. Coach parking by prior arrangement at The South Stack Kitchen Tel: 01407 762 181 (privately owned).
Facilities: Free access to Ellin's Tower which has windows overlooking main auk colony open daily (10am-5.30pm Easter-Sep).
Public transport: Mainline station Holyhead. Infrequent local bus service, Holyhead-South Stack. Tel. 0870 608 2608.
Habitat: Sea cliffs, maritime grassland, maritime heath, lowland heath.
Key birds: Peregrine, Chough, Fulmar, Puffin, Guillemot, Razorbill, Rock Pipit, Sky Lark, Stonechat, Linnet, Shag, migrant warblers and passage seabirds.
Contact: Dave Bateson, Plas Nico, South Stack, Holyhead, Anglesey LL65 1YH. 01407 764 973. www.rspb.org.uk

NATURE RESERVES - WALES

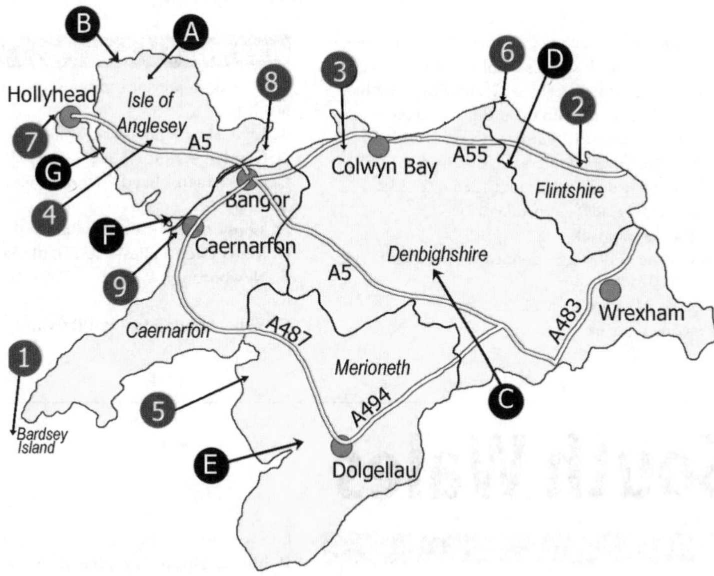

8. TRAETH LAFAN

Gwynedd Council.

Location: NE of Bangor, stretching to Llanfairfechan. 1) Minor road from old A55 near Tal-y-Bont (SH 610 710) to Aber Ogwen car park by coast (SH 614 723). 2) Also access from minor road from Abergwyngregyn village to Morfa Aber Reserve (SH 646 731) 3) Access on foot to Morfa Madryn Reserve 1 mile W from Llanfairfechan promenade (SH 679 754).

Access: Open access from 1, 2, and 3. All sites are wheelchair accessible. Public transport available.

Facilities: Public paths. 1) Car park, hides 200m away at Spinnies Reserve. 2) Car park and hide. 3) Car and coach park with toilets and café, hides at reserve.

Public transport: For local bus and train timetables call 0870 60 82 608 or log on to www.gwynedd.gov.uk or www.conwy.gov.uk

Habitat: Intertidal sands and mudflats, wetlands, streams. SPA SAC SSSI and LNR.

Key birds: Third most important area in Wales for wintering waders; of national importance for moulting Great Crested Grebe and Red-breasted Merganser; internationally important for Oystercatcher and Curlew; passage waders; winter concentrations of Goldeneye and Greenshank, and of regional significance for wintering populations of Black-throated, Red-throated and Great Northern Divers and Black-necked and Slavonian Grebes and breeding Lapwings at Morfa Madryn.

Contact: Countryside Wardens, Countryside and Access Unit, Gwynedd Council, Council Offices, Caernarfon LL55 1SH. Countryside Wardens on 01286 679 281; e-mail: CefnGwlad@gwynedd.gov.uk wwwgwynedd.gov.uk

Conwy CBCl Countryside Service on 01492 575 200. e-mail: cg.cs@conwy.gov.uk

www.conwy.gov.uk

9. Y FORYD

Gwynedd Council.

Location: SW of Caernarfon, at W end of Menai Straits. 1) Minor road along shore from A487 S of Caernarfon (SH 483 617), and also minor road S to Llanfaglan, Llandwrog and Dinas Dinlle from above, or W from A499 (SH 452 555)

Access: Several minor roads lead to the bay. The picnic site and hide are wheelchair accessible. Public transport available.

Facilities: Car park and picnic site on E shore (SH 453 604), bird hide on E shore (SH 452 586) – phone Countryside Warden to arrange access to hide.

Public transport: Buses available to neighbouring villages, with access on foot to bay within 1 mile, contact 0870 6082 608 or www.gwynedd.gov.uk

Habitat: Partially enclosed intertidal bay, sand and mud flats, salt marsh. SSSI, SAC, and LNR.

Key birds: Large wintering populations of Wigeon,

Shellduck, Oystercatcher, Curlew, Lapwing, Dunlin, and Redshank, with smaller numbers of Golden and Grey Plover, Knot, Greenshank, and Black and Bar-tailed Godwit, along with other ducks and divers.
Contact: Countryside Wardens, Countryside and Access Unit, Gwynedd Council, Caernarfon LL55 1SH. Countryside Wardens on 01286 672 255;
e-mail: CefnGwlad@gwynedd.gov.uk
wwwgwynedd.gov.uk
Conwy County Borough Council Countryside Service on 01492 575 200.
e-mail: cg.cs@conwy.gov.uk
www.conwy.gov.uk

OTHER SITES

Full details in previous editions, (year indicated in brackets).
A. Llyn Alaw – Jim Clark, 01407 730 762 (07).
B. Cemlyn – North Wales WT, 01970 612 367 (06).
C. Gors Maen Llwyd – North Wales WT, 01970 612 367 (06).
D. Loggerheads Country Park –01352 810 586 (07).
E. Mawddach Valley – RSPB, 01654 700 222 (06).
F. Newborough Warren – CCW, 01248 716 422 (06).
G. Valley Wetlands – RSPB Cymru, 01248 363 800 (07).

South Wales

1. CWM CLYDACH

RSPB (South Wales Office).
Location: SN 584 026. Three miles N of J45 on M4, through the village of Clydach on B4291.
Access: Open at all times along public footpaths and waymarked trails. Coach parking not available.
Facilities: Nature trails, car park, information boards.
Public transport: Buses from Swansea stop at reserve entrance. Nearest railway station is eight miles away in Swansea.
Habitat: Oak woodland on steep slopes lining the banks of the fast-flowing Lower Clydach River.
Key birds: *Spring/summer*: Nesting Buzzard, Sparrowhawk and Raven. Nestboxes are used by Pied Flycatcher, Redstart and tits while Wood Warbler, all three species of woodpecker, Nuthatch, Treecreeper and Tawny Owl also nest. Dipper and Grey Wagtail frequent the river.
Contact: Martin Humphreys, 2 Tyn y Berllan, Craig Cefn Parc, Clydach, Swansea SA6 5TL. 01792 842 927.

2. KENFIG NNR

Bridgend County Borough Council.
Location: SS 802 811. Seven miles W of Bridgend. From J37 on M4, drive towards Porthcawl, then North Cornelly, then follow signs.
Access: Open at all times. Unsurfaced sandy paths, not suitable for wheelchairs. Flooding possible in winter and spring. Coach parking available.
Facilities: Toilets, hides, free car parking and sign-posted paths. Visitor centre open weekends and holidays (10am-4.30pm), weekdays (2pm-4.30pm).
Public transport: Local bus service – contact reserve for details.
Habitat: 1,300 acre sand dune system, freshwater lake with reeds, numerous wet dune slacks, sandy coastline with some rocky outcrops.
Key birds: *Summer*: Warblers including Cetti's, Grasshopper, Sedge, Reed and Willow Warbler, Blackcap and Whitethroat. One of the UK's best sites for orchids. *Winter*: Wildfowl, Water Rail, Bittern, grebes.
Contact: David Carrington, Ton Kenfig, Bridgend, CF33 4PT. 01656 743 386.
e-mail: carridg@bridgend.gov.uk

3. LAVERNOCK POINT

The Wildlife Trust of South and West Wales.
Location: ST 182 680. Public footpaths S of B4267 between Barry & Penarth.
Access: No restrictions.
Facilities: None.
Public transport: Call Trust for advice.
Habitat: Cliff top, unimproved grassland, dense scrub.
Key birds: Seawatching in late summer; Glamorgan's best migration hotspot in autumn.
Contact: Trust HQ, 01656 724 100.
e-mail: information@wtsww.cix.co.uk

4. MAGOR MARSH

Gwent Wildlife Trust.
Location: ST 427 867. S of Magor. Leave M4 at exit

23, turning R onto B4245. Follow signs for Redwick in Magor village. Take first L after railway bridge – reserve entrance is half mile further on R.
Access: Open all year. Keep to path. Wheelchair access to bird hide..
Facilities: Hide. Car park, footpaths and boardwalks.
Public transport: Bus service to Magor village. Reserve is approx 10 mins walk along Redwick road.
Habitat: Sedge fen, reedswamp, willow carr, damp hay meadows and open water.
Key birds: Important for wetland birds. *Spring*: Reed, Sedge and Grasshopper Warbler, occasional Garganey and Green Sandpiper on passage, Hobby. *Winter*: Teal, Peregrine, Jack Snipe, Snipe, occasional Shoveler and Gadwall, Bittern records in two recent years. *All year*: Little Egret, Little Grebe, Reed Bunting, Cetti's Warbler and Water Rail.
Contact: Gwent Wildlife Trust, Seddon House, Dingestow, Monmouth NP25 4DY. 01600 740 358; Fax 01600 740 299. e-mail: info@gwentwildlife.co.uk www.gwentwildlife.org

5. OXWICH

CCW (Swansea Office).
Location: SS 872 773. 12 miles from Swansea, off A4118.
Access: NNR open at all times. No permit required for access to foreshore. Dunes, woodlands and facilities.
Facilities: Private car park, summer only. Toilets summer only. Marsh boardwalk and marsh lookout. No visitor centre, no facilities for disabled visitors.
Public transport: Bus service Swansea/Oxwich. First Cymru, tel 01792 580 580.
Habitat: Freshwater marsh, saltmarsh, foreshore, dunes, woodlands.
Key birds: *Summer*: Breeding Reed, Sedge and Cetti's Warblers, Treecreeper, Nuthatch, woodpeckers. *Winter*: Wildfowl.
Contact: Countryside Council for Wales, RVB House, Llys Tawe, King's Road, Swansea SA1 8PG. 01792 634 960.
e-mail: enquiries@ccw.gov.uk
www.ccw.gov.uk

6. PARC SLIP NATURE PARK

The Wildlife Trust of South and West Wales.
Location: SS 880 840. Tondu, half mile W of Aberkenfig. From Bridgend take A4063 N, turning L onto B4281 after passing M4. Reserve is signposted from this road.
Access: Open dawn to dusk. Space for coach parking.
Facilities: Three hides, nature trail, interpretation centre.
Public transport: None.
Habitat: Restored opencast mining site, wader scrape, lagoons.
Key birds: *Summer*: Breeding Tufted Duck, Lapwing, Sky Lark. Migrant waders (inc. Little Ringed Plover, Green Sandpiper), Little Gull. Kingfisher, Green Woodpecker.
Contact: Trust HQ, 01656 724 100.
e-mail: information@wtsww.cix.co.uk

7. WHITEFORD NNR

Location: SS 450 960. Pass through Llanmadoc village, downhill, turn R at church to Cwm Ivy. Lane leads from here downhill to Whiteford Plantation. Follow footpath through Plantation, across Burrows to hide on Berges Island.
Access: Free access. Best to get to hide before a.m. high water for waders and wildfowl.
Facilities: None. Area not recommended for those with restricted mobility but excellent view of Whiteford Marsh from hillside road above Britannia Inn at Cheriton.
Public transport: None.
Habitat: Conifer plantation, marsh, mudflats.
Key birds: *Autumn/winter*: Divers, Red-necked,

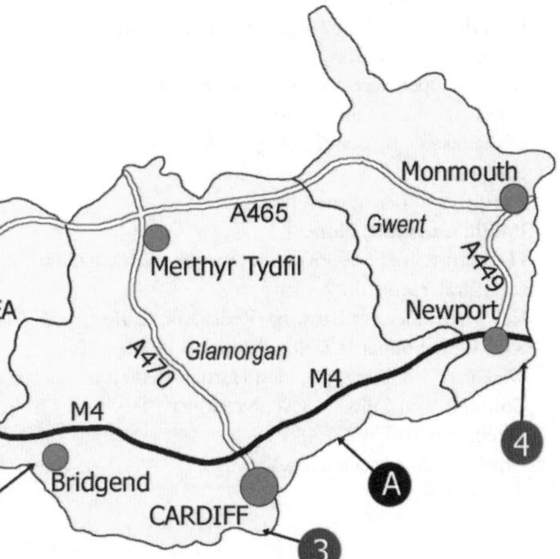

Slavonian and Black-necked Grebes, Brent Goose, Wigeon, Teal, Pintail and Eider. Common and Jack Snipe occur, with Whimbrel and Spotted Redshank on passage. Turnstone and Purple Sandpiper at Whiteford Point.

OTHER SITES

Full details in previous editions, (year indicated in brackets).

A. Peterstone Wentlooge – Gwent WT, 01600 715 501.

West Wales

1. CASTLE WOODS

The Wildlife Trust of South and West Wales.
Location: SN 615 217. About 60 acres of woodland overlooking River Tywi, W of Llandeilo town centre.
Access: Open all year by footpath from Tywi Bridge, Llandeilo (SN 627 221).
Facilities: Call for advice.
Public transport: None.
Habitat: Old mixed deciduous woodlands.
Key birds: All three woodpeckers, Buzzard, Raven, Sparrowhawk. *Summer*: Pied and Spotted Flycatchers, Redstart, Wood Warbler. *Winter*: On water meadows below, look for Teal, Wigeon, Goosander, Shoveler, Tufted Duck and Pochard.
Contact: Steve Lucas, Area Officer, 35 Maesquarre Road, Betws, Ammanford, Carmarthenshire SA18 2LF. 01269 594 293.
e-mail: information@wtsww.cix.co.uk
www.wildlifetrust.org.uk/wtsww

2. CORS CARON

CCW (West Wales Area).
Location: SN 697 632 (car park). Reached from B4343 N of Tregaron.
Access: Open access to S of car park along the railway to boardwalk, out to SE bog. Access to rest of the reserve by permit. Dogs on lead. Access for coaches.
Facilities: None at present.
Public transport: None.
Habitat: Raised bog, river, fen, wet grassland, willow woodland, reedbed.
Key birds: *Summer*: Lapwing, Redshank, Curlew, Red Kite, Grasshopper Warbler, Whinchat. *Winter*: Teal, Wigeon, Whooper Swan, Hen Harrier, Red Kite.
Contact: Paul Culyer, CCW, Neuaddlas, Tregaron, Ceredigion. 01974 298 480.
e-mail: p.culyer@ccw.gov.uk
www.ccw.gov.uk

3. DINAS & GWENFFRWD

RSPB (South Wales Office).
Location: SN 788 472. North of Llandovery. From A483 take B road signposted to Llyn Brianne Reservoir.
Access: Public nature trail at Dinas open at all times.
Facilities: Nature trails.
Public transport: Nearest station at Llandovery, 10 miles away.
Habitat: Hillside oakwoods, streams, bracken slopes and moorland.
Key birds: Buzzard, Pied Flycatcher, Redstart, Wood Warbler, Tree Pipit, Red Kite and Peregrine in area. Dipper, Goosander, Raven.
Contact: Reserve Warden, RSPB Ynys-Hir Reserve, Eglwys-fach, Machynlleth, Powys SY20 8TA. 01654 700 222. e-mail: ynyshir@rspb.org.uk

4. DYFI

CCW (West Wales Area).
Location: SN 610 942. Large estuary area W of Machyalleth. Public footpaths off A493 E of Aberdyfi, and off B4353 (S of river); minor road from B4353 at Ynyslas to dunes and parking area.
Access: Ynyslas dunes and the estuary have unrestricted access. No access to Cors Fochno (raised bog) for casual birdwatching; permit required for study and research purposes. Good views over the bog and Aberleri marshes from W bank of Afon Leri.
Facilities: Public hide overlooking marshes beside footpath at SN 611 911.
Public transport: None.
Habitat: Sandflats, mudflats, saltmarsh, creeks, dunes, raised bog, grazing marsh.
Key birds: *Winter*: Greenland White-fronted Goose, wildfowl, waders and raptors. *Summer*: Breeding wildfowl and waders (inc. Teal, Shoveler, Merganser, Lapwing, Curlew, Redshank).
Contact: Mike Bailey, CCW Warden, Plas Gogerddan, Aberystwyth, Ceredigion SY23 3EE. 01970 821 100.

5. THE NATIONAL WETLANDS CENTRE, WALES

The Wildfowl & Wetlands Trust.
Location: SS 533 984. Leave M4 at junction 48. Signposted from A484, E of Llanelli.
Access: Open daily (9.30am-6.00pm summer, earlier in winter) except Christmas Eve and Christmas Day.
Facilities: Visitor centre, restaurant, hides, education facilities, disabled access. Overlooks Burry Inlet.
Public transport: None.
Habitat: Inter-tidal mudflats, reedbeds, pools, marsh, waterfowl collection.
Key birds: Large flocks of Curlew, Oystercatcher, Redshank on saltmarsh. *Winter*: Pintail, Wigeon, Teal. Also Little Egret, Short-eared Owl, Peregrine.
Contact: Mr Nigel Williams, Centre Manager,The National Wetlands Centre, Llwynhendy, Llanelli SA14 9SH. 01554 741 087; Fax 01554 744 101. e-mail: info.llanelli@wwt.org.uk www.wwt.org.uk

6. RAMSEY ISLAND

RSPB (South Wales Office).
Location: SM 706 237. One mile offshore from St Justinians slipway, two miles W of St Davids.
Access: Open every day, Easter-Oct 31. No wheelchair access. Coach parking available at St Justinians. For boat bookings contact: Thousand Island expeditions: 01437 721 686 or e-mail: sales@thousandislands.co.uk
Facilities: Toilets, small RSPB shop, tuck shop, hot drinks and snacks, self-guiding trail.
Public transport: Trains to Haverfordwest Station. Hourly buses to St Davids, bus to St Justinians.
Habitat: Acid grassland, maritime heath, seacliffs.
Key birds: *Spring/summer*: Cliff-nesting auks (Guillemot, Razorbill). Kittiwake, Lesser, Great Black-backed, Herring Gulls, Shag, Wheatear, Stonechat. *All year*: Peregrine, Raven, Chough, Lapwing.
Other notable flora and fauna: Mammals: Grey seal, red deer, porpoise seen most days.
Contact: RSPB Ramsey Island Reserve, Warden: 07836 535 733. www.rspb.org.uk

7. SKOKHOLM ISLAND

The Wildlife Trust of South and West Wales.
Location: SM 735 050. Island lying S of Skomer.
Access: Occasional day visits, also 3 or 4 night stays available. Weekly accomm. Apr-Sep, tel 01239 621 212 for details and booking.
Facilities: Call for details.
Public transport: None.
Habitat: Cliffs, bays and inlets.
Key birds: *Summer*: Large colonies of Razorbill, Puffin, Guillemot, Manx Shearwater, Storm Petrel, Lesser Black-backed Gull. Migrants inc. rare species.
Contact: Trust HQ, 01239 621 212.

8. SKOMER ISLAND

The Wildlife Trust of South and West Wales.
Location: SM 725 095. Fifteen miles from Haverfordwest. Take B4327 turn-off for Marloes, embarkation point at Martin's Haven, two miles past village.
Access: Apr 1-Oct 31. Boats sail at 10am, 11am and noon every day except Mon (Bank Holidays excluded). Closed four days beginning of Jun for seabird counts. Not suitable for infirm (steep landing steps and rough ground).
Facilities: Information centre, toilets, two hides, wardens, booklets, guides, nature trails.
Public transport: None.
Habitat: Maritime cliff, bracken, bluebells and red campion, heathland, freshwater ponds.
Key birds: Largest colony of Manx Shearwater in the world (overnight). Puffin, Guillemot, Razorbill (Apr-end Jul). Kittiwake (until end Aug), Fulmar (absent Oct), Short-eared Owl (during day Jun and Jul), Chough, Peregrine, Buzzard (all year), migrants.
Contact: Juan Brown, Skomer Island, Marloes, Pembs SA62 2BJ. 07971 114 302. e-mail: skomer@wtww.co.uk

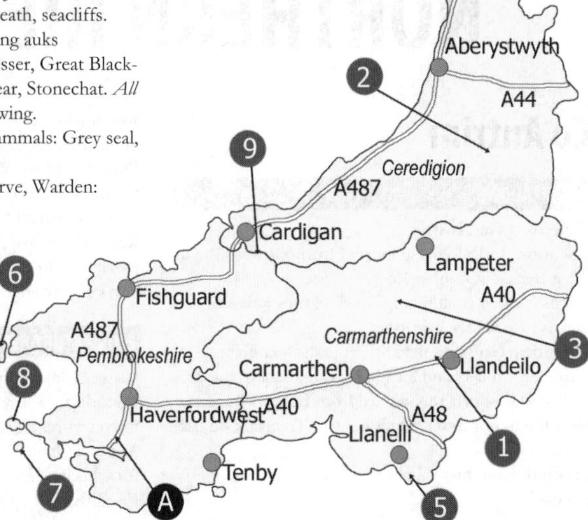

9. WELSH WILDLIFE CENTRE

The Wildlife Trust of South and West Wales.
Location: SN 188 451. Two miles SE of Cardigan. River Teifi is N boundary. Sign posted from Cardigan to Fishguard Road.
Access: Open 10.30am-5pm all year. Free parking for WTSWW members, £3 non-members. Dogs on leads welcome. Disabled access to visitor centre, paths, four hides.
Facilities: Visitor centre, restaurant, network of paths and seven hides.
Public transport: Train station, Haverfordwest (23 miles). Bus station in Cardigan. Access on foot from Cardigan centre, ten mins.
Habitat: Wetlands, marsh, swamp, reedbed, open water, creek (tidal), river, saltmarsh, woodland.
Key birds: Cetti's Warbler, Kingfisher, Water Rail, Greater Spotted Woodpecker, Dipper, gulls, Marsh Harrier, Sand Martin, Hobby, Redstart, occasional Bittern and Red Kite.
Contact: The Welsh Wildlife Centre, Cilgerran, Cardigan SA43 2TB. 01239 621 212.
e-mail: wwc@welshwildlife.org
www.welshwildlife.org

10. YNYS-HIR

RSPB (CYMRU).
Location: SN 68 29 63. Off A487 Aberystwyth - Machynlleth road in Eglwys-fach village. Six miles SW of Machynlleth.
Access: Open every day (9am-9pm or dusk if earlier). Visitor centre open daily Apr-Oct (10am-5pm), Wed-Sun Nov-Mar (10am-4pm). Coaches welcome but please call for parking information. Sorry, no dogs allowed.
Facilities: Visitor centre and toilets. Numerous trails, six hides, drinks machine.
Public transport: Bus service to Eglwys-fach from either Machynlleth or Aberystwyth, tel. 01970 617 951. Rail service to Machynlleth.
Habitat: Estuary, freshwater pools, woodland and wet grassland.
Key birds: *Winter*: Greenland White-fronted Goose, Wigeon, Hen Harrier, Barnacle Goose. *Spring/* summer: Wood Warbler, Redstart, Pied Flycatcher. *All year*: Peregrine, Red Kite, Buzzard, Goshawk, Little Egret.
Contact: Reserve Warden, RSPB Ynys-Hir Reserve, Eglwys-fach, Machynlleth, Powys SY20 8TA. 01654 700 222. e-mail: ynyshir@rspb.org.uk

OTHER SITES

Full details in previous editions, (year indicated in brackets).
A. Westfield Pill – Trust HQ, 01239 621 212 (06).

NORTHERN IRELAND

Co Antrim

BOG MEADOWS

Ulster Wildlife Trust.
Location: J 315 726. Signposted from the Falls Road, West Belfast. (OS map 15).
Access: Open at all times. Coach parties welcome. Suitable for wheelchair users.
Facilities: Car park, network of paths – contact warden for toilets and bird hide access arrangements.
Public transport: Bus service from Belfast city along Falls Road. For more details contact Translink on 028 9066 6630.
Habitat: Unimproved grassland, scrub, ponds, reedbeds.
Key birds: *Summer*: Passage waders, Grey Wagtail, Stonechat, Sedge and Grasshopper Warblers, Reed Bunting. *Winter*: Water Rail, Snipe, Teal.
Contact: Ross Towers, Bog Meadows Reserve Warden, Belfast UWT Office, 163 Stewartstown Road, Dunmurry, Belfast BT17 0HW. 028 9062 8647.
e-mail: info@ulsterwildlifetrust.org
www.ulsterwildlifetrust.org

ECOS NATURE RESERVE

Ulster Wildlife Trust.
Location: D 118 036. 0.5 miles NE of Ballymena town centre. Signposted off M2 (OS map 9).
Access: Open at all times. Coaches welcome. Suitable for wheelchair users.
Facilities: Environmental centre (028 2566 4400), car

park, toilets, bird hide, network of paths.
Public transport: Bus from Ballymena town centre or within easy walking distance. For more details contact Translink on 028 9066 6630.
Habitat: Lake, wet meadows, willow coppice, scrub.
Key birds: *Summer*: Breeding Snipe, Sedge Warbler, Grasshopper Warbler, Reed Bunting. *Winter*: Teal, Goldeneye, Lapwing, Curlew. Rarities have included, White-winged Black Tern and Hoopoe in recent years.
Contact: Reserves Manager, Ulster Wildlife Trust, 3 New Line, Crossgar, Co Down BT19 9EP. 028 4483 0282. e-mail: info@ulsterwildifetrust.org www.ulsterwildlifetrust.org

LAGAN MEADOWS

Ulster Wildlife Trust.
Location: J 335 703. Signposted off Malone Road, South Belfast (OS map 15).
Access: Open at all times. Suitable for coach parties. Suitable for wheelchair users along Lagan towpath.
Facilities: Network of paths.
Public transport: Bus service from Belfast city centre along Malone/Stranmillis Roads. For more details contact Translink on 028 9066 6630.
Habitat: Species-rich meadows, marsh, pond and scrub.
Key birds: *Summer*: Sedge and Grasshopper Warblers, Blackcap and Reed Bunting. *Winter*: Water Rail, Snipe, Redpoll and Siskin.
Contact: Rachael Bryers, Reserve warden, Belfast UWT office, 163 Stewartstown Road, Dunmurry, Belfast BT17 0HW. 028 9062 8647.
e-mail: info@ulsterwildlifetrust.org
www.ulsterwildlifetrust.org

PORTMORE LOUGH

RSPB (Northern Ireland Office).
Location: J 107 685. Eight miles from Lurgan. Signposted from Aghalee village.
Access: Open every day, unmanned. Limited disabled facilities.
Facilities: Car park, toilets, information shelter and one hide.
Public transport: None.
Habitat: Lowland wet grassland, scrub and reedbed.
Key birds: *Spring/summer*: Breeding Curlew, Snipe, Lapwing. *Winter*: Greylag Goose, Whooper Swan and a variety of wildfowl.
Contact: John Scovell, 028 9510 097; mobile 07736 792516. e-mail: john.scovell@rspb.org.uk

RATHLIN ISLAND

RSPB (Northern Ireland Office).
Location: Off NE coast of County Antrim. Five mile ferry journey from Ballycastle.
Access: Open Apr 1-Aug 31. Four miles from harbour plus approx 100 steps.
Facilities: Toilets and visitor reception with interpretation material. RSPB viewpoint at the West Lighthouse.
Public transport: Caledonian MacBrayne ferry service from Ballycastle to Rathlin, tel 028 2076 9299. Minibus tel 028 2076 3451.
Habitat: Sea cliffs and offshore stacks.
Key birds: *Spring/summer*: Puffin, Guillemot, Razorbill, Fulmar, Kittiwake.
Contact: Liam Mcfaul/Alison McFaul, RSPB, South Cleggan, Rathlin Island, Ballycastle, Co Antrim, 02820 763 948.

STRAIDKILLY

Ulster Wildlife Trust.
Location:D 302 165. Situated midway between Glenarm and Carnlough in the Glens of Antrim (OS map 9).
Access: Open at all times. Not suitable for coach parties or wheelchair users.
Facilities: Waymarked trail, picnic area and interpretation viewpoint.
Public transport: 128 Ballymena-Carnlough or 162 Larne-Cushendun. For more details contact Translink on 028 9066 6630.
Habitat: Semi-natural woodland.
Key birds: *Summer*: Buzzard, Raven, Blackcap and Bullfinch. *Winter*: Woodcock.
Contact: Reserves Manager, Ulster Wildlife Trust, 3 New Line, Crossgar, Co Down BT19 9EP. 028 4483 0282. e-mail: info@ulsterwildifetrust.org www.ulsterwildlifetrust.org

Co Armagh

OXFORD ISLAND

Craigavon Borough Council.
Location: J 061 608. On shores of Lough Neagh, 2.5 miles from Lurgan, Co Armagh. Signposted from J10 of M1.
Access: Site open at all times. Car parks locked at varying times (see signs). Coach parking available. Lough Neagh Discovery Centre open every day Apr-Sept (10am-5pm Mon-Sat, 10am-7pm Sun), Oct-Mar (10am-5pm every day) Closed Christmas Day. Dogs on leads please. Most of site and all of Centre

accessible for wheelchairs. Wheelchairs and mobility scooters available for visitors.
Facilities: Public toilets, Lough Neagh Discovery Centre with exhibitions, loop system for hard-of-hearing, shop and café. Four miles of footpaths, five birdwatching hides, children's play area, picnic tables, public jetties. Guided walks available (pre-booking essential). Varied programme of events.
Public transport: Ulsterbus Park'n Ride at Lough Road, Lurgan is 0.5 miles from reserve entrance. Tel 028 9033 3000. Lurgan Railway Station, 3 miles from reserve entrance.
Habitat: Freshwater lake, ponds, wet grassland, reedbed, woodland.
Key birds: *Winter*: Large flocks of wildfowl, especially Pochard, Tufted Duck, Goldeneye and Scaup (mainly Dec/Jan). Whooper and Bewick's Swans (Oct-Apr). *Summer*: Sedge Warbler, Grasshopper Warbler and Great Crested Grebe.
Contact: Rosemary Mulholland, Conservation Officer, Lough Neagh Discovery Centre, Oxford Island NNR, Lurgan, Co Armagh, N Ireland BT66 6NJ. 02838 322 205. www.oxfordisland.com
e-mail: oxford.island@craigavon.gov.uk

Co Down

BELFAST LOUGH RESERVE

RSPB (Northern Ireland Office).
Location: Take A2 N from Belfast and follow signs to Belfast Harbour Estate. Both entrances to reserve have checkpoints. From Dee Street 2 miles to reserve, from Tillysburn entrance 1 mile.
Access: Dawn to dusk.
Facilities: Lagoon overlooked by observation room (check for opening hours), two view points.
Public transport: None.
Habitat: Mudflats, wet grassland, freshwater lagoon.
Key birds: Noted for Black-tailed Godwit numbers and excellent variety of waterfowl in spring, autumn and winter, with close views. Rarities have included Buff-breasted, Pectoral, White-rumped and Semi-palmated Sandpipers, Spotted Crake, American Wigeon, Laughing Gull.
Contact: Warden, Anthony McGeehan, 028 9147 9009.

CASTLE ESPIE

The Wildfowl & Wetlands Trust.
Location: J 474 672. On Strangford Lough 10 miles E of Belfast, signposted from A22 in the Comber area.
Access: Open daily except Christmas Day (10.30am Mon-Sat, 11.30am Sun).
Facilities: Visitor centre, educational facilities, views over lough, three hides, woodland walk.
Public transport: Call for advice.
Habitat: Reedbed filtration system with viewing facilities.
Key birds: *Winter*: Wildfowl esp. pale-bellied Brent Goose, Scaup. *Summer*: Warblers. Wader scrape has attracted Little Egret, Ruff, Long-billed Dowitcher, Killdeer.
Contact: James Orr, Centre Manager, The Wildfowl & Wetlands Trust, Castle Espie, Ballydrain Road, Comber, Co Down BT23 6EA. 02891 874 146.

COPELAND BIRD OBSERVATORY

Location: Situated on a 40-acre island on outer edge of Belfast Lough, four miles N of Donaghadee.
Access: Access is by chartered boat from Donaghadee.
Facilities: Observatory open Apr-Oct most weekends and some whole weeks. Hostel-type accommodation for up to 20. Daily ringing, bird census, sea passage recording. General bookings: Neville McKee, 67 Temple Rise, Templepatrick, Co. Antrim BT39 0AG (tel 028 9443 3068).
Public transport: None.
Habitat: Grassy areas, rock foreshore.
Key birds: Large colony of Manx Shearwaters; Black Guillemot, Eider, Water Rail also nest. *Summer*: Visiting Storm Petrels. Moderate passage of passerine migrants.
Contact: Dr Peter Munro, Talisker Lodge, 54B Templepatrick Road, Ballyclare, Co Antrim BT39 9TX. 028 9332 3421.

MURLOUGH

National Trust.
Location: J 394 338. Ireland's first nature reserve, between Dundrum and Newcastle, close to Mourne Mountains.
Access: Permit needed except on marked paths.
Facilities: Visitor centre.
Public transport: Local bus service from Belfast-Newcastle passes reserve entrances.
Habitat: Sand dunes, heathland.
Key birds: Waders and wildfowl occur in Inner Dundrum Bay adjacent to the reserve; divers and large numbers of Scoter (inc. regular Surf Scoter) and Merganser in Dundrum Bay.
Contact: Head Warden, Murlough NNR, The Stable Yard, Keel Point, Dundrum, Newcastle, Co Down BT33 0NQ. Tel/Fax 028 4375 1467;
e-mail umnnrw@smtp.ntrust.org.uk.

NORTH STRANGFORD LOUGH

National Trust.
Location: J 510 700. View from adjacent roads and car parks; also from hide at Castle Espie (J 492 675).
Access: Call for advice.
Facilities: Hide.
Public transport: Bus service from Newtownards to Portaferry.
Habitat: Extensive tidal mudflats, limited saltmarsh.
Key birds: Major feeding area for pale-bellied Brent Goose, also Pintail, Wigeon, Whooper Swan. Waders (inc. Dunlin, Knot, Oystercatcher, Bar-tailed Godwit).
Contact: Head Warden, National Trust, Strangford Lough Wildlife Scheme, Castle Ward, Strangford, Co Down BT30 7LS. Tel/Fax 028 4488 1411;
e-mail uslwcw@smtp.ntrust.org.uk.
e-mail: strangford@nationaltrust.org.uk

SLIEVENACLOY

Ulster Wildlife Trust.
Location:J 255 712. Situated in the Belfast Hills, take Ballycolin Road off A501 (OS map 14,15).
Access: Contact Reserve Warden. Unsuitable for coach parties and wheelchair users.
Facilities: Car park, waymarked trails.
Public transport: Bus service from Belfast to Glenavy. For more details contact Translink on 028 9066 6630.
Habitat: Unimproved grassland, scrub.
Key birds: *Summer*: Snipe, Curlew, Sky Lark, Grey Wagtail, Stonechat, Wheatear, Grasshopper Warbler and Reed Bunting. *Winter*: Hen Harrier, Merlin, Fieldfare and Snow Bunting.
Contact: Catherine Bertrand, Slievenacloy Reserve Warden, Belfast UWT office, 163 Stewartstown Road, Dunmurry, Belfast BT17 0HW. 028 9062 8647.
e-mail: info@ulsterwildlifetrust.org
www.ulsterwildlifetrust.org

Co Londonderry

LOUGH FOYLE

RSPB (Northern Ireland Office).
Location: C 545 237. Large sea lough NE of Londonderry. Take minor roads off Limavady-Londonderry road to view-points (choose high tide) at Longfield Point, Ballykelly, Faughanvale.
Access: Open all year. No permit, but keep to trails.
Facilities: None.
Public transport: None.
Habitat: Beds of eel-grass, mudflats, surrounding agricultural land.
Key birds: Staging-post for migrating wildfowl (eg. 15,000 Wigeon, 4,000 Pale-bellied Brent Geese in Oct/Nov). *Winter*: Slavonian Grebe, divers, Bewick's and Whooper Swans, Bar-tailed Godwit, Golden Plover, Snow Bunting. *Autumn*: Waders (inc. Ruff, Little Stint, Curlew Sandpiper, Spotted Redshank).
Contact: RSPB N Ireland HQ (01232 491 547), 028 9049 1547.

UMBRA

Ulster Wildlife Trust.
Location: C 725 355. Ten miles W of Coleraine on A2 – entrance beside automatic railway crossing about 1.5 miles W of Downhill. OS 1:50 000 sheet 4.
Access: Wildlife Trust members. Not suitable for coaches. Unsuitable for wheelchair users.
Facilities: Informal paths.
Public transport: Ulsterbus service to Downhill from Coleraine. For more details contact Translink on 028 9066 6630.
Habitat: Sand dunes.
Key birds: *Summer*: Breeding Sky Lark. *Winter*: Woodcock, Peregrine, plus Great Northern Diver offshore.
Contact: Andrew Upton, Ulster Wildlife Trust, 3 New Line, Crossgar, Co Down BT30 9EP. 028 4483 0282. e-mail: andrew.upton@ulsterwildifetrust.org
www.ulsterwildlifetrust.org

OTHER SITES

Full details in previous editions, (year indicated in brackets).
Blessingbourne – Andrew Upton (Ulster WT), 02844 830 282.
Crawfordsburn Country Park – 02892 853 621 (07).
Isle of Muck – Ulster WT, 02890 628 647 (07).
Kebble, Rathlin Island – Dept of Environment, 02870 823 600 (07).
Quoile Pondage – Dept of Environment, 02844 615 520 (07).

ISLE OF MAN

BREAGLE GLEN

Manx Wildlife Trust/Castletown Town Commissioners Habitats.
Location: SC 196 688. In Port Erin from St Georges Crescent, which forms the whole N and W boundary.
Access: Open all year. Facilities: None.
Public transport: Regular bus service from Douglas to Port Erin and then short walk.
Habitat: Small woodland area, shrubs.
Key birds: *Passage*: Yellow-browed Warbler, Barred Warbler, Firecrest, Red-breasted Flycatcher have been recorded.
Contact: Tricia Sayle, Reserves Officer, Manx Wildlife Trust, Tynwald Mills, St John's, Isle of Man IM4 3AE. 01624 801 985.
e-mail: manxwt@cix.co.uk
www.wildlifetrust.org.uk/manxwt

CALF OF MAN BIRD OBSERVATORY

Manx National Heritage.
Location: SC 15 65. Small island off the SW of the Isle of Man.
Access: Landings by private craft all year. No dogs, fires, camping or climbing.
Facilities: Accommodation for 8 people plus 2 volunteers sharing from Apr-Sept. Bookings: at contact address. Bird ringers welcome to join in ringing activities with prior notice.
Public transport: Local boat from Port Erin (Apr-Sept) or Port St Mary all year.
Habitat: Heather/bracken moor and seabird cliffs.
Key birds: *All year*: Hen Harrier, Peregrine and Chough. Breeding seabirds including Shag, Razorbill, Manx Shearwater etc. Excellent spring and autumn migration, seabird passage best in autumn.
Contact: Ben Jones, (Warden), Manx National Heritage, Douglas, Isle of Man IM1 3LY.

CLOSE SARTFIELD

Manx Wildlife Trust.
Location: SC 361 956. From Ramsey drive W on A3. Turn on to B9, take third R and follow this road for nearly a mile. Reserve entrance is on R.
Access: Open all year round. No dogs. Path and boardwalk suitable for wheelchairs from car park through wildflower meadow and willow scrub to hide. Facilities: Car park, hide, reserve leaflet (50p, available from office) outlines circular walk.
Public transport: None.
Habitat: Wildflower-rich hay meadow, marshy grassland, willow scrub/developing birch woodland, bog.
Key birds: *Winter*: Large roost of Hen Harrier. *Summer*: Corn Crake (breeding 1999 and 2000 after 11 years' absence), Curlew, warblers.
Contact: Manx Wildlife Trust, 01624 801 985.
e-mail: manxwt@cix.co.uk
www.wildlifetrust.org.uk/manxwt

CRONK Y BING

Manx Wildlife Trust.
Location: NX 381 017. Take A10 coast road N from Jurby. Approx two miles along there is a sharp R hand turn over a bridge. Before the bridge there is a track to the L. A parking area is available at the end of the track.
Access: Open all year round. Dogs to be kept on a lead. Not suitable for the disabled.
Facilities: None.
Public transport: None.
Habitat: Open dune and dune grassland.
Key birds: *Summer*: Terns. *Winter*: Divers, grebes, skuas, gulls.
Contact: Manx Wildlife Trust, 01624 801 985.
e-mail: manxwt@cix.co.uk
www.wildlifetrust.org.uk/manxwt

COUNTY DIRECTORY

Grey Heron by Steve Knell

ENGLAND

THE INFORMATION in the directory has been obtained either from the persons listed or from the appropriate national or other bodies. In some cases, where it has not proved possible to verify the details directly, alternative responsible sources have been relied upon. When no satisfactory record was available, previously included entries have sometimes had to be deleted. Readers are requested to advise the editor of any errors or omissions.

AVON

See Somerset.

BEDFORDSHIRE

Bird Atlas/Avifauna
An Atlas of the Breeding Birds of Bedfordshire 1988-92 by R A Dazley and P Trodd (Bedfordshire Natural History Society, 1994).

Bird Recorders
Dave Odell, 136 Bedford Road, Wootton, Bedford, MK43 9JD. e-mail: daveodell@tiscali.co.uk

Bird Report
BEDFORDSHIRE BIRD REPORT (1946-), from Mary Sheridan, 28 Chestnut Hill, Linslade, Leighton Buzzard, Beds LU7 2TR. 01525 378 245.

BTO Regional Representative & Regional Development Officer
RR. Nigel Willits, 93 High Street, Wrestlingworth, Beds SG19 2EL. e-mail: willits1960@hotmail.com

Club
BEDFORDSHIRE BIRD CLUB. (1992; 293). Miss Sheila Alliez, Flat 61 Adamson Court, Adamson Walk, Kempston, Bedford, MK42 8QZ.
e-mail: alliezsec@peewit.freeserve.co.uk
www.bedsbirdclub.org.uk
Meetings: 8.00pm, last Tuesday of the month (Sep-Mar), Maulden Village Hall, Maulden, Beds.

Ringing Groups
IVEL RG. Errol Newman, 29 Norse Road, Goldington, Bedford, MK41 0NR. 01234 312 787;
e-mail: lew.n1@ntlworld.com

RSPB. WB Kirby, e-mail: will.kirby@rspb.org.uk

RSPB Local Groups
BEDFORD. (1970; 80). Bob Montgomery, 36 Princes Road, Bromham, Beds MK43 8QD. 01234 822 035;
www.rspb.org.uk/groups/bedford/
Meetings: 7.30pm, 3rd Thursday of the month, A.R.A. Manton Lane, Bedford.

LUTON AND SOUTH BEDFORDSHIRE. (1973; 120+). Mick Price, 120 Common Road, Kensworth, Beds LU6 3RG. 01582 873 268.
Meetings: 7.45pm, 2nd Wednesday of the month, Houghton Regis Social Cnetre, Parkside Drive, Houghton Regis, LU5 5QN.

Wildlife Trust
See Cambridgeshire,

BERKSHIRE

BirdAtlas/Avifauna
The Birds of Berkshire by P E Standley et al (Berkshire Atlas Group/Reading Ornithological Club, 1996).

Bird Recorder
RECORDER (Records Committee and rarity records). Chris DR Heard, 3 Waterside Lodge, Ray Mead Road, Maidenhead, Berkshire SL6 8NP. 01628 633 828; e-mail: chris.heard@virgin.net

ASSISTANT RECORDER (Rare breeding records, bird survey data). Derek J Barker, 40 Heywood Gardens, Woodlands Park, Maidenhead, Berkshire SL6 3LZ. 01628 820 125.

Bird Reports
BERKSHIRE BIRD BULLETIN (Monthly, 1986-), from Brian Clews, 118 Broomhill, Cookham, Berks SL6 9LQ. 01628 525 314;
e-mail: brian.clews@btconnect.com

BIRDS OF BERKSHIRE (1974-), from The Secretary of the Berkshire Ornithological Club,

BIRDS OF THE THEALE AREA (1988-), from The Secretary, Theale Area Bird Conservation Group.

BTO Regional Representative
RR. Chris Robinson, 2 Beckfords, Upper Basildon, Reading, RG8 8PB. 01491 671 420;
e-mail: berks_bto_rep@btinternet.com

Clubs
BERKSHIRE BIRD BULLETIN GROUP. (1986; 100). Berkshire Bird Bulletin Group, PO Box 680, Maidenhead, Berks SL6 9ST. 01628 525 314;
e-mail: brian.clews@btconnect.com

ENGLAND

NEWBURY DISTRICT ORNITHOLOGICAL CLUB. (1959; 110). Trevor Maynard, 15 Kempton Close, Newbury, Berks RG14 7RS. 01635 36752; e-mail: info1@ndoc.org.uk www.ndoc.org.uk

BERKSHIRE ORNITHOLOGICAL CLUB. (1947; 320). Renton Righelato, 63 Hamilton Road, Reading RG1 5RA. 0787 981 2564; e-mail: renton.righelato@berksoc.org.uk www.berksoc.org.uk
Meetings: 8pm, alternate Wednesdays (Oct-Mar). University of Reading.

THEALE AREA BIRD CONSERVATION GROUP. (1988; 75). Brian Uttley, 65 Omers Rise, Burghfield Common, Reading RG7 3HH. 0118 983 2894. www.freewebs.com/tabcg/index.htm
Meetings: 8pm, 1st Tuesday of the month, Englefield Social Club.

Ringing Groups
NEWBURY RG. J Legg, 31 Haysoms Drive, Greenham, Nr Newbury, Berks, RG19 8EY. e-mail: janlegg@btinternet.com www.newburyrg.co.uk

RUNNYMEDE RG. D G Harris, 22 Blossom Waye, Hounslow, TW5 9HD. e-mail: daveharris@tinyonline. co.uk

RSPB Local Groups
EAST BERKSHIRE. (1974; 200). Gerry Studd, 5 Cherry Grove, Holmer Green, High Wycombe, Bucks HP15 6RG. 01494 715 609; e-mail: gerrystudd@aol.com www.eastberksrspb.org.uk
Meetings: 7.30pm, Thursdays (Sept-April), Methodist Church Hall, High Street, Maidenhead.

READING. (1986; 80). David Glover. 0118 983 3812; e-mail: davidglover@hotmail.co.uk www.reading-rspb.org.uk

WOKINGHAM & BRACKNELL. (1979; 200). Les Blundell, Folly Cottage, Buckle Lane, Warfield RG42 5SB. 01344 861 964; e-mail: les@folly-cottage.fsnet.co.uk www.wbrspb.btinternet.co.uk
Meetings: 8.00pm, 2nd Tuesday of the month (Sep-Jun), Finchampstead Memorial Hall, Wokingham, RG40 4JU.

Wildlife Hospitals
KESTREL LODGE. D J Chandler, 101 Sheridan Avenue, Caversham, Reading, RG4 7QB. 01189 477 107. Birds of prey, ground feeding birds, waterbirds, seabirds. Temporary homes for all except large birds of prey. Veterinary support. Small charge.

LIFELINE. Wendy Hermon, Treatment Centre Co-ordinator, Swan Treatment Centre, Cuckoo Weir Island, South Meadow Lane, Eton, Windsor, Berks, SL4 6SS. 01753 859 397; (Fax) 01753 622 709; e-mail: wendyhermon@aol.com www.zen117019.zen.co.uk
Registered charity. Thames Valley 24-hour swan rescue and treatment service. Veterinary support and hospital unit. Operates membership scheme.

Wildlife Trust
Director, See Oxfordshire,

BUCKINGHAMSHIRE

BirdAtlas/Avifauna
The Birds of Buckinghamshire ed by P Lack and D Ferguson (Buckinghamshire Bird Club, 1993). Now out of print.

Bird Recorder
Andy Harding, 15 Jubilee Terrace, Stony Stratford, Milton Keynes, MK11 1DU. (H) 01908 565 896; (W) 01908 653 328; e-mail: a.v.harding@open.ac.uk

Bird Reports
BUCKINGHAMSHIRE BIRD REPORT (1980-), from John Gearing, Valentines, Dinton, Aylesbury, Bucks, HP17 8UW. e-mail: john_gearing@hotmail.com

NORTH BUCKS BIRD REPORT (12 pa), from The Recorder.

BTO Regional Representative & Regional Development Officer
RR. Position vacant

RDO. Peter Hearn, 160 High Street, Aylesbury, Bucks HP20 1RE. 01296 424 145; (Fax) 01296 581 520.

Clubs
BUCKINGHAMSHIRE BIRD CLUB. (1981; 340). Roger S Warren, The Old Chapel, Skirmett, Henley-on-Thames, Oxon RG9 6TD. 01491 638 691. www.bucksbirdclub.co.uk

NORTH BUCKS BIRDERS. (1977; 40). Andy Harding, 15 Jubilee Terrace, Stony Stratford, Milton Keynes, MK11 1DU. (H) 01908 565 896; (W) 01908 653 328; e-mail: a.v.harding@open.ac.uk
Meetings: Last Tuesday of the month (Nov, Jan, Feb, Mar), The Cock, High Street, Stony Stratford.

Ringing Groups
HUGHENDEN RG. Peter Edwards, 8 The Brackens, Warren Wood, High Wycombe, Bucks, HP11 1EB. 01494 535 125.

RSPB Local Groups
See also Herts: Chorleywood,

AYLESBURY. (1981; 220). Ann Wallington, 01295 253 330, e-mail: Jenny.wallington@tesco.net

NORTH BUCKINGHAMSHIRE. (1976; 430). Chris Ward, 41 William Smith Close, Woolstone, Milton Keynes, MK15 0AN. 01908 669 448;
e-mail:cwphotography@hotmail.com
www.rspb.org.uk/groups/northbucks
Meetings: 7.30pm, 2nd Thursday of the month, Heronsbrook Meeting Place, Walnut Tree, Milton Keynes, MK7 7ED.

Wildlife Hospitals
WILDLIFE HOSPITAL TRUST. St Tiggywinkles, Aston Road, Haddenham, Aylesbury, Bucks HP17 8AF. 01844 292 292; (Fax) 01844 292 640;
e-mail: mail@sttiggywinkles.org.uk
www.tiggywinkles.com
Registered charity. All British species. Veterinary referrals and helpline for vets and others on wild bird treatments. Full veterinary unit and staff. Pub: *Bright Eyes* (free to members - sae).

Wildlife Trust
Director, See Oxfordshire,

CAMBRIDGESHIRE

BirdAtlas/Avifauna
An Atlas of the Breeding Birds of Cambridgeshire (VC 29) P M M Bircham et al (Cambridge Bird Club, 1994).

The Birds of Cambridgeshire: checklist 2000 (Cambridge Bird Club)

Bird Recorders
CAMBRIDGESHIRE. Mark Hawkes, 7 Cook Drive, Eynesbury, St Neots, Cambs PE19 2JU. 01480 215 305; e-mail: marklhawkes@yahoo.co.uk

HUNTINGDON & PETERBOROUGH. John Clark, 7 West Brook, Hilton, Huntingdon, Cambs, PE28 9NW. 01480 830 472.

Bird Reports
CAMBRIDGESHIRE BIRD REPORT (1925-), from Bruce Martin, 178 Nuns Way, Cambridge, CB4 2NS. 01223 700 656;
e-mail: bruce.s.martin@ntlworld.com

PAXTON PITS BIRD REPORT (1994-)
£3.50 inc postage, from Trevor Gunton, 15 St James Road, Little Paxton, Cambs PE19 6QW. (Tel/Fax) 01480 473 562.

PETERBOROUGH BIRD CLUB REPORT (1999-), see contact for Peterborough Bird Club.
www.pbc.codehog.co.uk

BTO Regional Representatives
CAMBRIDGESHIRE RR. Tony Fulford, 19 Mallow Close, Ely, Cambs CB6 3WH. 01353 659 524;
e-mail: tonyfulford@googlemail.com

HUNTINGDON & PETERBOROUGH. Phillip Todd, 01733 810 832; e-mail: huntspbororr@yahoo.co.uk

Clubs
CAMBRIDGESHIRE BIRD CLUB. (1925; 310). John Harding, 3 Cotton's Field, Dry Drayton, Cambs CB23 8DG.
e-mail: jch@theleys.net
Meetings: 2nd Friday of the month, St John's Church Hall, Hills Road, Cambridge/Milton CP Visitors Centre, Milton, Cambridge.

PETERBOROUGH BIRD CLUB. (1999; 210) David Cromack (Chairman), 55 Thorpe Park Road, Peterborough, PE3 6LJ. 01733 566 815.
e-mail: d.cromack@btinternet.com
www.pbc.codehog.co.uk
Meetings: Indoor: 7.30pm last Tuesday of each month (Sep-Apr), Burghley Club, Burghley Square, Peterborough. Outdoor: monthly throughout most of year.

Ringing Group
WICKEN FEN RG. Dr C J R Thorne, 17 The Footpath, Coton, Cambs, CB23 7PX. 01954 210 566;
e-mail: cjrt@cam.ac.uk

Wetland Bird Survey Organisers
CAMBRIDGESHIRE OLD COUNTY. Bruce Martin, 178 Nuns Way, Cambridge, CB4 2NS. 01223 700 656;
e-mail: bruce.s.martin@ntlworld.com

NENE WASHES. Charlie Kitchin, RSPB Nene Washes, 21a East Delph, Whittlesey, Cambs PE7 1RH. 01733 205 140.

RSPB Local Groups
CAMBRIDGE. (1977; 150). Melvyn Smith, 01799 500 482; e-mail: mel_brensmith@hotmail.co.uk
www.rspb.org.uk/groups/cambridge.
Meetings: 3rd Wednesday of every month Jan-May and Sept-Dec 8pm. Chemistry Labs, Lensfield Road, Cambridge.

HUNTINGDONSHIRE. (1982; 180). Martyn Stanley-Williams, Babinda House, High Street, Bury, Huntingdon PE26 2NR. 01487 710 456;
e-mail: edunit@edunit.plus.com
www.huntsrspb.co.uk
Meetings: 7.30pm, last Wednesday of the month (Sep-Apr), Free Church, St Ives.

ENGLAND

Wildlife Trust
THE WILDLIFE TRUST FOR BEDFORDSHIRE, CAMBRIDGESHIRE, NORTHAMPTONSHIRE AND PETERBOROUGH. (1990; 33,000). The Manor House, Broad Street, Great Cambourne, Cambridgeshire CB23 6DH. 01954 713 500; (Fax) 01954 710 051;
e-mail: cambridgeshire@wildlifebcnp.org
www.wildlifebcnp.org

CHESHIRE

BirdAtlas/Avifauna
The Birds of Sandbach Flashes 1935-1999 by Andrew Goodwin and Colin Lythgoe (The Printing House, Crewe, 2000).

Bird Recorder (inc Wirral)
CHESHIRE & WIRRAL. Hugh Pulsford, 6 Buttermere Drive, Great Warford, Alderley Edge, Cheshire SK9 7WA. 01565 880 171; e-mail: countyrec@cawos.org.

Bird Report
CHESHIRE & WIRRAL BIRD REPORT (1969-), from David Cogger, 113 Nantwich Road, Middlewich, Cheshire, CW10 9HD. 01606 832 517;
e-mail: memsec@cawos.org www.cawos.org

HILBRE BIRD OBSERVATORY REPORT, from Hilbre Bird Observatory, c/o 129, Ennisdale Drive, West Kirby, Wirral, CH48 9UG, £3.

SOUTH EAST CHESHIRE ORNITHOLOGICAL SOCIETY BIRD REPORT (1985-), from The Secretary, South East Cheshire Ornithol Soc. 01270 582 642.

BTO Regional Representatives & Regional Development Officer
MID RR. Paul Miller, 01928 787 535;
e-mail: huntershill@worldonline.co.uk

NORTH & EAST RR. Charles Hull, Edleston Cottage, Edleston Hall Lane, Nantwich, Cheshire, CW5 8PL. 01270 628 194; e-mail: edleston@yahoo.co.uk

SOUTH RR & RDO. Charles Hull, Edleston Cottage, Edleston Hall Lane, Nantwich, Cheshire, CW5 8PL. 01270 628 194; e-mail: edleston@yahoo.co.uk

Clubs
CHESHIRE & WIRRAL ORNITHOLOGICAL SOCIETY. (1988; 375). David Cogger, 113 Nantwich Road, Middlewich, Cheshire, CW10 9HD. 01606 832 517;
e-mail: memsec@cawos.org www.cawos.org
Meetings: 7.45pm, 1st Friday of the month, Knutsford Civic Centre.

CHESTER & DISTRICT ORNITHOLOGICAL SOCIETY. (1967; 50). David King, 13 Bennett Close, Willaston, South Wirral, CH64 2XF. 0151 327 7212.
Meetings: 7.30pm, 1st Thursday of the month (Oct-Mar), Caldy Valley Community Centre.

KNUTSFORD ORNITHOLOGICAL SOCIETY. (1974; 45). Derek A Pike, 2 Lilac Avenue, Knutsford, Cheshire WA16 0AZ. 01565 653 811.
Meetings: 7.30pm, 4th Friday of the month (not Dec), Jubilee Hall, Stanley Road, Knutsford.

LANCASHIRE & CHESHIRE FAUNA SOCIETY. (1914; 140). Dave Bickerton, 64 Petre Crescent, Rishton, Blackburn, Lancs, BB1 4RB. 01254 886 257;
e-mail: bickertond@aol.com www.lacfs.org.uk

LYMM ORNITHOLOGY GROUP. (1975; 60). Mrs Ann Ledden, 4 Hill View, Widnes, WA8 9AL. 0151 424 0441; e-mail: secretary-log@tiscali.co.uk
Meetings: 8.00pm, last Friday of the month (Aug-May), Lymm Village Hall.

MID-CHESHIRE ORNITHOLOGICAL SOCIETY. (1963; 80). Paul Kenyon, 196 Chester Road, Hartford, Northwich, Cheshire CW8 1LG. 01606 779 60; e-mail: contact@midcheshireos.co.uk
www.midcheshireos.co.uk
Meetings: 7.30pm, 2nd Friday of the month (Oct-Mar), Hartford Village Hall.

MID-CHESHIRE ORNITHOLOGICAL SOCIETY

NANTWICH NATURAL HISTORY SOCIETY. (1979; 40). Dr P Griffiths, Vailima, Heatley Lane, Broomhall, Nantwich, Cheshire CW5 8BA. 01270 780 626.
Meetings: 7.30pm 3rd Tuesday of the month, RSPCA, Stapeley Grange.

SOUTH EAST CHESHIRE ORNITHOLOGICAL SOCIETY. (1964; 150). Colin Lythgoe, 11 Waterloo Road, Haslington, Crewe, CW1 5TF. 01270 582 642.
www.secos.org.uk
Meetings: 2nd Friday (Sept-Apr), 7.30pm, St Matthews Church Hall, Elworth.

WILMSLOW GUILD BIRDWATCHING GROUP. (1965; 67). Tom Gibbons, Chestnut Cottage, 37 Strawberry Lane, Wilmslow, Cheshire, SK9 6AQ. 01625 520 317.
Meetings: 7.30pm last Friday of the month, Wilmslow Guild, Bourne St, Wilmslow.

Ringing Groups
MERSEYSIDE RG. Bob Harris, 2 Dulas Road, Wavertree Green, Liverpool, L15 6UA. (Work) 0151 706 4311; e-mail: harris@liv.ac.uk

SOUTH MANCHESTER RG. C M Richards, Fairhaven, 13 The Green, Handforth, Wilmslow, Cheshire, SK9 3AG. 01625 524 527;
e-mail: cliveandkay.richards@care4free.net

ENGLAND

RSPB Local Groups
CHESTER. (1987; 220). Roger Nutter, Group Leader, 2 Lower Farm Court, Duckington, Malpas, Cheshire SY14 8LQ. 01829 782 237;
e-mail: lexeme@onetel.com
www.rspb.org.uk/groups/chester
Meetings: 7.30pm, 3rd Wednesday of the month (Sep-Apr), St Mary's Centre, Chester.

MACCLESFIELD. (1979; 394). Ray Evans, 01625 432 635; e-mail: ray@macclesfieldrspb.org.uk
www.macclesfieldrspb.org.uk

NORTH CHESHIRE. (1976; 100). Paul Grimmet. 01925 268 770; e-mail: paulw@ecosse.net
Meetings: 7.45pm, 3rd Friday (Jan-April and Sept-Nov), Appleton Parish Hall, Dudlow's Green Road, Appleton, Warrington.

Wildlife Hospitals
RSPCA STAPELEY GRANGE WILDLIFE CENTRE. London Road, Stapeley, Nantwich, Cheshire, CW5 7JW. 0870 442 7102. All wild birds. Oiled bird wash facilities and pools. Veterinary support.

Wildlife Trust
CHESHIRE WILDLIFE TRUST. Bickley Hall Farm, Bickley, Malpas, Cheshire SY14 8EF. 01948 820 728; (Fax) 0709 2888 469;
e-mail: info@cheshirewtcix.co.uk
www.wildlifetrust.org.uk/cheshire

CLEVELAND

Bird Atlas/Avifauna
The Breeding Birds of Cleveland. Due for publication 2007/2008.

Bird Recorder
CLEVELAND. Richard Taylor, Stoneybank, Dibdale Road, Neasham, Darlington DL2 1PF.
E-mail: RCT@teesmouth.plus.com

Bird Report
CLEVELAND BIRD REPORT (1974-), from Mr J Fletcher, 43 Glaisdale Avenue, Middlesbrough TS5 7PF. 01642 818 825.

BTO Regional Representative
CLEVELAND RR. Vic Fairbrother, 8, Whitby Avenue, Guisborough, Cleveland TS14 7AP. 01287 633 744; e-mail: vic.fairbrother@ntlworld.com.

Club
TEESMOUTH BIRD CLUB. (1960; 320). Chris Sharp (Hon Sec.), 20 Auckland Way, Hartlepool, TS26 0AN. 01429 865 163. www.teesmouthbc.com
Meetings: 7.30pm, 1st Monday of the month (Sep-Apr), Stockton Library, Church Road, Stockton.

Ringing Groups
TEES RG. E Wood, Southfields, 16 Marton Moor Road, Nunthorpe, Middlesbrough, Cleveland, TS7 0BH. 01642 323 563.

SOUTH CLEVELAND RG. W Norman, 2 Station Cottages, Grosmont, Whitby, N Yorks, YO22 5PB. 01947 895 226; e-mail: wilfgros@lineone.net

RSPB Local Group
CLEVELAND. (1974; 200). Terry Reeve, 01642 512 693; www.rspb.org.uk/groups/cleveland
Meetings: 7.30pm, 2nd Monday of the month (Sep-Apr), Lingfield Farm Countryside Centre, Mount Pleasant Way, Coulby Newham, Middlesbrough (£1.50 members, £2.50 non-members).

Wetland Bird Survey Organiser
TEES ESTUARY. Mike Leakey, c/o Natural England, British Energy, Tees Road, Hartlepool, TS25 2BZ. 01429 853 325;
e-mail: mike.leakey@naturalengland.org.uk

Wildlife Trust
TEES VALLEY WILDLIFE TRUST. (1979; 5,000). Margrove Heritage Centre, Margrove Park, Boosbeck, Saltburn-by-the-Sea, TS12 3BZ. 01287 636 382; (Fax) 01287 636 383;
e-mail: info@teeswildlife.org
www.teeswildlife.org

CORNWALL AND THE ISLES OF SCILLY

Bird Atlas/Avifauna
The Birds of the Isles of Scilly by P Robinson. Published by Christopher Helm 2003.

Bird Recorders
CORNWALL. Darrell Clegg, 55 Lower Fore Street, Saltash, Cornwall PL12 6JQ.
E-mail: secretary@cbwps.org.uk

ISLES OF SCILLY. Nigel Hudson, Post Office Flat, Hugh Street, St Mary's, Isles of Scilly TR21 0JE. 01720 422 267; e-mail: nigel-hudson@tiscali.co.uk

Bird Reports
BIRDS IN CORNWALL (1931-), from Cornwall Birdwatching and Preservation Society.

ISLES OF SCILLY BIRD REPORT and NATURAL HISTORY REVIEW 2000 (1969-), from The Recorder, Isles of Scilly Bird Group.

ISLES of SCILLY BIRD GROUP

BTO Regional Representative
CORNWALL. Stephen Jackson, 2, Trelawney Cottages, Falmouth, Cornwall TR11 3NY. 01326 313 533; e-mail: stephen.f.jackson@btinternet.com

ISLES OF SCILLY RR & RDO. Will Wagstaff, 42 Sally Port, St Mary's, Isles of Scilly, TR21 0JE. 01720 422 212; e-mail: william.wagstaff@virgin.net

Clubs
CORNWALL BIRDWATCHING & PRESERVATION SOCIETY. (1931; 990). Darrell Clegg, 55 Lower Fore Street, Saltash, Cornwall PL12 6JQ.
E-mail: secretary@cbwps.org.uk
www.cbwps.org.uk

CORNWALL WILDLIFE TRUST PHOTOGRAPHIC GROUP. (40). David Chapman, 41 Bosence Road, Townshend, Nr Hayle, Cornwall TR27 6AL. 01736 850 287; e-mail: david@ruralimages.freeserve.co.uk
www.ruralimages.freeserve.co.uk
Meetings: Mixture of indoor and outdoor meetings, please phone for details.

ISLES OF SCILLY BIRD GROUP. (2000; 510). Danni Borrett, Membership Secretary, ISBG, Post Office Flat, Hugh Town, St Mary's, Isles of Scilly TR21 0LL.
e-mail: dannibee@tiscali.co.uk
www.scillybirding.co.uk

Ringing Group
SCILLONIA SEABIRD GROUP. Peter Robinson, Secretary, 19 Pine Park Road, Honiton, Devon, EX14 2HR. (Tel/Fax) 01404 549 873; (M) 07768 538 132; e-mail: pjrobinson2@aol.com

RSPB Local Group
CORNWALL. (1972; 600). Gordon Mills, 11 Commercial Square, Camborne, Cornwall TR14 8JZ. 01209 718 144;
e-mail: grsdmillsflorists@camborne.fsbusiness.co.uk
www.rspbcornwall.org.uk.
Meetings: Indoor meetings (Oct-Apr), outdoor throughout the year.

Wetland Bird Survey Organisers
CORNWALL (excl. Tamar complex). Graham Hobin, Lower Drift Farmhouse, Drift, Buryas Bridge, Penzance TR19 6AA;
e-mail: graham.hobin@sky.com

TAMAR COMPLEX. Gladys Grant, 18 Orchard Crescent, Oreston, Plymouth, PL9 7NF. 01752 406 287; e-mail: gladysgrant@talktalk.net

MOUSEHOLE WILD BIRD HOSPITAL & SANCTUARY ASSOCIATION LTD. Raginnis Hill, Mousehole, Penzance, Cornwall, TR19 6SR. 01736 731 386. All species. No ringing.

Wildlife Trust
CORNWALL WILDLIFE TRUST. (1962; 13,600). Five Acres, Allet, Truro, Cornwall, TR4 9DJ. 01872 273 939; (Fax) 01872 225 476;
e-mail: info@cornwt.demon.co.uk
www.cornwallwildlifetrust.org.uk

THE ISLES OF SCILLY WILDLIFE TRUST. (460). Carn Thomas, Hugh Town, St Marys, Isles of Scilly TR21 0PT. (Tel/Fax) 01720 422 153;
e-mail: enquiries@ios-wildlifetrust.org.uk
www.ios-wildlifetrust.org.uk

CUMBRIA

BirdAtlas/Avifauna
The Breeding Birds of Cumbria by Stott, Callion, Kinley, Raven and Roberts (Cumbria Bird Club, 2002).

Bird Recorders
COUNTY. Colin Raven, 18 Seathwaite Road, Barrow-in-Furness, Cumbria, LA14 4LX;
e-mail: colin@walneyobs.fsnet.co.uk

NORTH EAST (Carlisle & Eden). R.H.Jones, 130 Greenacres, Wetheral, Carlisle, Cumbria CA4 8LU. 01228 561 684.

NORTH WEST (Allerdale & Copeland). Derek McAlone, 88 Whinlatter Road, Mirehouse, Whitehaven, Cumbria CA28 8DQ. 01946 691 370; e-mail: derek@derekmcalone3.wanadoo.co.uk

SOUTH (South Lakeland & Furness). Ronnie Irving, 24 Birchwood Close, Kendal, Cumbria, LA9 5BJ. 01539 727 523; e-mail: ronnie@wsi-sign.co.uk

Bird Reports
BIRDS AND WILDLIFE IN CUMBRIA (1970-), from Dave Piercy, 01768 777 246;
E-mail: daveandkathypiercy@tiscali.co.uk

WALNEY BIRD OBSERVATORY REPORT, from the Warden, see Reserves.

BTO Regional Representatives
CUMBRIA. Clive Hartley, Undercragg, Charney Well La, Grange Over Sands, LA11 6DB. 01539 532 856; e-mail: clive.hartley@tiscali.co.uk

Clubs
ARNSIDE & DISTRICT NATURAL HISTORY SOCIETY. (1967; 221). Mrs GM Smith, West Wind, Orchard Road, Arnside, via Carnforth, Cumbria, LA5 0DP. 01524 762 522.
Meetings: 7.30pm, 2nd Tuesday of the month (Sept-Apr). WI Hall, Arnside. (Also summer walks).

CUMBRIA BIRD CLUB. (1989; 230). Clive Hartley, Undercragg, Charney Well La Grange Over Sands, LA11 6DB. 01539 532 856;
e-mail: clive.hartley@tiscali.co.uk
www.cumbriabirdclub.freeserve.co.uk
Meetings: Various evenings and venues (Oct-

CUMBRIA RAPTOR STUDY GROUP

Mar) check on website for further details. £2 for non-members.

CUMBRIA RAPTOR STUDY GROUP. (1992). P N Davies, Snowhill Cottage, Caldbeck, Wigton, Cumbria, CA7 8HL. 01697 371 249;
e-mail: pete.caldbeck@virgin.net

Ringing Groups
EDEN RG. G Longrigg, Mere Bank, Bleatarn, Warcop, Appleby, Cumbria, CA16 6PX.

WALNEY BIRD OBSERVATORY. K Parkes, 176 Harrogate Street, Barrow-in-Furness, Cumbria, LA14 5NA. 01229 824 219.

RSPB Local Groups
CARLISLE. (1974; 400). Bob Jones, 130 Greenacres, Wetheral, Carlisle. 01225 561 684;
e-mail: bob@onethirty.force9.co.uk
Meetings: 7.30pm, Wednesday monthly, Tythe Barn, Carlisle.

SOUTH LAKELAND. (1973; 340). Mr Martin Baines, 101 Serpentine Road, Kendal, Cumbria, LA9 4PP. 01539 732 214.
Meetings: Contact above.

WEST CUMBRIA. (1986; 270). Neil Hutchin, 3 Camerton Road, Gt Broughton, Cockermouth, Cumbria, CA13 0YR. 01900 825 231;
e-mail: majoriehutchin@btinternet.com
Meetings: 7.30pm, 1st Tuesday (Sept-Apr), United Reformed Church, Main St, Cockermouth

Wetland Bird Survey Organiser
DUDDON ESTUARY. Rosalyn Gay, 8 Victoria Street, Millom, Cumbria LA18 5AS. 01229 773 820;
e-mail: colinathodbarrow@aol.com

Wildlife Trust
CUMBRIA WILDLIFE TRUST. (1962; 15,000). Plumgarths, Crook Road, Kendal, Cumbria LA8 8LX. 01539 816 300; (Fax) 01539 816 301;
e-mail: mail@cumbriawildlifetrust.org.uk
www.cumbriawildlifetrust.org.uk

DERBYSHIRE

BirdAtlas/Avifauna
The Birds of Derbyshire, ed. RA Frost (in preparation)

Bird Recorders
1. JOINT RECORDER. Roy A Frost, 66 St Lawrence Road, North Wingfield, Chesterfield, Derbyshire, S42 5LL. 01246 850 037;
e-mail: frostra66@btinternet.com

2. Records Committee & rarity records. Rodney W Key, 3 Farningham Close, Spondon, Derby, DE21 7DZ. 01332 678 571; e-mail: r_key@sky.com

3. JOINT RECORDER. Richard M R James, 10 Eastbrae Road, Littleover, Derby, DE23 1WA. 01332 771 787; e-mail: rmrjames@yahoo.co.uk

Bird Reports
CARSINGTON BIRD CLUB ANNUAL REPORT, from The Secretary.

DERBYSHIRE BIRD REPORT (1954-), from Bryan Barnacle, Mays, Malthouse Lane, Froggatt, Hope Valley, Derbyshire S32 3ZA. 01433 630 726;
e-mail: barney@mays1.demon.co.uk

OGSTON BIRD CLUB REPORT (1970-), from (see contact for Ogston Bird Club below).

BTO Regional Representatives
NORTH RR. Dave Budworth, 121 Wood Lane, Newhall, Swadlincote, Derbys, DE11 0LX. 01283 215 188; e-mail: dbud01@aol.com

SOUTH RR. Dave Budworth, 121 Wood Lane, Newhall, Swadlincote, Derbys, DE11 0LX. 01283 215 188; e-mail: dbud01@aol.com

Clubs
BAKEWELL & DISTRICT BIRD STUDY GROUP. (1987; 80). Bill Millward, Dale House, The Dale, Hope Valley, Derbys S32 1AQ.
Meetings: 7.30pm, 2nd Monday of the month, Friends Meeting House, Bakewell.

BUXTON FIELD CLUB. (1946; 68). B Aries, 1 Horsefair Avenue, Chapel-en-le-Frith, High Peak, Derbys, SK23 9SQ. 01298 815 291;
e-mail: brian.aries@horsefair.ndo.co.uk
Meetings: 7.30pm, Saturdays fortnightly (Oct-Mar), Methodist Church Hall, Buxton.

CARSINGTON BIRD CLUB. (1992; 257). Maria Harwood/ Pat Wain, Joint Membership Secretaries, Lydgate House, West End, Brassington, Derbyshire, DE4 4HL. 01629 823 693;
e-mail: membership@carsingtonbirdclub.co.uk
www.carsingtonbirdclub.co.uk
Meetings: 3rd Tuesday of the month (Sep-Mar), Hognaston Village Hall, (Apr-Aug), outdoors.

DERBYSHIRE ORNITHOLOGICAL SOCIETY. (1954; 550). Steve Shaw, 84 Moorland View Road, Walton, Chesterfield, Derbys, S40 3DF. 01246 236 090;
e-mail: steveshaw@ornsoc.freeserve.co.uk
www.derbyshireos.org.uk
Meetings: 7.30pm, last Friday of the winter months, various venues.

OGSTON BIRD CLUB. (1969; 1,126). Malcolm Hill, 2 Sycamore Avenue, Glapwell, Chesterfield, S44 5LH. 01623 812 159. www.ogstonbirdclub.co.uk

SOUTH PEAK RAPTOR STUDY GROUP. (1998; 12). M E Taylor, 76 Hawksley Avenue, Newbold, Chesterfield, Derbys, S40 4TL. 01246 277 749.

Ringing Groups

DARK PEAK RG. W M Underwood, Ivy Cottage, 15 Broadbottom Road, Mottram-in-Longdendale, Hyde, Cheshire SK14 6JB.
e-mail: w.m.underwood@talk21.com

SORBY-BRECK RG. Geoff P Mawson, Moonpenny Farm, Farwater Lane, Dronfield, Sheffield, S18 1RA.
e-mail: moonpenny@talktalk.net

SOUDER RG. Dave Budworth, 121 Wood Lane, Newhall, Swadlincote, Derbys, DE11 0LX. 01283 215 188.

RSPB Local Groups

CHESTERFIELD. (1987; 274). Sue Ottowell, 01246 569 431; e-mail: seottowell@tesco.net
www.rspb.org.uk/groups/chesterfield
Meetings: 7.15pm, usually 3rd Monday of the month, Winding Wheel, New Exhibition Centre, 13 Holywell Street, Chesterfield.

DERBY LOCAL GROUP. (1973; 400). Chris Hunt, 38 Spenbeck Drive, Allestree, Derby, DE22 2UH. 01332 551 701; e-mail: chris.hunt42@ntlworld.com.
Meetings: 7.30pm, 1st Wednesday of the month (Sep-Apr), Lund Pavilion, Derbyshire County Cricket Ground (see press for date of Jan meeting).

HIGH PEAK. (1974; 175). Peter Griffiths, 17 Clifton Drive, Marple, Stockport SK6 6PP. 0161 427 5325.
Meetings: 7.30pm, 3rd Monday of the month (Sep-May), Marple Senior Citizens Hall.

Wildlife Trust

DERBYSHIRE WILDLIFE TRUST. (1962; 11,500). East Mill, Bridge Foot, Belper, Derbyshire DE56 1XH. 01773 881 188; (Fax) 01773 821 826;
e-mail: enquiries@derbyshirewt.co.uk
www.derbyshirewildlifetrust.org.uk

DEVON

BirdAtlas/Avifauna

Tetrad Atlas of Breeding Birds of Devon by H P Sitters (Devon Birdwatching & Preservation Society, 1988).

The Birds of Darmoor by R Smaldon, published by Isabelline Books, 2005. (£18.95 from the publishers at 6 Bellevue, Enys , Penryn, Cornwall TR10 9LB).

The Birds of Lundy due Autumn 2007 by Tim Davis and Tim Jones (see www.birdsoflunday.org.uk for further details),

Bird Recorder

Mr MW Tyler, The Acorn, Shute Road, Kilmington, Axminster, Devon EX13 7ST. 01297 34958.
e-mail: clonwayteam@btopenworld.com

Bird Reports

DEVON BIRD REPORT (1971) Previous annual reports since 1929, from DBWPS, PO Box 71, Okehampton, Devon EX20 1WF. From 2007 this report will be part of *Devon Birds* the journal of the DBWPS.

LUNDY FIELD SOCIETY ANNUAL REPORT (1946-), from Secretary. Index to Report is on Society's website.

BTO Regional Representative

RR. John Woodland, Glebe Cottage, Dunsford, Exeter, EX6 7AA. 01647 252 494:
e-mail:
jwoodland@btodv.
fsnet.co.uk

BTO DEVON NATIONAL ATLAS ORGANISER. Mark Blacksell, Lower Hobey, Belstone, Okehampton EX20 1QY. 01837 840 808;
e-mail: mblacksell@plymouth.ac.uk

Clubs

DEVON BIRDWATCHING & PRESERVATION SOCIETY. (1928; 1200). Mrs Joy Vaughan, 28 Fern Meadow, Okehampton, Devon, EX20 1PB. 01837 53360; e-mail: joy@vaughan411.freeserve.co.uk

KINGSBRIDGE & DISTRICT NATURAL HISTORY SOCIETY. (1989; 130). Martin Catt, Migrants Rest, East Prawle, Kingsbridge, Devon, TQ7 2DB. 01548 511 443; e-mail: martin.catt@btinternet.com
Meeting: 7.30pm 4th Monday of the month (Sept-Apr), phone for venue.

LUNDY FIELD SOCIETY. (1946; 450). Frances Stuart, 3 Lower Linden Road, Clevedon, North Somerset BS21 7SU. 01275 871 434;
e-mail: lfssec@hotmail.com www.lundy.org.uk
Meeting: AGM 1st Saturday in March, 1.45pm, Exeter University.

TOPSHAM BIRDWATCHING & NATURALISTS' SOCIETY. (1969; 140). Mrs Janice Vining, 2 The Maltings, Fore Street, Topsham, Exeter, EX3 0HF. 01392 873 514; e-mail: tbnsociety@hotmail.com
www.members.tripod.co.uk/tbns
Meetings: 7.30pm, 2nd Friday of the month (Sep-May), Matthews Hall, Topsham.

Ringing Groups

AXE ESTUARY RINGING GROUP. Mike Tyler, The Acorn, Shute Road, Kilmington, Axminster, EX13 7ST. 01297 349 58;
e-mail: mwtyler2@googlemail.com

DEVON & CORNWALL WADER RG. R C Swinfen, 72 Dunraven Drive, Derriford, Plymouth, PL6 6AT. 01752 704 184.

LUNDY FIELD SOCIETY. A M Taylor, 26 High Street, Spetisbury, Blandford, Dorset, DT11 9DJ. 01258 857 336; e-mail: ammataylor@yahoo.co.uk

SLAPTON BIRD OBSERVATORY. Nick Ward, 36 Shaftesbury Road, St Thomas, Exeter, EX2 0BR. 01392 425 689;
email: nik@ward2898.freeserve.co.uk.

RSPB Local Groups
EXETER & DISTRICT. (1974; 466). John Allan, Coxland-by-Sigford, Sigford, Near Newton Abbot, TQ12 6LE. 01626 821 344;
e-mail: johnallan@coxland.e7even.com
www.exeter-rspb.org.uk
Meetings: 7.30p, various evenings, Southernhay United Reformed Church Rooms, Dix's Field, EXETER.

NORTH DEVON. (1976; 68). Contact RSPB South West Regional Office, Exeter (see National Directory).
Meetings: 7 for 7.30pm, last Friday of the month, The Civic Centre, Barnstaple.

PLYMOUTH. (1974; 600). Mrs Eileen Willey, 11 Beverstone Way, Roborough, Plymouth, PL6 7DY. 01752 208 996.

Wetland Bird Survey Organiser
DEVON. Peter Reay, 10 Devon House, Bovey Tracey, Devon TQ13 9HB. 01626 834 486;
e-mail: peter.p.j.reay@btinternet.com

TAMAR COMPLEX. Gladys Grant, 18 Orchard Crescent, Oreston, Plymouth, PL9 7NF. 01752 406 287; e-mail: gladysgrant@talktalk.net

Wildlife Hospitals
BIRD OF PREY CASUALTY CENTRE. Mrs J E L Vinson, Crooked Meadow, Stidston Lane, South Brent, Devon, TQ10 9JS. 01364 72174.
Birds of prey, with emergency advice on other species. Aviaries, rehabilitation facilities. Veterinary support.

HURRELL, Dr L H. Dr Hurrell, 201 Outland Road, Peverell, Plymouth, PL2 3PF. 01752 771 838.
Birds of prey only. Veterinary support.

Wildlife Trust
DEVON WILDLIFE TRUST. (1962; 33,000). Shirehampton House, 35-37 St David's Hill, Exeter, EX4 4DA. 01392 279 244; (Fax) 01392 433 221;
e-mail: contactus@devonwildlifewt.org
www.devonwildlifetrust.org

DORSET

BirdAtlas/Avifauna
Dorset Breeding Bird Atlas (working title). In preparation.

The Birds of Dorset by Dr George Green (Christopher Helm 2004)

Bird Recorder
James Lidster, 35 Napier Road, Poole, Dorset BH15 4LX. 01202 672 406;
e-mail: dorsetbirds@btopenworld.com

Bird Reports
DORSET BIRDS (1977-), from Miss J W Adams, 16 Sherford Drive, Wareham, Dorset, BH20 4EN. 01929 552 299.

THE BIRDS OF CHRISTCHURCH HARBOUR (1956-), from Ian Southworth, 1 Bodowen Road, Burton, Christchurch, Dorset BH23 7JL.
e-mail: ianbirder@aol.com

PORTLAND BIRD OBSERVATORY REPORT, from the Warden, see Reserves,

BTO Regional Representatives
Mike Pleasants, 10 Green Lane, Bournemouth, BH10 5LB. 07762 987 115 or 01202 593 500;
e-mail: mike@btorepdorset.org
www.btorepdorset.org

Clubs
CHRISTCHURCH HARBOUR ORNITHOLOGICAL GROUP. (1956; 225). Mr. I.H. Southworth, Membership Secretary,1 Bodowen Road, Burton, Christchurch, Dorset BH23 7JL. 01202 478 093.
www.chog.org.uk.

DORSET BIRD CLUB. (1987; 525). Mr Chris Chapleo, 15 Stour Way, Christchurch, Dorset BH23 2PF. 01202 419 867.
www.dorsetbirdclub.org.uk
Meetings: Usually 7.30pm, no set day or venue.

DORSET BIRD CLUB

DORSET NATURAL HISTORY & ARCHAEOLOGICAL SOCIETY. (1845; 2188). Dorset County Museum, High West Street, Dorchester, Dorset, DT1 1XA. 01305 262 735;
e-mail: secretary@dorsetcountymuseum.org
www.dorsetcountymuseum.org

Ringing Groups
CHRISTCHURCH HARBOUR RS. E C Brett, 3 Whitfield Park, St Ives, Ringwood, Hants, BH24 2DX.
e-mail: ed_brett@lineone.net

PORTLAND BIRD OBSERVATORY. Martin Cade, Old Lower Light, Portland Bill, Dorset, DT5 2JT. 01305 820 553; e-mail: obs@btinternet.com
www.portlandbirdobs.btinternet.co.uk

STOUR RG. R Gifford, 62 Beacon Park Road, Upton, Poole, Dorset, BH16 5PE.

ENGLAND

RSPB Local Groups
BLACKMOOR VALE. (1981; 106). Mrs Margaret Marris, 15 Burges Close, Marnhull, Sturminster Newton, Dorset, DT10 1QQ. 01258 820 091.
Meetings: 7.30pm, 3rd Friday in the month, Gillingham Primary School.

EAST DORSET. (1974; 435). Tony Long (Group Leader: S. Cresswell), 93 Wimborne Road, Corfe Mullen, Wimborne, BH21 3DS. 01202 880 508; e-mail: tony@joan1206.fsnet.co.uk
Meetings: 7.30pm, 2nd Wednesday of the month, St Mark's church Hall, Talbot Village, Wallisdown, Bournemouth.

POOLE. (1982; 305). John Derricott, 49 Medbourne Close, Blandford, Dorset, DT11 7UA. 01258 450 927; e-mail: johnmal@derricott.fslife.co.uk www.rspb.org.uk/groups/poole
Meetings: 7.30pm, Upton Community Centre, Poole Road, Upton.

SOUTH DORSET. (1976; 422). Marion Perriss, Old Barn Cottage, Affpuddle, Dorchester, Dorset, DT2 7HH. 01305 848 268; e-mail: affpuddle@btinternet.com; www.southdorset-rspb.org.uk.
Meetings: 3rd Thursday of each month (Sep-Apr), Dorchester Town Hall.

Wildlife Hospital
SWAN RESCUE SANCTUARY. Ken and Judy Merriman, The Wigeon, Crooked Withies, Holt, Wimborne, Dorset, BH21 7LB. 01202 828 166; (mobile) 0385 917 457;
e-mail: ken@swan-rescue.fsnet.co.uk
www.www.swan-rescue.fsnet.co.uk
24 hr rescue service for swans. Large sanctuary of 40 ponds and lakes. Hospital and intensive care. Veterinary support. Free advice and help line. Three fully equipped rescue ambulances. Rescue water craft for all emergencies. Viewing by appointment only.

Wetland Bird Survey Organisers
THE FLEET & PORTLAND HARBOUR. Steve Groves, Abbotsbury Swannery, New Barn Road, Abbotsbury, Dorset, DT3 4JG. (W) 01305 871 684;
e-mail: swannery@gotadsl.co.uk

RADIPOLE & LODMOOR. Nick Tomlinson, RSPB Visitor Centre, Swannery Carpark, Weymouth, Dorset, DT4 7TZ. 01305 778 313.

Wildlife Trust
DORSET WILDLIFE TRUST. (1961; 24,500). Brooklands Farm, Forston, Dorchester, Dorset, DT2 7AA. 01305 264 620; (Fax) 01305 251 120;
e-mail: enquiries@dorsetwildlife.co.uk
www.dorsetwildlife.co.uk

DURHAM

BirdAtlas/Avifauna
A Summer Atlas of Breeding Birds of County Durham by Stephen Westerberg/Keith Bowey. (Durham Bird Club, 2000)

Bird Recorders
Mark Newsome, 69 Cedar Drive, Jarrow, NE32 4BF.
e-mail: mvnewsome@hotmail.com

Bird Reports
BIRDS IN DURHAM (1971-), from D Sowerbutts, 9 Prebends Fields, Gilesgate, Durham, DH1 1HH. H:0191 386 7201; e-mail: d16lst@tiscali.co.uk

BTO Regional Representatives
David L Sowerbutts, 9 Prebends Field, Gilesgate Moor, Durham, DH1 1HH. H:0191 386 7201;
e-mail: david.sowerbutts@dunelm.org.uk

Clubs
DURHAM BIRD CLUB. (1975; 280). Steve Evans, Secretary, 07979 601 231;
www.durhambirdclub.org
Meetings: Monthly indoor meetings (Sept-Apr), in Durham and Sunderland.

SUMMERHILL (HARTLEPOOL) BIRD CLUB. (2000; 75). Kevin Spindloe, 118 West Auckland Road, Darlington DL3 0LG. 07766 406 157;
e-mail:kevinspindloe@aol.com
www.summerhillbirdclub.co.uk
Meetings: 7pm, 2nd Tuesday of the month (Sept-May), Summerhill Visitors Centre, Catcote Road, Hartlepool.

Ringing Groups
DURHAM DALES RG. J R Hawes, Fairways, 5 Raby Terrace, Willington, Crook, Durham, DL15 0HR.

RSPB Local Group
DURHAM. (1974; 125). David Gibson, 9 Frosterley Close, Newton Hall, Durham, DH1 5SN. 0191 386 9793.
Meetings: 7.30pm, 2nd Tuesday of the month (Oct-Mar), Room CG83, adjacent to Scarborough Lecture Theatre, University Science Site, Stockton Road entrance.

Wildlife Trust
DURHAM WILDLIFE TRUST. (1971; 4,000). Rainton Meadows, Chilton Moor, Houghton-le-Spring, Tyne & Wear, DH4 6PU. 0191 5843 112; (Fax) 0191 5843 934; e-mail: info@durhamwt.co.uk
www.durhamwildlifetrust.org.uk

ENGLAND

ESSEX

Bird Atlas/Avifauna
The Birds of Essex by Simon Wood (A&C Black, due August 2007).

The Breeding Birds of Essex by M K Dennis (Essex Birdwatching Society, 1996).

Bird Recorder
JOINT RECORDER. Roy Ledgerton (joint), 25 Bunyan Road, Braintree, Essex CM7 2PL. 01376 326 103; e-mail: r.ledgerton@virgin.net

JOINT RECORDER. Howard Vaughan, 103 Darnley Road, Strood, Rochester, Kent ME2 2EY. 01634 325 864; e-mail: howardebs@blueyonder.co.uk

JOINT RECORDER. Bob Flindall, 60 Lady Lane, Chelmsford, Essex CM2 0TH. 01245 344 206; e-mail: robert.flindall@btinternet.com

Bird Report
ESSEX BIRD REPORT (inc Bradwell Bird Obs records) (1950-), from Peter Dwyer, Sales Officer, 48 Churchill Avenue, Halstead, Essex, CO9 2BE. (Tel/Fax) 01787 476 524; e-mail: petedwyer@petedwyer.plus.com or pete@northessex.co.uk

BTO Regional Representatives & Regional Development Officer
NORTH-EAST RR & RDO. Position vacant.

NORTH-WEST RR. Graham Smith, 01277 354 034; e-mail: silaum.silaus@tiscali.co.uk

SOUTH RR. Lynn Parr, 01702 486 990; e-mail: lynn.parr@tesco.net

Club
ESSEX BIRDWATCHING SOCIETY. (1949; 700). Carol O'Leary, 24 Horeshoe Crescent, The Garrison, Shoeburyness, Essex SS3 9WL. www.essexbirdwatchsoc.co.uk
Meetings: 1st Friday of the month (Oct-Mar), Friends' Meeting House, Rainsford Road, Chelmsford.

Ringing Groups
ABBERTON RG. C P Harris, Wylandotte, Seamer Road, Southminster, Essex, CM0 7BX.

BRADWELL BIRD OBSERVATORY. C P Harris, Wyandotte, Seamer Road, Southminster, Essex, CM0 7BX.

RSPB Local Groups
CHELMSFORD AND CENTRAL ESSEX. (1976; 5500). Mike Logan Wood, Highwood, Ishams Chase, Wickham Bishops, Essex, CM8 3LG. 01621 892 045; e-mail: mike.lw@tiscali.co.uk
www.rspb.org.uk/groups/chelmsford
Meetings: 8pm, Thursdays, eight times a year. The Cramphorn Theatre, Chelmsford.

COLCHESTER. (1981; 250). Mrs V Owen, Tawnies, Hall Lane, Langenhoe, Colchester, CO5 7NA.
Meetings: 7.45pm, 2nd Thursday of the month (Sep-Apr), Shrub End Community Hall, Shrub End Road, Colchester.

SOUTHEND. (1983; 200). Graham Mee, 24 Sunbury Court, North Shoebury, Essex SS3 8TB. 01702 297 554; e-mail: grahamm@southendrspb.co.uk
www.southendrspb.co.uk
Meetings: 7.30pm, usually 1st Tuesday of the month (Sep-May), Belfairs School Hall, School Way, Leigh-on-Sea SS9 4HX.

Wetland Bird Survey Organisers
STOUR ESTUARY. Rick Vonk, RSPB, Unit 13 Court Farm, 3 Stutton Road, Brantham, Suffolk CO11 1PW. (D) 01473 328 006;
e-mail:rick.vonk@rspb.org.uk

LEE VALLEY. Cath Patrick, Myddelton House, Bulls Cross, Enfield, Herts EN2 9HG; 01992 717 711; e-mail: cpatrick@leevalleypark.org.uk

ESSEX (Other Sites). Howard Vaughan, 103 Darnley Road, Strood, Rochester, Kent ME2 2EY. 01634 325 864 (after 7pm);
e-mail; howardebs@blueyonder.co.uk

Wildlife Trust
ESSEX WILDLIFE TRUST. (1959; 36,000). The Joan Elliot Visitor Centre, Abbots Hall Farm, Great Wigborough, Colchester, CO5 7RZ. 01621 862 960; (Fax) 01621 862 990;
e-mail: admin@essexwt.org.uk
www.essexwt.org.uk

GLOUCESTERSHIRE

Bird Atlas/Avifauna
Atlas of Breeding Birds of the North Cotswolds. (North Cotswold Ornithological Society, 1990)

Bird Recorder
GLOUCESTERSHIRE EXCLUDING S.GLOS (AVON). Richard Baatsen, e-mail: baatsen@surfbirder.com

Bird Reports
CHELTENHAM BIRD CLUB BIRD REPORT (1998-), from The Secretary.

GLOUCESTERSHIRE BIRD REPORT (1953-), from David Cramp, 2 Ellenor Drive, Alderton, Tewkesbury, GL20 8NZ. e-mail: djcramp@btinternet.com

NORTH COTSWOLD ORNITHOLOGICAL SOCIETY ANNUAL REPORT (1983-), from T Hutton, 15 Green Close, Childswickham, Broadway, Worcs, WR12 7JJ. 01386 858 511.

ENGLAND

BTO Regional Representative
Mike Smart, 143 Cheltenham Road, Gloucester, GL2 0JH. Home/work 01452 421 131;
e-mail: smartmike@btinternet.com

Clubs
CHELTENHAM BIRD CLUB. (1976; 94). Mrs Frances Meredith, 14 Greatfield Drive, Charlton Kings, Cheltenham, GL53 9BU. 01242 516 393;
e-mail: chelt.birds@virgin.net
www.beehive.thisisgloucestershire.co.uk/cheltbirdclub
Meetings: 7.15pm, Mondays (Oct-Mar), Bournside School, Warden Hill Road, Cheltenham.

DURSLEY BIRDWATCHING & PRESERVATION SOCIETY. (1953; 350). Jennifer Rogers, 15 Shadwell, Uley, Dursley, Glos, GL11 5BW. 01453 860 128. email: j.rogers@btinternet.com
Meetings: 7.45pm, 2nd and 4th Monday (Sept-Mar), Dursley Community Centre.

GLOUCESTERSHIRE NATURALISTS' SOCIETY. (1948; 500). Mike Smart, 143 Cheltenham Road, Gloucester, GL2 0JH. 01452 421 131;
e-mail: smartmike@btinternet.com
www.glosnats.org.uk

NORTH COTSWOLD ORNITHOLOGICAL SOCIETY. (1982; 70). T Hutton, 15 Green Close, Childswickham, Broadway, Worcs, WR12 7JJ. 01386 858 511.
Meetings: Monthly field meetings, usually Sunday 9.30pm.

Ringing Groups
COTSWOLD WATER PARK RG. John Wells, 25 Pipers Grove, Highnam, Glos, GL2 8NJ.
e-mail: john.wells2@btinternet.com

SEVERN ESTUARY GULL GROUP. M E Durham, 6 Glebe Close, Frampton-on-Severn, Glos, GL2 7EL. 01452 741 312.

SEVERN VALE RG. John Wells, 25 Pipers Grove, Highnam, Glos, GL2 8NJ.
e-mail: john.wells2@btinternet.com

WILDFOWL & WETLANDS TRUST. Robin Ward, Wildfowl & Wetlands Trust, Slimbridge, Glos, GL2 7BT. 01453 891 272;
e-mail: robin.ward@wwt.org.uk

RSPB Local Group
GLOUCESTERSHIRE. (1972; 740). David Cramp, 2 Ellenor Drive, Alderton, Tewkesbury, GL20 8NZ. 01242 620 281; www.rspbgloucestershire.co.uk
Meetings: 7.30pm, 3rd Tuesday of the month, Sir Thomas Rich's School, Gloucester.

Wildlife Hospital
GLOUCESTER WILDLIFE RESCUE CENTRE. Alan and Louise Brockbank, 1 Moorend Lodge, Moorend, Hartpury, Glos GL19 3DG. 01452 700 038;
e-mail: info@gloswildliferescue.org.uk
www.gloswildliferescue.org.uk
Intensive care, treatment and rehabilitation facilities. Vetinary support. No restrictions or conditions. Not open to the public.

VALE WILDLIFE RESCUE - WILDLIFE HOSPITAL + REHABILITATION CENTRE. Any staff member, Station Road, Beckford, Tewkesbury, Glos, GL20 7AN. 01386 882 288; (Fax) 01386 882 299;
e-mail: info@vwr.org.uk www.vwr.org.uk
All wild birds. Intensive care. Registered charity. Veterinary support.

Wetland Bird Survey Organisers
GLOUCESTERSHIRE (Severn Estuary). Colette Hall, WWT Slimbridge, Gloucester, GL2 7BT. 01453 890 333.

GLOUCESTERSHIRE (Inland). Jenny Worden, Wildfowl and Wetlands Trust, Slimbridge, Glos GL2 7BT. 01453 890 333;
e-mail: jenny.worden@wwt.org.uk

COTSWOLD WATER PARK. Gareth Harris, Keynes Country Park, Spratsgate Lane, Shorncote, Glos GL7 6DF. 01285 861 459;
e-mail: gareth.harris@waterpark.org

Wildlife Trust
GLOUCESTERSHIRE WILDLIFE TRUST. (1961; 20,000). Conservation Centre, Robinswood Hill Country Park, Reservoir Road, Gloucester, GL4 6SX. 01452 383 333; (Fax) 01452 383 334;
e-mail: info@gloucestershirewildlifetrust.co.uk
www.gloucestershirewildlifetrust.co.uk

HAMPSHIRE

Bird Atlas/Avifauna
Birds of Hampshire by J M Clark and J A Eyre (Hampshire Ornithological Society, 1993).

Bird Recorder
RECORDER. John Clark, 4 Cygnet Court, Old Cove Road, Fleet, Hants, GU51 2RL. (Tel/Fax) 01252 623 397; e-mail: johnclark@cygnetcourt.demon.co.uk

Bird Reports
HAMPSHIRE BIRD REPORT (1955-), from Mrs Margaret Boswell, 5 Clarence Road, Lyndhurst, Hants, SO43 7AL. 023 8028 2105;
e-mail: magbos@btinternet.com
2004 edition £10 including p&p.

BTO Regional Representative
RR. Glynne C Evans, Waverley, Station Road, Chilbolton, Stockbridge, Hants, SO20 6AL. 01264 860 697; e-mail: hantsbto@hotmail.com

Clubs
HAMPSHIRE ORNITHOLOGICAL SOCIETY. (1979; 1,200). Barrie Roberts, Honarary Secretary, 149 Rownhams Lane, North Baddesley, Southampton, SO52 9LU. 023 8073 7023;
e-mail: robertsbarrie@hotmail.com

SOUTHAMPTON & DISTRICT BIRD GROUP. (1994; 68). Vic Short, 20 Westbroke Gardens, Romsey, SO51 7RQ. 01794 511 843;
e-mail: vicshort@btopenworld.com
Meetings: Programme available.

Ringing Groups
FARLINGTON RG. D A Bell, 38 Holly Grove, Fareham, Hants, PO16 7UP.

ITCHEN RG. W F Simcox, 10 Holdaway Close, Kingsworthy, Winchester, SO23 7QH.
e-mail: wsimcox@sparsholt.ac.uk

RSPB Local Groups
BASINGSTOKE. (1979; 90). Peter Hutchins, 35 Woodlands, Overton, Whitchurch, RG25 3HN. 01256 770 831; e-mail: fieldfare@jaybry.gotadsl.co.uk
Meetings: 7.30pm 3rd Wednesday of the month (Sept-May), The Barn, Church Cottage, St Michael's Church, Church Square, Basingstoke.

NORTH EAST HAMPSHIRE. (1976; 250). The Group leader, 4 Buttermer Close, Farnham, Surrey, GU10 4PN. 01252 724 093.
www.northeasthantsrspb.org.uk
Meetings: See website.

PORTSMOUTH. (1974; 210). Gordon Humby, 19 Charlesworth Gardens, Waterlooville, Hants, PO7 6AU. 02392 353 949.
Meetings: 7.30pm, 4th Saturday of every month. Colmans' Church Hall, Colman's Ave, Cosham. Programme and news letter issued to paid up members of the group who must be RSPB members.

WINCHESTER & DISTRICT LOCAL GROUP. (1974; 175). Maurice Walker, Jesmond, 1 Compton Way, Olivers Battery, Winchester, SO22 4EY. 01962 854 033. www.rspb.org.uk/groups/winchester
Meetings: 7.30pm, 1st Wednesday of the month (not Jul or Aug), Shalford Parish Hall, Pearson Lane, Shalford.

Wetland Bird Survey Organisers
HAMPSHIRE (Inland - excluding Avon Valley). Keith Wills, 51 Peabody Road, Farnborough, GU14 6EB. 01252 548 408; e-mail: keithb.wills@ukgateway.net

AVON VALLEY. John Clark, 4 Cygnet Court, Old Cove Road, Fleet, Hants GU51 2RL. 01252 623 397;
e-mail johnclark@cygnetcourt.demon.co.uk

Wildlife Trust
HAMPSHIRE & ISLE OF WIGHT WILDLIFE TRUST. (1960; 27,000). Beechcroft House, Vicarage Lane, Curdridge, Hampshire SO32 2DP. 01489 774 400; (Fax) 01489 774 401; e-mail: feedback@hwt.org.uk
www.hwt.org.uk

WIGHT WILDLIFE. 2 High Street, Newport, Isle of Wight PO30 1SS. 01983 533 180;
e-mail: feedback@hwt.org.uk

HEREFORDSHIRE

Bird Atlas/Avifauna
The Birds of Herefordshire 2004, published by the Herefordshire Ornithological Club.

Bird Recorder
Steve Coney, 5 Springfield Road, Withington, Hereford, HR1 3RU. 01432 850 068;
e-mail: coney@bluecarrots.com

Bird Report
THE YELLOWHAMMER - Herefordshire Ornithological Club annual report, (1951-), from Mr I Evans, 12 Brockington Drive, Tupsley, Hereford , HR1 1TA. 01432 265 509; e-mail: iforelaine@btinternet.com

BTO Regional Representative
Steve Coney, 5 Springfield Road, Withington, Hereford, HR1 3RU. 01432 850 068;
e-mail: coney@bluecarrots.com

Club
HEREFORDSHIRE ORNITHOLOGICAL CLUB. (1950; 360). TM Weale, Foxholes, Bringsty Common, Worcester, WR6 5UN.
01886 821 368;
e-mail: weale@tinyworld.co.uk
www.herefordshirebirds.org
Meetings: 7.30pm, 2nd Thursday of the month (Autumn/winter), Holmer Parish Centre, Holmer, Hereford.

HEREFORDSHIRE ORNITHOLOGICAL CLUB
Reg. Charity No. 1068608
1950
PRO AVES

Ringing Group
LLANCILLO RG. Dr G R Geen, 6 The Copse, Bannister Green, Felsted, Dunmow, Essex, CM6 3NP. 01371 820 189;
e-mail: grahamgeen@talktalk.net

Wildlife Hospital

Wildlife Trust
HEREFORDSHIRE NATURE TRUST. (1962; 2,535). Lower House Farm, Ledbury Road, Tupsley, Hereford, HR1 1UT. 01432 356 872; (Fax) 01432 275 489; e-mail: enquiries@herefordshirewt.co.uk
www .wildlifetrust.org.uk/hereford

ENGLAND

HERTFORDSHIRE

Bird Atlas/Avifauna
Birds at Tring Reservoirs by R Young et al (Hertfordshire Natural History Society, 1996).

Mammals, Amphibians and Reptiles of Hertfordshire by Hertfordshire NHS in association with Training Publications Ltd, 3 Finway Court, Whippendell Road, Watford WD18 7EN, (2001).

The Breeding Birds of Hertfordshire by K W Smith et al (Herts NHS, 1993). Purchase from HNHS at £5 plus postage.
E-mail: herts.naturalhistorysociety@aol.com

Bird Recorder
Tony Blake, 9 Old Forge Close, Stanmore, Middx HA7 3EB. E-mail: recorder@hertsbirdclub.org.uk

Bird Report
HERTFORDSHIRE BIRD REPORT (1908-2004), from Ted Fletcher, Beech House, Aspenden, Buntingford, Herts SG9 9PG. 01763 272 979.
www.hertsbirdclub.org.uk

BTO Regional Representative & Regional Development Officer
RR & RDO. Chris Dee, 26 Broadleaf Avenue, Thorley Park, Bishop's Stortford, Herts, CM23 4JY. 01279 755 637; e-mail: hertsbto@hotmail.com

Clubs
FRIENDS OF TRING RESERVOIRS. (1993; 350). Rose Barr, Secretary, PO Box 1083, Tring HP23 5WU. 01296 424 145; (Fax) 01296 581 520.
www.fotr.org.uk
Meetings: See website.

HERTFORDSHIRE BIRD CLUB. (1971; 310) Part of Hertfordshire NHS. Ted Fletcher, Beech House, Aspenden, Buntingford, Herts SG9 9PG. 01763 272 979. www.hertsbirdclub.org.uk

HERTFORDSHIRE NATURAL HISTORY SOCIETY AND HERTS BIRD CLUB. (1875; 320)Linda Smith, 24 Mandeville Rise, Welwyn Garden City, Herts AL8 7JU.
e-mail: herts.naturalhistorysociety@ntlworld.com
www.hnhs.org and www.hertsbirdclub.org.uk

Ringing Groups
AYLESBURY VALE RG (main activity at Marsworth). S M Downhill, 12 Millfield, Berkhamsted, Herts, HP4 2PB. 01442 865 821; e-mail: smdjbd@waitrose.com

MAPLE CROSS RG. P Delaloye,
e-mail: pdelaloye@tiscali.co.uk

RYE MEADS RG. Chris Dee, 26 Broadleaf Avenue, Thorley Park, Bishop's Stortford, Herts, CM23 4JY. 01279 755 637;
e-mail: ringingsecretary@rmrg.org.uk

TRING RG. Mick A'Court, 6 Chalkshire Cottages, Chalkshire Road, Butlers Cross, Bucks, HP17 0TW. (H) 01296 623 610; (W) 01494 462 246;
e-mail: mick@focusrite.com or
e-mail: a.arundinaceous@virgin.net

RSPB Local Groups
CHORLEYWOOD & DISTRICT. (1977; 142). Sam Thomas, 36 Field Way, Rickmansworth, Herts WD3 2EJ. 01923 449 917.
Meetings: 8pm, last Thursday of the month (Sept-May).

HARPENDEN. (1974; 1000). Geoff Horn, 41 Ridgewood Drive, Harpenden, Herts AL5 3LJ. 01582 765 443; e-mail: geoffrhorn@yahoo.co.uk
Meetings: Check with group contact for details.

HEMEL HEMPSTEAD. (1972; 150). Paul Green, 207 Northridge Way, Hemel Hempstead, Herts, HP1 2AU. 01442 266 637;
e-mail: paul@310nrwhh.freeserve.co.uk
www.hemelrspb.org.uk
Meetings: 8pm, 1st Monday of the month (Sep-Jun), The Cavendish School.

HITCHIN & LETCHWORTH. (1973; 120). Dr Martin Johnson, 1 Cartwright Road, Royston, Herts, SG8 9ET. 01763 249 459;
e-mail: martinrjspc@hotmail.com
Meetings: 7.30pm, 1st Friday of the month, The Settlement, Nevells Road, Letchworth.

POTTERS BAR & BARNET. (1977; 1800). Stan Bailey, 23 Bowmans Close, Potters Bar, Herts, EN6 5NN. 01707 646 073.
Meetings: 2.00pm, 2nd Wednesday of the month, St Johns URC Hall, Mowbray Road, Barnet, 8.00pm, changeable Mondays, Wyllyotts Centre, Potters Bar.

ST ALBANS. (1979; 1550 in catchment area). John Maxfield, 46 Gladeside, Jersey Farm, St Albans, Herts, AL4 9JA. 01727 832 688;
e-mail: peter@antram.demon.co.uk
www.antram.demon.co.uk/
Meetings: 8.00pm, 2nd Tuesday of the month (Sep-Feb; Apr-May), St Saviours Church Hall, Sandpit Lane, St Albans.

SOUTH EAST HERTS. (1971; 2,400 in catchment area). Terry Smith, 31 Marle Gardens, Waltham Abbey, Essex EN9 2DZ. 01992 715 634;
e-mail: se_herts_rspb@yahoo.co.uk
www.rspb.org.uk/groups/southeasthertfordshire
Meetings: 7.30pm, usually last Tuesday of the month (Sept-June), URC Church Hall, Mill Lane, Broxbourne.

STEVENAGE. (1982; 1300 in the catchment area). Mrs Ann Collis, 16 Stevenage Road, Walkern, Herts, 01483 861 547.
Meetings: 7.30pm, 3rd Tuesday of the month, Friends Meeting House, Cuttys Lane, Stevenage.

WATFORD. (1974; 590). Janet Reynolds, 01923 249 647; e-mail: janet.reynolds@whht.nhs.uk http://members.lycos.co.uk/watford_RSPB/
Meetings: 7.30pm, 2nd Wednesday of the month (Sep-Jun), St Thomas' Church Hall, Langley Road, Watford.

Wildlife Hospital
SWAN CARE. Secretary, Swan Care, 14 Moorland Road, Boxmoor, Hemel Hempstead, Herts, HP1 1NH. 01442 251 961. Swans. Sanctuary and treatment centre. Veterinary support.

Wildlife Trust
HERTS & MIDDLESEX WILDLIFE TRUST. (1964; 17,000). Grebe House, St Michael's Street, St Albans, Herts, AL3 4SN. 01727 858 901; (Fax) 01727 854 542; e-mail: info@hmwt.org www.wildlifetrust.org.uk/herts/

ISLE OF WIGHT

Bird Recorder
G Sparshott, Leopards Farm, Main Road, Havenstreet, Isle of Wight, PO33 4DR. 01983 882 549; e-mail: grahamspa@aol.com

Bird Reports
ISLE OF WIGHT BIRD REPORT (1986-) (Pre-1986 not available), from Mr DJ Hunnybun, 40 Churchill Road, Cowes, Isle of Wight, PO31 8HH. 01983 292 880; email: davehunnybun@hotmail.com

BTO Regional Representative
James C Gloyn, 3 School Close, Newchurch, Isle of Wight, PO36 0NL. 01983 865 567; e-mail: gloynjc@yahoo.com

Clubs
ISLE OF WIGHT NATURAL HISTORY & ARCHAEOLOGICAL SOCIETY. (1919; 500). The Secretary, Salisbury Gardens, Dudley Road, Ventnor, Isle of Wight, PO38 1EJ. 01983 855 385.

ISLE OF WIGHT ORNITHOLOGICAL GROUP. (1986; 155). Mr DJ Hunnybun, 40 Churchill Road, Cowes, Isle of Wight, PO31 8HH. 01983 292 880; email: davehunnybun@hotmail.com

Wildlife Trust
Director, See Hampshire,

KENT

Bird Atlas/Avifauna
Birding in Kent by D W Taylor et al 1996. Pica Press.

Bird Recorder
Don Taylor, 1 Rose Cottages, Old Loose Hill, Loose, Maidstone, Kent, ME15 0BN. 01622 745 641; e-mail: don@collared.free-online.co.uk

Bird Reports
DUNGENESS BIRD OBSERVATORY REPORT (1989-), from the Warden, see Reserves.

KENT BIRD REPORT (1952-), from Dave Sutton, 61 Alpha Road, Birchington, Kent, CT7 9ED. 01843 842 541; e-mail: dave@suttond8.freeserve.co.uk

SANDWICH BAY BIRD OBSERVATORY REPORT, from Warden, see Reserves,

BTO Regional Representative
RR. Sally Hunter, 01304 612 425; e-mail: sally.hunter@tesco.net

Club
KENT ORNITHOLOGICAL SOCIETY. (1952; 720). Mrs Ann Abrams, 4 Laxton Way, Faversham, Kent ME13 8LJ. 01795 533 453; e-mail: annie@chrisabrams.plus.com www.kentos.org.uk
Meetings: Indoor: October-April at various venues; the AGM in April is at St Paul's Church Hall, Boxley Road, Maidstone. See website for details: www.kentos.org.uk

Ringing Groups
DARTFORD RG. R Taylor, 21 Dallin Road, Plumstead, London SE18 3NY.

DUNGENESS BIRD OBSERVATORY. David Walker, Dungeness Bird Observatory, Dungeness, Romney Marsh, Kent, TN29 9NA. 01797 321 309; e-mail: dungeness.obs@tinyonline.co.uk www.dungenessbirdobs.org.uk

RECULVER RG. Chris Hindle, 42 Glenbervie Drive, Herne Bay, Kent, CT6 6QL. 01227 373 070; e-mail: christopherhindle@hotmail.com

SANDWICH BAY BIRD OBSERVATORY. Mr KB Ellis, 6 Alderney Gardens, St Peters, Broadstairs, Kent CT10 2TN. 01304 617 341; e-mail: sbbot@talk21.com

SWALE WADER GROUP. Rod Smith, 67 York Avenue, Chatham, Kent, ME5 9ES. 01634 865 863; www.swalewader.co.uk

RSPB Local Groups
CANTERBURY. (1973; 216). Jean Bomber, St Heliers, 30a Castle Road, Tankerton, Whitstable, Kent, CT5 2DY. 01227 277 725. www.canterburyrspb.co.uk
Meetings: 8.00pm, 2nd Wednesday of the month (Sept-Apr), Chaucer Technology School, Spring Lane, Canterbury.

GRAVESEND & DISTRICT. (1977; 278). Malcolm Jennings, 206 Lower Higham Road, Gravesend, Kent DA12 2NN. 01474 322 171.
Meetings: 7.45pm, 2nd Wednesday of the month (Sep-May), St Botolph's Hall, North Fleet, Gravesend.

MAIDSTONE. (1973; 250). Dick Marchese, 11 Bathurst Road, Staplehurst, Tonbridge, Kent, TN12 0LG. 01580 892 458. www.vidler23.freeserve.co.uk/
Meetings: 7.30pm, 3rd Thursday of the month, Grove Green Community Hall, Penhurst Close, Grove Green, opposite Tesco's.

MEDWAY. (1974; 230). Sue Carter, 31 Ufton Lane, Sittingbourne, ME10 1JB. 01795 427 854. www.medway-rspb.pwp.blueyonder.co.uk
Meetings: 7.45pm 3rd Tuesday of the month (except Aug), Strood Library, Bryant Road, Strood.

SEVENOAKS. (1974; 300). Bernard Morris, New House, Kilkhampton, Bude, Cornwall, EX23 9RZ. 01288 321 727 or 07967 564 699;(Fax) 01288 321 838; e-mail: bernard.morris5@btinternet.com
Meetings: 7.45pm 1st Thursday of the month, Otford Memorial Hall.

SOUTH EAST KENT. (1981; 165). Pauline McKenzie-Lloyd, Hillside, Old Park Avenue, Dover, Kent CT16 2DY. 01304 826 529;
email: pauline.mcklloyd@tiscali.co.uk
www.rspb.org.uk/groups/southeastkent
Meetings: 7.30pm, 3rd Wednesday of the month (Sep-May), United Reform Church, Folkestone. See details of field trips on website.

THANET. (1975; 119). Peter Radcliffe, Cottage of St John, Caterbury Road, Sarre, Kent CT7 0JY. 01843 847 345.
Meetings: 7.30pm last Tuesday of the month (Jan-Nov), Portland Centre.

TONBRIDGE. (1975; 150 reg attendees/1700 in catchment). Ms Gabrielle Sutcliffe, 1 Postern Heath Cottages, Postern Lane, Tonbridge, Kent, TN11 0QU. 01732 365 583.
Meetings: 7.45pm 3rd Wednesday of the month (Sept-Apr), St Phillips Church, Salisbury Road.

Wetland Bird Survey Organisers
EAST KENT. Ken Lodge, 14 Gallwey Avenue, Birchington, Kent CT7 9PA. 01843 843 105;
e-mail: kenlodge@minnisbay15.freeserve.co.uk

MEDWAY ESTUARY & NORTH KENT MARSHES. Sally Jennings, RSPB, Bromhey Farm, Cooling, Rochester, Kent ME3 8DS. 01634 222 480 .

SWALE ESTUARY. Sally Jennings, RSPB, Bromhey Farm, Cooling, Rochester, Kent ME3 8DS. 01634 222 480.

Wildlife Hospital
RAPTOR CENTRE. Eddie Hare, Ivy Cottage, Groombridge Place, Groombridge, Tunbridge Wells, Kent, TN3 9QG. 01892 861 175; (Fax) 01892 863 761. www.raptorcentre.co.uk Birds of prey. Veterinary support. 24hr rescue service for sick and injured birds of prey that covers the South-East.

Wildlife Trust
KENT WILDLIFE TRUST. (1958; 10500). Tyland Barn, Sandling, Maidstone, Kent, ME14 3BD. 01622 662 012; (Fax) 01622 671 390;
e-mail: info@kentwildlife.org.uk
www.kentwildlifetrust.org.uk

LANCASHIRE

Bird Atlas/Avifauna
An Atlas of Breeding Birds of Lancaster and District by Ken Harrison (Lancaster & District Birdwatching Society, 1995).

Breeding Birds of Lancashire and North Merseyside (2001), sponsored by North West Water. Contact: Bob Pyefinch, 12 Bannistre Court, Tarleton, Preston PR4 6HA.

Bird Recorder
(See also Manchester).

Inc North Merseyside. Steve White, 102 Minster Court, Crown Street, Liverpool, L7 3QD. 0151 707 2744; e-mail: stephen.white2@tesco.net

Bird Reports
BIRDS OF LANCASTER & DISTRICT (1959-), from Secretary, Lancaster & District BWS, 01524 734 462.

EAST LANCASHIRE ORNITHOLOGISTS' CLUB BIRD REPORT (1982-), from Secretary, 01282 612 870;
e-mail: john.plackett@eastlancsornithologists.org.uk
www.eastlancsornithologists.org.uk

BLACKBURN & DISTRICT BIRD CLUB ANNUAL REPORT (1992-), from Doreen Bonner, 6 Winston Road, Blackburn, BB1 8BJ. (Tel/Fax) 01254 261 480; www.blackburnbirds.freeuk.com

CHORLEY & DISTRICT NATURAL HISTORY SOCIETY BIRD REPORT (1975-), from The Secretary.

FYLDE BIRD REPORT (1983-), from The Secretary, Fylde Bird Club.

LANCASHIRE BIRD REPORT (1914-), from The Secretary, Lancs & Cheshire Fauna Soc.

ROSSENDALE ORNITHOLOGISTS' CLUB BIRD REPORT (1977-). from The Secretary, Rossendale Ornithologists Club.

BTO Regional Representatives & Regional Development Officer
EAST RR. Tony Cooper, 28 Peel Park Avenue, Clitheroe, Lancs, BB7 1ET. 01200 424 577;
e-mail: tony.cooper@eastlancsornithologists.org.uk

NORTH & WEST RR. Jean Roberts, 01524 770 295; e-mail: JeanRbrts6@aol.com

SOUTH RR. Position Vacant.

Clubs

BLACKBURN & DISTRICT BIRD CLUB. (1991; 134). Jim Bonner, 6 Winston Road, Blackburn, BB1 8BJ. (Tel/Fax) 01254 261 480.
www.blackburnbirds.freeuk.com
Meetings: Normally 7.30pm, 1st Monday of the month, (Sept-Apr), Church Hall, Preston New Road. Check website for all indoor and outdoor meetings.

CHORLEY & DISTRICT NATURAL HISTORY SOCIETY. (1979; 170). Phil Kirk, Millend, Dawbers Lane, Euxton, Chorley, Lancs, PR7 6EB. 01257 266 783; e-mail: secretary@chorleynats.org.uk
www.chorleynats.org.uk
Meetings: 7.30pm, 3rd Thursday of the month (Sept-Apr), St Mary's Parish Centre, Chorley

EAST LANCASHIRE ORNITHOLOGISTS' CLUB. (1955; 45). Dr JCW Plackett, 77 Walton Lane, Nelson, Lancs BB9 6BB. 01282 612 870;
e-mail: john.plackett@eastlancsornithologists.org.uk
www.eastlancsornithologists.org.uk
Meetings: 7.30pm, 1st Monday of the month, St Anne's Church Hall, Feuce, Nr Burnley.

FYLDE BIRD CLUB. (1982; 110). Paul Ellis, 18 Staining Rise, Blackpool, FY3 0BU. 01253 891 281; e-mail: paul.ellis24@btopenworld.com
or kinta.beaver@man.ac.uk
www.fyldebirdclub.org

Meetings: 7.45pm, 4th Tuesday of the month, River Wyre Hotel, Breck Road, Poulton le Fylde.

FYLDE NATURALISTS' SOCIETY. (1946; 140). Julie Clarke, 7 Cedar Avenue, Poulton-le-Fylde, Blackpool, FY6 8DQ. 01253 883 785;
e-mail: julie-p-clarke@hotmail.com.
Meetings: 7.30pm, fortnightly (Sep-Mar), Fylde Coast Alive, Church Hall, Raikes Parade, Blackpool unless otherwise stated in the Programme.

LANCASHIRE & CHESHIRE FAUNA SOCIETY. (1914; 150). Dave Bickerton, 64 Petre Crescent, Rishton, Lancs, BB1 4RB. 01254 886 257;
e-mail: bickertond@aol.com
www.lacfs.org.uk

LANCASHIRE BIRD CLUB. (1996). Dave Bickerton, 64 Petre Crescent, Rishton, Lancs, BB1 4RB. 01254 886 257; e-mail: bickertond@aol.com
www.lacfs.org.uk

LANCASTER & DISTRICT BIRD WATCHING SOCIETY. (1959; 200). Andrew Cadman, 57 Greenways, Over Kellet, Carnforth, Lancs, LA6 1DE. 01524 734 462; e mail: andrewokuk@yahoo.co.uk or: ldbws@yahoo.co.uk
www.lancasterbirdwatching.org.uk
Meetings: 7.30pm, last Monday of the month (Sep-Nov, Feb-Mar), Bare Methodist Church Hall, St Margarets Road, Morecambe; (Jan and Apr) the Hornby Institute, Hornby.

ROSSENDALE ORNITHOLOGISTS' CLUB. (1976; 35). Ian Brady, 25 Church St, Newchurch, Rossendale, Lancs, BB4 9EX. 01706 222 120.
Meetings: 7.30pm, 3rd Monday of the month, Weavers Cottage, Bacup Road, Rawtenstall.

Ringing Groups

FYLDE RG. G Barnes, 17 Lomond Avenue, Marton, Blackpool, FY3 9QL.

MORECAMBE BAY WADER RG. J Sheldon, 140 Oxford Street, Barrow-in-Furness, Cumbria, LA14 5PJ.

NORTH LANCS RG. John Wilson BEM, 40 Church Hill Avenue, Warton, Carnforth, Lancs, LA5 9NU.
E-mail: johnwilson711@btinternet.com

SOUTH WEST LANCASHIRE RG. I H Wolfenden, 35 Hartdale Road, Thornton, Liverpool, Merseyside L23 1TA. 01519 311 232.

RSPB Local Groups

BLACKPOOL. (1983; 170). Alan Stamford, 6 Kensington Road, Cleveleys, FY5 1ER. 01253 859 662.
Meetings: 7.30pm, 2nd Friday of the month (Sept-June), Frank Townend Centre, Beach Road, Cleveleys.

BOLTON. (1978; 320). Mrs Alma Schofield, 29 Redcar Road, Little Lever, Bolton, BL3 1EW. 01204 791 745. http://boltonrspb.users.btopenworld.com
Meetings: 7.30pm, Thursdays (dates vary), Main Hall, Smithills School, Smithills Dean Road, Bolton.

LANCASTER. (1972; 176). Jill Blackburn, 13 Coach Road, Warton, Carnforth, Lancs LA5 9PR.
e-mail: jill.blackburn@quista.net
www.rspb.org.uk/localgroups/lancaster

Wetland Bird Survey Organisers

NORTH LANCASHIRE (Inland). Mr Pete Marsh, Leck View Cottage, Ashley's farm, High Tatham, Lancaster, LA2 8PH. 01524 264 944;
e-mail: pbmarsh@btopenworld.com

Wildlife Trust

THE WILDLIFE TRUST FOR LANCASHIRE, MANCHESTER AND NORTH MERSEYSIDE. (1962; 16,000). Mr Peter Mallon, Communications Officer, The Barn, Berkeley Drive, Bamber Bridge, Preston, PR5 6BY. 01772 324 129; (Fax) 01772 628 849;
e-mail: pmallon@lancswt.org.uk
www.lancswt.org.uk

ENGLAND

LEICESTERSHIRE & RUTLAND

Bird Atlas/Avifauna
Leicestershire and Rutland County Avifauna by Rob Fray, Steve Lister, Roger Davies and Andrew Harrop. (Helm due 2007)

Bird Recorder
Steve Lister, 6 Albert Promenade, Loughborough, Leicestershire LE11 1RE. 01509 829 495; e-mail: stevelister@surfbirder.com

Bird Reports
LEICESTERSHIRE & RUTLAND BIRD REPORT (1941-), from Mrs S Graham, 5 Lycheate Close, Cropston, Leicestershire LE7 7HU. 0116 236 6474.

RUTLAND NAT HIST SOC ANNUAL REPORT (1965-), from The Secretary, 01572 747 302.

BTO Regional Representative
LEICESTER & RUTLAND RR. Tim Grove, 35 Clumber Street, Melton Mowbray, Leicestershire LE13 0ND. 01664 850 766; e-mail: k.grove1@ntlworld.com

Clubs
BIRSTALL BIRDWATCHING CLUB. (1976; 50). Mr KJ Goodrich, 6 Riversdale Close, Birstall, Leicester, LE4 4EH. 0116 267 4813.
Meetings: 7.30pm, 2nd Tuesday of the month (Oct-Apr), Longslade Community College, room 11.

LEICESTERSHIRE & RUTLAND ORNITHOLOGICAL SOCIETY. (1941; 580). Mrs Marion Vincent, 48 Templar Way, Rothley, Leicester, LE7 7RB. 0116 230 3405. www.lros.org.uk
Meetings: 7.30pm, 1st Friday of the month, Leicester Adult Education College, Wellington St, Leicester. Additional meeting at Rutland Water Birdwatching Centre.

MARKET HARBOROUGH & DISTRICT NATURAL HISTORY SOCIETY. (1971; 40). Mrs Marion Mills, 36 Nelson Street, Market Harborough, Leics LE16 9AY. 01858 462 346.
Meetings: 7.30pm, 2nd Monday in the month, Welland Park College

SOUTH LEICESTER BIRDWATCHERS. (2006;). Paul Seaton, 76 Roehampton Drive, Wigston, Leics LE18 1HU. 07973 156 060;
e-mail: paul.lseaton@ntlworld.com
Meetings: 7.30 pm, 2nd Wednesday of the month (Sep-Jun), County Scout Centre, Winchester Road, Blaby, Leicester LE8 4HN.

RUTLAND NATURAL HISTORY SOCIETY. (1964; 256). Mrs L Worrall, 6 Redland Close, Barrowden, Oakham, Rutland, LE15 8ES. 01572 747 302. www.rnhs.org.uk
Meetings: 7.30pm, 1st Tuesday of the month (Oct-Apr), Oakham C of E School, Burley Road, Oakham.

Ringing Groups
RUTLAND WATER RG. Tim Appleton, Fishponds Cottage, Stamford Road, Oakham, LE15 8AB. (Day) 01572 770 651;
e-mail: awbc@rutland water.org.uk

STANFORD RG. John Cranfield, 41 Main Street, Fleckney, Leicester LE8 8AP. 0116 240 4385;
e-mail: JacanaJohn@talktalk.ne

RSPB Local Groups
LEICESTER. (1969; 1,600 in catchement area). Chris Woolass, 136 Braunstone Lane, Leicester, LE3 2RW. 0116 2990 078;
e-mail: chris@jclwoolass.freeserve.co.uk
Meetings: 7.30pm, 3rd Friday of the month (Sep-May), Adult Education Centre, Wellington Street, Leicester

LOUGHBOROUGH. (1970; 300). Robert Orton, 12 Avon Road, Barrow-on-Soar, Leics, LE12 8LE. 077 4887 6798.
Meetings: Monthly Friday nights, Loughborough University.

Wetland Bird Survey Organisers
LEICESTERSHIRE & RUTLAND (excl Rutland Water. Tim Grove, 35 Clumber Street, Melton Mowbray, Leics LE13 0ND. 01664 850 766;
e-mail: k.grove1@ntlworld.com

RUTLAND WATER. Tim Appleton, Fishponds Cottage, Stamford Road, Oakham, LE15 8AB. (Day) 01572 770 651.
e-mail: awbc@rutland water.org.uk

Wildlife Trust
LEICESTERSHIRE & RUTLAND WILDLIFE TRUST. (1956; 10,000). Brocks Hill Environment Centre, Washbrook Lane, Oadby, Leicestershire LE2 5JJ. 0116 272 0444; (Fax) 0116 272 0404;
e-mail: info@lrwt.org.uk www.lrwt.org.uk

LINCOLNSHIRE

Bird Atlas/Avifauna
The Status of Birds in Lincolnshire 1991-1995 (covers a five-year period) from Mr W Sterling, LBC Sales, Newlyn, Carlton Avenue, Healing, Grimsby DN37 7PN.

Bird Recorders
Steve Keightley, Redclyffe, Swineshead Road, Frampton Fen, Boston PE20 1SG. 01205 290 233;
e-mail: steve.keightley@btinternet.com

Bird Reports
GIBRALTAR POINT OBSERVATORY BIRD REPORT, from observatory (see Reserves section).

LINCOLNSHIRE BIRD REPORT (1979-1996), (1990 now sold out), from Mr W Sterling, LBC Sales, Newlyn, Carlton Avenue, Healing, Grimsby DN37 7PN.

LINCOLNSHIRE RARE AND SCARCE BIRD REPORT (1997-1999) first edition, from Mr W Sterling, LBC Sales, Newlyn, Carlton Avenue, Healing, Grimsby DN37 7PN.

SCUNTHORPE & NORTH WEST LINCOLNSHIRE BIRD REPORT (1973-), from the Secretary, Scunthorpe Museum Society, Ornithological Section, (Day) 01724 402 871; (Eve) 1724 734 261.

BTO Regional Representatives & Regional Development Officer
EAST AND NORTH RR. Positions vacant.

SOUTH RR. Richard & Kay Heath, 56 Pennytoft Lane, Pinchbeck, Spalding, Lincs, PE11 3PQ. 01775 767055; e-mail: heathsrk@ukonline.co.uk

WEST RR. Peter Overton, Hilltop Farm, Welbourn, Lincoln, LN5 0QH. Work 01400 273 323; e-mail: nyika@biosearch.org.uk

RDO. Nicholas Watts, Vine House Farm, Deeping St Nicholas, Spalding, Lincs, PE11 3DG. 01775 630 208.

Club
LINCOLNSHIRE BIRD CLUB. (1979; 220). Janet Eastmead, 3 Oxeney Drive, Langworth, Lincoln LN3 5DD. 01522 754 522; e-mail: jee@freeuk.com
Meetings: Local groups hold winter evening meetings (contact Secretary for details).

SCUNTHORPE MUSEUM SOCIETY (Ornithological Section). (1973; 50). Keith Parker, 7 Ryedale Avenue, Winterton, Scunthorpe, Lincs DN15 9BJ.
Meetings: 7.15pm, 3rd Monday of the month (Sep-Apr), Scunthorpe Museum, Oswald Road.

Ringing Groups
MID LINCOLNSHIRE RG. J Mawer, 2 The Chestnuts, Owmby Road, Searby, Lincolnshire DN38 6EH. 01652 628 583.

WASH WADER RG. P L Ireland, 27 Hainfield Drive, Solihull, W Midlands, B91 2PL. 0121 704 1168; e-mail: enquiries@wwrg.org.uk

RSPB Local Groups
GRIMSBY AND CLEETHORPES. (1986; 2200 in catchment area). Barbara Stephenson. 01472 814 303; e-mail: terence@terencewhalin.wannado.co.uk www.grimsby-RSPB.co.uk.
Meetings: 7.30pm, 1st Monday of the month (Sept-May), Cromwell Banqueting Suite, Cromwell Road, Cleethorpes.

LINCOLN. (1974; 250). Peter Skelson, 26 Parksgate Avenue, Lincoln, LN6 7HP. 01522 695 747;
e-mail: peter.skelson@lincolnrspb.org.uk
www.lincolnrspb.org.uk
Meetings: 7.30pm, 2nd Thursday of the month (not Jun, Jul, Aug, Dec), The Lawn, Union Road, Lincoln.

SOUTH LINCOLNSHIRE. (1987; 350). Barry Hancock, The Limes, Meer Booth Road, Antons Gowt, Boston, Lincs, PE22 7BG. 01205 280 057;
e-mail: info@southlincsrspb.org.uk
www.southlincsrspb.org.uk

Wetland Bird Survey Organisers
HUMBER ESTUARY - MID SOUTH. Ian Shepherd, 38 Lindsey Road, Cleethorpes, Lincolnshire DN35 8TN. 01472 697 142

THE WASH. Jim Scott, RSPB, Barn A, Home Farm Barns, Common Road, Snettisham, King's Lynn, Norfolk PE31 7PD.

Wildlife Trust
LINCOLNSHIRE WILDLIFE TRUST. (1948; 26,000). Banovallum House, Manor House Street, Horncastle, Lincs, LN9 5HF. 01507 526 667; (Fax) 01507 525 732; e-mail: info@lincstrust.co.uk
www.lincstrust.org.uk

LONDON, GREATER

Bird Atlas/Avifauna
*The Breeding Birds of the London Area, 2002. (*ISBN 0901009 121) ed Jan Hewlett (London Natural History Society).

Bird Recorder (see also Surrey)
Andrew Self, 16 Harp Island Close, Neasden, London, NW10 0DF
e-mail: andrewself@lineone.net
www.londonbirders.com

Bird Report
CROYDON BIRD SURVEY (1995), from Secretary, Croydon RSPB Group, 020 8640 4578;
e-mail: johndavis.wine@care4free.net
www.croydon-rspb.org.uk.

LONDON BIRD REPORT (20-mile radius of St Paul's Cath) (1936-), from Catherine Schmitt, Publications Sales, London Natural History Society, 4 Falkland Avenue, London N3 1QR.

BTO Regional Representative & Regional Development Officer
LONDON, NORTH. Ian Woodward, 245 Larkshall Road, Chingford, London E4 9HY. 07931 705 437;
e-mail: ianw_bto_nlon@hotmail.co.uk

LONDON, SOUTH. Richard Arnold, 10 Leominster Road, Morden, Surrey SM4 6HN. 020 8646 2483;
e-mail: richard_arnold@blueyonder.co.uk

ENGLAND

Clubs

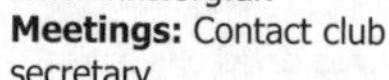

LONDON NATURAL HISTORY SOCIETY (Ornithology Section). (1858; 1000). Mrs Angela Linnell, 20 Eleven Acre Rise, Loughton, Essex IG10 1AN. 020 8508 2932; e-mail: Angela.Linnell@care4free.net. www.lnhs.org.uk
Meetings: Contact club secretary.

MARYLEBONE BIRDWATCHING SOCIETY. (1981; 110). Judy Powell, 7 Rochester Terrace, London, NW1 9JN. 020 7485 0863;
e-mail: birdsmbs@yahoo.com
www.geocities.com/birdsmbs
Meeting: 7.15pm 2nd Friday of month (Sept-May), Gospel Oak, Methodist Chapel, Lisburne Road, London NW3 2NR.

Ringing Groups

LONDON GULL STUDY GROUP - (SE including Hampshire, Surrey, Sussex, Berkshire and Oxfordshire). No longer in operation but able to give information on gulls. Mark Fletcher, 24 The Gowans, Sutton-on-the-Forest, York, YO61 1DJ.
e-mail: m.fletcher@csl.gov.uk

RUNNYMEDE RG. D G Harris, 22 Blossom Waye, Hounslow, TW5 9HD.
e-mail: daveharris@tinyonline.co.uk

RSPB Local Groups

BEXLEY. (1979; 180). Tony Banks, 15 Boundary Road, Sidcup, Kent DA15 8SS. 020 8859 3518;
email: Tony@banks76.freeserve.co.uk
www.bexleyrspb.org.uk
Meetings: 7.30pm, 3rd Friday of the month, Hurstmere School Hall, Hurst Road, Sidcup.

BROMLEY. (1972; 285). Bob Francis, 10 The Pantiles, Bickley, Bromley BR1 2BX. 020 8464 3844;
e-mail: rbrtfranc@netscape.net
www.bromleyrspb.org.uk
Meetings: 2nd Wednesday of the month (Sep-Jun), Large Hall, Bromley Central Library Building, Bromley High Street.

CENTRAL LONDON. (1974; 330). Jill Aldred,
e-mail: J.Aldred@janja.dircon.co.uk;
www.janja.dircon.co.uk/rspb
Meetings: 2nd Thursday of the month (Sep-May), St Columba's Church Hall, Pont St, London SW1.

CROYDON. (1973; 4,000 in catchment area). John Davies, 9 Cricket Green, Mitcham, CR4 4LB. 020 8640 4578; e-mail: johndavis.wine@care4free.net
www.croydon-rspb.org.uk
Meetings: 2nd Monday of each month at 2pm-4pm and again at 8pm-10pm at St Peter's Hall, Ledbury Road, South Croydon.

ENFIELD. (1971; 2,700). Norman G Hudson, 125 Morley Hill, Enfield, Middx, EN2 0BQ. 020 8363 1431.
Meetings: 8pm, 1st Thursday of the month, St Andrews Hall, Enfield Town.

HAVERING. (1972; 270). David Coe, 8 The Fairway, Upminster, Essex, RM14 1BS. 01708 220 710.
Meetings: 8pm, 2nd Friday of the month, Hornchurch Library, North Street, Hornchurch.

NORTH LONDON. (1974; 3,000). John Parsons, 65 Rutland Gardens, Harringay, London, N4 1JW. 020 8802 9537.

NORTH WEST LONDON RSPB GROUP. (1983; 2,000 in catchment area). Bob Husband, The Firs, 49 Carson Road, Cockfosters, Barnet, Herts, EN4 9EN. 020 8441 8742.
Meetings: 8pm, last Tuesday of the month (Sept-Apr), Union Church Hall, Eversfield Gardens, Mill Hill, NW7.

PINNER & DISTRICT. (1972; 300). Dennis Bristow, 118 Crofts Road, Harrow, Middx, HA1 2PJ. 020 8863 5026.
Meetings: 8pm, 2nd Thursday of the month (Sept-May), Church Hall, St John The Baptist Parish church, Pinner.

RICHMOND & TWICKENHAM. (1979; 375). Keith Birch, 32 Broom Lock, Teddington, TW11 9QP. 020 8977 6496; e-mail: keithgbirch@aol.com.
Meetings: 8.00pm, 1st Wednesday of the month, York House, Twickenham.

WEST LONDON. (1973; 400). Alan Bender, 020 8841 1952; e-mail: alan.bender@tesco.net
www.rspb.org.uk/groups/westlondon
Meetings: Ealing Town Hall, 22 Uxbridge Road, LONDON, W5 2BU

Wildlife Hospitals

WILDLIFE RESCUE & AMBULANCE SERVICE (ENFIELD). Barry Smitherman MBE, Trant Park Animal Centre and Wildlife Hospital, Trent Country Park, Snakes Lane, Enfield, Middx EN4 0PS. 020 8292 5377.
All categories of wild birds. Emergency ambulance with full rescue equipment, boats, ladders etc. Own treatment centre and aviaries. Veterinary support. Essential to telephone first.

Wildlife Trust

LONDON WILDLIFE TRUST. (1981; 7,500). Skyline House, 200 Union Street, London, SE1 0LX. 0207 261 0447; (Fax) 0207 633 0811;
e-mail: enquiries@wildlondon.org.uk
www.wildlondon.org.uk

MANCHESTER, GREATER

Bird Atlas/Avifauna
Breeding Birds in Greater Manchester by Philip Holland et al (1984).

Bird Recorder
RECORDER AND REPORT EDITOR. Mrs A Judith Smith, 12 Edge Green Street, Ashton-in-Makerfield, Wigan, WN4 8SL. 01942 712 615; e-mail: judith@gmbirds.freeserve.co.uk www.gmbirds.freeserve.co.uk

ASSISTANT RECORDER (Rarities). Ian McKerchar, 42 Green Ave, Astley, Manchester, M29 7EH. 01942 701 758; e-mail: ian@mckerchar1.freeserve.co.uk

ASSISTANT RECORDER (Database). Steve Atkins, 33 King's Grove, Wardle, Rochdale OL12 9HR. 01706 645 097; e-mail: steveatkins@tiscali.co.uk

Bird Reports
BIRDS IN GREATER MANCHESTER (1976-), from Mrs M McCormick, 91 Sinderland Road, Altrincham WA14 5JJ (only editions up to year 2000. Year 2001 onwards from County Recorder).

LEIGH ORNITHOLOGICAL SOCIETY BIRD REPORT (1971-), from J Critchley, 2 Albany Grove, Tyldesley, Manchester, M29 7NE. 01942 884 644.

BTO Regional Representative & Regional Development Officer
RR. Steve Suttill, 94 Manchester Road, Mossley, Ashton-under-Lyne, Lancashire OL5 9AY. 01457 836 360; e-mail: suttill.parkinson@virgin.net

RDO. Jim Jeffery, 20 Church Lane, Romiley, Stockport, Cheshire, SK6 4AA. 0161 494 5367; e-mail: jim_jeffery1943@yahoo.co.uk

Clubs
MANCHESTER ORNITHOLOGICAL SOCIETY. (1954; 70). Dr R Sandling, School of Mathematics, Manchester University, Manchester M13 9EP. e-mail: rsandling@manchester.ac.uk
Meetings: 7.30pm, Tuesdays, St James Church Hall, off Church Street, Gatley.

GREATER MANCHESTER BIRD RECORDING GROUP. (2002: 40) Restricted to contributors of the county bird report. Mrs A Judith Smith, 01942 712 615; e-mail: judith@gmbirds.freeserve.co.uk www.gmbirds.freeserve.co.uk

HALE ORNITHOLOGISTS. (1968; 77). Mrs E Hall, Flat 22 , Shirley Court, Wardle Road, Sale M33 3DQ.
Meetings: 7.30pm, 2nd Wednesday of the month (Sept-July), St Peters Assembly Rooms, Hale.

LEIGH ORNITHOLOGICAL SOCIETY. (1971; 118). Mr D Shallcross, 10 Holden Brook Close, Leigh, Lancs, WN7 2HL. E-mail: chairman@leighos.org.uk www.leighos.org.uk
Meetings: 7.15pm, Fridays, Leigh Library (check website for details).

ROCHDALE FIELD NATURALISTS' SOCIETY. (1970; 90). Mrs J P Wood, 196 Castleton Road, Thornham, Royton, Oldham, OL2 6UP. 0161 345 2012; www.rochdaleonline.org (listed under societies and events)
Meetings: Yearly syllabus states dates of lectures and outings.

STOCKPORT BIRDWATCHING SOCIETY. (1972; 80). Dave Evans, 36 Tatton Road South, Stockport, Cheshire, SK4 4LU. 0161 432 9513; e-mail: windhover@ntlworld.com
Meetings: 7.30pm, last Wednesday of the month, Tiviot Dale Church.

Ringing Groups
LEIGH RG. A J Gramauskas, 21 Elliot Avenue, Golborne, Warrington, WA3 3DU. 0151 929 215.

SOUTH MANCHESTER RG. C M Richards, Fairhaven, 13 The Green, Handforth, Wilmslow, Cheshire, SK9 3AG. 01625 524 527; e-mail: cliveandray.richards@care4free.net

RSPB Local Groups
BOLTON. (1978; 320). Mrs Alma Schofield, 29 Redcar Road, Little Lever, Bolton, BL3 1EW. 01204 791 745. http://boltonrspb.users.btopenworld.com
Meetings: 7.30pm, Thursdays (dates vary), Main Hall, Smithills School, Smithills Dean Road, Bolton.

HIGH PEAK. (1974; 175). Peter Griffiths, 17 Clifton Drive, Marple, Stockport SK6 6PP. 0161 427 5325.
Meetings: 7.30pm, 3rd Monday of the month (Sep-May), Marple Senior Citizens Hall.

MANCHESTER. (1972; 3,600 in catchment area). Peter Wolstenholme, 31 South Park Road, Gatley, Cheshire, SK8 4AL. 0161 428 2175.
Meetings: 7.30 pm, St James Parish Hall, Gatley Green, Church Road, Gatley, Cheadle.

STOCKPORT. (1979; 250). Gay Crossley, 5 Broadhill Close, Bramhall, Stockport, Cheshire SK7 3BY. 0161 439 3210.
http://beatrice.mcc.ac.uk/stockport-rspb
Meetings: 7.30pm, 2nd Monday of the month (Sep-Apr), Stockport College of Technology, Lecture Theatre B.

WIGAN. (1973; 80). Graham Tonge, 01942 248 238; e-mail: gandmtonge@blueyonder.co.uk www.rspb.org.uk/groups/wigan.
Meetings: 7.45pm. Wigan Council For Voluntary Youth Service, Penson Street, Wigan Lane, near Swinley Labour Club, WIGAN.

Wildlife Hospital
THREE OWLS BIRD SANCTUARY AND RESERVE. Trustee, Nigel Fowler, Wolstenholme Fold, Norden, Rochdale, OL11 5UD. 01706 642 162; Emergency helpline 07973 819 389;
e-mail: info@threeowls.co.uk www.threeowls.co.uk
Registered charity. All species of wild bird. Rehabilitation and release on Sanctuary Reserve. Open every Sunday 12pm-5pm, otherwise visitors welcome by appointment. Quarterly newsletter. Veterinary support.

Wildlife Trust
Director, See Lancashire,

MERSEYSIDE & WIRRAL

Bird Atlas see Cheshire

Bird Recorders see Cheshire; Lancashire.

Bird Reports see also Cheshire
HILBRE BIRD OBSERVATORY REPORT, from the Warden, see Reserves,

BTO Regional Representatives
MERSEYSIDE RR and RDO. Bob Harris, 2 Dulas Road, Wavertree Green, Liverpool, L15 6UA. Work 0151 706 4311; e-mail: harris@liv.ac.uk

WIRRAL RR. Paul Miller, 01928 787 535;
e-mail: huntershill@worldonline.co.uk

Clubs
MERSEYSIDE NATURALISTS' ASSOCIATION. (1938; 260). John Clegg, MNA Membership Secretary, 29 Barlow Lane, Liverpool L4 3QP.
www.geocities.com/mnahome
Meetings: 3rd Saturday afternoon (winter only), Bootle Cricket Club. Coach outings throughout the year.
New publication due 2008: *In the Footsteps of Eric Hardy* by David Bryant (John Bannon Press).

WIRRAL BIRD CLUB. (1977; 150). The Secretary, E-mail: info@wirralbirdclub.com
www.wirralbirdclub.com

Ringing Groups
MERSEYSIDE RG. Bob Harris, 2 Dulas Road, Wavertree Green, Liverpool, L15 6UA. Work 0151 706 4311; e-mail: harris@liv.ac.uk

SOUTH WEST LANCASHIRE RG. I H Wolfenden, 35 Hartdale Road, Thornton, Liverpool, Merseyside L23 1TA. 01519 311 232.

RSPB Local Groups
LIVERPOOL. (1966; 162). Chris Tynan, 10 Barker Close, Huyton, Liverpool, L36 0XU. 0151 480 7938; e-mail: christtynan@aol.com
www.rspbliverpool.org.uk
Meetings: 7 for 7.30pm, 3rd Monday of the month (Sep-Apr), Mossley Hill Parish Church, Junc. Rose Lane and Elmswood Rd.

SEFTON COAST. (1980; 195). Peter Taylor, 26 Tilston Road, Walton, Liverpool, L9 6AJ. 0151 524 1905; e-mail: ptaylor@liv.ac.uk
www.scmg-rspb.org.uk
Meetings: 7.30pm, 2nd Tuesday of the month, St Lukes Church Hall, Liverpool Road, Crosby.

SOUTHPORT. (1974; 300). Roy Ekins, 01704 875 898; e-mail: royekins@yahoo.co.uk
Meetings: 7.45pm, Lord Street West Church Hall, Duke Street, SOUTHPORT.

WIRRAL. (1982; 120). Jeremy Bradshaw. 0151 632 2364; email: info@wirralrspb.org.uk
www.jowitt1.org.uk/rspb.htm

Wetland Bird Survey Organiser
DEE ESTUARY. Colin Wells, Burton Farm Point, Station Road, Nr Neston, South Wirral CH64 5SB. 01513 367 681; e-mail: colinwells@rspb.org.uk

Wildlife Trust
Director, See Lancashire,

NORFOLK

Bird Atlas/Avifauna
The Birds of Norfolk by Moss Taylor, Michael Seago, Peter Allard & Don Dorling (Pica Press, 1999).

Bird Recorder
Until end of 2007. Giles Dunmore, 49 Nelson Road, Sheringham, Norfolk, NR26 8DA. 01263 822 550; e-mail: giles.dunmore@tiscali.co.uk

From Jan 2008. Dave and Jacquie Bryant, 27 Swan Close, Hempstead Road, Holt, Norfolk NR25 6DP. 01263 714 249.

Bird Reports
CLEY BIRD CLUB 10-KM SQUARE BIRD REPORT (1987-), from Peter Gooden, 45 Charles Road, Holt, Norfolk, NR25 6DA. 01263 712 368

NAR VALLEY ORNITHOLOGICAL SOCIETY ANNUAL REPORT (1976-), from The Secretary, Ian Black.

NORFOLK BIRD & MAMMAL REPORT (1953-), from DL Paull, 8 Lindford Drive, Eaton, Norwich NR4 6LT.

NORFOLK ORNITHOLOGISTS' ASSOCN ANNUAL REPORT (1961-), from The Secretary.

WENSUM VALLEY BIRDWATCHING SOCIETY (2003-) from; e-mail: admin@wvbs.co.uk
www.wvbs.co.uk

BTO Regional Representatives
NORTH-EAST RR. Chris Hudson, Cornerstones, 5 Ringland Road, Taverham, Norwich, NR8 6TG. 01603 868 805; (M) 07771 635 844; e-mail: Chris697@btinternet.com

NORTH-WEST RR. Allan Hale, 01366 328 421; e-mail: allan.heidi@eidosnet.co.uk

SOUTH-EAST RR. Rachel Warren, 01603 593 912; e-mail: campephilus@btinternet.com.

SOUTH-WEST RR. Vince Matthews, Rose's Cottage, The Green, Merton, Thetford, Norfolk, IP25 6QU.

Clubs
CLEY BIRD CLUB. (1986; 500). Peter Gooden, 45 Charles Road, Holt, Norfolk, NR25 6DA. 01263 712 368.
Meetings: 8.00pm, Wednesdays, monthly (Dec-Feb), White Horse Hotel, Blakeney.

GREAT YARMOUTH BIRD CLUB. (1989; 30). Keith R Dye, 104 Wolseley Road, Great Yarmouth, Norfolk, NR31 0EJ. 01493 600 705;
e-mail: keith@dye3833.freeserve.co.uk
www.gybc.org.uk
Meetings: 7.45pm, 4th Monday of the month, Rumbold Arms, Southtown Road.

NAR VALLEY ORNITHOLOGICAL SOCIETY. (1976; 125). Ian Black, Three Chimneys, Tumbler Hill, Swaffham, Norfolk, PE37 7JG. 01760 724 092;
e-mail: ian_a_black@hotmail.com
www.accessbs.com/narvos
Meetings: 7.30pm, last Tuesday of the month (Jul-Nov and Jan-May), Barn Theatre, Convent of The Sacred Heart, Mangate Street, Swaffham, PE37 7QW.

NORFOLK & NORWICH NATURALISTS' SOCIETY. (1869; 630). DL Paull, 8 Lindford Drive, Eaton, Norwich NR4 6LT. 01603 457 270;
www.nnns.org.uk
Meetings: 7.30pm, 3rd Tuesday of the month (Sep-Apr), Easton College, Norwich.

NORFOLK BIRD CLUB. (1992; 350). The Secretary, Norfolk Bird Club, North Haven, Marks Lane, Santon Downham, Norfolk IP27 0TG.

NORFOLK ORNITHOLOGISTS' ASSOCIATION. (1962; 1100). Jed Andrews, Broadwater Road, Holme-next-Sea, Hunstanton, Norfolk, PE36 6LQ. 01485 525 406; e-mail: info@noa.org.uk www.noa.org.uk

WENSUM VALLEY BIRDWATCHING SOCIETY. (2003; 110). Colin Wright, 7 Hinshalwood Way, Old Costessey, Norwich, Norfolk NR8 5BN. 01603 740 548; e-mail: admin@wvbs.co.uk www.wvbs.co.uk
Meetings: 7.30pm, 3rd Thursday of the month, Weston Longville village hall.

Ringing Groups
BTO NUNNERY RG. Dawn Balmer, c/o BTO, The Nunnery, Thetford, Norfolk IP24 2PU.
e-mail: dawn.balmer@bto.org

HOLME BIRD OBSERVATORY. Miss SA Barker, e-mail: info@noa.org.uk.

NORTH WEST NORFOLK RG. Mr J L Middleton, 18 Back Lane, Burnham Market, Norfolk PE31 8EY.
E-mail: middleton@bmarket.freeserve.co.uk

SHERINGHAM RG. D Sadler, 26 Abbey Road, Sheringham, Norfolk NR26 8NN. 01263 821 904.

WASH WADER RG. P L Ireland, 27 Hainfield Drive, Solihull, W Midlands, B91 2PL. 0121 704 1168;
e-mail: enquiries@wwrg.org.uk

RSPB Local Groups
NORWICH. (1971; 360). Robert Pindar, 01692 582 689: e-mail: r.pindar@uea.ac.uk.
Meetings: 7.30pm, 2nd Monday of the month (except Aug), Hellesdon Community Centre, Middletons Lane, Hellesdon, Norwich (entrance of Woodview Road).

WEST NORFOLK. (1977; 247). Ken Bayliss, 23 Church Lane, Roydon, King's Lynn, Norfolk PE32 1AR. 01485 600 446;
e-mail: ken.bayliss3@btopenworld.com
Meetings: 7.30pm, 3rd Wednesday of the month (Sep-Apr), South Wootton Village Hall, Church Lane, South Wootton, King's Lynn.

Wetland Bird Survey Organisers
NORTH NORFOLK COAST. Michael Rooney, English Nature, Hill Farm Offices, Main Road, Well-next-the –Sea, Norfolk NR23 1AB. 01485 210 515;
e-mail: michael.rooney@naturalengland.org.uk

INLAND. Tim Strudwick, RSPB Strumpshaw Fen, Staithe Cottage, Low Road, Strumpshaw, Norfolk NR13 4HS. 01603 715 191.

THE WASH. Jim Scott, RSPB, Barn A, Home Farm Barns, Common Road, Snettisham, King's Lynn, Norfolk PE31 7PD.

Wildlife Trust
NORFOLK WILDLIFE TRUST. (1926; 32,000). Bewick House, 22 Thorpe Road, Norwich, Norfolk NR1 1RY. 01603 625 540; (Fax) 01603 598 300;
e-mail: admin@norfolkwildlifetrust.org.uk
www.norfolkwildlifetrust.org.uk

ENGLAND

NORTHAMPTONSHIRE

Bird Recorder
Position vacant, Enquiries to Mike Alibone, 25 Harrier Park, East Hunsbury, Northants NN4 0QG. E-mail: northantsbirds@ntlworld.com

BTO Regional Representative
RR. Position vacant.

Clubs
NORTHAMPTONSHIRE BIRD CLUB. (1973; 100). Mrs Eleanor McMahon, Oriole House, 5 The Croft, Hanging Houghton, Northants, NN6 9HW. 01604 880 009. www.northamptonshirebirdclub.org.uk
Meetings: 7.30pm, 1st Wednesday of the month. Village Hall, Pound Lane, Moulton, Northants.

Ringing Group
NORTHANTS RG. D M Francis, 2 Brittons Drive, Billing Lane, Northampton, NN3 5DP.

RSPB Local Groups
MID NENE. (1975; 350). Michael Ridout, Melrose, 140 Northampton Road, Rushden, Northants, NN10 6AN. 01933 355 544;
e-mail: michael_ridout@btinternet.com
Meetings: 7.30pm, 2nd or 3rd Thursday of the month (Sep-Apr), The Saxon Hall, Thorpe Street/ Brook Street, Raunds.

NORTHAMPTON. (1978; 3,000 in catchment area). Liz Wicks, 6 Waypost Court, Lings, Northampton, NN3 8LN. 01604 513 991;
e-mail: lizydrip@ntlworld.com
Meetings: 7.30pm, 2nd Thursday of the month, Northants County Council staff sports and social club (Wootton Hall Pavilion), Wootton Hall Park, Wootton NN4 0JA.

Wetland Bird Survey Organiser
Robert Ratcliffe, 173 Montague Road, Bilton, Rugby, Warks CV22 6LG. 01788 336 983.

Wildlife Trust
Director, See Cambridgeshire.

NORTHUMBERLAND

Bird Atlas/Avifauna
The Atlas of Breeding Birds in Northumbria edited by J C Day et al (Northumberland and Tyneside Bird Club, 1995) now out of print.

The Atlas of Wintering Birds in Northumbria (Northumberland and Tyneside Bird Club).

Bird Recorder
Tim Dean, 2 Knocklaw Park, Rothbury, Northumberland NE65 7PW. 01669 621 460; (M) 07766 263 167; e-mail: t.r.dean@btopenworld.com

Bird Reports
BIRDS IN NORTHUMBRIA (1970-), from Trevor Blake, 6 Glenside, Ellington, Morpeth, Northumberland NE61 5LS. 01670 862 635;
e-mail: trevor@skyestorm2.wanadoo.co.uk

BIRDS ON THE FARNE ISLANDS (1971-), from Secretary, Natural History Society of Northumbria, 0191 2326 386; e-mail: nhsn@ncl.ac.uk

BTO Regional Representative & Regional Development Officer
RR. Tom Cadwallender, 22 South View, Lesbury, Alnwick, Northumberland, NE66 3PZ. (H) 01665 830 884; (W) 01670 533 039;
e-mail: tomandmurielcadwallender@hotmail.com

RDO. Muriel Cadwallender, 22 South View, Lesbury, Alnwick, Northumberland, NE66 3PZ. 01665 830 884;
e-mail: tomandmurielcadwallender@hotmail.com

Clubs
NATURAL HISTORY SOCIETY OF NORTHUMBRIA. (1829; 850). David C Noble-Rollin, Hancock Museum, Barras Bridge, Newcastle upon Tyne, NE2 4PT. 0191 232 6386; e-mail: nhsn@ncl.ac.uk
www.nhsn.ncl.ac.uk
Meetings: 7.00pm, every Friday (Oct-Mar), Percy Building, Newcastle University.

NORTH NORTHUMBERLAND BIRD CLUB. (1984; 210). Richard Narraway, Workshop Cottage, The Friary, Bamburgh, NE69 7AE. 01668 214 759 www.northnorthumberland birdclub.co.uk.
Meetings: 7.30pm, 2nd Friday of the month (Sep-Jun), Bamburgh Pavilion (below castle).

NORTHUMBERLAND & TYNESIDE BIRD CLUB. (1958; 270). Alan Watson, Secretary, 3 Green Close, Whitley Bay, Northumberland NE25 9SH. 0191 252 2744; e-mail: apusx@blueyonder.co.uk
www.ntbc.org.uk

Ringing Groups
NATURAL HISTORY SOCIETY OF NORTHUMBRIA. Dr C P F Redfern, Westfield House, Acomb, Hexham, Northumberland, NE46 4RJ.

NORTHUMBRIA RG. Secretary. B Galloway, 34 West Meadows, Stamfordham Road, Westerhope, Newcastle upon Tyne, NE5 1LS. 0191 286 4850.

Wetland Bird Survey Organisers
NORTHUMBERLAND COAST. J Roper, 1 Long Row, Howick, Alnwick, Northumberland, NE66 3LQ.

NORTHUMBERLAND (Inland). Steve Holliday, 2 Larriston Place, Cramlington, Northumberland NE23 8ER. 01670 731 963;
e-mail: steveholliday@hotmail.co.uk

Wildlife Hospitals
BERWICK SWAN & WILDLIFE TRUST. The Honorary Secretary, North Road Industrial Estate, Berwick upon Tweed, TD15 1UN. 01289 302 882;
e-mail: swan-trust@hotmail.co.uk
www.swan-trust.org
Registered charity. All categories of wildlife. Pools for swans and other waterfowl. Veterinary support.

Wildlife Trust
NORTHUMBERLAND WILDLIFE TRUST. (1962; 13,000). The Garden House, St Nicholas Park, Jubilee Road, Gosforth, Newcastle upon Tyne, NE3 3XT. 0191 284 6884; (Fax) 0191 284 6794;
e-mail: mail@northwt.org.uk www.nwt.org.uk

NOTTINGHAMSHIRE

Bird Recorders
Andy Hall, e-mail: andy.h11@ntlworld.com

Bird Reports
LOUND BIRD REPORT (1990-), from Gary Hobson, 23 Milne Rd, Bircotes, Doncaster DN11 8AL. 01302 742 779.

NETHERFIELD WILDLIFE GROUP ANNUAL REPORT (1999-), from Mr N Matthews, 4 Shellburne Close, Heronridge, Nottingham NG5 9LL, £4.50 inc postage.

BIRDS OF NOTTINGHAMSHIRE (1943-). £4.50 inc postage, from Ms Jenny Swindells, 21 Chaworth Road, West Bridgford, Nottingham NG2 7AE. 0115 9812 432; e-mail: j.swindells@btinternet.com
www.nottsbirders.net

BTO Regional Representative
RR. Mrs Lynda Milner, 6 Kirton Park, Kirton, Newark, Notts, NG22 9LR. 01623 862 025;
e-mail: lyndamilner@hotmail.com

Clubs
ATTENBOROUGH BIRD CLUB. John Ellis, 67 Springfield Avenue, Sandiacre, Nottingham NG10 5NA. E-mail: jellis@trent.83.freeserve.co.uk

LOUND BIRD CLUB. (1991; 48). Gary Hobson, 23 Milne Rd, Bircotes, Doncaster DN11 8AL. 01302 742 779; www.loundbirdclub.piczo.com

NETHERFIELD WILDLIFE GROUP. (1999; 130). Philip Burnham, 57 Tilford Road, Newstead Village, Nottingham, NG15 0BU. 01623 401 980;
e-mail: philip.burnham1@ntlworld.com.

NOTTINGHAMSHIRE BIRDWATCHERS. (1935; 420). Ms Jenny Swindells, 21 Chaworth Road, West Bridgford, Nottingham NG2 7AE. 0115 9812 432;
e-mail: j.swindells@btinternet.com
www.nottsbirders.net
Meetings: Monthly talks in winter, please see website for details.

WOLLATON NATURAL HISTORY SOCIETY. (1976; 99). Mrs P Price, 33 Coatsby Road, Hollycroft, Kimberley, Nottingham, NG16 2TH. 0115 938 4965.
Meetings: 7.30pm, 3rd Wednesday of the month, St Leonards Church Hall, Wollaton Village.

Integrated Population Monitoring Group
TRESWELL WOOD INTEGRATED POPULATION MONITORING GROUP. Chris du Feu, 66 High Street, Beckingham, Notts, DN10 4PF.
e-mail: chris@chrisdufeu.force9.co.uk

Ringing Groups
BIRKLANDS RG. A D Lowe, 12 Midhurst Way, Clifton Estate, Nottingham NG11 8DY.
e-mail: alowe@mansfield.gov.uk

NORTH NOTTS RG. Adrian Blackburn, Willows End, 27 Palmer Road, Retford, Notts DN22 6SS. 01777 706 516; (M) 07718 766 873:
e-mail: blackburns@suleska.freeserve.co.uk

SOUTH NOTTINGHAMSHIRE RG. K J Hemsley, 8 Grange Farm Close, Toton, Beeston, Notts, NG9 6EB. e-mail: k.hemsley@ntlworld.com

RSPB Local Groups
MANSFIELD AND DISTRICT. (1986; 200). John Barlow, 240 Southwell Road West, Mansfield, Notts NG18 4LB. 01623 626 647.
Meetings: Night and venue changing from Nov 1st, check www.rspb.org.uk/groups/mansfield for further details.

NOTTINGHAM. (1974; 514). Andrew Griffin, Hawthorn Cottage, Thoroton, Notts, NG13 9DS. 01949 851 426;
e-mail: andrew@thoroton.f.sworld.co.uk
www.notts-rspb.org.uk
Meetings: 7.30pm, 1st Wednesday of the month, Nottingham Mechanics, North Sherwood Street, Nottingham.

Wetland Bird Survey Organiser
Gary Hobson, 23 Milne Rd, Bircotes, Doncaster DN11 8AL. 01302 742 779.

Wildlife Trust
NOTTINGHAMSHIRE WILDLIFE TRUST. (1963; 4,300). The Old Ragged School, Brook Street, Nottingham, NG1 1EA. 0115 958 8242; (Fax) 0115 924 3175; e-mail: info@nottswt.co.uk
www.wildlifetrust.org.uk/nottinghamshire

ENGLAND

OXFORDSHIRE

Bird Atlas/Avifauna
Birds of Oxfordshire by J W Brucker et al (Oxford, Pisces, 1992).

The New Birds of the Banbury Area by T G Easterbrook (Banbury Ornithological Society, 1995).

Bird Recorder
Ian Lewington, 119 Brasenose Road, Didcot, Oxon, OX11 7BP. 01235 819 792;
e-mail: ian@recorder.fsnet.co.uk

Bird Reports
BIRDS OF OXFORDSHIRE (1921-), from Roy Overall, 30 Hunsdon Road, Iffley, Oxford, OX4 4JE. 01865 775 632.

BANBURY ORNITHOLOGICAL SOCIETY ANNUAL REPORT (1952-). £5 each including postage, from MJ Lewis, Old Mill Cottage, Avon Dassett, Southam, Warwickshire, CV47 2AE. 01295 690 643;
e-mail: mikelewisad@hotmail.com.

BTO Regional Representatives & Regional Development Officer
NORTH. Frances Buckel, Witts End, Radbones Hill, Over Norton, Chipping Norton, Oxon OX7 5RA. 01608 644 425; e-mail: fmarks@btinternet.com or fran.buckel@binternet.com

SOUTH RR & RDO. Mr John Melling, 17 Lime Grove, Southmoor, Nr Abingdon, Oxon OX13 5DN;
e-mail: bto-rep@oos.org.uk

OXFORDSHIRE (South). Catherine Ross, Duck End Cottage, 40 Sutton Lane, Witney, Oxfordshire, OX29 5RU. (H) 01865 881 552;
e-mail: catherine@duckend6332.freeserve.co.uk

Clubs
BANBURY ORNITHOLOGICAL SOCIETY. (1952; 100). Frances Buckel, Witts End, Radbones Hill, Over Norton, Chipping Norton, Oxon OX7 5RA. 01608 644 425; e-mail: fmarks@btinternet.com or fran.buckel@binternet.com
www.banburyornithologicalsociety.org.uk
Meetings: 7.30pm, 2nd Monday of the month, Freemason's Hall, Marlborough Road, Banbury.

OXFORD ORNITHOLOGICAL SOCIETY. (1921; 330). Barry Hudson, Pinfold, 4 Bushy Row, Bampton, Oxon OX18 2JU. 01993 852 028;
e-mail: secretary@oos.org.uk
www.oos.org.uk
Meetings: Various dates, Stratford Brake, Kidlington.

Ringing Group
EDWARD GREY INSTITUTE. Dr A G Gosler, c/o Edward Grey Institute, Department of Zoology, South Parks Road, Oxford, OX1 3PS. 01865 271 158; e-mail: andrew.gosler@zoo.ox.ac.uk

RSPB Local Groups
OXFORD. (1977; 100). Ian Kilshaw, 6 Queens Court, Bicester, Oxon, OX26 6JX. 01869 601 901;
e-mail: ian.kilshaw@ntlworld.com
www.rspb-oxford.org.uk
Meetings: 7.45pm, normally 1st Thursday of the month, Sandhills Primary School, Terret Avenue, Headington, Oxford (opposite Thornhill park and ride).

VALE OF WHITE HORSE. (1977; 330). Nigel Franklin, 14 Upper Road, Kennington, Oxford OX1 5LJ. 01865 327 854;
e-mail: chairman@rspb-vwh.org.uk
www.rspb-vwh.org.uk
Meetings: 7.30pm, 3rd Monday of the month (Sep-May). Didcot Civic Hall.

Wildlife Trust
BBOWT. (1959; 24,000). The Lodge, 1 Armstrong Road, Littlemore, Oxford, OX4 4XT. 01865 775 476; (Fax) 01865 711 301; e-mail: info@bbowt.org.uk
www.bbowt.org.uk

SHROPSHIRE

Bird Atlas/Avifauna
Atlas of the Breeding Birds of Shropshire (Shropshire Ornithological Society, 1995).

Bird Recorder
Geoff Holmes, 22 Tenbury Drive, Telford Estate, Shrewsbury, SY2 5YF. 01743 364 621;
e-mail: geoff.holmes4@tiscali.co.uk

Bird Report
SHROPSHIRE BIRD REPORT (1956-) Annual, from Helen Griffiths (Hon Secretary), 104 Noel Hill Road, Cross Houses, Shrewsbury SY5 6LD. 01743 761 507;
e-mail: helen.griffiths@english-nature.org.uk
www.shropshirebirds.com

BTO Regional Representative
RR. Allan Dawes, Rosedale, Chapel Lane, Trefonen, Oswestry, Shrops, SY10 9DX. 01691 654 245;
e-mail: allandawes@btinternet.com

Club
SHROPSHIRE ORNITHOLOGICAL SOCIETY. (1955; 800). Helen Griffiths, 104 Noel Hill Road, Cross Houses, Shrewsbury, SY5 6LD. 01743 761 507;
e-mail: helen.griffiths@english-nature.org.uk
www.shropshirebirds.com
Meetings: 7.15pm, 1st Thursday of month (Oct-Apr), Shirehall, Shrewsbury.

RSPB Local Group
SHROPSHIRE. (1992; 320). Roger M Evans, 31 The Wheatlands, Bridgnorth, WV16 5BD. 01746 766 042; e-mail: mort.evans@virgin.net

Meetings: 3rd Thursday of the month (Sep-Apr), Council Chamber, Shirehall, Shrewsbury. Also field trip year round. 3rd Wednesday in the month (Oct-March) Secret Hills Centre Craven Arms.

SOUTH SHROPSHIRE. Alan Botting (Group Leader, 01547 540 176 or Christine Bateman (Secretary), 01584 878 362. www.rspbsouthshropshire.co.uk
Meetings: 7.30pm (Sep-Apr), Shropshire Hills Discovery Centre (Secret Hills), Craven Arms.

Wildlife Trust
SHROPSHIRE WILDLIFE TRUST. (1962; 10,000). 193 Abbey Foregate, Shrewsbury, Shropshire SY2 6AH. 01743 284 280; (Fax) 01743 284 281; e-mail: shropshirewt@cix.co.uk
www.shropshirewildlifetrust.org.uk

SOMERSET & BRISTOL

Bird Atlas/Avifauna
A History of the Birds of Somerset by DK Ballance. (Isabelline Books, 6 Bellevue, Enys, Penryn, Cornwall TR10 9LB. 2006).

The Birds of Exmoor and the Quantocks by DK Ballance and BD Gibbs. (Isabelline Books, 6 Bellevue, Enys, Penryn, Cornwall TR10 9LB. 2003).

Bird Recorders
Brian D Gibbs, 23 Lyngford Road, Taunton, Somerset, TA2 7EE. 01823 274 887;
e-mail: brian.gibbs@virgin.net
www.somersetbirds.uko2.co.uk

BATH, NE SOMERSET, BRISTOL, S GLOS. Harvey Rose, 12 Birbeck Road, Bristol, BS9 1BD. 0117 968 1638; e-mail: h.e.rose@bris.ac.uk

Bird Reports
AVON BIRD REPORT (1977-), from Harvey Rose, 12 Birbeck Road, Bristol, BS9 1BD. 0117 968 1638; e-mail: h.e.rose@bris.ac.uk

EXMOOR NATURALIST (1974-), from the Secretary, Exmoor Natural History Society.

SOMERSET BIRDS (1913-), from Mr Brian Hill, 7 Mill Cottages, Creech St Michael, Taunton, Somerset TA3 5PU. 01823 443 503.
www.somersetbirds.uko2.co.uk

BTO Regional Representatives,
AVON RR. Richard L Bland, 11 Percival Road, Bristol, BS8 3LN. 01179 734 828;
e-mail: richardbland@blueyonder.co.uk

AVON ASSISTANT RR. John Tully, 6 Falcondale Walk, Westbury-on-Trym, Bristol, BS9 3JG. 0117 950 0992; e-mail: johntully4@aol.com

SOMERSET RR. Eve Tigwell, Hawthorne Cottage, 3 Friggle Street, Frome, Somerset, BA11 5LP. 01373 451 630; e-mail: eve.tigwell@zen.co.uk

Clubs
BRISTOL NATURALISTS' SOCIETY (Ornithological Section). (1862; 550). Dr Mary Hill, 15 Montrose Avenue, Redland, Bristol, BS6 6EH. 0117 942 2193; e-mail: mary@jhill15.fsnet.co.uk
www.bristolnats.org.uk
Meetings: 7.30pm, monthly Wednesday or Friday (check for dates, Oct-Mar), Westmorland Hall, Westmorland Road, Bristol

BRISTOL ORNITHOLOGICAL CLUB. (1966; 670). Mrs Judy Copeland, 19 St George's Hill, Easton-in-Gordano, North Somerset, BS20 0PS. (Tel/Fax) 01275 373 554;
e-mail: judy.copeland@ukgateway.net
www.boc-bristol.org.uk
Meetings: 7.30pm, 3rd Thursday of the month, Newman Hall, Grange Court Road, Westbury-on-Trym.

CAM VALLEY WILDLIFE GROUP. (1994: 356). André Fournier, 1 Boomfield Lane, Paulton, Bristol BS39 7QU. 01761 418 153.
e-mail: andre.fournier@btinternet.com
www.camvalleywildlifegroup.org.uk

EXMOOR NATURAL HISTORY SOCIETY. (1974; 480). Miss Caroline Giddens, 12 King George Road, Minehead, Somerset, TA24 5JD. 01643 707 624;
e-mail: carol.enhs@virgin.net
www.enhs.org.uk
Meetings: 7.30pm, 1st Wednesday of the month (Oct-Mar), Methodist Church Hall, The Avenue, Minehead.

SOMERSET ORNITHOLOGICAL SOCIETY. (1923; 350). Mr Brian Hill, 7 Mill Cottages, Creech St Michael, Taunton, Somerset TA3 5PU. 01823 443 503. www.somersetbirds.uko2.co.uk
Meetings: 7.30pm, various Thursdays (Oct-Apr), Ruishton Village Hall, Taunton.

Ringing Groups
GORDANO VALLEY RG. Lyndon Roberts, 20 Glebe Road, Long Ashton, Bristol, BS41 9LH. 01275 392 722; e-mail: mail@lyndonroberts.com

RSPCA. S Powell, 1 Rosemill Cottage, Rosemill Lane, Ilminster, Somerset, TA19 5PR.

STEEP HOLM RS. A J Parsons, Barnfield, Tower Hill Road, Crewkerne, Somerset, TA18 8BJ. 01460 73640.

ENGLAND

RSPB Local Groups
BATH AND DISTRICT. (1989; 220). Alan Barrett, . 01225 310 905;
e-mail: alan_w_h_barrett@yahoo.co.uk
www.rspb.org.uk/groups/bath
Meetings: 7.30pm, 3rd Wednesday of the month (Sep-Mar), Bath Society Meeting Room, Green Park Station, Bath

CREWKERNE & DISTRICT. (1979; 355). Denise Chamings, Daniels Farm, Lower Stratton, South Petherton, Somerset, TA13 5LP. 01460 240 740;
e-mail: denise.chamings@virgin.net
rspb.org.uk/groups/crewkerne
Meetings: 7.30pm, 3rd Thursday of the month (Sep-Apr), The Day Centre, Crewkerne.

TAUNTON. (1975; 148). Frances Freeman, 01823 674 182; e-mail: francesfreeman@yahoo.com

WESTON-SUPER-MARE (N SOMERSET). (1976; 215). Don Hurrell, Freeways, Star, Winscombe, BS25 1PS. 01934 842 717;
e-mail: hurrell@cpsmail.co.uk
www.rspb.org.uk/groups/westonsupermare
Meetings: 7.30pm, 1st Thursday of the month (Sep-Apr), St Pauls Church Hall, Walscote Road.

Wetland Bird Survey Organisers
SEVERN ESTUARY (Southern Coast). Harvey Rose, 12 Birbek Road, Stoke Bishop, Bristol, BS9 1BD. 0117 968 1638; e-mail: h.e.rose@bris.ac.uk

SOMERSET LEVELS. Steve Meen, RSPB West Sedgemoor, Dewlands Farm, Redhill, Curry Rivel, Langport, Somerset TA10 0PH. 01458 252 805;
e-mail: steve.meen@rspb.org.uk

Wildlife Trusts
AVON WILDLIFE TRUST. (1980; 7,000). The Old Police Station , 32 Jacobs Wells Road, Bristol, BS8 1DR. 0117 917 7270; (Fax) 0117 929 7273;
e-mail: mail@avonwildlifetrust.org.uk
www.avonwildlifetrust.org.uk

SOMERSET WILDLIFE TRUST. (1964; 19,500). Tonedale Mill, Tonedale, Wellington, Somerset TA21 0AW. 01823 652 400; (Fax) 01823 652 411;
e-mail: enquiries@somersetwildlife.org
www.somersetwildlife.org

STAFFORDSHIRE

Bird Recorder
Nick Pomiankowski, 22 The Villas, West End, Stoke ST4 5AQ; 01782 849 682;
e-mail: staffs-recorder@westmidlandbirdclub.com

Bird Report See West Midlands

BTO Regional Representatives
NORTH EAST. Gilly Jones, 4 The Poplars, Lichfield Road, Abbots Bromley, Rugeley, Staffs WS15 3AA. 01283 840 555; e-mail: g.n.jones@wlv.ac.uk.

SOUTH & CENTRAL. Gilly Jones, 4 The Poplars, Lichfield Road, Abbots Bromley, Rugeley, Staffs WS15 3AA. 01283 840 555;
e-mail: g.n.jones@wlv.ac.uk

WEST. Gilly Jones, 4 The Poplars, Lichfield Road, Abbots Bromley, Rugeley, Staffs WS15 3AA. 01283 840 555; e-mail: g.n.jones@wlv.ac.uk

Clubs
SOUTH PEAK RAPTOR STUDY GROUP. (1998; 12). M E Taylor, 76 Hawksley Avenue, Newbold, Chesterfield, Derbys, S40 4TL. 01246 277 749.

WEST MIDLAND BIRD CLUB (STAFFORD BRANCH). Gerald Ford, 01630 673 409;
e-mail: gerald.ford@westmidlandbirdclub.com
www.westmidlandbirdclub.com/stafford
Meetings: 7.30pm, 2nd Friday of the month (Oct-Mar), The Centre for The Blind, North Walls, Stafford.

WEST MIDLAND BIRD CLUB (TAMWORTH BRANCH). (1992). Barbara Stubbs, 19 Alfred Street, Tamworth, Staffs, B79 7RL. 01827 57865;
e-mail: tamworth@westmidlandbirdclub
www.westmidlandbirdclub.com/tamworth
Meetings: 7.30pm, 3rd Friday of the month (Sep-Apr), Phil Dix Centre, Corporation Street, Tamworth.

RSPB Local Groups
BURTON-ON-TRENT AND SOUTH DERBYSHIRE. (1973; 50). Dave Lummis, 121 Wilmot Road, Swadlincote, Derbys, DE11 9BN. 01283 219 902.
www.basd-rspb.co.uk
Meetings: 7.30pm 1st Wednesday of the month, All Saint's Church, Bronston Road, Burton.

LICHFIELD & DISTRICT. (1977; 1150). Ray Jennett, 12 St Margarets Road, Lichfield, Staffs, WS13 7RA. 01543 255 195.
Meetings: 7.30pm, 2nd Tuesday of the month (Jan-May, Sept-Dec), St Mary's Centre.

NORTH STAFFS. (1982; 187). John Booth, 32 St Margaret Drive, Sneyd Green, Stoke-on-Trent, ST1 6EW. 01782 262 082;
www.rspb.org.uk/groups/northstaffordshire
Meetings: 7.30pm, normally 3rd Wednesday of the month, North Staffs Conference Centre (Medical Institute).

SOUTH WEST STAFFORDSHIRE. (1972; 204). Mrs Theresa Dorrance, 39 Wilkes Road, Codsall, Wolverhampton, WV8 1RZ. 01902 847 041;
e-mail: dorrancesteve@fsmail.net
Meetings: 8.00pm, 2nd Tuesday of the month, Codsall Village Hall.

Wetland Bird Survey Organisers
Gilly Jones, 4 The Poplars, Lichfield Road, Abbots Bromley, Rugeley, Staffs WS15 3AA. 01283 840 555; e-mail: g.n.jones@wlv.ac.uk

Wildlife Hospitals
BRITISH WILDLIFE RESCUE CENTRE. Alfred Hardy, Amerton Working Farm, Stowe-by-Chartley, Stafford, ST18 0LA. 01889 271 308.
On A518 Stafford/Uttoxeter road. All species, including imprints and permanently injured. Hospital, large aviaries and caging. Open to the public every day. Veterinary support.

GENTLESHAW BIRD OF PREY HOSPITAL. Jenny Smith, Gentleshaw Wildlife Centre, Stone Road, Eccleshall, Staffs ST21 6JY. 01785 850 379;
e-mail: gentleshaw1@btconnect.com
www.gentleshawwildlife.co.uk Registered charity. All birds of prey (inc. owls). Hospital cages and aviaries; release sites. Veterinary support.

Also Gentleshaw Bird of Prey and Wildlife Centre, Fletchers Country Garden Centre, Stone Road, Eccleshall, Stafford. 01785 850 379.

Wildlife Trust
STAFFORDSHIRE WILDLIFE TRUST. (1969; 14,000). The Wolseley Centre, Wolseley Bridge, Stafford, ST17 0WT. 01889 880 100; (Fax) 01889 880 101;
e-mail: info@staffs-wildlife.org.uk
www.staffs-wildlife.org.uk

SUFFOLK

Bird Atlas/Avifauna
Birds of Suffolk by S H Piotrowski (February 2003).

Bird Recorders
NORTH EAST. David Fairhurst,
e-mail: davidfairhurst@lycos.com

SOUTH EAST (inc. coastal region from Slaughden Quay southwards). Eddie Marsh,
e-mail: marshharrier@btinternet.com

WEST (whole of Suffolk W of Stowmarket, inc. Breckland). Colin Jakes, 7 Maltward Avenue, Bury St Edmunds, Suffolk IP33 3XN. 01284 702 215;
e-mail: colin.jakes@stedsbc.gov.uk

Bird Report
SUFFOLK BIRDS (inc Landguard Bird Observatory Report) (1950-), from Ipswich Museum, High Street, Ipswich, Suffolk.

BTO Regional Representative
Mick T Wright, 15 Avondale Road, Ipswich, IP3 9JT. 01473 710 032; e-mail: micktwright@btinternet.com

Clubs
LAVENHAM BIRD CLUB. (1972; 54). Mike Lewis, 6 Grammar School Place, Sudbury, Suffolk CO10 2GE. 01787 324 488.

SUFFOLK ORNITHOLOGISTS' GROUP. (1973; 650). Andrew M Gregory, 1 Holly Road, Ipswich, IP1 3QN. 01473 253 816.
Meetings: Last Thursday of the month (Jan-Mar, Oct-Nov), Holiday Inn, Ipswich.

Ringing Groups
DINGLE BIRD CLUB. Dr D Pearson, 4 Lupin Close, Reydon, Southwold, Suffolk, IP18 6NW. 01502 722 348.

LACKFORD RG. Dr Peter Lack, 11 Holden Road, Lackford, Bury St Edmunds, Suffolk, IP28 6HZ.
e-mail: peter.diane@tinyworld.co.uk

MARKET WESTON RG. Dr R H W Langston, Walnut Tree Farm, Thorpe Street, Hinderclay, Diss, Norfolk, IP22 1HT. e-mail: rlangston@wntfarm.demon.co.uk

RSPB Local Groups
BURY ST EDMUNDS. (1982; 150). Trevor Hart, 7 Westgart Gardens, Bury St Edmunds, Suffolk, IP33 3LB. 01284 705 165; e-mail: trevor.hart@glv.com
Meetings: 7.30pm, 3rd Tuesday of the month (Sep-May), County Upper School, Beetons Way, Bury St Edmunds.

IPSWICH. (1975; 260). Mr Chris Courtney, St Elmo, 19 Marlborough Road, Ipswich, Suffolk IP4 5HT. 01473 423 213; e-mail: yogachris@yahoo.co.uk
www.ipswichrspb.org.uk.
Meetings: 7.30pm, 2nd Thursday of the month (Sep-Apr), Sidegate Primary School, Sidegate Lane, Ipswich.

LOWESTOFT & DISTRICT. (1976; 130). Mrs E Beaumont, 52 Squires Walk, Lowestoft, Suffolk, NR32 4LA. 01502 560 126;
e-mail: groupleader@lowestoft-rspb-group.org.uk
www.lowestoft-rspb-group.org.uk
Meetings: Friday 7.15pm 1st Monday in the month, St Marks Church Hall, Oulton Broad.

WOODBRIDGE. (1987; 450). Malcolm Key, Riverside, Parham, Suffolk, IP13 9LZ. 01728 723 155; e-mail: malcolm.key@btopenworld.com
Meetings: 7.30pm, 1st Thursday of the month (Oct-May), Woodbridge Community Hall.

Wetland Bird Survey Organisers
ALDE COMPLEX. Rodney West, Flint Cottage, Stone Common, Blaxhall, Woodbridge, IP12 2DP. (Office) 01728 689 171; e-mail: rodwest@ndirect.co.uk

DEBEN ESTUARY. Nick Mason, Evening Hall, Hollesley, Nr Woodbridge, Ipswich, IP12 3QU. (H)01359 411 150; e-mail: nick.mason4@btinternet.com

STOUR ESTUARY. Rick Vonk, RSPB, Unit 13 Court Farm, 3 Stutton Road, Brantham, Suffolk CO11 1PW. (Daytime) 01473 328 006;
e-mail: rick.vonk@rspb.org.uk

SUFFOLK (other sites). Alan Miller, Suffolk Wildlife Trust, 9 Valley Terrace, Valley Road, Leiston, IP16 4AP. (Daytime) 01728 833 405;
e-mail: alan.miller@suffolkwildlifetrust.org

Wildlife Trust
SUFFOLK WILDLIFE TRUST. (1961; 25,000). Brooke House, The Green, Ashbocking, Ipswich, IP6 9JY. 01473 890 089; (Fax) 01473 890 165;
e-mail: info@suffolkwildlifetrust.org
www.suffolkwildlifetrust.org

SURREY

Bird Atlas/Avifauna
Birds of Surrey by Jeffery Wheatley (Surrey Bird Club 2007).

Bird Recorder
SURREY (includes Greater London south of the Thames and east to the Surrey Docks, excludes Spelthorne). Jeffery Wheatley, 9 Copse Edge, Elstead, Godalming, Surrey, GU8 6DJ. 01252 702 450; (Fax) 01252 703 650.

Bird Report
SURBITON AND DISTRICT BIRD WATCHING SOCIETY (1972-), from Thelma Caine, 21 More Lane, Esher, Surrey KT10 8AJ.

SURREY BIRD REPORT (1952-), from J Gates, 5 Hillside Road, Weybourne, Farnham, Surrey GU9 9DW. 01252 315 047.

BTO Regional Representative
RR Postion vacant.

Clubs
SURBITON & DISTRICT BIRDWATCHING SOCIETY. (1954; 165). Gary Caine, 21 More Lane, Esher, Surrey KT10 8AJ. 01372 468 432;
e-mail: hockley@sdbws.ndo.co.uk
www.sdbws.ndo.co.uk
Meetings: 7.30pm, 3rd Tuesday of the month, Surbiton Library Annex.

SURREY BIRD CLUB. (1957; 350). Charlotte Gray, 24 Nursery Hill, Shamley Green, Surrey GU5 0UN. 01483 894 144; e-mail: webmaster@surreybirdclub.org.uk
www.sbclub.ukonline.co.uk

Ringing Groups
HERSHAM RG. A J Beasley, 29 Selbourne Avenue, New Haw, Weybridge, Surrey, KT15 3RB.
e-mail: abeasley00@hotmail.com

RUNNYMEDE RG. D G Harris, 22 Blossom Waye, Hounslow, TW5 9HD.
e-mail: daveharris@tinyonline.co.uk

RSPB Local Groups
DORKING & DISTRICT. (1982; 310). John Burge, Broughton Norrels Drive, East Horsley, Leatherhead KT24 5DR. 01483 283 803;
e-mail: burge@j-sburge.fsnet.co.uk
Meetings: 8.00pm, Fridays, Christian Centre, next to St Martin's Church, Dorking.

EAST SURREY. (1984; 150-200). Brian Hobley, 26 Alexandra Road, Warlingham, Surrey, CR6 9DU. 01883 625 404; www.eastsurreyrspb.co.uk
Meetings: 8.00pm, 2nd Wednesday of the month (Sep-Jul), Whitehart Barn, Godstone.

EPSOM & EWELL. (1974; 168). Janet Gilbert, 78 Fair(Fax) Avenue, Ewell, Epsom, Surrey, KT17 2QQ. 0208 394 0405;
e-mail: janetegilbert@btinternet.com
www.wsnhs.co.uk
Meetings: 7.45pm, 2nd Friday of the month, All Saints Church Hall, Fulford Road, West Ewell.

GUILDFORD AND DISTRICT. (1974; 580). Roger Beck, 14 Overbrook, West Horsley, KT24 6BH. 01483 282 417;
e-mail: rogerbeck@beck40.fsnet.co.uk
www.rspb.org.uk/groups/guildford
Meetings: 2.15pm 2nd Tuesday and 7.45pm 4th Wednesday, Onslow Village Hall, Guildford.

NORTH WEST SURREY. (1973; 140). Ms Mary Braddock, 20 Meadway Drive, New Haw, Surrey, KT15 2DT. 01932 858 692;
e-mail: mary@braddock3.wanadoo.co.uk
www.nwsurreyrspb.org.uk
Meetings: 7.45pm, 4th Wednesday of the month (not Dec, Jul, Aug), Sir William Perkins School, Chertsey.

Wetland Bird Survey Organiser
SURREY (includes Greater London south of the Thames and east to the Surrey Docks, excludes Spellthorne). Jeffery Wheatley, 9 Copse Edge, Elstead, Godalming, Surrey, GU8 6DJ. 01252 702 450; e-mail: j.j.wheatley@btinternet.com

Wildlife Hospitals
THE SWAN SANCTUARY. See National Directory

WILDLIFE AID. Randalls Farm House, Randalls Road, Leatherhead, Surrey, KT22 0AL. 01372 377 332; 24-hr emergline 09061 800 132 (50p/min); (Fax) 01372 375 183;
e-mail: wildlife@pncl.co.uk www.wildlifeaid.com
Registered charity. Wildlife hospital and rehabilitation centre helping all native British species. Special housing for birds of prey. Membership scheme and fund raising activities. Veterinary support.

Wildlife Trust
SURREY WILDLIFE TRUST. (1959; 25,700). School Lane, Pirbright, Woking, Surrey, GU24 0JN. 01483 795 440; (Fax) 01483 486 505;
e-mail: info@surreywt.org.uk
www.surreywildlifetrust.org

SUSSEX

Bird Atlas/Avifauna
The Birds of Selsey Bill and the Selsey Peninsula (a checklist to year 2000), from Mr O Mitchell, 21 Trundle View Close, Barnham, Bognor Regis, PO22 0JZ.

Birds of Sussex ed by Paul James (Sussex Ornithological Society, 1996).

Fifty Years of Birdwatching, a celebration of the acheivements of the Shoreham District OS from 1953 onwards. from Shoreham District Ornithological Society, 7 Berberis Court, Shoreham by Sea, West Sussex BN43 6JA. £15 plus £2.50 p&p.

Bird Recorder
Mr CW Melgar, 36 Victoria Road, Worthing, W Sussex, BN11 1XB. 01903 200 064;
e-mail: cwmelgar@yahoo.com

Bird Reports
BIRDS OF RYE HARBOUR NR ANNUAL REPORT (1977- published every 5 years), from Dr Barry Yates, see Clubs.

PAGHAM HARBOUR LOCAL NATURE RESERVE ANNUAL REPORT, from the Warden, see Reserves,

SHOREHAM DISTRICT ORNITHOLOGICAL SOCIETY ANNUAL REPORT (1953-) - back issues available, from Mrs. Shena Maskell, SDOS Membership Administrator, 41 St. Lawrence Avenue, Worthing, West Sussex BN14 7JJ.
www.sdos.org

SUSSEX BIRD REPORT (1963-), from J E Trowell, Lorrimer, Main Road, Icklesham, Winchelsea, E Sussex, TN36 4BS. www.sos.org.uk
e-mail: membership@sos.org.uk

BTO Regional Representative
Dr A Barrie Watson, 83 Buckingham Road, Shoreham-by-Sea, W Sussex, BN43 5UD. 01273 452 472.

Clubs
FRIENDS OF RYE HARBOUR NATURE RESERVE. (1973; 1800). Dr Barry Yates, 2 Watch Cottages, Nook Beach, Winchelsea, E Sussex, TN36 4LU. 01797 223 862; e-mail: yates@clara.net
www.wildrye.info
Meetings: Monthly talks in winter, monthly walks all year.

HENFIELD BIRDWATCH. (1999; 110). Mike Russell, 31 Downsview, Small Dole, Henfield, West Sussex, BN5 9YB. 01273 494 311;
e-mail: mikerussell@sussexwt.org.uk

SHOREHAM DISTRICT ORNITHOLOGICAL SOCIETY. (1953; 120). Mrs. Shena Maskell, SDOS Membership Administrator, 41 St. Lawrence Avenue, Worthing, West Sussex BN14 7JJ.
www.sdos.org.
Meetings: 7.30pm, 1st Tuesday of the month (Oct-Apr), St Peter's Church Hall, Shoreham-by-Sea. (7 indoor meetings, 16 field outings)

SDOS

SUSSEX ORNITHOLOGICAL SOCIETY. (1962; 1542). Mr Richard Cowser, Beavers Brook, The Thatchway, Angmering, BN16 4HJ. 01903 770 259;
e-mail:secretary@sos.org.uk
www.sos.org.uk

Ringing Groups
BEACHY HEAD RS. R D M Edgar, 32 Hartfield Road, Seaford, E Sussex BN25 4PW.

CUCKMERE RG. Tim Parmenter, 18 Chapel Road, Plumpton Green, East Sussex BN7 3DD. 01273 891 881.

RYE BAY RG. P Jones, Elms Farm, Pett Lane, Icklesham, Winchelsea, E Sussex, TN36 4AH. 01797 226 374; e-mail: philjones@beamingbroadband.com

STEYNING RINGING GROUP. B R Clay, Meghana, Honeysuckle Lane, High Salvington, Worthing, West Sussex BN13 3BT. e-mail: brian.clay@ntlworld.com

RSPB Local Groups
BATTLE. (1973; 100). Miss Lynn Jenkins, 61 Austen Way, Guestling, Hastings, E Sussex, TN35 4JH. 01424 432 076;
e-mail: lynn.jenkins@battlerspb.org.uk
www.battlerspb.org.uk
Meetings: 7.30pm, 4th Tuesday of the month, Battle and Langton Primary School, Battle.

BRIGHTON & DISTRICT. (1974; 350). Marion Couldery, 81 Hove Park Road, Hove, East Sussex BN3 6LN. e-mail: marioncouldery@aol.com
www.rspb.org.uk/groups/brighton
Meetings: 7.30pm, 4th Thursday of the month, All Saints Church Hall, Eaton Road, Hove.

CHICHESTER & SW SUSSEX. (1979; 245). David Hart, Heys Bridle Rd, Slindon Common, Arundel BN18 0NA. 01243 814 497;
www.RSPB.org.uk/groups/chichester
Meetings: 7.30 pm 2nd Thursday of each month, Newell Centre, Newell Centre, Tozer Way, St Pancras, Chichester.

CRAWLEY & HORSHAM. (1978; 148). Andrea Saxton, 104 Heath Way, Horsham, W Sussex, RH12 5XS. 01403 242 218.
Meetings: 8.00pm, 3rd Wednesday of the month (Sept-Apr), The Friary Hall, Crawley.

EAST GRINSTEAD. (1998; 185). Nick Walker, 14 York Avenue, East Grinstead, W Sussex, RH19 4TL. 01342 315 825.
Meetings: 8.00pm, last Wednesday of the month, Large Parish Hall, De La Warr Road, East Grinstead.

EASTBOURNE & DISTRICT. (1993; 520). Ian Muldoon, 01273 476 852;
e-mail: ian1muldoon@yahoo.co.uk
Meetings: 2.15 pm and 7.30 pm ,1st Wednesday of the month (Sep-Jun), St. Wilfreds Church Hall, Eastbourne Road, Pevensey Bay.

HASTINGS & ST LEONARDS. (1983; 110). Eric Stokes, 59 Parkstone Road, Hastings, E Sussex TN34 2NT. 01424 426 029.
Meetings: 7.30pm, 3rd Friday of the month, Taplin Centre, Upper Maze Hill.

Wildlife Hospital
BRENT LODGE BIRD & WILDLIFE TRUST. Penny Cooper, Brent Lodge, Cow Lane, Sidlesham, Chichester, West Sussex, PO20 7LN. 01243 641 672 (emergency number); www.brentlodge.org.
All species of wild birds and small mammals. Full surgical and medical facilities (inc. X-ray). Purpose-built oiled bird washing unit. Veterinary support.

Wildlife Trust
SUSSEX WILDLIFE TRUST. (1961; 24,000). Woods Mill, Shoreham Road, Henfield, W Sussex, BN5 9SD. 01273 492 630; (Fax) 01273 494 500;
e-mail: enquiries@sussexwt.org.uk
www.sussexwt.org.uk

TYNE & WEAR

Bird Recorders
See Durham; Northumberland.

Bird Report See Durham; Northumberland.

Clubs
NATURAL HISTORY SOCIETY OF NORTHUMBRIA. (1829; 900). David C Noble-Rollin, Hancock Museum, Barras Bridge, Newcastle upon Tyne, NE2 4PT. 0191 232 6386; e-mail: nhsn@ncl.ac.uk
Meetings: 7.00pm, every Friday (Oct-Mar), Percy Building, Newcastle University.

NORTHUMBERLAND & TYNESIDE BIRD CLUB. (1958; 270). Alan Watson, Secretary, 3 Green Close, Whitley Bay, Northumberland NE25 9SH. 0191 252 2744; e-mail: alan@watson53.freeserve.co.uk
www.ntbc.org.uk.

RSPB Local Groups
NEWCASTLE UPON TYNE. (1969; 250). Brian Moorhead, 07903 387 429;
e-mail: ncastlerspbgroup@btinternet.com
www.rspb.org.uk/groups/newcastle
Meetings: 7pm, (Mar, Jun, Sep, Nov), Northumbria University, Ellison Place, Newcastle upon Tyne.

WARWICKSHIRE

Bird Recorder
Jonathan Bowley, 17 Meadow Way, Fenny Compton, Southam, Warks, CV47 2WD. 01295 770 069;
e-mail: warwks-recorder@westmidlandbirdclub.com

Bird Report
See West Midlands.

BTO Regional Representatives
WARWICKSHIRE. Mark Smith, 01926 735 398;
e-mail: mark.smith36@ntlworld.com

RUGBY. Position vacant.

Clubs
NUNEATON & DISTRICT BIRDWATCHERS' CLUB. (1950; 78). Alvin K Burton, 23 Redruth Close, Horeston Grange, Nuneaton, Warwicks, CV11 6FG. 024 7664 1591.
Meetings: 7.30pm, 3rd Thursday of the month (Sep-Jun), Hatters Space Community Centre, Upper Abbey Street, Nuneaton.

Ringing Groups
ARDEN RG. Roger J Juckes, 24 Croft Lane, Temple Grafton, Alcester, Warks B49 6PA. 01789 778748.

BRANDON RG. David Stone, Overbury, Wolverton, Stratford-on-Avon, Warks, CV37 0HG. 01789 731 488.

RSPB Local Group
See West Midlands.

Wildlife Trust
WARWICKSHIRE WILDLIFE TRUST. (1970; 13,000). Brandon Marsh Nature Centre, Brandon Lane, Coventry, CV3 3GW. 024 7630 2912; (Fax) 024 7663 9556; e-mail: enquiries@wkwt.org.uk
www.warwickshire-wildlife-trust.org.uk

WEST MIDLANDS

Bird Atlas/Avifauna
The Birds of the West Midlands edited by Graham Harrison et al (West Midland Bird Club, 1982). Rev ed due 2000/2001.

Bird Recorder
Kevin Clements, 26 Hambrook Close, Dunstall Park, Wolverhampton, West Midlands WV6 0XA. e-mail: west-mids-recorder@westmidlandbirdclub.com

Bird Reports
THE BIRDS OF SMESTOW VALLEY AND DUNSTALL PARK (1988-), from the Secretary, Smestow Valley Bird Group.

THE BIRDS OF STAFFORDSHIRE, WARWICKSHIRE, WORCESTERSIRE AND THE WEST MIDLANDS (1934-), from Mr J Reeves, 9 Hintons Coppice, Knowle, Solihull, B93 9RF.

BTO Regional Representative
BIRMINGHAM & WEST MIDLANDS. Steve Davies. 07882 891 726;
e-mail:stevendavies907@btinternet.com

Clubs
SMESTOW VALLEY BIRD GROUP. (1988; 56). Frank Dickson, 11 Bow Street, Bilston, Wolverhampton, WV14 7NB. 01902 493 733.

WEST MIDLAND BIRD CLUB. (1929; 2000). Barbara Oakley, Hon Secretary, 147 Worlds End, Quinton, Birmingham B32 1JX. e-mail: secretary@westmidlandbirdclub.com
www.westmidlandbirdclub.com
Meetings: Check website for details of the different branches and their events.

WEST MIDLAND BIRD CLUB (BIRMINGHAM BRANCH). (1995; 800). Martin Kenrick, e-mail: birmingham@westmidlandbirdclub.com/birmingham www.westmidlandbirdclub.com/birmingham
Meetings: 7.30pm, usually last Tuesday (Oct-Apr), Birmingham Medical Institute, in Harborne Road, Edgbaston, near Five Ways.

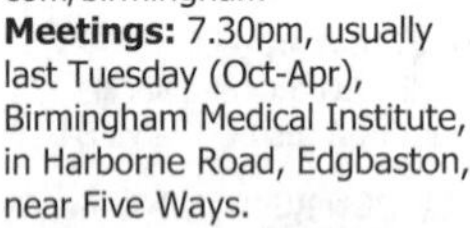

WEST MIDLAND BIRD CLUB (SOLIHULL BRANCH). Raymond Brown, The Spinney, 63 Grange Road, Dorridge, Solihull B93 8QS. 01564 772 550;
e-mail: solihull@westmidlandbirdclub
www.westmidlandbirdclub.com/solihull
Meetings: 7.30 pm, Fridays, Solihull College's, New Lecture Rooms, Blossomfield Road, Solihull.

Ringing Groups
MERCIAN RG (Sutton Coldfield). R L Castle, 91 Maney Hill Road, Sutton Coldfield, West Midlands, B72 1JT. 0121 686 7568.

RSPB Local Groups
BIRMINGHAM. (1975; 100). John Bailey, 52 Gresham Road, Hall Green, Birmingham, B28 0HY. 0121 777 4389; e-mail: jvbailey@btinternet.com
www.rspb-birmingham.org.uk
Meetings: 7.30pm, 3rd Thursday of the month (Sep-Jun), Salvation Army Citadel, St Chads, Queensway, Birmingham.

COVENTRY & WARWICKSHIRE. (1969; 130). Alan King, 69 Westmorland Road, Coventry, CV2 5BP. 024 7672 7348;
e-mail: alan.king.wyken@ntlworld.com.

SOLIHULL. (1983; 2,600 in catchment area). John Roberts, 115 Dovehouse Lane, Solihull, West Midlands, B91 2EQ. 0121 707 3101.
Meetings: 7.30pm, usually 2nd Tuesday of the month (Sep-Apr), Oliver Bird Hall, Church Hill Road, Solihull.

STOURBRIDGE. (1978; 150). Paul Banks, 4 Sandpiper Close, Wollescote, Stourbridge, DY9 8TD. 01384 898 948; e-mail: picapica@tinyworld.co.uk
www.rspb.org.uk/groups/stourbridge
Meetings: 2nd Wednesday of the month (Sep-May).

SUTTON COLDFIELD. (1986; 250). Martin Fisher, 0121 308 4400; e-mail: martinjfisher@care4free.net
Meetings: 7.30pm, 1st Monday of the month, Bishop Vesey's Grammer School.

WALSALL. (1970). Mike Pittaway, 2 Kedleston Close, Bloxwich, Walsall WS3 3TW. 01922 710 568;
e-mail: chair@rspb-walsall.org.uk
www.rspb-walsall.org.uk
Meetings: 7.30pm, 3rd Wednesday of the month, St Marys School, Jesson Road, Walsall.

WOLVERHAMPTON. (1974; 110). RSPB Midlands Regional Office, 46 South Bar, Banbury, Oxon OX16 9AB. 01295 253 330.
Meetings: 7.30pm, 2nd Wednesday of the month (Sept-Apr), The Newman Centre, Haywood Drive, Tettenhall, Wolverhampton.

Wildlife Hospitals
KIDD, D J. 20 Parry Road, Ashmore Park, Wednesfield, Wolverhampton, WV11 2PS. 01902 863 971.
All birds of prey, esp. owls. Aviaries, isolation pens. Veterinary support.

Wildlife Trust
THE WILDLIFE TRUST FOR BIRMINGHAM AND BLACK COUNTRY. (1980; 2,000). 28 Harborne Road, Edgbaston, Birmingham, B15 3AA. 0121 454 1199; (Fax) 0121 454 6556;
e-mail: info@bbcwildlife.org.uk

WILTSHIRE

Bird Atlas/Avifauna
Birds of Wiltshire by James Ferguson-Lees 2007

Bird Recorder
Rob Turner, 14 Ethendun, Bratton, Westbury, Wilts, BA13 4RX. 01380 830 862;
e-mail: robt14@btopenworld.com

Bird Report
Published in Hobby (journal of the Wiltshire OS) *(1975-)*, from John Osborne, 4 Fairdown Avenue, Westbury, Wiltshire BA13 3HS. 01373 864 598

BTO Regional Representatives
NORTH. Bill Quantrill, 01225 866 245;
e-mail: wquantrill@billg.fsnet.co.uk

SOUTH. Bill Quantrill, 01225 866 245;
e-mail: wquantrill@billg.fsnet.co.uk

Clubs
SALISBURY & DISTRICT NATURAL HISTORY SOCIETY. (1952; 151). J Pitman, 10 The Hardings, Devizes Road, Salisbury, SP2 9LZ. 01722 327 395.
Meetings: 7.30pm, 3rd Thursday of the month (Sept-Apr), Lecture Hall, Salisbury Museum, King House, The Close, Salisbury.

WILTSHIRE ORNITHOLOGICAL SOCIETY. (1974; 450). Phil Deacon, 12 Rawston Close, Nythe, Swindon, Wilts SN3 3PW. 01793 528 930;
e-mail: phil.deacon@ntlworld.com
www.wiltshirebirds.co.uk
Meetings: See website for details.

WILTSHIRE ORNITHOLOGICAL SOCIETY

Ringing Group
COTSWOLD WATER PARK RG. John Wells, 25 Pipers Grove, Highnam, Glos, GL2 8NJ.
e-mail: john.wells2@btinternet.com

WEST WILTSHIRE RG. Mr M.J. Hamzij, 13 Halfway Close, Trowbridge, Wilts, BA14 7HQ.
e-mail: m.hamzij@btinternet.com

RSPB Local Groups
NORTH WILTSHIRE. (1973; 115). Derek Lyford, 9 Devon Road, Swindon, SN2 1PQ. 01793 520 997;
e-mail: derek.lyford@virgin.net
www.rspb.org.uk/groups/northwiltshire
Meetings: 7.30pm, 1st Tuesday of the month (Sep-Jun), Even Swindon Community Centre, Jennings St, Swindon (SU 137 849).

SOUTH WILTSHIRE. (1986; 800). Tony Goddard, Clovelly, Lower Road, Charlton All Saints, Salisbury, SP5 4HQ. 01725 510 309.
Meetings: 7.30pm, Tuesday evenings (monthly), Salisbury Arts Centre, Salisbury.

Wildlife Hospital
VALE WILDLIFE RESCUE - WILDLIFE HOSPITAL + REHABILITATION CENTRE. Any staff member, Station Road, Beckford, Tewkesbury, Glos, GL20 7AN. 01386 882 288; (Fax) 01386 882 299;
e-mail: info@vwr.org.uk www.vwr.org.uk
All wild birds. Intensive care. Registered charity. Veterinary support.

Wetland Bird Survey Organiser
COTSWOLD WATER PARK. Gareth Harris, Keynes Country Park, Spratsgate Lane, Shorncote, Glos GL7 6DF. 01285 861 459;
e-mail: gareth.harris@waterpark.org

Wildlife Trust
WILTSHIRE WILDLIFE TRUST. (1962; 18,000). Elm Tree Court, Long Street, Devizes, Wilts, SN10 1NJ. 01380 725 670; (Fax) 01380 729 017;
e-mail: info@wiltshirewildlife.org
www.wiltshirewildlife.org

WORCESTERSHIRE

Bird Recorder
Andy Warr, 14 Bromsgrove Street, Worcester WR3 8AR. 01905 28281; e-mail:
worcs-recorder@westmidlandbirdclub.com

Bird Report See West Midlands.

BTO Regional Representative
G Harry Green MBE, Windy Ridge, Pershore Road, Little Comberton, Pershore, Worcs, WR10 3EW. 01386 710 377;
e-mail: harrygreen_worcs@yahoo.co.uk

Ringing Group
WYCHAVON RG. J R Hodson, 15 High Green, Severn Stoke, Worcester, WR8 9JS. (day) 01905 754 919, (eve) 01905 371 333;
e-mail: john.hodson@tesco.net

Club
WEST MIDLAND BIRD CLUB (KIDDERMINSTER BRANCH). Celia Barton, 28A Albert Street, Wall Heath, Kingswinford DY6 0NA. 01384 839 838;
e-mail: kidderminster@westmidlandbirdclub.com
Meetings: 7.30pm, 4th Wednesday of the month (Sep-Apr), St Oswalds Church Centre, Broadwaters, Kidderminster.

RSPB Local Group
WORCESTER & MALVERN. (1980; 300). Garth Lowe, Sunnymead, Old Storridge, Alfrick, Worcester, WR6 5HT. 01886 833 362.
Meetings: 7.30pm, 2nd Wednesday in month (Sept-May), Powick Village Hall.

Wildlife Trust
WORCESTERSHIRE WILDLIFE TRUST. (1968; 9,000). Lower Smite Farm, Smite Hill, Hindlip, Worcester, WR3 8SZ. 01905 754 919; (Fax) 01905 755 868; e-mail:
enquiries@worcestershirewildlifetrust.co.uk
www.worcswildlifetrust.co.uk
Charity no. 256618.

ENGLAND

YORKSHIRE

Bird Atlas/Avifauna

*An Atlas of the Breeding Birds of the Huddersfield Area, 1987-1992.*by Brian Armitage et al (2000) - very few copies left.

Atlas of Breeding Birds in the Leeds Area 1987-1991 by Richard Fuller et al (Leeds Birdwatchers' Club, 1994).

Birds of Barnsley by Nick Addey (Pub by author, 114 Everill Gate Lane, Broomhill, Barnsley S73 0YJ, 1998).

Birds of The Lower Derwent Valley by CS Ralston. English Nature (E and N Yorks) 2005.

The Birds of Halifax by Nick Dawtrey (only 20 left), 14 Moorend Gardens, Pellon, Halifax, W Yorks, HX2 0SD.

The Birds of Wintersett by S Denny. Wintersett Wildlife Group 2003, available from the author.

The Birds of Yorkshire by John Mather (Croom Helm, 1986).

Bird Recorders

VC61 (East Yorkshire) AND EDITOR. Geoff Dobbs, Silver Birches, 52 Common Lane, Welton, East Yorkshire HU15 1PT. 01482 666 092; e-mail: geoffdobbs@aol.com

VC62 (North Yorkshire East). Craig Thomas, 16 Scarborough Road, Filey, North Yorkshire YO14 9EF. 01723 513 055; e-mail: craigthomas@yahoo.co.uk

VC63 (South & West Yorkshire). Covering the following groups - Barnsley Bird Study, Blacktoft Sands RSPB, Doncaster and District OS, Rotherham and District OS, Sheffield Bird Study and SK58 Birders. John Wint, 9 Yew Tree Park, Whitley, Goole, DN14 0NZ. 01977 662 826; e-mail: john.wint@tiscali.co.uk

VC64 (West Yorkshire)/HARROGATE & CRAVEN. Jim Pewtress, 31 Piercy End, Kirbymoorside, York, YO62 6DQ. 01751 431 001; e-mail: trivialis@operamail.com

VC65 (North Yorkshire West). Steve Worwood, 18 Coltsgate Hill, Ripon HG4 2AB. 01765 602 518; e-mail: steve@worwood.entadsl.com

Bird Reports

BARNSLEY AREA BIRD REPORT (1971-), from the Secretary.

BRADFORD NATURALISTS' SOCIETY ANNUAL REPORT, from Mr I Hogg, 23 St Matthews Road, Bankfoot, Bradford, BD5 9AB. 01274 727902.

BRADFORD ORNITHOLOGICAL GROUP REPORT (1987-), from Jenny Barker, 3 Chapel Fold, Slack Lane, Oakworth, Keighley, BD22 0RQ.

DONCASTER BIRD REPORT (1955-), from Mr M Roberts, 8 Sandbeck court, Rossington, Doncaster, DN11 0FN. 01302 326 265.

FILEY BIRD REPORT (1976-), from Mr C Court, 12 Pinewood Avenue, Filey, YO14 9NS.

FIVE TOWNS BIRD REPORT (1995-), from Secretary, Five Towns Bird Group.

HALIFAX BIRDWATCHERS' CLUB ANNUAL REPORT (1991-), from Nick C Dawtrey, 14 Moorend Gardens, Pellon, Halifax, W Yorks, HX2 0SD. 01422 364 228.

HARROGATE & DISTRICT NATURALISTS' ORNITHOLOGY REPORT (1996-), from the Secretary.

HULL VALLEY WILDLIFE GROUP REPORT (2000-) incorporating Tophill Low recording area). from Geoff Dobbs, 12 Park Avenue, Hull, HU5 3ER. 01482 341 524; e-mail: geoffdobbs@aol.com

BIRDS IN HUDDERSFIELD (1966-), from Mr Brian Armitage, 106 Forest Road, Dalton, Huddersfield HD5 8ET.01484 305 054; e-mail: brian.armitage@ntlworld.com

LEEDS BIRDWATCHERS' CLUB ANNUAL REPORT (1949-), from the Secretary.

BIRDS OF ROTHERHAM (1975-), from the Secretary, Rotherham Orn Soc, www.rotherhambirds.co.uk (check website for current publication details).

BIRDS IN THE SHEFFIELD AREA (1973-), from Tony Morris, 4A Raven Road, Sheffield, S7 1SB. e-mail: ajmo@blueyonder.co.uk
www.sbsg.org

THE BIRDS OF SK58 (1993-), from Secretary, SK58 Birders. E-mail: sk58birders@sk58.freeserve.co.uk
www.sk58.freeserve.co.uk

SPURN BIRD WILDLIFE REPORT, from the Warden, see Reserves.

WINTERSETT AREA ANNUAL REPORT (1988-), from Steve Denny, 13 Rutland Drive, Crofton, Wakefield, WF4 1SA. 01924 864 487.

YORK ORNITHOLOGICAL CLUB ANNUAL REPORT (1970-), from Peter Watson, 1 Oak Villa, Hodgson Lane, Upper Poppleton, York YO26 6EA. 01904 795 063; e-mail: peterewwatson@aol.com.

YORKSHIRE NATURALISTS' UNION: BIRD REPORT (1940-), from John A Newbould, Stonecroft, 3 Brookmead Close, Sutton Poyntz, Wemouth, Dorset, DT3 6RS.

ENGLAND

BTO Regional Representatives & Regional Development Officers
NORTH-EAST RR. Michael Carroll, 01751 476 550.

NORTH-WEST RR. Gerald Light, 01756 753 720; e-mail: gerald@uwlig.plus.com.

SOUTH-EAST AND SOUTH-WEST RR. Position vacant.

EAST RR. Position vacant.

BRADFORD RR & RDO. Mike L Denton, 77 Hawthorne Terrace, Crosland Moor, Huddersfield, HD4 5RP. 01484 646 990.

YORKSHIRE (HARROGATE) RR. Mike Brown, 48 Pannal Ash Drive, Harrogate, N Yorks, HG2 0HU. 01423 567 382;
e-mail: mike@thebrownsathome.plus.com

LEEDS & WAKEFIELD RR. Position vacant.,

RICHMOND RR. John Edwards, 7 Church Garth, Great Smeaton, Northallerton, N Yorks, DL6 2HW. (H) 01609 881 476; (W) 01609 780 780 extn 2452; e-mail: john@jhedwards.plus.com

YORK RR. Rob Chapman, 12 Moorland Road, York, YO10 4HF. 01904 633 558;
e-mail: robert.chapman@tinyworld.co.uk

Clubs
BARNSLEY BIRD STUDY GROUP. (1970; 35). Christine Carr, 300 Higham Common Road, Higham, Barnsley, South Yorkshire S75 1PS. 01226 384 694; e-mail: geoffcarr300@fsmail.net
Meetings: 7.15pm, 1st Thursday in the month (Nov-Mar), RSPB Old Moor, Barnsley.

BRADFORD NATURALISTS' SOCIETY. (1875; 30). D R Grant, 19 The Wheatings, Ossett, W Yorks, WF5 0QQ. 01924 273 628.
Meetings: 7.30pm, Mondays, Richmond Building, University of Bradford.

BRADFORD ORNITHOLOGICAL GROUP. (1987; 180). Shaun Radcliffe, 8 Longwood Avenue, Bingley, W Yorks, BD16 2RX. 01274 770 960;
www.bradfordbirding.org
Meetings: 1st Tuesday of the month - see website for details.

CASTLEFORD & DISTRICT NATURALISTS' SOCIETY. (1956; 20). Michael J Warrington, 31 Mount Avenue, Hemsworth, Pontefract, W Yorks, WF9 4QE. 01977 614 954; e-mail: michael@warrington31mount.freeserve.co.uk.
Meetings: 7.30pm, Tuesdays monthly (Sep-Mar), Whitwood College, Castleford (check with above for dates).

DONCASTER & DISTRICT ORNITHOLOGICAL SOCIETY. (1955; 40). Dave Ward, Membership Secretary, 11 Newstead Road, Scawthorpe, Doncaster DN5 9JS.
www.birdingdoncaster.org.uk
Meetings: 7.15pm, last Thursday of the month (Jan-May and Sep-Nov), Parklands Sports and social club.

FILEY BRIGG ORNITHOLOGICAL GROUP. (1977; 100). Dr Sue Hull, 32 West Road, Filey, N Yorkshire, YO14 9LP. 01723 515 042;
e-mail:secretary-at-fbog.co.uk
www.fbog.co.uk

F.B.O.G. FILEY BRIGG ORNITHOLOGICAL GROUP BIRD OBSERVATORY

HALIFAX BIRDWATCHERS' CLUB. (1992). Nick C Dawtrey, 14 Moorend Gardens, Pellon, Halifax, W Yorks, HX2 0SD. 01422 364 228.

HARROGATE & DISTRICT NATURALISTS' SOCIETY. (1947; 350). Mike Brown, 48 Pannal Ash Drive, Harrogate, N Yorks, HG2 0HU. 01423 567 382;
e-mail: mike@thebrownsathome.plus.com
Meetings: 7.45pm, Wednesday fornightly from 10/10/05, St Robert's Centre, Harrogate.

HORNSEA BIRD CLUB. (1967; 42). John Eldret, 44 Rolston Road, Hornsea, HU18 1UH. 01964 532 854.
Meetings: 7.30pm, 3rd Friday of the month (Sep-Mar), Hornsea Library.

HUDDERSFIELD BIRDWATCHERS' CLUB. (1966; 80). Chris Abell, 57 Butterley Lane, New Mill, Holmfirth, HD9 7EZ. 01484 681 499;
e-mail: cdabell@gmail.com
www.huddersfieldbirdwatchersclub.org.uk
Meetings: 7.30pm, Tuesday's fortnightly (Sep-May), Children's Library (section), Huddersfield Library and Art Gallery, Princess Alexandra Walk, Huddersfield.

HULL VALLEY WILDLIFE GROUP. (1997; 175). The Secretary. www.hullvalleywildlifegroup.org.uk

LEEDS BIRDWATCHERS' CLUB. (1949; 60). Peter Murphy, 12 West End lane, Horsforth, Leeds LS18 5JP. 0113 293 0188;
e-mail: pandbmurphy@ntlworld.com
Meetings: 7.15pm Monday fortnightly, Quaker Meeting House, Woodhouse Lane, Leeds.

PUDSEY ORNITHOLOGY CLUB. (1989; 26). Alan Patchett, 102 Half Mile Lane, Leeds, LS13 1DB. 0113 229 9038.
Meetings: Contact for details.

ROTHERHAM & DISTRICT ORNITHOLOGICAL SOCIETY. (1974; 80). Malcolm Taylor, 18 Maple Place, Chapeltown, Sheffield, S35 1QW. 0114 246 1848. www.rotherhambirds.co.uk
Meetings: 7.30pm, 2nd Friday of the month, United Reform Church Hall, Herringthorpe.

SCARBOROUGH BIRDERS. (1993; 15). R.N.Hopper (Membership Secretary), 10A Ramshill Road, Scarborough, N Yorkshire, YO11 2QE. 01723 369 537. www.scarborough-birding.org.uk

SHEFFIELD BIRD STUDY GROUP. (1972; 160). Richard Dale, 109 Main Road, Wharncliffe Side, Sheffield S35 0DP. 0114 286 2513;
e-mail: richarddale9@hotmail.com
www.sbsg.org
Meetings: 7.15pm, 2nd Wednesday of the month (Sep-Jun), Lecture Theatre 5, Sheffield University Arts Tower.

SK58 BIRDERS. (1993; 66). Andy Hirst, 15 Hunters Drive, Dinnington, Sheffield, S25 2TG. 07947 068 125; e-mail: sk58birders@sk58.freeserve.co.uk
www.sk58.freeserve.co.uk
Chair: Mick Clay, 2 High St, S.Anston, Sheffield. 01909 566 000.
Meetings: 7.30pm, last Wednesday of the month (except Aug), Upstairs Room, Loyal Trooper pub, South Anston.

SORBY NHS (ORNITHOLOGICAL SECTION). (1918; 400). Dr Jim Monach, 100 Bole Hill Lane, Sheffield S10 1SD. e-mail: ornithology@sorby.org.uk
www.sorby.org.uk

SWILLINGTON INGS BIRD GROUP. (1989; 83). Nick Smith, 40 Holmsley Lane, Woodlesford, Leeds, LS26 8RN. 0113 282 6154;
e-mail: jnicoll.smith@talktalk.net.
Meetings: 7.30pm, 1st Thursday of even months, Two Pointers Inn, Woodlesford, Leeds.

WAKEFIELD NATURALISTS' SOCIETY. (1851; 40). Philip Harrison, 392 Dewsbury Road, Wakefield, W Yorks, WF2 9DS. 01924 373 604.
Meetings: 7.30pm, 2nd Tuesday of the month (Sep-Apr), Friends Meeting House, Thornhill Street, Wakefield.

YORK ORNITHOLOGICAL CLUB. (1967; 80). Peter Watson, 1 Oak Villa, Hodgson Lane, Upper Poppleton, York, YO26 6EA. 01904 795 063;
e-mail: secretary@
yorkbirding.org.uk
www.yorkbirding.org.uk
Meetings: 7.30pm, 1st Tuesday of the month, Friends' Meeting House, Friargate, York (see website).

YORKSHIRE NATURALISTS' UNION (Ornithological Section). (1875; 500). Jim Pewtress, 31 Piercy End, Kirby Moorside, York, YO62 6DQ;
e-mail: trivialis@operamail.com

Ringing Groups

BARNSLEY RG. M C Wells, 715 Manchester Road, Stocksbridge, Sheffield, S36 1DQ. 0114 288 4211;
e-mail: barnsleybsg-plus.com

DONCASTER RG. D Hazard, 41 Jossey Lane, Scawthorpe, Doncaster, S Yorks, DN5 9DB. 01302 788 044; e-mail: davehazard@btopenworld.com

EAST DALES RG. Mr P. Bone, 11 Dorrington Close, Pocklington, York YO42 2GS.
E-mail: p.bone@csl.gov.uk

EAST YORKS RG. Peter J Dunn, 43 West Garth Gardens, Cayton, Scarborough, N Yorks, YO11 3SF. 01723 583149; e-mail: pjd@fbog.co.uk

SORBY-BRECK RG. Geoff P Mawson, Moonpenny Farm, Farwater Lane, Dronfield, Sheffield, S18 1RA.
e-mail: moonpenny@talktalk.net

SPURN BIRD OBSERVATORY. I D Walker, 31 Walton Park, Pannal, Harrogate, N Yorks, HG3 1EJ. 01423 879 408.

WINTERSETT RG. P Smith, 16 Templar Street, Wakefield, W Yorks, WF1 5HB. 01924 375 082.

RSPB Local Groups

AIREDALE AND BRADFORD. (1972; 3,500 in catchement area). Ruth Porter, 01524 703 019;
e-mail: Carol.bamber@RSPB.org.uk
Meetings: 7.30pm, monthly on Fridays, Room 3, Shipley Library.

CRAVEN & PENDLE. (1986; 300). Ian Cresswell, Teal Cottage, 2 St. Robert Close, Gargrave, Skipton BD23 3PT. 01756 748 540;
e-mail: ian@cravenandpendlerspb.org
www.cravenandpendlerspb.org
Meetings: 7.30pm 2nd Wednesday of the month (Sep-May), St Andrews Church Hall, Newmarket Street, Skipton.

DONCASTER. (1984; 115). Sue Clifton, West Lodge, Wadworth Hall Lane, Wadworth, Doncaster, DN11 9BH. (Tel/Fax) 01302 854 956;
e-mail: sue@wlwad.wanadoo.co.uk
Meetings: 7.30pm 2nd Wednesday of the month (Sept-May), Salvation Army Community Church, Lakeside.

EAST YORKSHIRE. (1986;110). Trevor Malkin, 49 Taylors Field, Driffield, E Yorks, YO25 6FQ. 01377 257 325. www.eymg.free serve.co.uk

HUDDERSFIELD & HALIFAX. (1981; 200). David Hemingway, 267 Long Lane, Dalton, Huddersfield, HD5 9SH. 01484 301 920;
e-mail: d.hemingway@ntlworld.com

HULL & DISTRICT. (1983; 334). Betty Hilton. 01482 849 503; e-mail: betty-hilton@hotmail.com
Meetings: 7.30pm, Tuesdays (Sept-May), United Reformed Church, Southella Way, Kirkella, HULL. (£1.50 for Local Group Members and £2.00 for Non Members).

LEEDS. (1974; 450). Linda Jenkinson, 112 Eden Crescent, Burley, Leeds, LS4 2TR. 0113 230 4595; E-mail: linda.jenkinson@leeds.gov.uk www.rspb.org.uk/groups/leeds
Meetings: 7.30pm, 3rd Wednesday of the month (Sep-Apr), Lecture Theatre B, School of Mechanical Engineering, University of Leeds.

SHEFFIELD. (1981; 500). Malcolm Dyke, Flat 5, 648 Abbeydale Road, Sheffield, S7 2BB. 07947 031 172; www.rspb-sheffield.org.uk
Meetings: 7.30pm 1st Thursday of the month (Sept-May), Central United Reformed Church, Norfolk St, Sheffield.

WAKEFIELD. (1987; 150). Bob Coursey, 21 Greenside, Walton, Wakefield, West Yorkshire WF2 6NN. 01924 256 289.
www.rspb.org.uk/groups/wakefield
Meetings: 7.30pm, 4th Thursday of the month (Sep-Apr), Ossett War Memorial Community Centre, Prospect Road, Ossett, WF5 8AN.

WHITBY. (1977; 120). John Woolley, 2 Upgang Lane, Whitby, N Yorks, YO21 3EA. 01947 604 505.
Meetings: 7.15pm, 2nd Wednesday of the month, St John Ambulance Hall, back St Hilda's Terrace, Whitby.

YORK. (1973; 600). Chris Lloyd, 7 School Lane, Upper Poppleton, York, YO26 6JS. 01904 794 865; e-mail: chris.a.lloyd@care4free.net
www.yorkrspb.org.uk
Meetings: 7.30pm, Tues, Wed or Thurs, Temple Hall, York St John College, Lord Mayors Walk, York.

Wildlife Hospital
ANIMAL HOUSE WILDLIFE WELFARE. Mrs C Buckroyd, 14 Victoria Street, Scarborough, YO12 7SS. 01723 371 256 (please leave a message on the answer machine and callers will be contacted as soon as possible); e-mail: cynthiabuckroyd@talktalk.net or cindybuckroyd@hotmail.com.
All species of wild birds. Oiled birds given treatment before forwarding to cleaning stations. Incubators, hospital cages, heat pads, release sites. Birds ringed before release. Prior telephone call requested. Collection if required. Veterinary support. Charity shop at 127 Victoria Road.

Wildlife Trusts
SHEFFIELD WILDLIFE TRUST. (1985; 4,200). 37 Stafford Road, Sheffield, S2 2SF. 0114 263 4335; (Fax) 0114 263 4345;
e-mail: mail@wildsheffield.com
www.wildsheffield.com

YORKSHIRE WILDLIFE TRUST. (1946; 21,500). 1 St George's Place, Tadcaster Road, York YO24 1GN. 01904 659 570; (Fax) 01904 613 467;
e-mail: info@ywt.org.uk www.ywt.org.uk

SCOTLAND

Bird Report
SCOTTISH BIRD REPORT from: The SOC, The Scottish Birdwatching Resource Centre, Waterston House, Aberlady, East Lothian, EH32 0PY.

Club
See Scottish Ornithologists' Club in National Directory.

ANGUS & DUNDEE

Bird Recorder
ANGUS & DUNDEE. Graham Christer, 1 Balzeordie Cottages, Menmuir by Brechin, Angus DD9 7RQ. 01356 660 375;
e-mail: rec_glendoll@angus.sol.co.uk

Bird Report
ANGUS & DUNDEE BIRD REPORT (1974-), from The Woodlands, School Road, Luthermuir, Laurencekirk, AB30 1YX.

BTO Regional Representative & Regional Development Officer
ANGUS RR & RDO. Ken Slater, Braedownie Farmhouse, Glen Clova, Kirriemuir, Angus, DD8 4RD. 01575 550 233;
e-mail: rec_glendoll@angus.sol.co.uk

Clubs
ANGUS & DUNDEE BIRD CLUB. (1997; 202). Bob McCurley, 22 Kinnordy Terrace, Dundee, DD4 7NW. 01382 462 944; e-mail: lunanbay@onetel.net
www.angusbirding.homestead.com
Meetings: 7.30pm, Tuesdays, Montrose Basin Wildlife Centre.

SOC TAYSIDE BRANCH. (145). Brian Boag, Birch Brae, Knapp, Inchture, Perthshire PH14 9RN.

Ringing Group
TAY RG. Ms S Millar, Edenvale Cottage, 1 Lydox Cottages, Dairsie, Fife, KY15 4RN.
e-mail: les@lydox.fsnet.co.uk

RSPB Members' Group
DUNDEE. (1972;110). Graham Smith, 01382 532 461; e-mail: grahamnjen@hotmail.com
www.RSPB.org.uk/groups/dundee
Meetings: 7.30 pm, monthly on a Wednesday (Sep-Mar), Methodist Church, 20, West Marketgait, DUNDEE. Admission £1.00 for all, including refreshments.

Wetland Bird Survey Organisers
ANGUS INLAND (Excluding Montrose Basin). Graham Christer, The Ivy, 8 West Hemming Street, Letham, Forfar, Angus DD8 2PU.

MONTROSE BASIN. The Warden, SWT, Montrose Basin Wildlife Centre, Rossie Braes, Montrose, DD10 9JT. 01674 676336;
e-mail montrosebasin@swt.org.uk

ARGYLL

Bird Atlas/Avifauna
Birds of Argyll (Argyll Bird Club 2007), available from Bob Furness, The Cnoc, Tarbert, Arrochar, Dunbartonshire G83 7DG. 01301 702 603

Bird Recorder
ARGYLL. Paul Daw, Tigh-na-Tulloch, Tullochgorm, Minard, Argyll, PA32 8YQ. 01546 886 260;
e-mail: monedula@globalnet.co.uk

Bird Reports
ARGYLL BIRD REPORT (1984-), from Dr Bob Furness, The Cnoc, Tarbet, Dunbartonshire G83 7DG. 01301 702 603;
e-mail: r.furness@bio.gla.ac.uk

MACHRIHANISH SEABIRD OBSERVATORY REPORT (1992-), from the Observatory, see Reserves & Observatories.

BTO Regional Representatives
ARGYLL (MULL, COLL, TIREE AND MORVERN). Sue Dewar, 01680 812 594;
e-mail: sue.dewar@btconnect.com

ARGYLL MAINLAND, BUTE, GIGHA AND ARRAN. Richard Allen, e-mail: richardallan@compuserve.com

ISLAY, JURA, COLONSAY RR. John S Armitage, Airigh Sgallaidh, Portnahaven, Isle of Islay, PA47 7SZ. 01496 860 396;
e-mail: jsa@ornquest.plus.com

Clubs
ARGYLL BIRD CLUB. (1983;270). Sue Furness, The Cnoc, Tarbet, Argyll, G83 7DG. 01301 702 603;
e-mail: r.furness@bio.gla.ac.uk
www.argyllbirdclub.org

ISLE OF MULL BIRD CLUB. (2001;140), Mrs Janet T Hall, Membership Secretary, Druim Mhor, Craignure, Isle of Mull, Argyll PA65 6AY. 01680 812 441;
e-mail: oystercatcher@dee-emm.co.uk
www.mullbirdclub.org.uk
Meetings: 7 for 7.30pm start, 3rd Friday of the month (Oct-Apr), Craignure Village Hall.

Ringing Groups
TRESHNISH AUK RG. S W Walker,
e-mail: simon.walker9@btinternet.com

HELENSBURGH. (1975; 62). Steve Chadwin, 01436 670 158.

Wildlife Hospital
WINGS OVER MULL. Richard and Sue Dewar, Auchnacroish House, Torosay, Craignure, Isle of Mull PA65 6AY. (Tel/Fax) 01680 812 594;
email: dewars@wingsovermull.com
www.wingsovermull.com

AYRSHIRE

Bird Recorder
AYRSHIRE. Fraser Simpson, 4 Inchmurrin Drive, Kilmarnock, Ayrshire KA3 2JD.
e-mail: recorder@ayrshire-birding.org.uk

Bird Report
AYRSHIRE BIRD REPORT (1976-), from The Recorder or Dr RG Vernon, 29 Knoll Park, Ayr KA7 4RH.

BTO Regional Representative
AYRSHIRE RR. Brian Broadley, 01290 424 241;
e-mail: maggie_broadley@hotmail.com

Club
SOC AYRSHIRE. (1962; 154). Duncan Watt, Wildings Studio, 28 Greenbank, Dalry, Ayrshire, KA24 5AY. 01294 832 361; www.ayrshire-birding.org.uk
Meetings: 7.30pm, Tuesdays monthly, Monkton Community Church, Monkton by Prestwick.

RSPB Members' Groups
CENTRAL AYRSHIRE LOCAL GROUP. (1978; 85). Tony Scott (Group Leader), 4 Hilltop Place, Ayr, KA7 3PB. 01292 281 045; e-mail: da.scott@tiscali.co.uk
Meetings: 7.40pm, 3rd Monday of the month (Sep-Apr), Carnegie Library, Main Street, Ayr.

SCOTLAND

NORTH AYRSHIRE. (1976; 180). Duncan Watt, 28 Greenbank, Dalry, Ayrshire, KA24 5AY.
www.narspb.org.uk
Meetings: 7.30pm, various Fridays (Aug-Apr), Ardrossan Civic Centre, open to all. Full list available.

Wetland Bird Survey Organiser
AYRSHIRE. Mr David Grant, 16 Thorn Avenue, Coylton, Ayr KA6 6NL. (H) 01292 570 491;
e-mail: d.grant@au.sac.as.uk

Wildlife Hospital
HESSILHEAD WILDLIFE RESCUE CENTRE. Gay & Andy Christie, Gateside, Beith, Ayrshire, KA15 1HT. 01505 502 415; e-mail: info@hessilhead.org.uk
www.hessilhead.org.uk
All species. Releasing aviaries. Veterinary support. Visits only on open days please.

BORDERS

Bird Atlas/Avifauna
The Breeding Birds of South-east Scotland, a tetrad atlas 1988-1994 by R D Murray et al. (Scottish Ornithologists' Club, 1998).

Bird Recorder
Ray Murray, 4 Bellfield Crescent, Eddleston, Peebles, EH45 8RQ. 01721 730 677;
e-mail: ray.d.murray@ukgateway.net

Bird Report
BORDERS BIRD REPORT (1979-), From Malcolm Ross, Westfield Cottage, Smailholm, Kelso TD5 7PN. 01573 460 699;
e-mail: eliseandmalcolm@btinternet.com

BTO Regional Representative
RR. Graham Pyatt. 01721 740 319;
e-mail: d.g.pyatt@btinternet.com

Club
SOC BORDERS BRANCH. (100). Vicky McLellan, 18 Glen Crescent, Peebles,EH45 9BS. 01721 724 580.
Meetings: 7.30pm, 2nd Monday of the month, George & Abbotsford Hotel, Melrose.

Ringing Group
BORDERS RG. (1991; 10). Dr T W Dougall, 38 Leamington Terrace, Edinburgh, EH10 4JL. (Office) 0131 344 2536; (Fax) 0131 344 2600.

RSPB Members' Group
BORDERS. (1995; 94). Jim Stillie, 0175 020 660;
e-mail: jimstillie@selkirk4hs.freeserve.co.uk

CAITHNESS

Bird Recorder
CAITHNESS. Stan Laybourne, Old Schoolhouse, Harpsdale, Halkirk, Caithness, KW12 6UN. 01847 841 244; e-mail:stanlaybourne@talk21.com

Bird Report
CAITHNESS BIRD REPORT (1983-97). Now incorporated into *The Highland Bird Report*, From Julian Smith, St John's, Brough, Dunnet, Caithness; KW14 8YD. e-mail: designsmith@madasafish.com

BTO Regional Representative
CAITHNESS. D Omand, 9 Skiall, Shebster, Thurso, Caithness. 01847 811 403;
e-mail: achreamie@yahoo.co.uk

Club
SOC CAITHNESS BRANCH. (51). Stan Laybourne, Old Schoolhouse, Harpsdale, Halkirk, Caithness, KW12 6UN. 01847 841 244;
e-mail:stanlaybourne@talk21.com

CLYDE

Bird Recorders
CLYDE ISLANDS. Bernard Zonfrillo, 28 Brodie Road, Glasgow, G21 3SB. e-mail:b.zonfrillo@bio.gla.ac.uk

CLYDE. Iain P Gibson, 8 Kenmure View, Howwood, Johnstone, Renfrewshire, PA9 1DR. 01505 705 874;
e-mail:iain.gibson@land.glasgow.gov.uk

Bird Report
CLYDE BIRDS (1973-), incorporates the *Clyde Islands Bird Report*. From Jim & Valerie Wilson, 76 Laigh Road, Newton Mearns, Glasgow, G77 5EQ.
e-mail: jim.val@btinternet.com

BTO Regional Representative
LANARK, RENFREW, DUMBARTON. John Knowler, 0141 584 9117; e-mail: john.knowler@ntlworld.ocm

Club
SOC CLYDE BRANCH. (300). Sandra Hutchinson, 52 Station Road, Bearsden, Glasgow, G61 4AL. 0141 943 1816; e-mail: hutchinson_80hotmail.com

Ringing Group
CLYDE RG. (1979; 18)I Livingstone, 57 Strathview Road, Bellshill, Lanarkshire, ML4 2UY. 01698 749 844; e-mail: iainlivcrg@blueyonder.co.uk

RSPB Members' Groups
GLASGOW. (1972;141). Agnes Gunn, 43 Dickens Avenue, Clydebank, G81 3EP. 07811 550 142;
e-mail: agnesgunn2@aol.com
Meetings: 7.30pm, generally 1st Wednesday of the month (Sep-Apr), Woodside Halls or Fotheringay Centre.

HAMILTON. (1976;90). Jim Lynch, 0141 583 1044;
e-mail: birder45a@yahoo.co.uk
www.baronshaugh.co.uk
Meetings: 7.30pm, 3rd Thursday of the month (Sept-May), Watersports Centre, Motherwell (next to Strathclyde Loch).

RENFREWSHIRE. (1986; 200). Jim Sutherland, 0141 639 7028; e-mail: sutherland.jim@btopenworld.com

Wetland Bird Survey Organisers
CLYDE ESTUARY. Jim & Valerie Wilson, 76 Laigh Road, Newton Mearns, Glasgow G77 5EQ. (H)0141 639 2516; e-mail: Jim.Val@btinternet.com

GLASGOW/RENFREWSHIRE/LANARKSHIRE. Jim & Valerie Wilson, 76 Laigh Road, Newton Mearns, Glasgow G77 5EQ. (H)0141 639 2516; e-mail: Jim.Val@btinternet.com

DUMFRIES & GALLOWAY

Bird Recorder
Paul Collin, Gairland, Old Edinburgh Road, Minnigaff, Newton Stewart, DG8 6PL. 01671 402 861; e-mail: paul.collin@rspb.org.uk

Bird Report
DUMFRIES & GALLOWAY REGION BIRD REPORT (1985-), from Peter Norman, Low Boreland, Tongland Road, Kirkcudbright, DG6 4UU. 01557 331 429.

BTO Regional Representatives
DUMFRIES RR. Edmund Fellowes, 01387 262 094; e-mail: edmundfellowes@aol.com

KIRKCUDBRIGHT RR. Andrew Bielinski, 41 Main Street, St Johns Town of Dalry, Castle Douglas, Kirkcudbright, DG7 3UP. 01644 430 418 (evening); e-mail: andrewb@bielinski.fsnet.co.uk

WIGTOWN RR. Geoff Sheppard, The Roddens, Leswalt, Stranraer, Wigtownshire, DG9 0QR. 01776 870 685; e-mail: geoff.sheppard@tesco.net

Clubs
SOC DUMFRIES BRANCH. (1961; 105). Mrs Pat Abery, East Daylesford, Colvend, Dalbeattie, Dumfries, DG5 4QA. 01556 630 483.
Meetings: 7.30pm, 2nd Wednesday of the month (Sept-Apr), Cumberland St Day Centre.

SOC STEWARTRY BRANCH. (1976; 80). Miss Joan Howie, 60 Main Street, St Johns Town of Dalry, Castle Douglas, Kirkcudbrightshire, DG7 3UW. 01644 430 226.
Meetings: 7.30pm, usually 2nd Thursday of the month (Sep-Apr), Kells School, New Galloway.

SOC WEST GALLOWAY BRANCH. (1975; 50). Geoff Sheppard, The Roddens, Leswalt, Stranraer, Wigtownshire, DG9 0QR. 01776 870 685;
e-mail: geoff.sheppard@tesco.net
Meetings: 7.30pm, 2nd Tuesday of the month (Oct-Mar), Stranraer Library.

Ringing Group
NORTH SOLWAY RG. Geoff Sheppard, The Roddens, Leswalt, Stranraer, Wigtownshire, DG9 0QR. 01776 870 685; e-mail: geoff.sheppard@tesco.net

RSPB Members' Group
GALLOWAY. (1985;150). Cynthia Douglas, Midbark, Balmaclellan, Castle Douglas, DG7 3PX. 01644 420 605; www.gallowayrspb-localgroup.org.uk
Meetings: 7.30pm 3rd Tuesday in the month, Castle Douglas High School.

Wetland Bird Survey Organisers
AUCHENCAIRN. Euan MacAlpine, Auchenshore, Auchencairn, Castle Douglas, Galloway DG7 1QZ . 01556 640 244; e-mail: js.auchen@virgin.net

DUMFRIES & GALLOWAY (OTHER SITES). Steve Cooper, Wildfowl & Wetlands Trust, Eastpark Farm, Caerlaverock, Dumfries DG1 4RS. 01387 770 200; e-mail: steve.cooper@wwt.org.uk

LOCH RYAN. Geoff Shepherd, The Roddens, Leswalt, Stranraer, Wigtonshire DG9 0QR. 01776 870 685; e-mail: geoff.sheppard@tesco.net

SOLWAY ESTUARY (NORTH). Steve Cooper, Wildfowl & Wetlands Trust, Eastpark Farm, Caerlaverock, Dumfries DG1 4RS. 01387 770 200; e-mail: steve.cooper@wwt.org.uk

WIGTOWN. Paul Collin, Gairland, Old Edinburgh Road, Minnigaff, Newton Stewart, DG8 6PL. 01671 402 861; e-mail: paul.collin@rspb.org.uk

FIFE

Bird Atlas/Avifauna
The Fife Bird Atlas 2003 by Norman Elkins, Jim Reid, Allan Brown, Derek Robertson & Anne-Marie Smout. Available from Allan W. Brown (FOAG), 61 Watts Gardens, Cupar, Fife KY15 4UG, Tel. 01334 656 804, email: swans@allanwbrown.co.uk

Bird Recorders
FIFE REGION INC OFFSHORE ISLANDS (NORTH FORTH). Rab Shand.
e-mail: rabshand@blueyonder.co.uk

ISLE OF MAY BIRD OBSERVATORY. Iain English, 19 Nethan Gate, Hamilton, S Lanarks, ML3 8NH.
e-mail: i.english@talk21.com

Bird Reports
FIFE BIRD REPORT (1988-) (FIFE & KINROSS BR 1980-87), from Willie McBay, 41 Shamrock Street, Dunfermline, Fife, KY12 0JQ. 01383 723 464; e-mail: wmcbay@aol.com

ISLE OF MAY BIRD OBSERVATORY REPORT (1985-), from Jonathon Osborne, The Shieling, Halcombe Crescent, Earlston, Berwickshire TD4 6DA.

SCOTLAND

BTO Regional Representative
FIFE & KINROSS RR. Norman Elkins, 18 Scotstarvit View, Cupar, Fife, KY15 5DX. 01334 654 348; e-mail: jandnelkins@btinternet.com

Clubs
FIFE BIRD CLUB. (1985; 250). Willie McBay, 41 Shamrock Street, Dunfermline, Fife, KY12 0JQ. 01383 723 464; www.fifebirdclub.org.uk
Meetings: 7.30pm, (various evenings), Dean Park Hotel, Chapel Level, Kirkcaldy.

SOC FIFE BRANCH. (1956;170). Howard Chapman, 5 Woodville Park, Dairsie, Cupar, Fife KY15 4TE. 01334 870 768.
Meetings: 7.30pm, 2nd Wednesday of the month (Sep-Apr), St Andrews Town Hall.

Ringing Groups
ISLE OF MAY BIRD OBSERVATORY. David Grieve, 50 Main Street, Symington, Biggar, South Lancs ML12 6LJ. 01899 309 176/180.

TAY RG. Ms S Millar, Edenvale Cottage, 1 Lydox Cottages, Dairsie, Fife, KY15 4RN.
e-mail: les@lydox.fsnet.co.uk

Wetland Bird Survey Organisers
EDEN ESTUARY. Norman Elkins, 18 Scotstarvit View, Cupar, Fife KY15 5DX. 01334 654 348;
e-mail: jandnelkins@btinternet.com

TAY ESTUARY. Norman Elkins, 18 Scotstarvit View, Cupar, Fife KY15 5DX. 01334 654 348;
e-mail: jandnelkins@btinternet.com

Wildlife Hospital
SCOTTISH SPCA WILD LIFE REHABILITATION CENTRE. Middlebank Farm, Masterton Road, Dunfermline, Fife, KY11 8QN. 01383 412 520
All species. Open to visitors, groups and school parties. Illustrated talk on oiled bird cleaning and other aspects of wildlife rehabilitation available. Veterinary support.

FORTH

Bird Recorder
UPPER FORTH (Does not include parts of Stirling in Loch Lomondside/Clyde Basin). Dr C J Henty, Edgehill East, 7b Coneyhill Road, Bridge of Allan, Stirling, FK9 4EL. 01786 832 166;
e-mail: cjh@cliffhenty.plus.com

Bird Report
FORTH AREA BIRD REPORT (1975-) - enlarged report published annually in The Forth Naturalist and Historian, University of Stirling, From Dr Roy Sexton, 22 Alexander Drive, Bridge of Allan, Stirling FK9 4QB. 01786 833 409.

BTO Regional Representative
CENTRAL RR. Neil Bielby, 56 Ochiltree, Dunblane, Perthshire, FK15 0DF. 01786 823 830;
e-mail: n.bielby@sky.com

Club
SOC CENTRAL SCOTLAND BRANCH. (1968; 101). Mr RL Gooch, The Red House, Dollarfield, Dollar, Clacks FK14 7LX. 01259 742326.
Meetings: 7.30pm, 1st Thursday of the month (Sep-Apr), The Smith Art Gallery and Museum, Dumbarton Road, Stirling.

RSPB Members' Group
FORTH VALLEY. (1996; 150). David Redwood, 8 Strathmore Avenue, Dunblane, Perthshire FK15 9HX. 01786 825 493;
e-mail: david.redwood1@btinternet.com
http://forthrspb.p5.org.uk
Meetings: 7.30pm, 3rd Thursday of the month (Sept-Apr), Hillpark Centre, Stirling.

Wetland Bird Survey Organiser
CENTRAL (excl Forth Estuary. Neil Bielby, 56 Ochiltree, Dunblane, Perthshire FK15 0DF. 01786 823 830; e-mail: n.bielby@sky.com

HIGHLAND

Bird Atlas/Avifauna
The Birds of Sutherland by Alan Vittery (Colin Baxter Photography Ltd, 1997).

Sky Birds by R. McMillan (skyebirds.com 2005). Available from the author at 11 Elgol, Broadford, Isle of Skye IV49 9BL.

Bird Recorders
ROSS-SHIRE, INVERNESS-SHIRE, SUTHERLAND. Alastair McNee, Liathach, 4 Balnafettack Place, Inverness IV3 8TQ. 01463 220 493; (M)07763 927 814; e-mail: aj.mcnee@care4free.net

Bird Reports
HIGHLAND BIRD REPORT (1991-), from The Recorder. 2004 edition £7.50, 2005 £9.50 including p&p.

SUTHERLAND BIRD REVIEW (2002-), (sold out).

BTO Regional Representatives & Regional Development Officers
INVERNESS & SPEYSIDE RR & RDO. Hugh Insley, 1 Drummond Place, Inverness,IV2 4JT. 01463 230 652; e-mail: hugh.insley@btinternet.com

RUM, EIGG, CANNA & MUCK RR & RDO. Bob Swann, 14 St Vincent Road, Tain, Ross-shire, IV19 1JR. 01862 894 329;
e-mail: robert.swann@homecall.co.uk

ROSS-SHIRE RR. Simon Cohen,
E-mail: saraandsimon@hotmail.com

SUTHERLAND. Position vacant.

SKYE. Robert McMillan, 01471 866 305;
e-mail: Bob@Skye-birds.com

Clubs
EAST SUTHERLAND BIRD GROUP. (1976; 100). Tony Mainwood, 13 Ben Bhraggie Drive, Golspie, Sutherland KW10 6SX. 01408 633 247;
e-mail: tony.mainwood@btinternet.com
Meetings: 7.30pm, Last Monday of the month (Oct, Nov, Jan, Feb, Mar), Golspie Community Centre.

SOC HIGHLAND BRANCH. (1955; 151). Ann Sime, Drumrunie House, Myrtlefield Lane, Westhill, Inverness IV2 5UE. 01463 790 249.
Meetings: 7.45pm, 1st Tuesday of the month (Sep-Mar), Culloden Library.

Ringing Group
HIGHLAND RG. Bob Swann, 14 St Vincent Road, Tain, Ross-shire, IV19 1JR.
e-mail: robert.swann@homecall.co.uk

RSPB Members' Group
HIGHLAND. (1987; 214). Richard Prentice, Lingay, Lewiston, Drumnadrochit, Inverness, IV63 6UW. 01456 450 526;
e-mail: richard@rprentice.wanadoo.co.uk
www.rspb.org.uk/groups/highland

Wetland Bird Survey Organisers
MORAY & NAIRN (Inland). Martin Cook, Rowanbrae, Clochan, Buckie, Banffshire AB56 5EQ. (H) 01542 850 296.

SKYE & LOCHALSH. Bob McMillan, 10/11 Elgol, Nr Broadford, Isle of Skye IV49 9BL. 01471 866 305;
e-mail: bob@skye-birds.com

LOTHIAN

Bird Atlas/Avifauna
The Breeding Birds of South-east Scotland, a tetrad atlas 1988-1994 by R D Murray et al. (Scottish Ornithologists' Club, 1998).

Bird Recorder
David J Kelly, 01875 6140 72;
e-mail: dj_kelly@btinternet.com

Bird Reports
LOTHIAN BIRD REPORT (1979-), from the Lothian SOC Branch Secretary.

WEST LOTHIAN BIRD CLUB REPORT (1991-), from The Secretary, West Lothian Bird Club.

BTO Regional Representative
RR. Alan Heavisides, 9 Addiston Crescent, Balerno, Edinburgh, EH14 7DB. 0131 449 3816;
e-mail: a.heavisides@napier.ac.uk

Clubs
EDINBURGH NATURAL HISTORY SOCIETY. (1869; 200). Miss Joan Fairlie, 14 Relugas Road, Edinburgh EH9 2ND. 0131 668 1470.
www.edinburghnaturalhistory society.org.uk

EDINBURGH NATURAL HISTORY SOCIETY

LOTHIAN SOC. (1936; 450). John Hamilton, 30 Swanston Gardens, Edinburgh, EH10 7DL. 0131 445 5317; e-mail: john.r.hamilton31@btopenworld.com
www.lsoc.btinternet.co.uk
Meetings: 7.30pm, 2nd Tuesday (Sep-Dec and Jan-Apr), Lounge 2, Meadowbank Sports Stadium.

Ringing Group
LOTHIAN RG. Mr M Cubitt, 12 Burgh Mills Lane, Linlithgow, West Lothian EH49 7TA.

RSPB Members' Group
EDINBURGH. (1974;480). Mark Stephen, 36-5 Bryson Road, Edinburgh EH11 1DX.
e-mail: markbirder@blueyonder.co.uk
http://rspb-edin.pwp.blueyonder.co.uk
Meetings: 7.30pm, 3rd Tuesday or Wednesday of the month (Sep-Apr), Napier University, Craiglockhart Campus, Edinburgh.

Wetland Bird Survey Organisers
FORTH ESTUARY (North). Alastair Inglis, 5 Crowhill Road, Dalgety Bay, Fife KY11 5LJ.

FORTH ESTUARY (Outer South). Duncan Priddle, 19c High Street, Haddington, East Lothian EH41 3ES. 01620 827 459;
e-mail: dpriddle@eastlothian.gov.uk

LOTHIAN (excl estuaries). Joan Wilcox, 18 Howdenhall Gardens, Edinburgh, Midlothian EH16 6UN. (H)0131 6648 893.

TYNINGHAME ESTUARY. John Muir Country Park, Town House, Dunbar, East Lothian EH42 1ER. (W) 01368 863 886;
e-mail: randerson@eastlothian.gov.uk

MORAY & NAIRN

Bird Atlas/Avifauna *The Birds of Moray and Nairn* by Martin Cook (Mercat Press, 1992.

Bird Recorders
NAIRN. Martin J H Cook, Rowanbrae, Clochan, Buckie, Banffshire, AB56 5EQ. 01542 850 296;
e-mail: martin.cook9@virgin.net

MORAY. Martin J H Cook, Rowanbrae, Clochan, Buckie, Banffshire, AB56 5EQ. 01542 850 296;
e-mail: martin.cook9@virgin.net

Bird Reports
BIRDS IN MORAY AND NAIRN (1999-), From the Moray Recorder, 01542 850 296;
e-mail: martin.cook9@virgin.net

MORAY & NAIRN BIRD REPORT (1985-1998), From the Moray Recorder, 01542 850 296; e-mail: martin.cook9@virgin.net

BTO Regional Representatives
NAIRN RR. Bob Proctor, 78 Marleon Field, Elgin, Moray, IV30 4GE. 01343 548 395; (W) 01343 547 371; e-mail: bobandlouise@proctor8246.fsnet.co.uk

MORAY RR. Bob Proctor, 78 Marleon Field, Elgin, Moray, IV30 4GE. 01343 548 395; (W) 01343 547 371; e-mail: bobandlouise@proctor8246.fsnet.co.uk

Wetland Bird Survey Organisers
LOSSIE ESTUARY. Bob Proctor, 78 Marleon Field, Silvercrest, Bishopmill, Elgin, IV30 4GE; e-mail: bob.proctor@rspb.org.uk

MORAY & NAIRN (Inland). Martin Cook, Rowanbrae, Clochan, Buckie, Banffshire, AB56 5EQ. 01542 850 296.

NORTH-EAST SCOTLAND

Bird Atlas/Avifauna
The Birds of North-East Scotland by S T Buckland, M V Bell & N Picozzi (North-East Scotland Bird Club, 1990).

Bird Recorder
NORTH-EAST SCOTLAND. Hywel Maggs, 4 Merlin Terrace, Newburgh, Ellon, Aberdeenshire AB41 6FA. 01358 788 106; e-mail: hywelmaggs@hotmail.com

Bird Reports
NORTH-EAST SCOTLAND BIRD REPORT (1974-), from Dave Gill, Drakemyre Croft, Cairnorrie, Methlick, Aberdeenshire, AB41 7JN. 01651 806 252; e-mail: dave@drakemyre.freeserve.co.uk

NORTH SEA BIRD CLUB ANNUAL REPORT (1979-), From Andrew Thorpe, Ocean Laboratory and Centre for Ecology, Aberdeen University, Newburgh, Ellon, Aberdeenshire, AB41 6AA. 01224 274 428; e-mail: nsbc@abdn.ac.uk

BTO Regional Representatives
ABERDEEN. Paul Doyle, 01358 751 365; e-mail: paul@albaecology.co.uk

KINCARDINE & DEESIDE. Graham Cooper, Westbank, Beltie Road, Torphins, Banchory, Aberdeen, AB31 4JT. 01339 882 706; e-mail: grahamwcooper@beeb.net

Clubs
SOC GRAMPIAN BRANCH. (1956; 110). John Wills, Bilbo, Monymusk, Inverurie, Aberdeenshire, AB51 7HA. 01467 651 296; e-mail: bilbo@monymusk.freeserve.co.uk
Meetings: 7.30pm, 1st Monday of the month (Sep-Apr), venue to be arranged.

Ringing Groups
ABERDEEN UNIVERSITY RG. Andrew Thorpe, e-mail: andrewthorpe4@aol.com

GRAMPIAN RG. R Duncan, 86 Broadfold Drive, Bridge of Don, Aberdeen, AB23 8PP. E-mail: Raymond@waxwing.fsnet.co.uk

RSPB Members' Group
ABERDEEN & DISTRICT. (1975; 210). Rodney Payne, 2 Arbuthnott Court, Stonehaven, AB39 2GW. 01569 763 742; www.rspb-abdn-mbrsgp.org.uk.
Meetings: 7.30pm, monthly in the winter, Lecture Theatre, Zoology Dept, Tillydrone Av, Aberdeen. Two birding trips monthly throughout the year.

Wildlife Hospital
GRAMPIAN WILDLIFE REHABILITATION TRUST. 40 High Street, New Deer, Turriff, Aberdeenshire, AB53 6SX. 01771 644 489; (M) 07803 235 383; e-mail: laurence.brain@btconnect.com
Veterinary surgeon. Access to full practice facilities. Will care for all species of birds.

ORKNEY

Bird Atlas/Avifauna
The Birds of Orkney by CJ Booth et al (The Orkney Press, 1984).

Bird Recorder
Mr EJ Williams, Fairholm, Finstown, Orkney, KW17 2EQ. e-mail: jim@geniefea.freeserve.co.uk

Bird Report
ORKNEY BIRD REPORT (inc North Ronaldsay Bird Report) (1974-), From Mr EJ Williams, Fairholm, Finstown, Orkney, KW17 2EQ. e-mail: jim@geniefea.freeserve.co.uk

BTO Regional Representative
Colin Corse, Garrisdale, Lynn Park, Kirkwall, Orkney, KW15 1SL. 01856 874 484; e-mail: ccorse@aol.com

Club
SOC ORKNEY BRANCH. (1993; 15). Colin Corse, Garrisdale, Lynn Park, Kirkwall, Orkney, KW15 1SL. H:01856 874 484; e-mail: ccorse@aol.com.

Ringing Groups
NORTH RONALDSAY BIRD OBSERVATORY. Ms A E Duncan, Twingness, North Ronaldsay, Orkney, KW17 2BE. e-mail: alison@nrbo.prestel.co.uk www.nrbo.f2s.com

ORKNEY RG. Colin Corse, Garrisdale, Lynn Park, Kirkwall, Orkney, KW15 1SL. 01856 874 484; e-mail: ccorse@aol.com

SULE SKERRY RG. Dave Budworth, 121 Wood Lane, Newhall, Swadlincote, Derbys, DE11 0LX. 0121 6953 384.

SCOTLAND

RSPB Members' Group
ORKNEY. (1985; 300 in catchment area). Mrs Pauline Wilson, Sunny Bank, Deerness, Orkney KW17 2QQ. 01856 741 382; e-mail: pwilso@tiscali.co.uk
Meetings: Meetings advertised in newsletter and local press, held at Kirkwall Community Centre.

Wetland Bird Survey Organiser
ORKNEY (other sites). Eric Meek, RSPB, 12/14 North End Road, Stromness, Orkney KW16 3AG. 01856 850 176.

OUTER HEBRIDES

Bird Recorder
OUTER HEBRIDES AND WESTERN ISLES. Brian Rabbitts, 01876 580 328;
e-mail: rabbitts@hebrides.net

Bird Report
OUTER HEBRIDES BIRD REPORT (1989-), from the Recorder.

BTO Regional Representatives & Regional Development Officer
BENBECULA & THE UISTS RR & RDO.
Brian Rabbitts. 01876 580 328;
e-mail: rabbitts@hebrides.net

LEWIS & HARRIS RR. Chris Reynolds, 11 Reef, Isle of Lewis, HS2 9HU. 01851 672 376;
e-mail: cmreynolds@btinternet.com

Ringing Groups
SHIANTS AUK RG. David Steventon, Welland House, 207 Hurdsfield Road, Macclesfield, Cheshire, SK10 2PX. 01625 421 936.

UISTS AND BENBECULA. Brian Rabbitts, 01876 580 328; e-mail: rabbitts@hebrides.net

PERTH & KINROSS

Bird Recorder
PERTH & KINROSS. Ron Youngman, Blairchroisk Cottage, Ballinluig, Pitlochry, Perthshire, PH9 0NE. 01796 482324; e-mail: blairchroisk@aol.com

Bird Report
PERTH & KINROSS BIRD REPORT (1974-), from the Recorder.

BTO Regional Representative
PERTHSHIRE RR. Richard Paul. 01882 632 212;
e-mail: richard@rannoch.net
www.perthshire-birds.org.uk

Club
PERTHSHIRE SOCIETY OF NATURAL SCIENCE (Ornithological Section). (1964; 40). Miss Esther Taylor, 23 Verena Terrace, Perth, PH2 0BZ. 01738 621 986.
Meetings: 7.30pm, Wednesdays monthly (Oct-Mar), Perth Museum.

Wetland Bird Survey Organiser
TAY ESTUARY. Norman Elkins, 18 Scotstarvit View, Cupar, Fife KY15 5DX. 01334 654 348;
e-mail: jandnelkins@rapidial.co.uk

SHETLAND

Bird Recorders
FAIR ISLE. Deryk Shaw, Bird Observatory, Fair Isle, Shetland, ZE2 9JU.
e-mail: fairisle.birdobs@zetnet.co.uk

SHETLAND Paul Harvey, Shetland Biological Records Centre, Shetland Amenity Trust, 22-24 North Road, Lerwick, Shetland, ZE1 3NG. (Day) 01595 694 688;
e-mail: shetamenity.trust@zetnet.co.uk

Bird Reports
FAIR ISLE BIRD OBSERVATORY REPORT (1949-). From the Scottish Ornithologists' Club, 21 Regent Terrace, Edinburgh, EH7 5BT. 0131 556 6042.

SHETLAND BIRD REPORT (1969-) no pre 1973 available. From Martin Heubeck, East House, Sumburgh Lighthouse, Virkie, Shetland, ZE3 9JN.
e-mail: martinheubeck@btinternet.com

BTO Regional Representative and Regional Development Officer
RR and RDO. Dave Okill, Heilinabretta, Cauldhame, Trondra, Shetland, ZE1 0XL. 01595 880 450.

Club
SHETLAND BIRD CLUB. (1973; 200). Roger Riddington, Spindrift, Eastshore, Virkie, Shetland, ZE3 9JS. 01950 460 080. e-mail: editor@britishbirds.co.uk
www.nature-shetland.co.uk

Ringing Groups
FAIR ISLE BIRD OBSERVATORY. Deryk Shaw, Bird Observatory, Fair Isle, Shetland, ZE2 9JU.
e-mail: fairisle.birdobs@zetnet.co.uk

SHETLAND RG. Dave Okill, Heilinabretta, Cauldhame, Trondra, Shetland, ZE1 0XL. (H) 01595 880 450; (W) 01595 696 926

Wetland Bird Survey Organiser
Paul Harvey, Shetland Biological Records Centre, Shetland Amenity Trust, 22-24 North Road, Lerwick, Shetland, ZE1 3NG. (Day) 01595 694 688;
e-mail: shetamenity.trust@zetnet.co.uk

WALES

BTO Honorary Wales Officer
BTO WALES OFFICER. John Lloyd, Cynghordy Hall, Cynghordy, Llandovery, Carms SA20 0LN.
e-mail: the.lloyds@dsl.pipex.com

EAST WALES

Bird Atlas/Avifauna
The Gwent Atlas of Breeding Birds by Tyler, Lewis, Venables & Walton (Gwent Ornithological Society, 1987).

Bird Recorders
BRECONSHIRE. Andrew King, Heddfan, Pennorth, Brecon, Powys LD3 7EX. 01874 658 351;
e-mail: andrew.king53@virgin.net

GWENT. Chris Jones,
e-mail: countyrecorder@gwentbirds.org.uk.

MONTGOMERYSHIRE. Brayton Holt, Scops Cottage, Pentrebeirdd, Welshpool, Powys, SY21 9DL. 01938 500 266; e-mail: brayton.wanda@virgin.net

RADNORSHIRE, Pete Jennings, Penbont House, Elan Valley, Rhayader, Powys, LD6 5HS. (H) 01597 811 522; (W) 01597 810 880;
e-mail: petejelanvalley@hotmail.com

Bird Reports
BRECONSHIRE BIRDS (1962-), from Brecknock Wildlife Trust.

GWENT BIRD REPORT (1964-), from Jerry Lewis, Y Bwthyn Gwyn, Coldbrook, Abergavenny, Monmouthshire, NP7 9TD. (H) 01873 855 091; (W) 01633 644 856

MONTGOMERYSHIRE BIRD REPORT (1981-82-), from Montgomeryshire Wildlife Trust.

RADNOR BIRDS (1987/92-), from Radnorshire Recorder.

BTO Regional Representatives
BRECKNOCK RR. John Lloyd, Cynghordy Hall, Cynghordy, Llandovery, Carms, SA20 0LN.
e-mail: the.lloyds@dsl.pipex.com

GWENT RR. Jerry Lewis, Y Bwthyn Gwyn, Coldbrook, Abergavenny, Monmouthshire, NP7 9TD. (H) 01873 855 091; (W) 01633 644 856

MONTGOMERY RR. Jane Kelsall, Holly Bank, Moel y Garth, Welshpool, Powys SY21 9JA. 01938 556 438;
e-mail: janekelsall@phonecoop.coop

RADNORSHIRE RR. Brian Jones,
e-mail: jones.brn10@virgin.net

Clubs
THE GWENT ORNITHOLOGICAL SOCIETY. (1964; 420). T J Russell, The Pines, Highfield Road, Monmouth, Gwent, NP25 3HR. 01600 716 266;
e-mail: secretary@GwentBirds.org.uk
www.gwentbirds.org.uk
Meetings: 7.30pm, alternate Saturdays (Sept-Apr), Goytre Village Hall.

MONTGOMERYSHIRE FIELD SOCIETY. (1946; 190). Maureen Preen, Ivy House, Deep Cutting, Pool Quay, Welshpool, Powys, SY21 9LJ. Tel: Mary Oliver, 01686 413 518.
Meetings: 2.30pm, 2nd Saturday of the month (Nov, Jan, Feb, Mar), Methodist Church Hall, Welshpool. Field trips (Apr-Oct) weekdays.

MONTGOMERYSHIRE WILDLIFE TRUST BIRD GROUP. (1997; 110). A M Puzey, Four Seasons, Arddleen, Llanymynech, Powys, SY22 6RU. 01938 590 578.
Meetings: 7.30pm, Welshpool Methodist Hall.

RADNOR BIRD GROUP. (1986; 60). Pete Jennings, Penbont House, Elan Valley, Rhayader, Powys, LD6 5HS. 01597 811 522;
e-mail: petejelanvalley@hotmail.com

Ringing Groups
LLANGORSE RG. (1987; 15). Jerry Lewis, Y Bwthyn Gwyn, Coldbrook, Abergavenny, Monmouthshire, NP7 9TD. (H) 01873 855 091; (W) 01633 644 856

Wetland Bird Survey Organisers
RADNORSHIRE. Peter Jennings, Pentbont House, Elan Valley, Rhayader, Powys, LD6 5HS. (H) 01597 811 522; (W) 01597 810 880;
e-mail: petejelanvalley@hotmail.com

BRECONSHIRE and POWYS. Andrew King, Heddfan, Pennorth, Brecon LD3 7EX;
e-mail: heddfan25@hotmail.com

Wildlife Trusts
BRECKNOCK WILDLIFE TRUST. (1963; 893). Lion House, Bethel Square, Brecon, Powys, LD3 7AY. 01874 625 708; (Fax) 01874 610 552;
e-mail: brecknockwt@cix.co.uk
www.brecknockwildlifetrust.org.uk

GWENT WILDLIFE TRUST. (1963; 5,000). Seddon House, Dingestow, Monmouth NP25 4DY. 01600 740 358; (Fax) 01600 740 299;
e-mail: info@gwentwildlife.org
www.gwentwildlife.org

MONTGOMERYSHIRE WILDLIFE TRUST. (1982; 1,000). Collot House, 20 Severn Street, Welshpool,

Powys, SY21 7AD. 01938 555 654; (Fax) 01938 556 161; e-mail: info@montwt.co.uk www.montwt.co.uk

RADNORSHIRE WILDLIFE TRUST. (1987; 789). Warwick House, High Street, Llandrindod Wells, Powys, LD1 6AG. 01597 823 298; (Fax) 01597 823 274; e-mail:info@radnorshirewildlifetrust.org.uk www.radnorshirewildlifetrust.org.uk

NORTH WALES

Bird Atlas/Avifauna

Birds of Anglesey/Adar Môn by PH Jones and P Whalley. (Menter Mon, 2004)

The Birds of Caernarfonshire by John Barnes (1998, from Lionel Pilling, 51 Brighton Close, Rhyl LL18 3HL).

Bird Recorders

ANGLESEY. Stephen Culley, Millhouse, Penmynydd Road, Menai Bridge, Anglesey, LL59 5RT. e-mail: SteCul10@aol.com

CAERNARFON. John Barnes, Fach Goch, Waunfawr, Caernarfon, LL55 4YS. 01286 650 362.

DENBIGHSHIRE & FLINTSHIRE. Ian Spence, 43 Blackbrook, Sychdyn, Mold, Flintshire, CH7 6LT. Tel/fax 01352 750 118; e-mail: ianspence.cr@btinternet.com

MEIRIONNYDD. Jim Dustow, Afallon, 7 Glan y Don, Rhiwbryfdir, Blaenau Ffestiniog, Gwynedd LL41 3LW e-mail: Jim.Dustow@rspb.org.uk.

Bird Reports

BARDSEY BIRD OBSERVATORY ANNUAL REPORT, from the Warden, see Reserves.

CAMBRIAN BIRD REPORT (sometime Gwynedd Bird Report) (1953-), covers Anglesey, Meirionndd and Caernarfon, from Stephen Culley, Millhouse, Penmynydd Road, Menai Bridge, Anglesey, LL59 5RT. e-mail: SteCul10@aol.com

MEIRIONNYDD BIRD REPORT, published in Cambrian Bird Report (above).

NE WALES BIRD REPORT – was *Clwyd Bird Report (2002-),* from Dr Anne Brenchley, Ty'r Fawnog, 43 Black Brook, Sychdyn, Mold, Flints, CH7 6LT. 01352 750 118; e-mail: anne.brenchley@btinternet.com

WREXHAM BIRDWATCHERS' SOCIETY ANNUAL REPORT (1982-), from The Secretary, Wrexham Birdwatchers' Society.

BTO Regional Representatives

ANGLESEY RR. Tony White, 01407 710 137; e-mail: wylfor@treg5360.freeserve.co.uk

CAERNARFON RR. Geoff Gibbs, 01248 681 936; e-mail: geoffkate.gibbs@care4free.net

CLWYD EAST RR. Dr Anne Brenchley, Ty'r Fawnog, 43 Black Brook, Sychdyn, Mold, Flints, CH7 6LT. 01352 750 118; e-mail: anne.brenchley@btinternet.com

CLWYD WEST RR. Mel ab Owain, 31 Coed Bedw, Abergele, Conwy, LL22 7EH. 01745 826 528; e-mail: melabowain@btinternet.com

MEIRIONNYDD RR. David Anning. 01654 761 481; e-mail: davidanning@freeuk.com

Clubs

BANGOR BIRD GROUP. (1947; 100). Jane Prosser, 15 Victoria Street, Bangor, Gwynedd LL57 2HD.

CAMBRIAN ORNITHOLOGICAL SOCIETY. (1952; 190). Mr Rhion Pritchard, Pant Afonig, Hafod Lane, Bangor, Gwynedd, LL57 4BU. (H) 01248 671 301; e-mail: rhion@pritchardr.freeserve.co.uk
Meetings: 7.30pm, 1st Friday of the month, Pensychnant Centre, Sychnant Pass.

CLWYD BIRD RECORDING GROUP. Dr Anne Brenchley, Ty'r Fawnog, 43 Black Brook, Sychdyn, Mold, Flints, CH7 6LT. e-mail: anne.brenchley@btinternet.com

CLWYD ORNITHOLOGICAL SOCIETY. (1956; 45). EE Jones, Sandiway, Llanasa, Holywell, Flintshire CH8 9NE. 01745 852 984.

DEE ESTUARY CONSERVATION GROUP. (1973; 25 grps). Tony Perry, 10 Ridgeway Close, Connah's Quay, Deeside, CH5 4LZ. e-mail: decg@deeestuary.co.uk www.deeestuary.co.uk/decg.htm

DEESIDE NATURALISTS' SOCIETY. (1973; 700). Mrs Janice Jones, Secretary, 21 Woodlands Court, Hawarden, Deeside, Flints, CH5 3NB. 01244 537 440; e-mail: deenaturalists@btinernet.com www.deesidenaturalists.org.uk

WREXHAM BIRDWATCHERS' SOCIETY. (1974; 90). Miss Marian Williams, 10 Lake View, Gresford, Wrexham, Clwyd, LL12 8PU. 01978 854 633.
Meetings: 7.30pm, 1st Friday of the month (Sep-Apr), Gresford Memorial Hall, Gresford.

Ringing Groups

BARDSEY BIRD OBSERVATORY. Steven Stansfield, Bardsey Island, off Aberdaron, Pwllheli, Gwynedd, LL53 8DE. 07855 264 151; e-mail: warden@bbfo.org.uk

WALES

MERSEYSIDE RG. Bob Harris, 2 Dulas Road, Wavertree Green, Liverpool, L15 6UA. Work 0151 706 4311; e-mail: harris@liv.ac.uk

SCAN RG. Dr D. Moss
e-mail: dorian@dorianmoss.com

RSPB Local Group
NORTH WALES. (1986; 130). Maureen Douglas, 57 Penrhyn Beach East, Penrhyn Bay, Llandudno, Conwy LL30 3RW. 01492 547 768
Meetings: 3rd Friday of the month (Sep-Apr), St Davids Church Hall, Penrhyn Bay, LLANDUDNO, Gwynedd, LL30 3EJ.

Wetland Bird Survey Organisers
ANGLESEY (other sites). Ian Sims, Plas Nico, South Stack, Holyhead, LL65 1TH.

CONWY ESTUARY. Alan Davies, RSPB Conwy Reserve, Llandudno Junction, LL31 9XZ. 01492 584 091: e-mail: alan.davies@rspb.org.uk

CAERNARFONSHIRE (excl Traeth Lafan). Rhion Pritchard, Pant Afonig, Hafod Lane, Bangor, Gwynedd LL57 4BU. (H) 01248 671 301;
e-mail: rhion@pritchardr.freeserve.co.uk

CLWYD (Coastal). Mr Peter Wellington, 4 Cheltenham Avenue, Rhyl, Clwyd LL18 4DN. (H) 01745 3542 32.

CLWYD (INLAND), Elvet Jones, Sandiway, Llanasa, Holywell, Flints, CH8 9NE. 01745 852 984.

DEE ESTUARY. Colin Wells, Burton Point Farm, Station Road, Burton, Nr Neston, South Wirral, CH64 5SB. 0151 336 7681.

FORYD BAY. Simon Hugheston-Roberts, Oakhurst, St David's Road, Caernarfon, LL55 1EL.
e-mail: sm.roberts@ccw.gov.uk

MEIRIONNYDD (other sites). Mr Trefor Owen, Crochendy Twrog, Maentwrog, Blaenau Ffestiniog, LL41 3YU. (H) 01766 590 302.

TRAETH LAFAN. Mr Rhion Pritchard, Pant Afonig, Hafod Lane, Bangor, Gwynedd LL57 4BU. (H) 01248 671 301; e-mail: rhion@pritchardr.freeserve.co.uk

Wildlife Trust
NORTH WALES WILDLIFE TRUST. (1963; 4,609). 376 High Street, Bangor, Gwynedd, LL57 1YE. 01248 351 541; (Fax) 01248 353 192;
e-mail: nwwt@cix.co.uk
www.wildlifetrust.org.uk/northwales

SOUTH WALES

Bird Atlas/Avifauna
An Atlas of Breeding Birds in West Glamorgan by David M Hanford et al (Gower Ornithological Society, 1992).

Birds of Glamorgan by Clive Hurford and Peter Lansdown (Published by the authors, c/o National Museum of Wales, Cardiff, 1995)

Bird Recorders
GLAMORGAN (EAST). Geri Thomas, 9 Julian's Close, Gelligaer, Glamorgan CF82 8DT. (H) 01443 836 949; (M) 07984 591 983;
e-mail: geri.thomas@btopenworld.com

GOWER (WEST GLAMORGAN). Robert Taylor, 285 Llangyfelach Road, Brynhyfryd, Swansea, SA5 9LB. 01792 464 780; (M) 07970 567 007;
e-mail: rob@birding.freeserve.co.uk

Bird Reports
EAST GLAMORGAN BIRD REPORT (title varies 1963-95) 1996-2003, from Richard G Smith, 35 Manor Chase, Gwaun Miskin, Pontypridd, Rhondda Cynon Taff, S Wales, CF38 2JD.
e-mail: rgsmith@birdpix.freeserve.co.uk

GOWER BIRDS (1965-), from Jane Jones, 22 Kilfield Road, Bishopston, Swansea, SA3 3DL. 01792 232 316; e-mail: gowerbirdsf@hotmail.com
www.glamorganbirds.org.uk

BTO Regional Representatives
EAST GLAMORGAN (former Mid & South Glam) RR. Rob Nottage, 32 Village Farm, Bonvilston, Cardiff, CF5 6TY. e-mail: rob@nottages.freeserve.co.uk

WEST RR. Bob Howells, Ynys Enlli, 14 Dolgoy Close, West Cross, Swansea, SA3 5LT.
e-mail: bobhowells31@hotmail.com

Clubs
CARDIFF NATURALISTS' SOCIETY. (1867; 225). Stephen R Howe, National Museum of Wales, Cardiff, CF10 3NP.
e-mail: steve.howe@museumwales.ac.uk
www.cardiffnaturalists.org.uk
Meetings: 7.30pm, various evenings, Lecture Theatre EO.02, Llandaff Campus UWIC, Western Avenue, Cardiff.

GLAMORGAN BIRD CLUB. (1990; 300+). Pat Everett, 6 South View, Frampton Cotterell, Bristol, BS36 2HT. 01454 772 564;
e-mail: pat.everett@glamorganbirds.org.uk
Meetings: 7.30pm, 2nd Tuesday of winter months, Kentig Reserve Centre.

GOWER ORNITHOLOGICAL SOCIETY. (1956; 120). Jane Jones, 22 Kilfield Road, Bishopston, Swansea, SA3 3DL. 01792 232 316;
e-mail:
gowerbirdsf@hotmail.com
www.glamorganbirds.org.uk

Meetings: 7.15pm, last Friday of the month (Sep-Mar), The Environment Centre, Pier Street, Swansea.

Ringing Groups
FLAT HOLM RG. Brian Bailey, Tamarisk House, Wards Court, Frampton-on-Severn, Glos, GL2 7DY. e-mail: brian@sandbservices.fsnet.co.uk

KENFIG RG. Mr D.G. Carrington, 44 Ogmore Drive, Nottage, Porthcawl, Mid Glamorgan, CF36 3HR.

RSPB Local Groups
CARDIFF & DISTRICT. -1973. Joy Lyman, 5 Dros-Y-Morfa, Rumney, Cardiff, CF3 3BL. 02920 770 031; e-mail: joy@lyman.plus.com
www.RSPB.org.uk/groups/cardiff.
Meetings: 7.30pm, various Fridays (Sept-May), UWIC, Cyncoed Road, Cardiff.

WEST GLAMORGAN. (1985; 346). Maggie Cornelius, 01792 229 244; www.westglam-rspb.org.uk
e-mail: maggie@westglam-rspb.org.uk

Wetland Bird Survey Organisers
EAST GLAMORGAN (former Mid & South Glam), Rob Nottage, 32 Village Farm, Bonvilston, Cardiff, CF5 6TY. e-mail: rob@nottages.freeserve.co.uk

SEVERN ESTUARY, Niall Burton, c/o BTO, The Nunnery, Thetford, Norfolk, IP24 2PU.
e-mail: niall.burton@bto.org

WEST GLAMORGAN, Bob Howells, Ynys Enlli, 14 Dolgoy Close, West Cross, Swansea, SA3 5LT. 01792 405 363; e-mail: bobhowells31@hotmail.com

Wildlife Hospital
GOWER BIRD HOSPITAL. Karen Kingsnorth and Simon Allen, Valetta, Sandy Lane, Pennard, Swansea, SA3 2EW. 01792 371 630;
e-mail: info@gowerbirdhospital.org.uk
www.gowerbirdhospital.org.uk
All species of wild birds, also hedgehogs and small mammals. Prior phone call essential. Gower Bird Hospital cares for sick, injured and orphaned wild birds and animals with the sole intention of returning them to the wild. Post release radio tracking projects, ringing scheme. Contact us for more information.

Wildlife Trust
WILDLIFE TRUST OF SOUTH AND WEST WALES. (1961; 6,000). Nature Centre, Parc Slip, Fountain Road, Tondu, Bridgend CF32 0EH. 01656 724 100; (Fax) 01656 729 880; e-mail: info@welshwildlife.org
www.welshwildlife.org

WEST WALES

Bird Atlas/Avifauna
Birds of Pembrokeshire by Jack Donovan and Graham Rees (Dyfed Wildlife Trust, 1994).

Bird Recorders
CARMARTHENSHIRE. Derek Moore, Rowan HoweGors Road, Salem, Llandeilo, Carmarthenshire, SA19 7LY. 01558 823 708;
e-mail: DerekBirdBrain@aol.com

CEREDIGION. Hywel Roderick, 32 Prospect Street, Aberystwyth, Ceredigion, SY23 1JJ. 01970 617 681, e-mail: hywel@adar.freeserve.co.uk

PEMBROKESHIRE 1. Stephen Berry, 1 Cunard House, Quay Road, Goodwick SA64 0BS. 01348 872 233; e-mail: stephen.berry16@btinternet.com.

PEMBROKESHIRE 2. Jon Green, Crud Yr Awel, Bowls Road, Blaenporth, Ceredigion SA43 2AR. 01239 811 561; e-mail: jonrg@tiscali.co.uk.

Bird Reports
CARMARTHENSHIRE BIRD REPORT (1982-), from Mrs Angela Lovegrove, Newton Park Farm House, Cynwyl Elfed, Carmarthenshire SA33 6SP.

CEREDIGION BIRD REPORT (biennial 1982-87; annual 1988-), from Wildlife Trust West Wales.

PEMBROKESHIRE BIRD REPORT (1981-), from TJ Price, 2 Wordsworth Ave, Haverfordwest, Pembrokeshire, SA61 1SN.
e-mail: trevjprice@hotmail.com

BTO Regional Representatives
CARDIGAN RR. Moira Convery, 41 Danycoed, Aberystwyth SY23 2HD. 01970 612 998;
e-mail: moira@mconvery.freeserve.co.uk

CARMARTHEN RR. Colin Jones, 01554 821 632;
e-mail: colinjones25@yahoo.co.uk

PEMBROKE RR. Annie and Bob Haycock, 1 Rushmoor, Martletwy, Pembrokeshire, SA67 8BB. 01834 891 667;
e-mail: rushmoor1@tiscali.co.uk

Clubs
LLANELLI NATURALISTS. (1971; 100). Richard Pryce, Trevethin, School Road, Pwll, Llanelli, Carmarthenshire, SA15 4AL.
e-mail: pryceeco@aol.com
Meetings: 1st Thursday of the month, YWCA Llanelli (see programme in local libraries).

PEMBROKESHIRE BIRD GROUP. (1993; 60). T J Price, 2 Wordsworth Ave, Haverfordwest, Pembs, SA61 1SN. 01437 779667.
Meetings: 7.30pm, 1st Tuesday of the month (Oct-Apr), The Patch, Furzy Park, Haverfordwest.

Ringing Group
PEMBROKESHIRE RG. J Hayes, 3 Wades Close, Holyland Road, Pembroke, SA71 4BN. 01646 687 036; e-mail: hayes313@btinternet.com.

WALES

Wetland Bird Survey Organisers
BURRY INLET, NORTH, Graham Rutt, Springfield, Ffynone Road, Uplands, Swansea, SA1 6DE. 01792 325 603.

DYFI & DYSINNI ESTUARIES , Dick Squires, Cae'r Berllan, Eglwysfach, Machynlleth, Powys, SY20 8TA. e-mail: dick.squires@rspb.org.uk

CARDIGAN, Dick Squires, Cae'r Berllan, Eglwysfach, Machynlleth, Powys, SY20 8TA. e-mail: dick.squires@rspb.org.uk

CARMARTHEN, BAY AND INLAND. Ian Hainsworth, 23 Rhyd y Defaid Drive, Swansea, SA2 8AJ. 01792 205 693; e-mail: ian.hains@ntlworld.com www.carmarthenshirebirds.co.uk

Wildlife Hospitals
NEW QUAY BIRD HOSPITAL. Jean Bryant, Penfoel, Cross Inn, Llandysul, Ceredigion, SA44 6NR. 01545 560 462. All species of birds. Fully equipped for cleansing oiled seabirds. Veterinary support.

WEST WILLIAMSTON OILED BIRD CENTRE. Mrs J Hains, Lower House Farm, West Williamston, Kilgetty, Pembs, SA68 0TL. 01646 651 236. Facilities for holding up to 200 Guillemots, etc. for short periods. Initial treatment is given prior to despatch to other washing centres during very large oil spills; otherwise birds are washed at the Centre with intensive care and rehabilitation facilities. Also other species. Veterinary support.

Wildlife Trust
See South Wales.

ISLE OF MAN

Bird Atlas/Avifauna
Manx Bird Atlas. 5-yr BBS and Winter Atlas research completed. (Liverpool University 2007). Contact: Chris Sharpe (see below, BTO Representative).

Bird Recorder
Dr Pat Cullen, Troutbeck, Cronkbourne, Braddan, Isle of Man, IM4 4QA. Home: 01624 623308; Work 01624 676774; e-mail: bridgeen@mcb.net

Bird Reports
MANX BIRD REPORT (1947-), published in *Peregrine*. Mrs A C Kaye, Cronk Ny Ollee, Glen Chass, Port St Mary, Isle of Man, IM9 5PL.

CALF OF MAN BIRD OBSERVATORY ANNUAL REPORT, from The Secretary, Manx National Heritage, Manx Museum, Douglas, Isle of Man, IM1 3LY.

BTO Regional Representative & Regional Development Officer
RR. Dr Pat Cullen, as above, 01624 623 308.

RDO. Chris Sharpe, 33 Mines Road, Laxey, Isle of Man, IM4 7NH. 01624 861 130; e-mail: chris@manxbirdatlas.org.uk

Club
MANX ORNITHOLOGICAL SOCIETY. (1967; 150). Mrs A C Kaye, Cronk Ny Ollee, Glen Chass, Port St Mary, Isle of Man, IM9 5PL. 01624 834 015
Meetings: 1st Tues in month, 7.30pm, Union Mills Hall.

Ringing Group
MANX RINGING GROUP. Chris Sharpe, 33 Mines Road, Laxey, Isle of Man, IM4 7NH. 01624 861130; e-mail: chris@manxbirdatlas.org.uk

Wetland Bird Survey Organiser
Pat Cullen, Troutbeck, Cronkbourne, Braddan, Isle of Man, IM4 4QA. (H)01624 623 308; (W)01624 676 774; e-mail: bridgeen@mcb.net

Dr Pat Cullen, Troutbeck, Cronkbourne, Braddan, Isle of Man, IM4 4QA. (H) 01624 623 308; (W) 01624 676 774; e-mail: bridgeen@mcb.net

Wildlife Trust
MANX WILDLIFE TRUST. (1973; 900). The Courtyard, Tynwald Mills, St Johns, Isle of Man IM4 3AE. 01624 801 985; (Fax) 01624 801 022; e-mail: manxwt@cix.co.uk
www.wildlifetrust.org.uk/manxwt/

CHANNEL ISLANDS

ALDERNEY

Bird Recorder
Mark Atkinson. E-mail: atkinson@cwgsy.net.

Bird Report
ALDERNEY SOCIETY ORNITHOLOGY REPORT (1992-), from the Recorder.

BTO Regional Representative
Jamie Hooper, 1 Trinity Cottages, Torteval, Guernsey, GY8 0QD. (Tel/Fax) 01481 266 924; e-mail: jamie.hooper@cwgsy.net

Wildlife Trust
ALDERNEY WILDLIFE TRUST (2002; 460). Alderney Information Centre, 34 Victoria Street, St Anne Alderney GY9 3AA. 01481 822 935; (Fax) 01481 822 935; e-mail: info@alderneywildlife.org www.alderneywildlife.org

GUERNSEY

Bird Atlas/Avifauna
Birds of the Bailiwick of Guernsey (working title). In preparation.

Bird Recorder
Mark Lawlor; e-mail: mplawlor@cwgsy.net

Bird Report
REPORT & TRANSACTIONS OF LA SOCIETE GUERNESIAISE (1882-), from the Recorder.

BTO Regional Representative
Jamie Hooper, 1 Trinity Cottages, Torteval, Guernsey, GY8 0QD. (Tel/Fax) 01481 266 924; e-mail: jamie.hooper@cwgsy.net

Clubs
LA SOCIÉTIÉ GUERNESIAISE (Ornithological Section). (1882; 30). The Secretary, e-mail: societe@cwgsy.net
www.societe.org.gg
Meetings: First Thurs of month, 8pm, Candie Gardens lecture theatre.

RSPB Local Group
GUERNSEY. (1975; 350+). Michael Bairds, Les Quatre Vents, La Passee, St Sampsons, Guernsey, GY2 4TS. 01481 255 524; e-mail: mikebairds@cwgsy.nett
www.rspbguernsey.co.uk

Wetland Bird Survey Organiser
GUERNSEY COAST. Mary Simmons, Les Maeures, Mont d'Aval, Castel, Guernsey, GY5 7UQ. 01481 256 016; e-mail: msim@cwgsy.net

Wildlife Hospital
GUERNSEY. GSPCA ANIMAL SHELTER. Mrs Jayne Le Cras, Rue des Truchots, Les Fiers Moutons, St Andrews, Guernsey, Channel Islands, GY6 8UD. 01481 257 261; e-mail: jaynelecras@gspca.org.gg. All species. Modern cleansing unit for oiled seabirds. 24-hour emergency service. Veterinary support.

JERSEY

Bird Recorder
Tony Paintin, 16 Quennevais Gardens, St Brelade, Jersey, Channel Islands, JE3 8FQ. 01534 741 928; e-mail: cavokjersey@hotmail.com

Bird Report
JERSEY BIRD REPORT, from La Société Jersiaise, 7 Pier Road, St Helier, Jersey JE2 4XW.
e-mail: societe@societe-jersiaise.org

BTO Regional Representative
Tony Paintin, 16 Quennevais Gardens, St Brelade, Jersey, Channel Islands, JE3 8FQ. 01534 741 928; e-mail: cavokjersey@hotmail.com

Club
SOCIÉTIÉ JERSIAISE (Ornithological Section). (1948; 40). C/O La Société Jersiaise, 7 Pier Road, St Helier, Jersey JE2 4XW. 01534 758 314;
e-mail: societe@societe-jersiaise.org
www.societe-jersiaise.org
Meetings: 8.00pm, alternate Thursdays throughout the year, Museum in St.Helier.

Wildlife Hospital
JERSEY. JSPCA ANIMALS' SHELTER. The Secretary, 89 St Saviour's Road, St Helier, Jersey, JE2 4GJ. 01534 724 331; (Fax) 01534 871797;
e-mail: info@jspca.org.je
www.jspca.org.je All species. Expert outside support for owls and raptors. Oiled seabird unit. Veterinary surgeon on site. Educational Centre.

NORTHERN IRELAND

Bird Recorder
George Gordon, 2 Brooklyn Avenue, Bangor, Co Down, BT20 5RB. 028 9145 5763; e-mail: gordon@ballyholme2.freeserve.co.uk

Bird Reports
NORTHERN IRELAND BIRD REPORT, from Secretary, Northern Ireland, Birdwatchers' Association (see National Directory).

IRISH BIRD REPORT, Included in Irish Birds, BirdWatch Ireland in National Directory.

COPELAND BIRD OBSERVATORY REPORT, from the observatory, see Reserves.

BTO Regional Representatives
BTO IRELAND OFFICER. Shane Wolsey, 028 9146 7947; e-mail: shane@swolsey.biz

ANTRIM & BELFAST. Position vacant.

ARMAGH. David W A Knight, 20 Mandeville Drive, Tandragee, Craigavon, Co Armagh, BT62 2DQ. 028 38 840 658; e-mail: david.knight@niwater.com

DOWN. Position vacant.

FERMANAGH. Position vacant.

LONDONDERRY. Charles Stewart, Bravallen, 18 Duncrun Road, Bellarena, Limavady, Co Londonderry, BT49 0JD. 028 7775 0468; e-mail: charles.stewart2@btinternet.com

TYRONE. Position vacant.

Clubs
NORTHERN IRELAND BIRDWATCHERS' ASSOCIATION see National Directory.

NORTHERN IRELAND ORNITHOLOGISTS' CLUB, see National Directory.

CASTLE ESPIE BIRDWATCHING CLUB. (1995; 60). Dot Blakely, 8 Rosemary Park, Bangor, Co Down, BT20 3EX. 028 9145 0784.

Ringing Groups
COPELAND BIRD OBSERVATORY. C W Acheson, 28 Church Avenue, Dunmurry, Belfast, BT17 9RS.

NORTH DOWN RINGING GROUP. Hugh Thurgate, 16 Inishmore, Killyleagh, Downpatrick, Co Down, BT30 9TP.

RSPB Local Groups
ANTRIM. (1977; 23). Agnes Byron, 028 9446 2207.
Meetings: 8pm, 2nd Monday of the month, College of Agriculture Food & Rural Enterprise, 22 Greenmount Road.

BANGOR. (1973; 25). Fulton Somerville.
E-mail: fulton.somerville@newryandmourne.gov.uk
Meetings: Trinity Presbyterian Church Hall, Main Street, BANGOR, County Down.

BELFAST. (1970; 130). Ron Houston.028 9079 6188.
Meetings: Cooke Centenary Church Hall, Cooke Centenary Church Hall, Ormeau Rd, BELFAST.

COLERAINE. (1978; 45). Peter Robinson, 34 Blackthorn Court, Coleraine, Co Londonderry, BT52 2EX. 028 7034 4361;
e-mail: robinson493@btinternet.com
Meetings: 7.30pm, third Monday of the month (Sept-Apr), St Patricks Church, Minor Church Hall, Corner of Brook St and Circular Road, Coleraine.

FERMANAGH. (1977; 28). Barbara Johnston028 6634 1708; e-mail: johnston.cb@googlemail.com
Meetings: 7.30pm, 4th Tuesday of the month, St Macartans Church Hall.

FOYLE. Andrea Mitchell, 028 7134 9125;
e-mail: mitchellandrea@hotmail.com
Meetings: 4th Monday of the month, Loughs Agency Building, 22 Victoria Road, PREHEN

LARNE. (1974; 35). Jimmy Christie, 314 Coast Road, Ballygally, Co Antrim, BT40 2QZ. 028 2858 3223;
e-mail: candjchristie@btinternet.com
Meetings: 7.30pm, 1st Wednesday of the month, Larne Grammar School.

LISBURN. (1978; 30). David McCreedy, 10 Downside Avenue, Banbridge, Co Down, BT32 4BP. 028 4062 6125; e-mail: david@dmccreedy@wanadoo.co.uk
www.rspblisburn.com
Meetings: 7.30pm, 4th Monday of the month, Friends Meeting House, 4 Magheralave Road,

Wetland Bird Survey Organisers
ANTRIM, BELFAST LOUGH. John O'Boyle, Environment & Heritage Service, Commonwealth House, 35 Castle Street, Belfast BT1 1GU. 028 9054 6521; e-mail: john.oboyle@doeni.gov.uk

ANTRIM, LOUGHS NEAGH & BEG. Steve Foster, Peatlands Park, 33 Derryhubbert Road, Verner's Bridge, Dungannon BT71 6NW. (W) 028 3832 2398; e-mail: Stephen.foster@doeni.gov.uk

DOWN, BELFAST LOUGH. John O'Boyle, Environment & Heritage Service, Commonwealth House, 35 Castle Street, Belfast BT1 1GU. 028 9054 6521; e-mail: john.oboyle@doeni.gov.uk

DOWN, CARLINGFORD LOUGH. Frank Carroll, 292 Barcroft Park, Newry, Co. Down BT35 8ET. (H) 01693 68015

DOWN, OUTER ARDS. Neil McCulloch, Environment & Heritage Service, Commonwealth House, 35 Castle Street, Belfast BT1 1GU. 01232 251 477; e-mail: neil.mcCulloch@doeni.gov.uk

DOWN, STRANGFORD LOUGH. Paddy Mackie, Mahee island, Comber, Newtonards, Co. Down, BT23 6EP. (Tel/Fax) 028 9754 1420

FERMANAGH. Neil McCulloch, Environment & Heritage Service, Commonwealth House, 35 Castle Street, Belfast BT1 1GU. 01232 251 477; e-mail: neil.mcCulloch@doeni.gov.uk

LONDONDERRY, BANN ESTUARY. Hill Dick, 33 Hopefield Avenue, Portrush, Co. Antrim BT56 8HB.

Wildlife Hospital

TACT WILDLIFE CENTRE. Mrs Patricia Nevines, 2 Crumlin Road, Crumlin, Co Antrim, BT29 4AD. (Tel/Fax) 028 9442 2900; e-mail: tactwildlife@btinternet.com All categories of birds treated and rehabilitated; released where practicable, otherwise given a home. Visitors (inc. school groups and organisations) welcome by prior arrangement. Veterinary support.

Wildlife Trust

ULSTER WILDLIFE TRUST. (1978; 6,000). 3 New Line, Crossgar, Co Down, BT30 9EP. 028 4483 0282; (Fax) 028 4483 0888;
e-mail: info@ulsterwildlifetrust.org
www.ulsterwildlifetrust.org

REPUBLIC OF IRELAND

Bird Recorders

BirdWatch Ireland, P.O. Box 12, Greystones, Co. Wicklow, Ireland. 353 (0)1 2819 878 (Fax) 353 (0)1 2810 997; e-mail: info@birdwatchireland.ie
www.birdwatchireland.ie

Rarities. Paul Milne, 100 Dublin Road, Sutton, Dublin 13, +353 (0)1 832 5653;
e-mail: paul.milne@oceanfree.net

CLARE. John Murphy, e-mail: jemurphy@esatclearie

CORK. Mark Shorten, e-mail: mshorten@indigo.ie

DONEGAL. Ralph Sheppard,
e-mail: rsheppard@eircom.net

EAST COAST. Tom Cooney,
e-mail: tom.cooney@oceanfree.net

GALWAY. Tim Griffin, 74 Monalee Heights, Knocknacarra.

KERRY. Edward Carty, 3 The Orchard, Ballyrickard, Tralee.

LIMERICK. Tony Mee, Ballyorgan, Kilfinane, Co. Limerick.

MAYO. Tony Murray, National Parks and Wildlife, Lagduff More, Ballycroy, Westport.

MID-SHANNON. Stephen Heery,
e-mail: sheery@eircom.net

MONAGHAN. Joe Shannon,
e-mail: vjoeshan@eircom.net

WATERFORD. Paul Walsh, 16 Castlepoint, Crosshaven, Co. Cork;
e-mail: pmwalsh@waterfordbirds.com

WEXFORD. Chris Wilson, Wexford Wildfowl Reserve, North Slob.

Bird Reports

IRISH BIRD REPORT, contact BirdWatch Ireland in National, Directory).

CAPE CLEAR BIRD OBSERVATORY ANNUAL REPORT, from the observatory.

CORK BIRD REPORT (1963-71; 1976-), Cork Bird Report Editorial Team, Long Strand, Castlefreke, Clonakilty, Co. Cork; e-mail: cbr@corkecology.net

EAST COAST BIRD REPORT (1980-), Contact BirdWatch Ireland.

BirdWatch Ireland Branches

Branches may be contacted in writing via BirdWatch Ireland HQ (see entry in National Directory).

Ringing Groups

CAPE CLEAR B.O, Mr M.E. O'Donnell, Barnlands, Killinieran, Gorey, Co Wexford,
e-mail: micealodonnell@eircom.net

GREAT SALTEE RINGING STATION, Mr O J Merne, 20 Cuala Road, Bray, Co Wicklow, Ireland,
e-mail: omerne@eircom.net

MUNSTER RG, Mr K.P.C. Collins, Ballygambon, Lisronagh, Clonmel, County Tipperary,
e-mail: kcsk@eircom.net

NAT. PARKS & WILDLIFE SERVICE, Mr A.J. Walsh, Wildfowl Reserve, North Slob, Wexford, Eire,
e-mail: alynwalsh@eircom.net

SHANNON WADER RG, Mr P.A. Brennan, The Crag, Stonehall, Newmarket-On-Fergus, Co. Clare,
e-mail: philip@philipbrennan.com

ARTICLES IN BIRD REPORTS

Angus and Dundee Bird Report 2005
- Laughing Gull, Carnoustie Bay by Richard Bramhall
- Yellowhammers in a Monifieth garden by Arthur c Bastable
- The first Rustic Bunting for Angus by Richard Bramhall
- Breeding terns at GlaxoSmithKline, Montrose by Les Hatton
- First Isabelline Shrike for Angus by Richard Bramhall
- NB: The articles by Richard Bramhall have previously been published in *Birding Scotland*

Avon Bird Report 2005
- Unusual ornithological events in the Avon area 1945-1980 by AH Davis
- Historical perspective of Feral Pigeon populations by J Tully
- Identification of Marsh and Willow Tits by JP Martin
- Upland Sandpiper at Channel View Farm by R Hunt
- The Waxwing invasion by RL Bland
- BBS for Avon 2005 by J Tully
- Avon Ringing report by LF Roberts

Ayrshire Bird Report 2006
- The birds of the Hunterston area 1968-1999 by Marco McGinty and James Towill
- Skuas at Saltcoats in 2006 by Jason McManus
- Analysis of Barn Owl pellets in East Ayrshire by Alistair Murdoch
- Kestrel in Ayrshire 2006 by Gordon Riddle
- Sparrow breeding details 2006 by Ian Todd

Birds of Berkshire 2000-7
- Cormorant breeding survey 2000 by Pat Martin
- House Sparrows in College Town by Des Sussex
- Honey Buzzard influx in 2000 by Chris Heard
- Autumn passage of Yellow Wagtails by Pete Standley and Richard Crawford
- A Black Kite in West Berkshire by Chris Heard

Borders Bird Report No. 23 2005
- Ringing in Borders 2005
- Tree Sparrow Survey 1998-9
- Bird crime report for Borders 2005

Cambridgeshire Bird Report 2005
- Great Fen Project by Chris Gerrard
- Numbers of water birds at Grafham Water reservoir 1964-2002 by Daniel Piec
- An exceptional influx of Tundra Bean Geese in winter 2004/5 by Mark Ward
- The breeding birds of Monks Wood by Richard Broughton, Shelley Hinsley, Paul Bellamy

Carmarthenshire Birds 2004-5
- The BTO in Carmarthenshire by Colin Jones
- National Wetland Centre - ringing report 2005 by Heather Coats
- Ceredigion Bird Report 2004-2005
- Bonaparte's Gull - first county record by Mark Hughes
- Nightjar Survey by Ray Bamford
- Ringing Report by Dave Reed

Cheshire and Wirral Bird Report 2005
- Report on bird ringing in Cheshire and Wirral by Prof D Norman
- Chimney Swift at Wooston Eyes by D Riley
- Black Kite at Moore by A Wraithnel et al
- Pallas's Warbler wintering in Cheshire by RM Blindell et al
- Whiskered Terns at Ashtons Flash by M Fearn
- Long-billed Dowitcher at IMF RSPB reserve by S Hinde
- Cetti's Warblers at Neston reedbed by S Williams
- Breeding Little Egrets on the Dee Estuary 2005 by C Wells
- Waxwing influx 2004/5 by P Oddy
- 'Channel' Wagtail by AM Pulsford

Birds and Wildlife in Cumbria 2005
- Birds wintering in the Kendal/Killington area 2005/6 by Clive Hartley

Derbyshire Bird Report 2005
- Surf Scoter (at Foremark Reservoir - a new species for Derbyshire by RW Key
- White-tailed Eagle at Bueley Moor and Harland Edge - a new species for Derbyshire by ME Taylor
- Dartford Warbler at The Sanctuary, Derby - a new species for the society by RW Key
- Cormorants apparently rearing two broods by T Cockburn
- Pale female Yellowhammer at Barlow Edge during spring/summer 2005 by RW Key

Birds in Dumfries and Galloway 2005
- Donald Watson 1918-2005 an appreciation
- Systematic species accounts 2002-5
- Table summarising Galloway Mute Swan survey 2002
- North Solway Ringing Group constant effort site 2005, Lochfoot summary table

Birds in Greater Manchester; County Report 2006
- The breeding Peregrines in the City Centre by Judith Smith
- Greater Manchester County Year List 2006 (Birding on the edge!) by Robert Adderley
- Wintering birds in SD91 East Rochdale and Littleborough area (The Atlas 2007-11 winter pilot) by Steve Adkins and Steve Suttill.
- The BTO/RSPB/JNCC Breeding Bird Survey in the Manchester Region, 2006 by Judith Smith

Hampshire Bird Report 2005
- Tawny Owl Survey 2005 by BS Sharkey
- The Hobby in The Twilight Zone by I Pibworth
- Corn Bunting survey 2005 by KF Betton
- Birding by Bike by JM Clark
- Desert Wheatear by AC Johnson and SK Woolley
- First for Hampshire - Laughing Gull by JA Norton and PN Raby
- First for Hampshire - Radde's Warbler by NJ Montefriffo and A Pink

ARTICLES IN BIRD REPORTS

The Hertfordshire Bird Report 2004
- Review of the year by Ted Fletcher
- Bird Ringing report 2004 by Chris Dee
- BTO Breeding Bird Survey results for 2004 by Chris Dee
- Winter Gull Roost Survey January 2004 by Joan Thompson

Highland Bird Report 2005
- Highland Ringing Group report 2005 by Bob Swan et al
- The dynamics of a Highland Swallow Roost by Hugh Insley et al
- *Birds of the Cromarty Firth 1867* by W Vincent Legge (reprint of historical article)

Kent Bird Report 2005
- Marsh Harriers in Kent and the 2005 Breeding Survey by Peter Oliver
- Changes in Bird Populations at Bough Beech 1969-71 to 2005-7 by Chas Langton

The Leicestershire and Rutland Bird Report 2005
- Review of the year by Rob Fray
- Leicestershire and Rutland Wetland Bird Survey counts Rob Fray
- The arrival and departure of summer migants by Rob Fray
- Long-billed Dowitcher - new to county list by Steve Lister
- Visible migration at Deans Lane in autumn 2005 by Steve Lister
- Waxwings in Leicestershire and Rutland in 2005 by Rob Fray

Lincolnshire Rare and Scarce Bird report 1997-1999
- Summary of rare and scarce birds in Lincolnshire, reviews for 1997, 1998, 1999 by Steve Keightley
- Selected systematic list 1997-1999 by J Eastmead et al
- Accounts of Lincolnshire rarities 1997-1999
- Whistling Swan by Kevin Durose
- Franklin's Gull by Kevin Durose
- River Warbler by Kevin Durose
- Little Swift by Graham Catley
- Red flanked Bluetail by Kevin Durose

London Bird Report 2004
- Ringing report by Roger Taylor
- Breeding bird survey by Ian Woodward
- House Sparrow monitoring 1995-2003 by Helen Baker
- Meadow Pipits at Walton Heath by Alan Prowse

The Manx bird Report for 2005 by Pat Cullen
- Red Grouse in the Isle of Man 2005 by Bruce Walker
- Early and late dates of migrants in 2005 by Allen S. Moore
- Choughs in the Isle of Man 2005 by Allen S. Moore
- 2004 - a very good year for Choughs in the Isle of Man by Allen S. Moore
- Welsh Choughs in the Isle of Man by Allen S. Moore
- Report of the Manx Ringing Group 1997-2005 by Kevin Scott

Norfolk Bird Report 2006
- The Rook/Jackdaw roost at Buckenham Carrs by Mark Cocker
- Population explosion of nesting gulls in Great Yarmouth by Peter Allan
- First recorded roof-nesting of Common Terns in Norfolk by C Dye
- An interesting Pied Flycatcher on Blakeney Point by Mick Fiszer and Keith Dye
- Rose-breasted Grosbeak at Holme - addition to the Norfolk list by Jed Andrews

North East Scotland Bird Report 2005
- Black Grouse in NE Scotland in 2005 by I Francis and A Pout
- Barrow's Goldeneye at Meikle Loch - the first record for NE Scotland by P Shepard
- Bonaparte's Gull at Peterhead - a first for NE Scotland by A Thiel
- Belted Kingfisher in Aberdeen - the first Scottish record by K Landsman

Northern Ireland Bird Report 2003-4
- Little Shearwater at Ramore Head by Anthony McGeehan
- Polygamy - A new phase in Hen Harrier ecology by Don Scott

Birds in Northumbria 2005
- Franklin's Gull at Woodhorn by Jimmy Steele
- Chimney Swift at Holt Island by Michael Frankis
- Wetland bird survey 2005 by Steve Holliday et al
- Breeding bird survey report 2003-5 by Tom and Muriel Cadwallender
- Historical bird notes from Seaton sluice to Tynemouth by Peter Tapsell
- Rare birds in Northumberland by Andy Mould

Orkney Bird Report 2006
- Ringing report 2006 by Jim Williams
- North Ronaldsay Bird Observatory report 2006 by Alison Duncan
- Breeding Red-breasted Mergansers by Chris Booth
- Red-throated Diver survey 2006 by Stuart J Williams
- Hen Harriers in Orkney 2002-6 by Jim Williams
- The North Ronaldsay seawatch on Aug 31 by Bob Simpson

The Sussex Bird Report no.58 - 2005
- The Sussex Ringing Report for 2005 by RDM Edgar and S McKenaie
- Ivory Gulls in Sussex by RJ Fairbank
- Diseases of Garden Birds by RT Pepper
- The 2004/5 Waxwing invasion by A.Thomas
- Expansion of the Breeding Bird Survey in Sussex by Dr H. Crabtree
- Gull-billed Tern Lingering on the Sussex Coast, Summer 2005 by CW Melgar
- A Review of the Results of the WeBs in Sussex by Dr JA Newnham et al.

Hobby 2005 (Wiltshire OS)
- Species new to Wiltshire - Red-rumped Swallow at Corsham Lake
- Porton Down breeding bird survey 2005
- Salisbury Plain breeding bird survey 2005
- Stonehenge World Heritage Site breeding bird survey 2005
- Wiltshire Yellow Wagtail survey 2004

NATIONAL DIRECTORY

Goosander by Nick Williams

NATIONAL ORGANISATIONS

ARMY ORNITHOLOGICAL SOCIETY (founded 1960; membership 200).
Open to MOD employees and civilians who have an interest in their local MOD estate. Activities include field meetings, expeditions, the preparation of checklists of birds on Ministry of Defence property, conservation advice and an annual bird count. Annual journal *The Osprey*, published with the RNBWS and RAFOS from Easter 2001. Bulletins/ newsletters twice a year.
Contact: Secretary AOS, Army Ornithological Society, JAMES Project Team, Battlesbury Brks, Warminster, BA12 9DT. 01264 382 910;
e-mail: secretary@aos.org.uk
www.aos.org.uk

ASSOCIATION FOR THE PROTECTION OF RURAL SCOTLAND (1926).
Works to protect Scotland's countryside from unnecessary or inappropriate development, recognising the needs of those who live and work there and the necessity of reconciling these with the sometimes competing requirements of recreational use.
Contact: Association for the Protection of Rural Scotland, Gladstone's Land, 3rd Floor, 483 Lawnmarket, Edinburgh EH1 2NT. 0131 225 7012;
e-mail: info@ruralscotland.org
www.ruralscotland.org

ASSOCIATION OF COUNTY RECORDERS AND EDITORS (1993; 120).
The basic aim of ACRE is to promote best practice in the business of producing county bird reports, in the work of Recorders and in problems arising in managing record systems and archives. Organises periodic conferences and publishes *NewsACRE*.
Contact: Association of County Recorders & Editors, c/o Mrs A Judith Smith, 12 Edge Green Street, Ashton-in-Makerfield, Wigan, WN4 8SL. 01942 712 615;
e-mail: judith@gmbirds.freeserve.co.uk

BARN OWL TRUST (1988)
Registered charity. Aims to conserve the Barn Owl and its environment through conservation, education, research and information. Free leaflets on all aspects of Barn Owl conservation. Educational material inc. video and resource pack. Book *Barn Owls on Site*, a guide for planners and developers. Works with and advises landowners, farmers, planners, countryside bodies and others to promote a brighter future for Britain's Barn Owls. Currently providing training for ecological consultants via a one-day training course, 'Barn Owl Ecology, Searches and Signs'. Open to phone calls Mon-Fri (9.am-5.pm). Send SAE for information.

Contact: Secretary, Barn Owl Trust, Waterleat, Ashburton, Devon TQ13 7HU. 01364 653 026;
e-mail: info@barnowltrust.org.uk
www.barnowltrust.org.uk

BIRD OBSERVATORIES COUNCIL (1970).
Objectives are to provide a forum for establishing closer links and co-operation between individual autonomous observatories and to help co-ordinate the work carried out by them. All accredited bird observatories affiliated to the Council undertake a ringing programme and provide ringing experience to those interested. Most also provide accommodation for visiting birdwatchers.
Contact: Peter Howlett, Bird Observatories Council, c/o Dept of Biodiversity, National Museum Wales, Cardiff CF10 3NP. 0292 057 3233; (Fax) 0292 023 9009;
e-mail: info@birdobscouncil.org.uk
www.birdobscouncil.org.uk

BIRD STAMP SOCIETY (1986; 220).
Quarterly journal *Flight* contains philatelic and ornithological articles. Lists all new issues and identifies species. Runs a quarterly Postal Auction; number of lots range from 400 to 800 per auction. UK subs £14 per annum from August 1.
Contact: Mrs R Bradley, Bird Stamp Society, 31 Park View, Crossway Green, Chepstow NP16 5NA. 01291 625 412. e-mail: bradley666@lycos.co.uk
www.bird-stamps.org

BIRDWATCH IRELAND (1968; 10,000).
The trading name of the Irish Wildbird Conservancy, a voluntary body founded in 1968 by the amalgamation of the Irish Society for the Protection of Birds, the Irish Wildfowl Conservancy and the Irish Ornithologists' Club. Now the BirdLife International partner in Ireland with 21 voluntary branches. Conservation policy is based on formal research and surveys of birds and their habitats. Owns or manages an increasing number of reserves to protect threatened species and habitats. Publishes *Wings* quarterly and *Irish Birds* annually, in addition to annual project reports and survey results.
Contact: BirdWatch Ireland, P.O. Box 12, Greystones, Co. Wicklow, Ireland. 353 (0)1 2819 878 (Fax) 353 (0)1 2810 997;
e-mail: info@birdwatchireland.ie
www.birdwatchireland.ie

BRITISH BIRDS RARITIES COMMITTEE (1959).
The Committee adjudicates records of species of rare occurrence in Britain (marked `R' in the Log Charts). Its annual report is published in *British Birds*. The BBRC also assesses records from the Channel Islands. In the case of rarities trapped for ringing, records should be sent to the Ringing Office of the British Trust for Ornithology, who will in turn forward them to the BBRC.
Contact: Hon Secretary, British Birds Rarities Committee, Mr N Hudson, Post Office Flat, Hugh Street, St Mary's, Isles of Scilly TR21 0JE. 01736 796 223; e-mail: secretary@bbrc.org.uk www.bbrc.org.uk

BRITISH DRAGONFLY SOCIETY (1983; 1604).
The BDS aims to promote the conservation and study of dragonflies. Members receive two issues of *Dragonfly News* and *BDS Journal* each year in spring and autumn. There are countrywide field trips, an annual members day and training is available on aspects of dragonfly ecology.
Contact: Hon Secretary, British Dragonfly Society, Mr H Curry, 23 Bowker Way, Whittlesey, Peterborough PE7 1PY.
e-mail: bdssecretary@dragonflysoc.org.uk
www.dragonflysoc.org.uk

BRITISH FALCONERS' CLUB (1927; 1,200).
Largest falconry club in Europe, with regional branches. Its aim is to encourage responsible falconers and conserve birds of prey by breeding, holding educational meetings and providing facilities, guidance and advice to those wishing to take up the sport. Publishes T*he Falconer* annually and newsletter twice yearly.
Contact: The British Falconers' Club, Westfield, Meeting Hill, Worstead, North Walsham, Norfolk, NR28 9LS. 01692 404 057;
e-mail: admin@britishfalconersclub.co.uk
www.britishfalconersclub.co.uk

BRITISH MUSEUM (NAT HIST)
see Walter Rothschild Zoological Museum.

BRITISH ORNITHOLOGISTS' CLUB (1892; 525).
A registered charity, the Club's objects are `the promotion of scientific discussion between members of the BOU, and others interested in ornithology, and to facilitate the publication of scientific information in connection with ornithology'. The Club maintains a special interest in avian systematics, taxonomy and distribution. About eight dinner meetings are held each year. Publishes the *Bulletin of the British Ornithologists' Club* quarterly, also (since 1992) a continuing series of occasional publications.
Contact: British Ornithologists' Club, BOC Office, PO Box 417, Peterborough PE7 3FX. 01733 844 820; e-mail: boc.admin@bou.org.uk
www.boc-online.org

BRITISH ORNITHOLOGISTS' UNION (1858; 1,250).
Founded by Professor Alfred Newton FRS and one of the world's oldest and most respected ornithological societies. It aims to promote ornithology within the scientific and birdwatching communities, both in Britain and around the world. This is largely achieved by the publication of its quarterly international journal, *Ibis* (1859-), featuring work at the cutting edge of our understanding of the world's birdlife. An active programme of meetings, seminars and conferences on the major current ornithological and bird conservation themes are run to inform birdwatchers and ornithologists about the work being undertaken around the world. Recent events have covered Avian Influenza and other Bird Diseases, Renewable Energy and Birds, Climate Change and Coastal Birds. The proceedings of many of these events can be viewed free of charge via the BOU website. The BOU also runs an annual grant scheme providing valuable funding for research and bird conservation projects around the world. Copies of exchange journals, books reviewed in Ibis and offprints are held as part of the Alexander Library in the Zoology Department of the University of Oxford (see Edward Grey Institute). The BOU Records Committee maintains the official British List (see below).
Contact: British Ornithologists' Union, Steve Dudley, PO Box 417, Peterborough PE7 3FX. 01733 844 820; e-mail: bou@bou.org.uk
www.bou.org.uk www.ibis.ac.uk

BRITISH ORNITHOLOGISTS' UNION RECORDS COMMITTEE.
The BOURC is a standing committee of the British Ornithologists' Union. Its function is to maintain the British List, the official list of birds recorded in Great Britain. The up-to-date list can be viewed on the BOU website. Where vagrants are involved it is concerned only with those which relate to potential additions to the British List (ie first records).
In this it differs from the British Birds Rarities Committee (qv). In maintaining the British List, it also differs from the BBRC in that it examines, where necessary, important pre-1950 records,

monitors introduced species for possible admission to or deletion from the List, and reviews taxonomy and nomenclature generally. BOURC reports are published in *Ibis*. Decisions contained in these reports which affect the List are also announced via the popular birdwatching press.
Contact: British Ornithologists' Union, Steve Dudley, PO Box 417, Peterborough PE7 3FX. 01733 844 820; e-mail: bourc@bou.org.uk www.bou.org.uk

BRITISH TRUST FOR ORNITHOLOGY (1933; 12,500).
A registered charity governed by an elected Council, it has a rapidly growing membership and enjoys the support of a large number of county and local birdwatching clubs and societies through the BTO/Bird Clubs Partnership. Its aims are: `To promote and encourage the wider understanding, appreciation and conservation of birds through scientific studies using the combined skills and enthusiasm of its members, other birdwatchers and staff.' Through the fieldwork of its members and other birdwatchers, the BTO is responsible for the majority of the monitoring of British birds, British bird population and their habitats. BTO surveys include the National Ringing Scheme, the Nest Record Scheme, the Breeding Bird Survey (in collaboration with JNCC and RSPB), and the Waterways Breeding Bird Survey --- all contributing to an integrated programme of population monitoring. The BTO also runs projects on the birds of farmland and woodland, also (in collaboration with WWT, RSPB and JNCC) the Wetland Bird Survey, Garden BirdWatch, which started in 1995, now has more than 16,000 participants. The Trust has 130 voluntary regional representatives (see County Directory) who organise fieldworkers for the BTO's programme of national surveys in which members participate. The results of these co-operative efforts are communicated to government departments, local authorities, industry and conservation bodies for effective action. For details of current activities see National Projects. Members receive *BTO News* six times a year and have the option of subscribing to the thrice-yearly journal, *Bird Study* and twice yearly *Ringing & Migration*. Local meetings are held in conjunction with bird clubs and societies; there are regional and national birdwatchers' conferences, and specialist courses in bird identification and modern censusing techniques. Grants are made for research, and members have the use of a lending and reference library at Thetford and the Alexander Library at the Edward Grey Institute of Field Ornithology (qv).

Contact: British Trust for Ornithology, The Nunnery, Thetford, Norfolk IP24 2PU. 01842 750 050; (Fax) 01842 750 030;
e-mail: info@bto.org www.bto.org

BTO SCOTLAND (2000; 13,000).
BTO Scotland is now in its seventh year of operation. Its main functions are to promote the work of the BTO in Scotland, to encourage greater participation in BTO survey work by Scottish birdwatchers, and to develop contract research income within Scotland. BTO Scotland ensures that the work the Trust does is not just related to the priorities of the UK as a whole but is also focused on the priorities of Scotland, with a landscape and wildlife so different from the rest of the UK.
Contact: BTO Scotland, School of Biological and Environmental Sciences, Cottrell Building, University of Stirling, Stirling, FK9 4LA. 01786 466 560 (Fax) 01786 466 561; www.bto.org
e-mail: scot.info@bto.org

BRITISH WATERFOWL ASSOCIATION
The BWA is an association of enthusiasts interested in keeping, breeding and conserving all types of waterfowl, including wildfowl and domestic ducks and geese. It is a registered charity, without trade affiliations, dedicated to educating the public about waterfowl and the need for conservation as well as to raising the standards of keeping and breeding ducks, geese and swans in captivity.
Contact: British Waterfowl Association, Mrs Sue Schubert, PO Box 163, Oxted RH8 0WP. 01892 740212; e-mail: info@waterfowl.org.uk www.waterfowl.org.uk

BRITISH WILDLIFE REHABILITATION COUNCIL (1987).
Its aim is to promote the care and rehabilitation of wildlife casualties through the exchange of information between people such as rehabilitators, zoologists and veterinary surgeons who are active in this field. Organises an annual symposium or workshop. Publishes a regular newsletter. Supported by many national bodies including the Zoological Society of London, the British Veterinary Zoological Society, the RSPCA, the SSPCA, and the Vincent Wildlife Trust.
Contact: Secretary, British Wildlife Rehab Council, Tim Thomas, Wildlife Department, RSPCA, Wilberforce Way, Southwater, Horsham, W Sussex RH13 9RS. e-mail: tim@bwrc.org.uk
www.bwrc.org.uk

NATIONAL ORGANISATIONS

BTCV (formerly British Trust for Conservation Volunteers) (1959).
It's mission is to create a more sustainable future by inspiring people and improving places. Between 2004 and 2008 it aims to enrich the lives of one million people, through involvement with BTCV, through volunteering opportunities, employment, improved health, and life skills development; to improve the biodiversity and local environment of 20,000 places and to support active citizenship in 5,000 community-based groups. BTCV is governed by a board of 6 volunteer trustees elected by the charity membership and currently supports 140,000 volunteers to take practical action to improve their urban and rural environments. Publishes a quarterly newsletter, *The Conserver,* a series of practical handbooks and a wide range of other publications. Further information and a list of local offices is available from the above address.
Contact: BTCV, Conservation Centre, Sedum House, Mallard Way, Potteric Carr, Doncaster, DN4 8DB. 01302 388 888;
e-mail: Information@btcv.org.uk
www.btcv.org.uk

BTCV CYMRU,
The Conservation Centre, Forest Farm Road, Whitchurch, Cardiff CF14 7JJ. 029 2052 0990; (Fax) 029 2052 2181; e-mail: wales@btcv.org.uk
www.btcvcymru.org

BTCV SCOTLAND
Runs 7-14 day `Action Breaks' in Scotland during which participants undertake conservation projects; weekend training courses in environmental skills; midweek projects in Edinburgh, Glasgow, Aberdeen, Stirling and Inverness.
Contact: BTCV Scotland, Balallan House, 24 Allan Park, Stirling FK8 2QG. 01786 479 697; (Fax) 01786 465359; e-mail: scotland@btcv.org.uk
www.btcv.org.uk

BTCV CONSERVATION VOLUNTEERS NORTHERN IRELAND (1983).
Conservation Volunteers Northern Ireland, Beech House, 159 Ravenhill Road, BELFAST BT6 0BP. 028 9064 5169; (Fax) 028 9064 4409;
e-mail: CVNI@btcv.org.uk www.cvni.org

CAMPAIGN FOR THE PROTECTION OF RURAL WALES (1928; 2,800)
Its aims are to help the conservation and enhancement of the landscape, environment and amenities of the countryside, towns and villages of rural Wales and to form and educate opinion to ensure the promotion of its objectives. It recognises the importance of the indigenous cultures of rural Wales and gives advice and

information upon matters affecting protection, conservation and improvement of the visual environment.
Contact: Director, CPRW, Peter Ogden, Tŷ Gwyn, 31 High Street, Welshpool, Powys SY21 7YD. 01938 552 525/556 212; (Fax) 552 741;
www.cprw.org.uk

CENTRE FOR ECOLOGY & HYDROLOGY
The work of the CEH, a component body of the Natural Environment Research Council, includes a range of ornithological research, covering population studies, habitat management and work on the effects of pollution. The CEH has a long-term programme to monitor pesticide and pollutant residues in the corpses of predatory birds sent in by birdwatchers, and carries out detailed studies on affected species. The Biological Records Centre (BRC), which is part of the CEH, is responsible for the national biological data bank on plant and animal distributions (except birds).
Contact: Centre for Ecology and Hydrology, Polaris House, North Star, Swindon SN2 1EU. 01793 442 516; (Fax) 01793 442 528.
e-mail: director@ceh.ac.uk
www.ceh.ac.uk

COUNTRY LAND AND BUSINESS ASSOCIATION (1907; 50,000).
The CLA is at the heart of rural life and is the voice of the countryside for England and Wales, campaigning on issues which directly affect those who live and work in rural communities. Its members together manage 60% of the countryside. CLA members range from some of the largest landowners, with interests in forest, moorland, water and agriculture, to some of the smallest with little more than a paddock or garden.
Contact: Secretary, Country Land and Business Association, 16 Belgrave Square, London, SW1X 8PQ. 020 7235 0511; (Fax) 020 7235 4696;
e-mail: mail@cla.org.uk
www.cla.org.uk

COUNTRYSIDE AGENCY
This is now part of Natural England (see page 314).

COUNTRYSIDE COUNCIL FOR WALES
The Government's statutory adviser on wildlife, countryside and maritime conservation matters in Wales. It is the executive authority for the conservation of habitats and wildlife. Through partners, CCW promotes protection of landscape,

opportunities for enjoyment, and support of those who live, work in, and manage the countryside. It enables these partners, including local authorities, voluntary organisations and interested individuals, to pursue countryside management projects through grant aid. CCW is accountable to the National Assembly for Wales which appoints its Council members and provides its annual grant-in-aid.
Contact: Countryside Council for Wales, Maes-y-Ffynnon, Penrhosgarnedd, Bangor, Gwynedd LL57 2DL. 0845 1306 229; (Fax) 01248 355 782; e-mail: enquiries@ccw.gov.uk
www.ccw.gov.uk

CPRE (formerly Council for the Protection of Rural England) (1926; 60,000).
Patron HM The Queen. CPRE now has 43 county branches and 200 local groups. Its members are people who care passionately about our countryside and campaign for it to be protected and enhanced for the benefit of everyone. Membership open to all.
Contact: CPRE National Office, 128 Southwark Street, London SE1 0SW. 020 7981 2800; (Fax) 020 7981 2899; e-mail: info@cpre.org.uk
www.cpre.org.uk

DEPARTMENT OF THE ENVIRONMENT FOR NORTHERN IRELAND
Responsible for the declaration and management of National Nature Reserves, the declaration of Areas of Special Scientific Interest, the administration of Wildlife Refuges, the classification of Special Protection Areas under the EC Birds Directive, the designation of Special Areas of Conservation under the EC Habitats Directive and the designation of Ramsar sites under the Ramsar Convention. It administers the Nature Conservation and Amenity Lands (Northern Ireland) Order 1985, the Wildlife (Northern Ireland) Order 1985, the Game Acts and the Conservation (Natural Habitats, etc) Regulations (NI) 1995 and the Environment (Northern Ireland) Order 2002.
Contact: Department of the Environment (NI), Environment and Heritage Service, Klondyke Building, Cromac Avenue, Gasworks Business Park, Lower Ormeau Road, Belfast BT7 2JA. (028) 9056 9515; (polution hotline; 0800 807 060).
www.ehsni.gov.uk

DISABLED BIRDER'S ASSOCIATION (2,000; 600).
The DBA is a registered charity and international movement, which aims to promote access to reserves and other birding places and to a range of services, so that people with different needs can follow the birding obsession as freely as able-bodied people. Membership is currently free and open to all, either disabled or able-bodied. We are keen for new members to help give a strong voice to get our message across to those who own and manage nature reserves to ensure that they think about access when planning and improving their facilities. We are also seeking to influence those who provide birdwatching services and equipment. The DBA also runs overseas trips. Chairman, Bo Beolens.

Contact: The Membership Secretary, Margaret Read MBE, Disabled Birder's Association, 121 Lavernock Road, Pengarth, Vale of Glamorgan CF64 3QG. e-mail: bo@fatbirder.com
www.disabledbirdersassociation.co.uk

EDWARD GREY INSTITUTE OF FIELD ORNITHOLOGY (1938).
The EGI takes its name from Edward Grey, first Viscount Grey of Fallodon, a life-long lover of birds and former Chancellor of the University of Oxford, who gave his support to an appeal for its foundation capital. The Institute now has a permanent research staff; it usually houses some 12-15 research students, five or six senior visitors and post-doctoral research workers. Field research is carried out mainly in Wytham Woods near Oxford and on the island of Skomer in West Wales. In addition there are laboratory facilities and aviary space for experimental work. The Institute houses the Alexander Library, one of the largest collections of 20th Century material on birds in the world. The library is supported by the British Ornithologists Union who provides much of the material. Included in its manuscript collections are diaries, notebooks and papers of ornithologists. It also houses the British Falconers Club library. The Library is open to members of the BOU and the Oxford Ornithological Society; other bona fide ornithologists may use the library by prior arrangement.
Contact: Edward Grey Institute, Department of Zoology, South Parks Road, Oxford OX1 3PS. 01865 271 274, Alexander Library 01865 271 143; e-mail:clare.rowsell@zoo.ox.ac.ukweb-site, EGI: http://egizoosrv.zoo.ox.ac.uk/EGI/EGIhome.htm web-site library http://users.ox.ac.uk/~zoolib/

ENVIRONMENT AGENCY (THE)
A non-departmental body that aims to protect and improve the environment and to contribute towards the delivery of sustainable development through the integrated management of air, land and water. Functions include pollution prevention and control, waste minimisation, management of

water resources, flood defence, improvement of salmon and freshwater fisheries, conservation of aquatic species, navigation and use of inland and coastal waters for recreation. Sponsored by the Department of the Environment, Transport and the Regions, MAFF and the Welsh Office.

Contact: National Customer Contact Centre, PO Box 544, Rotherham, S60 1BY. General Enquiries: 08708 506 506 (Mon-Fri 8am-6pm), Incident hotline: 0800 807 060 (Freephone* 24 Hour); e-mail: enquiries@environment-agency.gov.uk www.environment-agency.gov.uk

Regional Offices:

Anglian. The Environment Agency, Kingfisher House, Goldhay Way, Orton Goldhay, Peterborough PE2 5ZR. 01733 371 811; fax 01733 231 840.

North East. The Environment Agency, Rivers House, 21 Park Square South, Leeds LS1 2QG. 0113 244 0191; fax 0113 246 1889.

North West. The Environment Agency, PO Box 12, Warrington WA4 1HG. 01925 653 999; fax 01925 415 961.

Midlands. The Environment Agency, Sapphire East, 550 Streetsbrook Road, Solihull B91 1QT. 08708 506 506; (Fax) 0121 711 5824.

Southern. The Environment Agency, Guildbourne House, Chatsworth Road, Worthing, W Sussex BN11 1LD. 01903 832 000; fax 01903 821 832.

South West. The Environment Agency, Manley House, Kestrel Way, Exeter EX2 7LQ. 08708 506 506.

Thames. The Environment Agency, Kings Meadow House, Kings Meadow Road, Reading RG1 8DQ.

Wales. The Environment Agency, Rivers House, St Mellons Business Park, St Mellons, Cardiff CF3 0EY. 08708 506 506.

FARMING AND WILDLIFE ADVISORY GROUP (FWAG) (1969).

An independent UK registered charity led by farmers and supported by government and leading countryside organisations. Its aim is to unite farming and forestry with wildlife and landscape conservation. Active in most UK counties. There are 120 Farm Conservation Advisers who give practical advice to farmers and landowners to help them integrate environmental objectives with commercial farming practices.
www.fwag.org.uk

Contact:

English Head Office, FWAG, National Agricultural Centre, Stoneleigh Park, Kenilworth, Warwickshire CV8 2RX. 02476 696 699;(Fax) 02476 696 699; e-mail: info@fwag.org.uk

Northern Ireland, FWAG, National Agricultural Centre, 46b Rainey Street, Magherafelt, Co. Derry BT45 5AH. 028 7930 0606; (Fax) 028 7930 0599; e-mail: n.ireland@fwag.org.uk

Scottish Head Office, FWAG Scotland, Algo Business Centre, Glenearn Road, Perth PH2 ONJ. 01738 450 500; (Fax) 01738 450 495; e-mail: steven.hunt@fwag.org.uk

Wales Head Office. FWAG Cymru, Ffordd Arran, Dolgellau, Gwynedd LL40 1LW. 01341 421 456; (Fax) 01341 422 757; e-mail: cymru@fwag.org.uk

FIELD STUDIES COUNCIL (1943).

Manages Centres where students from schools, universities and colleges of education, as well as individuals of all ages, can stay and study various aspects of the environment under expert guidance. The courses include many for birdwatchers, providing opportunities to study birdlife on coasts, estuaries, mountains and islands. There are some courses demonstrating bird ringing and others for members of the BTO. The length of the courses varies: from a weekend up to seven days' duration. Research workers and naturalists wishing to use the records and resources are welcome.

Contact: Field Studies Council, Preston Montford, Montford Bridge, Shrewsbury SY4 1HW. 01743 852 100; (Fax) 01743 852 101;
e-mail: fsc.headoffice@field-studies-council.org
www.field-studies-council.org

Centres:

Blencathra Field Centre, Threlkeld, Keswick, Cumbria CA12 4SG, 01768 77 9601;
e-mail: enquiries.bl@field-studies-council.org

Castle Head Field Centre, Grange-over-Sands, Cumbria LA11 6QT, 0845 330 7364;
e-mail: enquiries.ch@field-studies-council.org

Dale Fort Field Centre, Haverfordwest, Pembs SA62 3RD, 0845 330 7365;
e-mail: enquiries.df@field-studies-council.org

Epping Forest Field Centre, High Beach, Loughton, Essex, IG10 4AF, 020 8502 8500;
e-mail: enquiries.ef@field-studies-council.org

Flatford Mill Field Centre, East Bergholt, Suffolk, CO7 6UL, 0845 330 7368;
e-mail: enquiries.fm@field-studies-council.org

Derrygonnelly Field Centre, Tir Navar, Creamery St, Derrygonnelly, Co Fermanagh, BT93 6HW. 028 686 416 73;
e-mail: enquiries.dg.@field-studies-council.org

Juniper Hall Field Centre, Dorking, Surrey, RH5 6DA, 0845 458 3507; e-mail: enquiries.jh@field-studies-council.org

Kindrogan Field Centre, Enochdhu, Blairgowrie, Perthshire PH10 7PG. 01250 870 150; e-mail: enquiries.kd@field-studies-council.org

Margam Park Field Centre, Port Talbot SA13 2TJ. 01639 8956 36; e-mail: margam_sustainable_centre@hotmail.com

Malham Tarn Field Centre, Settle, N Yorks, BD24 9PU, 01729 830 331; e-mail: enquiries.mt@field-studies-council.org

Nettlecombe Court, The Leonard Wills Field Centre, Williton, Taunton, Somerset, TA4 4HT, 01984 640 320; e-mail: enquiries.nc@field-studies-council.org

Orielton Field Centre, Pembroke, Pembs,SA71 5EZ, 0845 330 7372; e-mail: enquiries.or@field-studies-council.org

Preston Montford Field Centre, Montford Bridge, Shrewsbury, SY4 1DX, 0845 330 7378; e-mail: enquiries.pm@field-studies-council.org

Rhyd-y-creuau, The Drapers' Field Centre Betws-y-coed, Conwy, LL24 0HB, 01690 710 494; e-mail: enquiries.rc@field-studies-council.org

Slapton Ley Field Centre, Slapton, Kingsbridge, Devon, TQ7 2QP, 01548 580 466; e-mail: enquiries.sl@field-studies-council.org

FLIGHTLINE

Northern Ireland's daily bird news service. Run under the auspices of the Northern Ireland Birdwatchers' Association (qv).
Contact: Flightline, George Gordon, 2 Brooklyn Avenue, Bangor, Co Down BT20 5RB. 028 9146 7408; e-mail: gordon@ballyholm2.freeserve.co.uk

FORESTRY COMMISSION

The Forestry Commission of Great Britain is the government department responsible for the protection and expansion of Britain's forests and woodlands. The organisation is run from national offices in England, Wales and Scotland, working to targets set by Commissioners and Ministers in each of the three countries. Its objectives are to protect Britain's forests and resources, conserve and improve the biodiversity, landscape and cultural heritage of forests and woodlands, develop opportunities for woodland recreation and increase public understanding and community participation in forestry.
Contact: Forestry Commission, Silvan House, 231 Corstorphine Road, Edinburgh, EH12 7AT; 0131 334 0303; (Fax) 0131 334 3047; Media enquiries: 0131 314 6500. Public enquiries: 0845 367 3787 e-mail: enquiries@forestry.gsi.gov.uk www.forestry.gov.uk

Details of wildlife viewing sites aross the country can be found on www.forestry.gov.uk/forestry/wildwoods

Forestry Commission National Offices:
England: Great Eastern House, Tenison Road, Cambridge CB1 2DU. 01223 314 546; (Fax) 01223 460 699, e-mail: fc.nat.off.eng@forestry.gsi.gov.uk

Scotland: Address as contact above, 0131 334 0303, (Fax) 0131 314 6152; e-mail: fcscotland@forestry.gsi.gov.uk

Wales: Victoria Terrace, Aberystwyth, Ceredigion SY23 2DQ. 0845 604 0845; (Fax) 01970 626 177.

FRIENDS OF THE EARTH (1971; 100,000).

The largest international network of environmental groups in the world, represented in 68 countries. It is one of the leading environmental pressure groups in the UK. It has a unique network of campaigning local groups, working in 200 communities in England, Wales and Northern Ireland. It is largely funded by supporters with more than 90% of income coming from individual donations, the rest from special fundraising events, grants and trading.
Contact: Friends of the Earth, 26-28 Underwood Street, London, N1 7JQ. 020 7490 1555; (Fax) 020 7490 0881; e-mail: info@foe.co.uk www.foe.co.uk

GAME CONSERVANCY TRUST (1933; 22,000).

A registered charity which researches the conservation of game and other wildlife in the British countryside. More than 60 scientists are engaged in detailed work on insects, pesticides, birds (30 species inc. raptors), mammals (inc. foxes), and habitats. The results are used to advise government, landowners, farmers and conservationists on practical management techniques which will benefit game species, their habitats, and wildlife. Each June an Annual Review of 100 pages lists about 50 papers published in the peer-reviewed scientific press.

Contact: Deputy Director of Research, Game Conservancy Trust, Dr Aebischer, Fordingbridge, Hampshire, SP6 1EF. 01425 652 381; (Fax) 01425 655 848; e-mail: info@gct.org.uk www.gct.org.uk

GAY BIRDERS CLUB (1995; 300+).

A voluntary society for lesbian, gay and bisexual birdwatchers, their friends and supporters, over the age of consent, in the UK and worldwide.

The club has 3-400 members and a network of regional contacts. It organises day trips, weekends and longer events at notable birding locations in the UK and abroad; about 200+ events in a year. Members receive a quarterly newsletter with details of all events. There is a Grand Get Together every 18 months. Membership £12 waged and £5 unwaged.
Contact: Membership, Gay Birders Club, GeeBeeCee, BCM-Mono, London, WC1N 3XX. e-mail: contact@gbc-online.org.uk www.gbc-online.org.uk

GOLDEN ORIOLE GROUP (1987; 15).
Organises censuses of breeding Golden Orioles in parts of Cambridgeshire, Norfolk and Suffolk. Maintains contact with a network of individuals in other parts of the country where Orioles may or do breed. Studies breeding biology, habitat and food requirements of the species.
Contact: Golden Oriole Group, Jake Allsop, 5 Bury Lane, Haddenham, Ely, Cambs CB6 3PR. 01353 740 540; e-mail: goldenoriolegroup@yahoo.com www.goldenoriolegroup.org.uk

HAWK AND OWL TRUST (1969).
Registered charity dedicated to the conservation and appreciation of all birds of prey including owls. Publishes a newsletter *Peregrine* and educational materials for all ages. The Trust achieves its major aim of creating and enhancing wild habitats for birds of prey, through projects which involve practical research, creative conservation and education. Projects are often conducted in close partnership with landowners, farmers and others. Members are invited to take part in population studies, field surveys, etc. Studies of Barn and Little Owls, Hen Harrier, and Goshawk are in progress. The Trust's National Conservation and Education Centre at Newland Park, Gorelands Lane, Chalfont St Giles, Bucks, is open to the public and offers schools and other groups cross-curricular environmental activities.

Contact: Hawk and Owl Trust, PO Box 100, Taunton TA4 2WX. 0870 990 3889; e-mail: enquiries@hawkandowl.org www.hawkandowl.org
Membership administration: 11 St Mary's Close, Abbotskerswell, Newton Abbot, Devon, TQ12 5QF.

INTERNATIONAL WADER STUDY GROUP (1970; 500).
An association of wader enthusiasts, both amateur and professional, from all parts of the world. The Group aims to maintain contact between them, to help in the organisation of co-operative studies, and to provide a vehicle for the exchange of information. Publishes the *Wader Study Group Bulletin* three times a year and holds annual meetings throughout Europe.
Contact: International Wader Study Group, The National Centre for Ornithology, The Nunnery, Thetford, Norfolk IP24 2PU. www.waderstudygroup.org

IRISH RARE BIRDS COMMITTEE (1985).
Assesses records of species of rare occurrence in the Republic of Ireland. Details of records accepted and rejected are incorporated in the Irish Bird Report, published annually in *Irish Birds*. In the case of rarities trapped for ringing, ringers in the Republic of Ireland are required to send their schedules initially to the National Parks and Wildlife Service, 51 St Stephen's Green, Dublin 2. A copy is taken before the schedules are sent to the British Trust for Ornithology.
Contact: Hon Secretary, Irish Rare Birds Committee, Paul Milne, 100 Dublin Road, Sutton, Dublin 13. +353 (0)1 8325 653; e-mail: paul.milne@oceanfree.net

JOINT NATURE CONSERVATION COMMITTEE (1990).
A committee of the three country agencies (Natural England, Scottish Natural Heritage, and the Countryside Council for Wales), together with independent members and representatives from Northern Ireland and the Countryside Agency. It is supported by specialist staff. Its statutory responsibilities include the establishment of common standards for monitoring; the analysis of information and research; advising Ministers on the development and implementation of policies for or affecting nature conservation; the provision of advice and the dissemination of knowledge to any persons about nature conservation; and the undertaking and commissioning of research relevant to these functions. JNCC additionally has the UK responsibility for relevant European and wider international matters. The Species Team, located at the HQ address above, is responsible for terrestrial bird conservation.
Contact: Joint Nature Conservation Committee, Monkstone House, City Road, Peterborough PE1 1JY. 01733 562 626; (Fax) 01733 555 948; e-mail: comment@jncc.gov.uk www.jncc.gov.uk

LINNEAN SOCIETY OF LONDON (1788, 2,000).
Named after Carl Linnaeus, the 18th century Swedish biologist, who created the modern

system of scientific biological nomenclature, the Society promotes all aspects of pure and applied biology. It houses Linnaeus's collection of plants, insects and fishes, library and correspondence. The Society has a major reference library of some 100,000 volumes. Publishes the *Biological, Botanical and Zoological* Journals, and the *Synopses of the British Fauna.*
Contact: Executive Secretary, Linnean Society of London, Adrian Thomas, Burlington House, Piccadilly, London W1J 0BF. 020 7434 4479; (Fax) 020 7287 9364; e-mail: info@linnean.org www.linnean.org

LITTLE OWL STUDY GROUP (2002; 37).
Formed to promote the study and conservation of Little Owls (Athene noctua) in Britain and to develop a population monitoring network for Little Owls. The LOSG is part of the International Little Owl Working Group, a Europe-wide organisation networking Little Owl research and conservation. The Little Owl is declining at an alarming rate across Europe and is endangered in at least three Western European countries. To combat this, a European Species Action Plan is being developed, to put in place the necessary monitors, conservation, and education measures for its long term survival. Project Athene is the British leg of this SAP.(See National Projects).
Contact: Little Owl Study Group, Roy Leigh, c/o Biota, The Old Barn, Moseley Hall Farm, Chilford Road, Knutsford, Cheshire WA16 8RB. 0871 734 0111; (Fax) 0871 734 0555; e-mail: rsl@biota.co.uk

MANX ORNITHOLOGICAL SOCIETY
see County Directory

MANX WILDLIFE TRUST
see County Directory

NATIONAL BIRDS OF PREY CENTRE (1967).
Concerned with the conservation and captive breeding of all raptors. Approx 85 species on site. Birds flown daily. Open all year (except Christmas Day and Boxing Day) - 10.30am to 5.30pm. The Centre takes in many injured, sick, rescued and confiscated birds each year. Where possible they are treated by the Centre, many are just weak or very young and once recovered and strong, they are released back into the wild.
Contact: National Birds of Prey Centre, Newent, Glos, GL18 1JJ. 0870 990 1992;
e-mail: kb@nbpc.org
www.nbpc.co.uk

NATIONAL TRUST (1895; 3.5 million).
Charity that works for the preservation of places of historic interest or natural beauty in England, Wales and Northern Ireland for ever, for everyone. They rely on their 3.5 million members, 49,000 volunteers, 500,000 school children and millions of visitors, donors and supporters. The Trust protects and opens to the public more than 300 historic houses and gardens, 49 industrial monuments and mills, plus more than 617,500 acres of land and 700 miles of coast. About 10% of SSSIs and ASSIs in England, Wales and Northern Ireland are wholly or partially owned by the Trust, as are 63 NNRs (e.g. Blakeney Point, Wicken Fen, Murlough and Dinefwr Estate). 33% of Ramsar sites include Trust land as do 45% of SPAs.
Central Office: Heelis, Kemble Drive, Swindon, Wiltshire SN2 2NA. Tel: 01793 817 400; (Fax) 01793 817 401.
Enquiries: PO Box 39, Warrington, WA5 7WD. Tel: 0870 458 4000; (Fax) 0870 609 0345.
e-mail: enquiries@thenationaltrust.org.uk
www.nationaltrust.org.uk

NATIONAL TRUST FOR SCOTLAND (1931; 297,000).
An independent charity, its 128 properties open to the public are described in its annual guide. It manages 76,000 hectares of countryside, including seven NNRs.
Contact: Marketing Department, National Trust for Scotland, Wemyss House, 28 Charlotte Square, Edinburgh, EH2 4ET. 0844 493 2100; (Fax) 0131 243 9301. e-mail: information@nts.org.uk
www.nts.org.uk

NATURAL ENGLAND
Natural England has been formed by bringing together English Nature, the landscape, access and recreation elements of the Countryside Agency and the environmental land management functions of the Rural Development Service.

Natural England works for people, places and nature, to enhance biodiversity, landscapes and wildlife in rural, urban, coastal and marine areas; promoting access, recreation and public well-being; and contributing to the way natural resources are managed so that they can be enjoyed now and in the future.

Natural England is working towards the delivery of four strategic outcomes:

- A healthy natural environment: England's natural environment will be conserved and enhanced.
- Enjoyment of the natural environment: more people enjoying, understanding and acting to improve, the natural environment, more often.

- Sustainable use of the natural environment: the use and management of the natural environment is more sustainable.

A secure environmental future: decisions which collectively secure the future of the natural environment.

Contact: Natural England, Northminster House, Peterborough, PE1 1UA. 0845 600 3078; (Fax) 01733 455 103;
e-mail: enquiries@naturalengland.org.uk
www.naturalengland.org.uk

NATURE PHOTOGRAPHERS' PORTFOLIO (1944; 66).
A society for photographers of wildlife, especially birds. Circulates postal portfolios of prints and transparencies. Annual conference held each autumn.
Contact: Hon Secretary, Nature Photographers' Portfolio, A Winspear-Cundall, 8 Gig Bridge Lane, Pershore, Worcs WR10 1NH. 01386 552 103.
www.nature-photographers-portfolio.co.uk

NORTHERN IRELAND BIRDWATCHERS' ASSOCIATION (1991; 120).
The NIBA Records Committee, established in 1997, has full responsibility for the assessment of records in N Ireland. NIBA also publishes the *Northern Ireland Bird Report*.
Contact: Hon Secretary, Northern Ireland Birdwatchers' Assoc, Wilton Farrelly, 24 Cabin Hill Gardens, Knock, Belfast BT5 7AP. 028 9022 5818;
e-mail: wilton.farrelly@ntlworld.com

NORTHERN IRELAND ORNITHOLOGISTS' CLUB (1965; 150).
Club formed to focus the ornithological interests of birdwatchers in the region. Operates a Tree Sparrow and Barn Owl nestbox scheme and a winter feeding programme for Yellowhammers. Has a regular programme of lectures and field trips for members. Publishes *The Harrier* quarterly.
Contact: Northern Ireland Ornithologists Club, Mrs Carol Gillespie, 4 Demesne Gate, Saintfield, Co. Down BT24 7BE;
e-mail: maurice.hughes@nioc.fsnet.co.uk
www.nioc.fsnet.co.uk

NORTH SEA BIRD CLUB (1979; 200).
The stated aims of the Club are to: provide a recreational pursuit for people employed offshore; obtain, collate and analyse observations of all birds seen offshore; produce reports of observations, including an annual report; promote the collection of data on other wildlife offshore. Currently it holds in excess of 100,000 records of birds, cetaceans and insects reported since 1979.
Contact: The North Sea Bird Club, Ocean Laboratory and Culterty Field Station, University of Aberdeen, Newburgh, Aberdeenshire AB41 6AA. 01224 274 428 (Fax) 01224 274 402;
e-mail: nsbc@abdn.ac.uk
www.abdn.ac.uk/nsbc

PEOPLE'S DISPENSARY FOR SICK ANIMALS (1917).
Registered charity. Provides free veterinary treatment for sick and injured animals whose owners qualify for this charitable service.
Contact: PDSA, Whitechapel Way, Priorslee, Telford, Shrops TF2 9PQ. 01952 290 999; (Fax) 01952 291 035; e-mail: pr@pdsa.org.uk
www.pdsa.org.uk

RAPTOR RESCUE, BIRD OF PREY REHABILITATION.
Birds of prey only. Heated hospital units. Indoor flights, secluded aviaries, hacking sites, rehabilitation aviaries/flights. Falconry rehabilitation techniques, foster birds for rearing young to avoid imprinting. Veterinary support. Reg charity no. 283733.
Contact: Raptor Rescue, Bird of Prey Rehabilitation, Beardwood Farm, Ladypit Road, Furness Vale, Derbyshire SK23 7QF. (National advice line) 0870 241 0609;
e-mail: info@raptorrescue.org.uk
www.raptorrescue.org.uk

RARE BREEDING BIRDS PANEL (1973).
An independent body funded by the JNCC and RSPB. Both bodies are represented on the panel as are BTO and ACRE. It collects all information on rare breeding birds in the United Kingdom, so that changes in status can be monitored as an aid to present-day conservation and stored for posterity. Special forms are used (obtainable free from the secretary and the website) and records should if possible be submitted via the county and regional recorders. Since 1996 the Panel also monitors breeding by scarcer non-native species and seeks records of these in the same way. Annual report is published in *British Birds*. For details of species covered by the Panel see Log Charts and the websites.

Rare Breeding Birds Panel

Contact: Secretary, Rare Breeding Birds Panel, The Old Orchard, Grange Road, North Berwick, East Lothian EH39 4QT. 1620 894 037;
e-mail: secretary@rbbp.org.uk
www.rbbp.org.uk

NATIONAL ORGANISATIONS

ROYAL AIR FORCE ORNITHOLOGICAL SOCIETY (1965; 295).
RAFOS organises regular field meetings for members, carries out ornithological census work on MOD properties and mounts major expeditions annually to various UK and overseas locations. Publishes a Newsletter twice a year, a Journal annually, and reports on its expeditions and surveys.
Contact: Royal Air Force Ornithological Soc, General Secretary, RAFOS, 100 Moselle Drive, Churchdown, Glos GL3 2TA. www.rafos.org.uk e-mail: rafos_secretary@hotmail.com

ROYAL NAVAL BIRDWATCHING SOCIETY (1946; 167 full and 93 associate members and library).
Covers all main ocean routes, the Society has a system for reporting the positions and identity of seabirds and landbirds at sea by means of standard sea report forms. Maintains an extensive world-wide seabird database. Members are encouraged to photograph birds while at sea and a library of photographs and slides is maintained. Publishes a *Bulletin* and an annual report entitled *The Sea Swallow*.
The Simpson Scholarship provides assistance to embryonic ornithologists for studies regarding seabirds and landbirds at sea.
Contact: Hon Secretary, Royal Naval Birdwatching Society, Cdr FS Ward RN, 16 Cutlers Lane, Stubbington, Fareham, Hants PO14 2JN. +44 1329 665 931; e-mail: francisward@btopenworld.com www.rnbws.org.uk

ROYAL PIGEON RACING ASSOCIATION (1897; 39,000).
Exists to promote the sport of pigeon racing and controls pigeon racing within the Association. Organises liberation sites, issues rings, calculates distances between liberation sites and home lofts, and assists in the return of strays. May be able to assist in identifying owners of ringed birds caught or found.
Contact: Royal Pigeon Racing Association, The Reddings, Cheltenham, GL51 6RN. 01452 713 529; e-mail: gm@rpra.org or strays@rpra.org www.rpra.org

ROYAL SOCIETY FOR THE PREVENTION OF CRUELTY TO ANIMALS (1824; 43,690).
In addition to its animal centres, the Society also runs a woodland study centre and nature reserve at Mallydams Wood in East Sussex and specialist wildlife rehabilitation centres at West Hatch, Taunton, Somerset TA3 5RT (0870 0101847), at Station Road, East Winch, King's Lynn, Norfolk PE32 1NR (0870 9061420), and London Road, Stapeley, Nantwich, Cheshire CW5 7JW (not open to the public). Inspectors are contacted through their National Communication Centre, which can be reached via the Society's 24-hour national cruelty and advice line: 08705 555 999.
Contact: RSPCA Enquiry Services, Willberforce Way, Horsham, West Sussex RH13 9RS. 0870 010 1181; (Fax) 0870 753 0048. Advice line: 0300 1234 555. **Cruelty line:** 0300 1234 999. www.rspca.org.uk

ROYAL SOCIETY FOR THE PROTECTION OF BIRDS (1889; 1,000,000+).
UK Partner of BirdLife International, and Europe's largest voluntary wildlife conservation body. The RSPB, a registered charity, is governed by an elected body (see also RSPB Phoenix and RSPB Wildlife Explorers). Its work in the conservation of wild birds and habitats covers the acquisition and management of nature reserves; research and surveys; monitoring and responding to development proposals, land use practices and pollution which threaten wild birds and biodiversity; and the provision of an advisory service on wildlife law enforcement.

Work in the education and information field includes formal education in schools and colleges, and informal activities for children through Wildlife Explorers; publications (including *Birds*, a quarterly magazine for members), displays and exhibitions; the distribution of moving images about birds; and the development of membership activities through Members' Groups.

The RSPB currently manages 182 nature reserves in the UK, covering more than 313,000 acres; more than 50% of this area is owned. Sites are carefully selected, mostly as being of national or international importance to wildlife conservation. The aim is to conserve a countrywide network of reserves with all examples of the main bird communities and with due regard to the conservation of plants and other animals. Visitors are generally welcome to most reserves, subject to any restrictions necessary to protect the wildlife or habitats.

Current national projects include extensive work on agriculture, and conservation and campaigning for the conservation of the marine environment and to halt the illegal persecution of birds of prey. Increasingly, there is involvement with broader environmental concerns such as climate change and transport.

NATIONAL ORGANISATIONS

The RSPB's International Dept works closely with Birdlife International and its partners in other countries and is involved with numerous projects overseas, especially in Europe and Asia.

Contact: RSPB, The Lodge, Sandy, Beds SG19 2DL. Membership enquiries: 01767 693 680 (office hours). Wildlife enquiries: 01767 693 690 (office hours). All other enquiries: 01767 680 551 (office hours); e-mail: (firstname.name)@rspb.org.uk www.rspb.org.uk

Regional Offices:

ENGLAND

Eastern England Regional Office, Stalham House, 65 Thorpe Road, Norwich, Norfolk NR1 1UD. 01603 661 662.

London Office, RSPB London Office, 2nd Floor, 65 Petty France, London SW1H 9EU. 0207 808 1240.

Midlands Regional Office, 46 The Green, South Bar, Banbury, Oxfordshire OX16 9AB. 01295 253 330.

North East Regional Office, Newcastle Office, 1 Sirius House, Amethyst Road, Newcastle Business Park, Newcastle-upon-Tyne NE4 7YL. 0191 233 4300.

South East Regional Office, 2nd Floor, 42 Frederick Place, Brighton, East Sussex BN1 4EA. 01273 775 333.

South West Regional Office, Keble House, Southernhay Gardens, Exeter, Devon EX1 1NT. 01392 432 691.

SCOTLAND

RSPB Scotland HQ, Dunedin House, 25 Ravelston Terrace, Edinburgh EH4 3TP. 0131 311 6500; e-mail: rspb.scotland@rspb.org.uk

RSPB East Scotland, 10 Albyn Terrace, Aberdeen AB1 1YP. 01224 624 824.

RSPB North Scotland, Etive House, Beechwood Park, Inverness IV2 3BW. 01463 715 000.

RSPB South & West Scotland, 10 Park Quadrant, Glasgow G3 6BS. 0141 331 0993.

WALES

RSPB Wales HQ, Sutherland House, Castlebridge, Cowbridge Road East, Cardiff CF11 9AB. 029 2035 3000.

NORTHERN IRELAND

RSPB Northern Ireland, Belvoir Park Forest, Belfast BT8 7QT. 028 9049 1547;
e-mail: rspb.nireland@rspb.org.uk

RSPB WILDLIFE EXPLORERS and RSPB PHOENIX (formerly YOC) (1965; 168,000).
Junior section of the RSPB. There are more than 100 groups run by 300 volunteers. Activities include projects, holidays, roadshows, competitions, and local events for children, families and teenagers. Publishes 2 bi-monthly magazines, *Bird Life* (aimed at 8-12 year olds) and *Wild Times* (aimed at under 8s) and 1 quarterly magazine *Wingbeat* (aimed at teenagers).

Contact: Youth Manager, RSPB Youth and Education Dept, The Lodge, Sandy, Beds SG19 2DL. 01767 680551; e-mail: explorers@rspb.org.uk and phoenix@rspb.org.uk www.rspb.org.uk/youth

SCOTTISH BIRDS RECORDS COMMITTEE (1984; 7 members + secretary).
Set up by the Scottish Ornithologists' Club to ensure that records of species not deemed rare enough to be considered by the British Birds Rarities Committee, but which are rare in Scotland, are fully assessed; also maintains the official list of Scottish birds.

Contact: Secretary, Scottish Birds Records Committee, Angus Hogg, 11 Kirkmichael Road, Crosshill, Maybole, Ayrshire KA19 7RJ.
e-mail: dcgos@globalnet.co.uk
www.the-soc.org.uk

SCOTTISH NATURAL HERITAGE (1991).
The Scottish Executive's statutory advisor in respect to the conservation, enhancement, enjoyment, understanding and sustainable use of the natural heritage.

Contact: Scottish Natural Heritage, Great Glen HouseLeachkin Road, Inverness IV3 8NW. 01463 725 000; e-mail: fergus.macneill@snh.gov.uk www.snh.org.uk

SCOTTISH ORNITHOLOGISTS' CLUB (1936; 2,250).
The Club has 14 branches (see County Directory). each with a programme of winter meetings and field trips throughout the year. The SOC organises an annual weekend conference in the autumn and a joint SOC/BTO one-day birdwatchers' conference in spring. Publishes quarterly newsletter *Scottish Bird News*, the bi-annual *Scottish Birds*, the annual *Scottish Bird Report* and the *Scottish Raptor*.The SOC has opened a new resource centre in Scotland, at Aberlady, details of which can be found on the website.

Contact: The SOC, The Scottish Birdwatching Resource Centre, Waterston House, Aberlady, East

Lothian EH32 0PY. 01875 871 330; (Fax) 01875 871 035; e-mail: mail@the-soc.org.uk www.the-soc.org.uk

SCOTTISH SOCIETY FOR THE PREVENTION OF CRUELTY TO ANIMALS (1839).
Represents animal welfare interests to Government, local authorities and others. Educates young people to realise their responsibilities. Maintains an inspectorate to patrol and investigate and to advise owners about the welfare of animals and birds in their care. Maintains welfare centres, two of which include oiled bird cleaning centres. Bird species, including birds of prey, are rehabilitated and where possible released back into the wild.
Contact: Scottish SPCA, Braehead Mains, 603 Queensferry Road, Edinburgh EH4 6EA. 0131 339 0222; (Fax) 0131 339 4777;
e-mail: enquiries@scottishspca.org
www.scottishspca.org

SCOTTISH WILDLIFE TRUST (1964; 28,500).
Has members' groups throughout Scotland. Aims to conserve all forms of wildlife and has over 120 reserves, many of great birdwatching interest, covering some 20,000 hectares. Member of The Wildlife Trusts partnership and organises Scottish Wildlife Watch. Publishes *Scottish Wildlife* three times a year.
Contact: Scottish Wildlife Trust, Cramond House, Cramond Glebe Road, Edinburgh EH4 6NS. 0131 312 7765; (Fax) 0131 312 8705;
e-mail: enquiries@swt.org.uk www.swt.org.uk

SEABIRD GROUP (1966; 350).
Concerned with conservation issues affecting seabirds. Co-ordinates census and monitoring work on breeding seabirds; has established and maintains the Seabird Colony Register in collaboration with the JNCC; organises triennial conferences on seabird biology and conservation topics. Small grants available to assist with research and survey work on seabirds. Publishes the *Seabird Group Newsletter* every four months and the journal, *Atlantic Seabirds*, quarterly in association with the Dutch Seabird Group.
Contact: Seabird Group, Alan Leitch, 2 Burgess Terrace, Edinburgh, EH9 2BD.
e-mail: alan.leitch1@virgin.net
www.seabirdgroup.org.uk

SOCIETY OF WILDLIFE ARTISTS (1964; 76 Members, 6 Associates).
Registered charity set up to generate appreciatin of the natural world through all works of fine art. Annual exhibition held in Sept/Oct at the Mall Galleries, London.
Contact: Jill Moger, Society of Wildlife Artists, Federation of British Artists, 17 Carlton House Terrace, London SW1Y 5BD. 020 7930 6844.
e-mail: info@mallgalleries.com
www.swla.co.uk

SWAN SANCTUARY (THE)
Founded by Dorothy Beeson BEM. A registered charity which operates nationally. Has a fully equipped swan hospital with an operating theatre, x-ray facilities and a veterinary surgeon. New site has several nursing ponds and a four acre rehabilitation lake where around 4,000 swans and the same number of other forms of wildlife are treated. 24-hour service operated, with volunteer rescuers on hand to recover victims of oil spills, vandalism etc. Reg. charity number 1002582.
Contact: The Swan Sanctuary, Felix Lane, Shepperton, Middlesex TW17 8NN. 01932 240 790; e-mail: swans@swanuk.org.uk
www.swanuk.org.uk

SWAN STUDY GROUP (80).
An association of both amateur and professionals, from around the UK. Most are concerned with Mute Swans, but Bewick's and Whooper Swan biologists are also active members. The aim of the Group is to provide a forum for communication and discussion, and to help co-ordinate co-operative studies. Annual meetings are held at various locations in the UK at which speakers give presentations on their own fieldwork.
Contact: Swan Study Group, Dr Helen Chisholm, 14 Buckstone Howe, Edinburgh, EH10 6XF. 0131 445 2351; e-mail: h.chisholm@blueyonder.co.uk

THE BRITISH LIBRARY SOUND ARCHIVE WILDLIFE SECTION (1969).
(Formerly BLOWS - British Library of Wildlife Sounds). The most comprehensive collection of bird sound recordings in existence: over 150,000 recordings of more than 8,000 species of birds worldwide, available for free listening. Copies or sonograms of most recordings can be supplied for private study or research and, subject to copyright clearance, for commercial uses. Contribution of new material and enquiries on all aspects of wildlife sounds and recording techniques are welcome. Publishes *Bioacoustics* journal, CD guides to bird songs and other wildlife, including ambience titles. Comprehensive catalogue available on-line at http:\\cadensa.bl.uk
Contact: Cheryl Tipp, British Library Sound Archive Wildlife Sctn, 96 Euston Road, London NW1 2DB. 020 7412 7402/3;
e-mail: cheryl.tipp@bl.uk
www.bl.uk/collections/sound-archive/wild.html

THE MAMMAL SOCIETY (1954; 2,500).
The Mammal Society is the voice for British mammals and the only organisation solely dedicated to the study and conservation of all British mammals. They seek to raise awareness of mammals, their ecology and their conservation needs; to survey British mammals and their habitats to identify the threats they face; to promote mammal studies in the UK and overseas; to advocate conservation plans based on sound science; to provide current information on mammals through their publications; to involve people of all ages in their efforts to protect mammals; to educate people about British mammals and to monitor mammal population changes.
Contact: Enquiries, The Mammal Society, 2B Inworth Street, London SW11 3EP. 020 7350 2200; (Fax) 020 7350 2211;
e-mail: enquiries@mammal.org.uk
www.mammal.org.uk

UK400 CLUB AND BRITISH BIRDING ASSOCIATION.
Serves to monitor the nation's leading twitchers and their life lists, and to keep under review contentious species occurrences in Britain and Ireland. Publishes a bi-monthly magazine *Rare Birds* and operates a website; www.uk400clubonline.co.uk. Membership open to all. The UK400 Club email group offers a regularly updated Rare Bird Alert and allows members open and frank discussion on anything topical.
Contact: UK400 Club, L G R Evans, Chaffinch House, 8 Sandycroft Road, Little Chalfont, Amersham, Bucks HP6 6QL. 01494 763 010;
e-mail: LGREUK400@aol.com
www.uk400clubonline.co.uk

ULSTER WILDLIFE TRUST
See County Directory.

WADER STUDY GROUP (1970; 600).
An association of wader enthusiasts, both amateur and professional, from all parts of the world. The Group aims to maintain contact between them, to help in the organisation of co-operative studies, and to provide a vehicle for the exchange of information. Publishes the *Wader Study Group Bulletin* three times a year and holds annual meetings throughout Europe.

WADER STUDY GROUP

Contact: General Manager, Wader Study Group, The National Centre for Ornithology, The Nunnery, Thetford, Norfolk IP24 2PU.
www.waderstudygroup.org

THE NATURAL HISTORY MUSEUM OF TRING
Founded by Lionel Walter (later Lord) Rothschild, the Museum displays British and exotic birds (1,500 species) including many rarities and extinct species. Galleries open all year except Dec 24-26. Adjacent to the Bird Group of the Natural History Museum - with over a million specimens and an extensive ornithological library, an internationally important centre for bird research.
Contact: Walter Rothschild Zoological Museum, Akeman Street, Tring, Herts HP23 6AP. 020 7942 6171; (Fax) 020 7942 6150.
e-mail: tring-enquiries@nhm.ac.uk
www.nhm.ac.uk/visit-us/galleries/tring/

WELSH KITE TRUST (1996; 1200).
A registered charity that undertakes the conservation and annual monitoring of Red Kites in Wales. It attempts to locate all the breeding birds, to compile data on population growth, productivity, range expansion etc. The Trust liaises with landowners, acts as consultant on planning issues and with regard to filming and photography, and represents Welsh interests on the UK Kite Steering Group. Provides a limited rescue service for injured kites and eggs or chicks at risk of desertion or starvation. Publishes a newsletter *Boda Wennol* twice a year, sent free to subscribing Friends of the Welsh Kite and to all landowners with nesting Kites.
Contact: Welsh Kite Trust, Tony Cross, Samaria, Nantmel, Llandrindod Wells, Powys LD1 6EN. 01597 825 981; www.welshkitetrust.org
e-mail: tony.cross@welshkitetrust.org

WETLAND TRUST
Set up to encourage conservation of wetlands and develop study of migratory birds, and to foster international relations in these fields. Large numbers of birds are ringed each year in Sussex and applications are invited from individuals to train in bird ringing or extend their experience.
Contact: Wetland Trust, Phil Jones, Elms Farm, Pett Lane, Icklesham, Winchelsea, E Sussex TN36 4AH. 01797 226374; e-mail: phil@wetlandtrust.org

WILDFOWL & WETLANDS TRUST (THE) (1946; 130,000 members and 4,700 bird adopters).
Registered charity founded by the late Sir Peter Scott, its mission - to conserve wetlands and their biodiversity. WWT has nine centres with reserves (see Arundel, Caerlaverock, Castle Espie, Llanelli, Martin Mere, Slimbridge, Washington, Welney, and The London Wetland Centre in Reserves and Observatories section). The centres are nationally or internationally important for wintering wildfowl; they also aim to raise awareness of and appreciation for wetland species, the problems

they face and the conservation action needed to help them. Programmes of walks and talks are available for visitors with varied interests - resources and programmes are provided for school groups. Centres, except Caerlaverock and Welney, have wildfowl from around the world, inc. endangered species. Research Department works on population dynamics, species management plans and wetland ecology. The Wetland Advisory Service (WAS) undertakes contracts, and Wetland Link International promotes the role of wetland centres for education and public awareness.

Contact: Wildfowl and Wetlands Trust, Slimbridge, Glos, GL2 7BT. 01453 891 900; (Fax) 01453 890 827;
e-mail: info.slimbridge@wwt.org.uk
www.wwt.org.uk

WILDLIFE SOUND RECORDING SOCIETY (1968; 327).
Works closely with the Wildlife Section of the National Sound Archive. Members carry out recording work for scientific purposes as well as for pleasure. A field weekend is held each spring, and members organise meetings locally. Four CD sound magazines of members' recordings are produced for members each year, and a journal, *Wildlife Sound*, is published twice a year.

Contact: Hon Membership Secretary, WSRS, Wildlife Sound Recording Society,
e-mail: enquiries@wildlife-sound.org
www.wildlife-sound.org/

WILDLIFE TRUSTS (THE) (720,000+)

The largest UK charity exclusively dedicated to conserving all habitats and species, with a membership that includes 134,000 junior members. It campaigns for the protection of wildlife and invests in the future by helping people of all ages to gain a greater appreciation and understanding of wildlife. Collectively, the Trusts manage more than 2,200 nature reserves spanning over 80,000 hectares. The Wildlife Trusts also lobby for better protection of the UK's natural heritage and are dedicated to protecting wildlife for the future. Publ *Natural World*. See also *Wildlife Watch*.

Contact: The Wildlife Trusts, The Kiln, Waterside, Mather Road, Newark NG24 1WT. 01636 670 001; (Fax) 01636 670 001;
e-mail: enquiry@wildlifetrusts.org
www.wildlifetrusts.org

WILDLIFE WATCH (1971; 24,000+).
The junior branch of The Wildlife Trusts (see previous entry). It supports 1,500 registered volunteer leaders running Watch groups across the UK. Publishes *Watchword* and *Wildlife Extra* for children and activity books for adults working with young people.

Contact: People and Wildlife Manager, Wildlife Watch, Helen Freeston, The Wildlife Trusts, The Kiln, Waterside, Mather Road, Newark NG24 1WT. 0870 036 7711; (Fax) 00870 036 0101;
e-mail: watch@wildlife-trusts.cix.co.uk
www.wildlifewatch.org.uk

WWF-UK (1961).
WWF is the world's largest independent conservation organisation, comprising 27 national organisations. It works to conserve endangered species, protect endangered spaces, and address global threats to nature by seeking long-term solutions with people in government and industry, education and civil society. Publishes *WWF News* (quarterly magazine).

Contact: Chief Executive, WWF-UK (World Wide Fund for Nature), Robert Napier, Panda House, Weyside Park, Catteshall Lane, Godalming, Surrey GU7 1XR. 01483 426 444; (Fax) 01483 426 409;
www.wwf-uk.org

ZOOLOGICAL PHOTOGRAPHIC CLUB (1899).
Circulates black and white and colour prints of zoological interest via a series of postal portfolios.

Contact: Hon Secretary, Zoological Photographic Club, Martin B Withers, 93 Cross Lane, Mountsorrel, Loughborough, Leics LE12 7BX. 0116 229 6080.

ZOOLOGICAL SOCIETY OF LONDON (1826).
Carries out research, organises symposia and holds scientific meetings. Manages ZSL London Zoo (first opened in 1828) and ZSL Whipsnade Zoo near Dunstable, Beds, each with extensive collections of birds. The Society's library has a large collection of ornithological books and journals. Publications include the *Journal of Zoology*, *Animal Conservation*, *Conservation Biology* book series, *The Symposia* and *The International Zoo Yearbook*.

Contact: Zoological Society of London, Regent's Park, London, NW1 4RY. 020 7722 3333.
www.zsl.org

NATIONAL PROJECTS

National ornithological projects depend for their success on the active participation of amateur birdwatchers. In return they provide birdwatchers with an excellent opportunity to contribute in a positive and worthwhile way to the scientific study of birds and their habitats, which is the vital basis of all conservation programmes. The following entries provide a description of each particular project and a note of whom to contact for further information (full address details are in the previous section).

ACTION FOR SWIFTS

A Concern for Swifts Group project.

Endorsed by the BTO and the RSPB, the Group monitors Swift breeding colonies, especially where building restoration and maintenance are likely to cause disturbance. Practical information can be provided to owners, architects, builders and others. The help of interested birdwatchers is always welcome.
Contact: Jake Allsop, 01353 740 540; http://actionforswifts.com

ATLAS 2007-11

(BTO, run in partnership with BirdWatch Ireland and the Scottish Ornithologists' Club)
Atlases have provided a periodic stock-take of the birds of Britain and Ireland, and this latest Atlas will do just that, only this time in both the breeding season and in winter. It will generate range and abundance maps for all species while giving the opportunity to contrast past and present distributions and assess changes, for better or worse. Fieldwork will start in earnest in November 2007 and run for 4 winters and 4 summers. Observers will be able to submit their records and see periodic sneak previews of the results online. Mapping Britain and Ireland's birds is a major undertaking and the BTO will need your support.
Contact: birdatlas@bto.org
www.birdatlas.net

BARN OWL MONITORING PROGRAMME

A BTO project
Volunteers monitor nest sites to record site occupancy, clutch size, brood size and breeding success. Qualified ringers may catch and ring adults and chicks and record measurements. Volunteers must be qualified bird ringers or nest recorders with a Schedule 1 licence for Barn Owl.
Contact: Carl Barimore,
e-mail: barnowls@bto.org

BirdTrack

Organised by BTO on behalf of BTO, RSPB and BirdWatch Ireland.
BirdTrack is a year-round bird recording scheme, designed to collect large numbers of lists of birds. The idea is simple – you make a note of the birds seen at each site you visit and enter your daily observations on a simple-to-use web page. Birdwatchers can also send in other types of records, including counts and casual observations. The focus of the website (www.birdtrack.net) will be spring and autumn migration, seasonal movements and the distribution of scarce species. BirdTrack is also an ideal electronic notebook to store your own bird records, allowing queries and reports by sites and species.
Contact: Mark Grantham, BTO

BREEDING BIRD SURVEY

Supported by the BTO, JNCC and the RSPB.
Begun in 1994, the BBS is designed to keep track of the changes in populations of our common breeding birds. It is dependent on volunteer birdwatchers throughout the country who can spare about five hours a year to cover a 1x1km survey square. There are just two morning visits to survey the breeding birds each year.
Survey squares are picked at random by computer to ensure that all habitats and regions are covered. Since its inception it has been a tremendous success, with more than 3,000 squares covered and more than 200 species recorded each year.
Contact: Census Unit, e-mail: bbs@bto.org, or your local BTO Regional Representative (see County Directory).

CORE MONITORING CENSUS (formerly COMMON BIRDS CENSUS)

This survey has officially finished. This was the

main source of population monitoring in the wider countryside from 1962-2000, but has now been superceded by the Breeding Bird Survey. Nevertheless, CBC is still the best method to use at a local scale, producing maps showing the locations of bird's territories for a defined area. This is especially useful to study the relationship of breeding birds with their habitats. Although new participants are not needed currently, the method is still valuable and will be available on the BTO website.

CONSTANT EFFORT SITES SCHEME

A BTO project for bird ringers, funded by a partnership of the BTO, the JNCC, The Environment and Heritage Service in Northern Ireland - National Parks & Wildlife Service (Ireland) and the ringers themselves.

Participants in the scheme monitor common songbird populations by standardized mist-netting and ringing of birds throughout the summer at more than 130 sites across Britain and Ireland. Changes in numbers of adults captured provide an index of population changes between years, while the ratio of juveniles to adults gives a measure of productivity. Between-year recaptures of birds are used to study variations in adult survival rates. Information from CES complements that from other long-term BTO surveys.

Contact: Mark Grantham, BTO.

GARDEN BIRD FEEDING SURVEY

A BTO project.

The 2006/07 season completed 37 years of the GBFS. Each year 250 observers record the numbers and variety of garden birds fed by man in the 26 weeks between October and March. It is the longest running survey of its type in the world. Gardens are selected by region and type, from city flats, suburban semis and rural houses to outlying farms.

Contact: David Glue, BTO.

BTO/CJ GARDEN BIRDWATCH

A BTO project, supported by C J WildBird Foods.

Started in January 1995, this project is a year-round survey that monitors the use that birds make of gardens. Approximately 17,000 participants from all over the UK and Ireland keep a weekly log of species using their gardens. The data collected are used to monitor regional, seasonal and year-to-year changes in the garden populations of our commoner birds. To cover costs there is an annual fee of £12. There is a quarterly colour magazine and all new joiners receive a full-colour, garden bird handbook. Results and more information are available online: www.bto.org/gbw. E-mail: gbw@bto.org

Contact: Garden BirdWatch Team, BTO.

GOOSE CENSUSES

A WWT project

Britain and Ireland support internationally important goose populations. During the day, many of these feed away from wetlands and are therefore not adequately censused by the Wetland Bird Survey. Additional surveys are therefore undertaken to provide estimates of population size. These primarily involve roost counts, supplemented by further counts of feeding birds.

Most populations are censused up to three times a year, typically during the autumn, midwinter, and spring. In addition, counts of the proportion of juveniles in goose flocks are undertaken to provide estimates of annual productivity. Further volunteers are always needed. In particular, counters in Scotland, Lancashire and Norfolk are sought. For more information

Contact: Richard Hearn, Programme Manager,
E-mail: richard.hearn@wwt.org.uk
T: +44 (0)1453 891 185;
e-mail: monitoring@wwt.org.uk

HERONRIES CENSUS

A BTO project.

This survey started in 1928 and has been carried out under the auspices of the BTO since 1934. It represents the longest continuous series of population data for any European breeding bird. Counts are made at as many heronries as possible each year, throughout the UK to provide an index of the current population level; data from Scotland and Northern Ireland are scant and more contributions from these countries would be especially welcomed.

Herons may be hit hard during periods of severe weather but benefit by increased survival over mild winters. Their position at the top of a food chain makes them particularly vulnerable to pesticides and pollution.

Contact: John Marchant, BTO.

IRISH WETLAND BIRD SURVEY (I-WeBS)

I-WeBS

A joint project of BirdWatch Ireland, the National Parks & Wildlife Service of the Dept of Arts, Culture & the Gaeltacht, and WWT, and supported by the Heritage Council and WWF-UK.

Established in 1994, I-WeBS aims to monitor the numbers and distribution of waterfowl

populations wintering in Ireland in the long term, enabling the population size and spatial and temporal trends in numbers to be identified and described for each species.
Methods are compatible with existing schemes in the UK and Europe, and I-WeBS collaborates closely with the Wetland Bird Survey (WeBS) in the UK. Synchronised monthly counts are undertaken at wetland sites of all habitats during the winter.

Counts are straightforward and counters receive a newsletter and full report annually. Additional help is always welcome, especially during these initial years as the scheme continues to grow.
Contact: BirdWatch Ireland; www.birdwatchireland.ie

NEST RECORD SCHEME

A BTO Project forming part of the BTO's Integrated Population Monitoring programme carried out under contract with the JNCC.
All birdwatchers can contribute to this scheme by sending information about nesting attempts they observe into the BTO on standard Nest Record Cards or electronically via the IPMR computer package. The NRS monitors changes in the nesting success and the timing of breeding of Britain's bird species. Guidance on on how to record and visit nests safely, without disturbing breeding birds, is available in a free starter pack from the Nest Records Unit.
Contact: Carl Barimore;
e-mail: nest.records@bto.org

RAPTOR AND OWL RESEARCH REGISTER

A BTO project
The Register has helped considerably over the past 30 years in encouraging and guiding research, and in the co-ordination of projects. There are currently almost 500 projects in the card index file through which the Register operates.

The owl species currently receiving most attention are Barn and Tawny. As to raptors, the most popular subjects are Kestrel, Buzzard, Sparrowhawk, Hobby and Peregrine, with researchers showing increasing interest in Red Kite, and fewer large in-depth studies of Goshawk, Osprey and harriers.

Contributing is a simple process and involves all raptor enthusiasts, whether it is to describe an amateur activity or professional study. The nature of research on record varies widely – from local pellet analyses to captive breeding and rehabilitation programmes to national surveys of Peregrine, Buzzard and Golden Eagle.

Birdwatchers in both Britain and abroad are encouraged to write for photocopies of cards relevant to the species or nature of their work. The effectiveness of the Register depends upon those running projects (however big or small) ensuring that their work is included.
Contact: David Glue, BTO.

RED KITE RE-INTRODUCTION PROJECT

An English Nature/SNH/RSPB project supported by Forest Enterprise, Yorkshire Water and authorities in Germany and Spain
The project involves the translocation of birds from Spain, Germany and the expanding Chilterns population for release at sites in England and Scotland.

Records of any wing-tagged Red Kites in England should be reported to Natural Engand, Northminster House, Peterborough, PEI IUA (tel 01733 455 281). Scottish records should be sent to the RSPB's North Scotland Regional Office, Etive House, Beechwood Park, Inverness, IV2 3BW (tel 01463 715 000).

Sightings are of particular value if the letter/number code (or colour) of wing tags can be seen or if the bird is seen flying low over (or into) woodland. Records should include an exact location, preferably with a six figure grid reference.

RETRAPPING ADULTS FOR SURVIVAL PROJECT

A BTO project for bird ringers, funded by a partnership of the BTO, the JNCC, The Environment and Heritage Service in Northern Ireland - National Parks & Wildlife Service (Ireland) and the ringers themselves.
This project started in 1998 and is an initiative of the BTO Ringing Scheme. It aims to gather re-trap information for a wide range of species, especially those of conservation concern, in a variety of breeding habitats, allowing the monitoring of survival rates.

Detailed information about survival rates from the RAS Project will help in the understanding of changing population trends. Ringers choose a target species, decide on a study area and develop suitable catching techniques. The aim then is to catch all the breeding adults of the chosen species within the study area. This is repeated each breeding season for a minimum of five years. The results will be relayed to conservation organisations who can use the information to design effective conservation action plans.
Contact: John Marchant, BTO.

NATIONAL PROJECTS

RINGING SCHEME

A BTO project for bird ringers, funded by a partnership of the BTO, the JNCC, The National Parks & Wildlife Service (Ireland) and the ringers themselves.

The purpose of the Ringing Scheme is to study survival, productivity and movements by marking birds with individually numbered metal rings which carry a return address. About 2,000 trained and licensed ringers operate in Britain and Ireland, and together they mark around 800,000 birds each year.

All birdwatchers can contribute to the scheme by reporting any ringed or colour-ringed birds they find either. Reports can be submitted online at www.ring.ac or direct to the BTO in writing. Anyone finding a ringed bird should note the ring number, species (if known), when and where the bird was found, and what happened to it. If the bird is dead, please remove and keep the ring, or if writing, flatten it out and tape it to your letter and send it to us. If details are reported via the website, or phoned in, please keep the ring in case there is a query. Finders who send their name and address will be given details of where and when the bird was ringed. About 12,000 ringed birds are reported each year and an annual report is published.

Contact: Jacquie Clark, BTO.

TOOTH & CLAW

An independent project aimed at improving knowledge about Britain's predators and promoting discussion on the issues that surround them.

Tooth & Claw explores some of the complex issues surrounding our relationship with wild predators and questions how we really feel and why?

Through the web site, Tooth & Claw provides a meeting place between anecdotal input and scientific research and encourages constructive and imaginative dialogue on predator issues.

A series of case studies led by powerful imagery will provide insightful interviews and personal accounts of our lives alongside the likes of eagles and foxes with a glimpse into the future and the return of creatures we have not known for centuries.

Contact: Peter Cairns, Northshots, Ballintean, Glenfeshie, Kingussie, Scotland, PH21 1NX. (44) (0)1540 651 352;
e-mail: peter@toothandclaw.org.uk
www.toothandclaw.org.uk

WATERWAYS BREEDING BIRD SURVEY

A BTO project, supported by the Environment Agency

WBBS uses transect methods like those of the Breeding Bird Survey to record bird populations along randomly chosen stretches of river and canal throughout the UK. Just two survey visits are needed during April-June. WBBS began in 1998 and has now taken over from the Waterways Bird Survey as the main monitoring scheme for birds in this habitat.

Contact: BTO Regional Representative (see County Directory) to enquire if any local stretches require coverage, otherwise John Marchant at BTO HQ.

WETLAND BIRD SURVEY

A joint scheme of BTO, WWT, RSPB & JNCC.

The Wetland Bird Survey (WeBS) is the monitoring scheme for non-breeding waterbirds in the UK.

The principal aims are:

1. to determine the population sizes of waterbirds
2. to determine trends in numbers and distribution
3. to identify important sites for waterbirds

WeBS data are used to designate important waterbird sites and protect them against adverse development, for research into the causes of declines, for establishing conservation priorities and strategies and to formulate management plans for wetland sites and waterbirds.

Monthly, synchronised Core Counts are made at as many wetland sites as possible. Low Tide Counts are made on about 20 estuaries each winter to identify important feeding areas. Counts take just a few hours and are relatively straightforward. The 3,000 participants receive regular newsletters and a comprehensive annual report. New counters are always welcome.

Contacts: WeBS Office, BTO (Core Counts - Mark Collier, Low Tide Counts - Alex Banks and general enquiries - Andy Musgrove, at BTO HQ, E-mail WeBS@bto.org www.bto.org/webs

INTERNATIONAL DIRECTORY

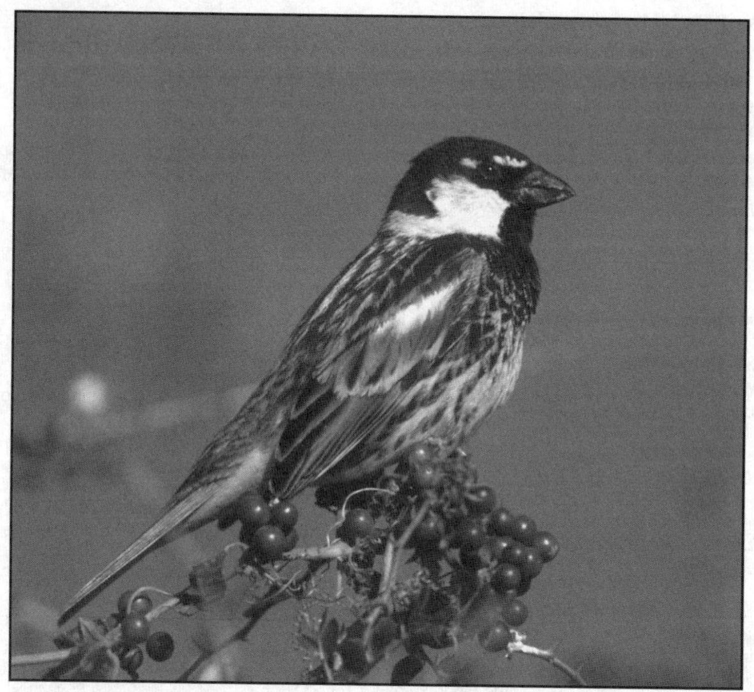

Spanish Sparrow by Keith Offord

The BirdLife Partnership

BirdLife is a Partnership of non-governmental organisations (NGOs) with a special focus on conservation and birds. Each NGO Partner represents a unique geographic territory/country.

The BirdLife Network explained

Partners: Membership-based NGOs who represent BirdLife in their own territory. Vote holders and key implementing bodies for BirdLife's Strategy and Regional Programmes in their own territories.

Partners Designate: Membership-based NGOs who represent BirdLife in their own territory, in a transition stage to becoming full Partners. Non-vote holders.

Affiliates: Usually NGOs, but also individuals, foundations or governmental institutions when appropriate. Act as a BirdLife contact with the aim of developing into, or recruiting, a BirdLife Partner in their territory.

Secretariat: The co-ordinating and servicing body of BirdLife International.

Secretariat Addresses

BirdLife Global Office
BirdLife International
Wellbrook Court
Girton Road
Cambridge CB3 0NA
UNITED KINGDOM
Tel. +44 1 223 277 318
Fax +44 1 223 277 200
E-mail: birdlife@birdlife.org.uk
www.birdlife.org

Birdlife Africa Regional Office
c/o ICIPE Campus
Kasarani Road, off Thika Road
Nairobi KENYA

Postal Address
PO Box 3502
00100 GPO
Nairobi KENYA
+254 20 862246
+254 20 862246
E-mail: birdlife@birdlife.or.ke
www.birdlife.org/regional/africa/partnership

BirdLife Americas Regional Office
Birdlife International
Vicente Cárdenas 120 y Japon,
3rd Floor
Quito ECUADOR

Postal address
BirdLife International
Casilla 17-17-717
Quito ECUADOR
Tel. +593 2 453 645
Fax +593 2 459 627
E-mail: birdlife@birdlife.org.ec
www.birdlife.org/regional/americas/partnership

BirdLife Asia Regional Office
Toyo-Shinjuku Building
2nd Floor, Shinjuku 1-12-15
Shinkuju-ku
Tokyo 160-0022, JAPAN
Tel.+3 3351 9981
Fax.+3 3351 9980
E-mail: info@birdlife-asia.org
www.birdlife.org/regional/asia/partnership

BirdLife European Regional Office
Droevendaalsesteeg 3a PO Box 127, NL- 6700 AC, Wageningen
THE NETHERLANDS
Tel. +31 317 478831
Fax +31 317 478844
E-mail: birdlife@birdlife.agro.nl

European Community Office (ECO)
BirdLife International
Avenue de la Toison d'Or 67
(2nd floor), B-1060 Brussels
BELGIUM
Tel. +32 2280 08 30
Fax +32 2230 38 02
E-mail: bleco@birdlifeeco.net
www.birdlife.org/regional/europe/partnership

BirdLife Middle East Regional Office
BirdLife International - Amman
P. O. Box 2295
Amman 11953
JORDAN
Tel: +962 (6) 566-2945
Fax: +962 (6) 569-1838
E-mail: birdlife@nol.com.jo
www.birdlife.org/regional/middle_east/partnership

AFRICA

PARTNERS

Burkina Faso
Fondation des Amis de la Nature (NATURAMA), 01 B.P. 6133, Ouagadougou 01.
e-mail: naturama@fasonet.bf

Ethiopia
Ethiopian Wildlife and Natural History Society, PO Box 13303, Addis Ababa, Pub: *Agazen; Ethiopian Wildl. and Nat. Hist. News. (& Annual Report); Ethiopian Wildl. and Nat. Hist. Soc. Quarterly News (WATCH); Walia (WATCH) (Ethiopia).*
e-mail: ewnhs@telecom.net.et
http://ewnhs.ble@telecom.net.et

Ghana
Ghana Wildlife Society, PO Box 13252, Accra, Pub: *Bongo News; NKO (The Parrots).*
e-mail: wildsoc@ighmail.com

Kenya
Nature Kenya, PO Box 44486, 00100 GPO. Nairobi. Pub: *Bulletin of the EANHS; Journal of East African Natural; Kenya Birds.*
e-mail: office@naturekenya.org
www.naturekenya.org

Nigeria
Nigerian Conservation Foundation, PO Box 74638, Victoria Island, Lagos. Pub: *NCF Matters/News/ Newsletter; Nigerian Conservation Foundation Annual Report.*
e-mail: enquiries@ncf-nigeria.org
www.africanconservation.org/ncftemp/

Seychelles
Nature Seychelles, Roche Caiman, Box 1310, Victoria, Mahe, Seychelles. Pub: *Zwazo - a BirdLife Seychelles Newsletter.*
e-mail: nature@seychelles.net
www.nature.org.sc

Sierra Leone
Conservation Society of Sierra Leone, PO BOX 1292, Freetown. Pub: *Rockfowl Link, The.*
e-mail: cssl@sierratel.sl

South Africa
BirdLife South Africa, PO Box 515, Randburg, Johannesburg 2125, South Africa, Pub: *Newsletter of BirdLife South Africa; Ostrich.*
e-mail: info@birdlife.org.za
www.birdlife.org.za

Tanzania
Wildlife Conservation Society of Tanzania, PO Box 70919, Dar es Salaam, Pub: *Miombo.*
e-mail: wcst@africaonline.co.tz

Uganda
Nature Uganda, PO Box 27034, Kampala. Pub: *Naturalist - A Newsletter of the East Africa Nat. His. Soc.*
e-mail: nature@natureuganda.org
www.natureuganda.org/

PARTNERS DESIGNATE

Tunisia
Association "Les Amis des Oiseaux", Avenue 18 Janvier 1952, Ariana Centre, App. C209, 2080 Ariana, Tunis. Pub: *Feuille de Liaison de l'AAO; Houbara, l'.* e-mail: aao.bird@planet.tn

Zimbabwe
BirdLife Zimbabwe, P O Box RV 100, Runiville, Harare, Zimbabwe. Pub: *Babbler (WATCH) (Zimbabwe); Honeyguide.*
e-mail: birds@zol.co.zw

AFFILIATES

Botswana
Birdlife Botswana, Private Bag 003 # Suite 348, Mogoditshane, Gaborone, Botswana
e-mail: blb@birdlifebotswana.org.bw
www.birdlifebotswana.org.bw

Burundi
Association Burundaise pour la Protection des Oiseaux, P O Box 7069, Bujumbura, Burundi
e-mail: aboburundi@yahoo.fr

Cameroon
Cameroon Biodiversity Conservation Society (CBCS), PO Box 3055, Messa, Yaoundé.
e-mail: gdzikouk@yahoo.fr

Egypt
Sherif Baha El Din, 3 Abdala El Katib St, Dokki, Cairo. e-mail: baha2@internetegypt.com

Rwanda
Association pour la Conservation de la Nature au Rwanda, P O Box 4290, Kigali,
e-mail: acnrwanda@yahoo.fr

Zambia
Zambian Ornithological Society, Box 33944, Lusaka 10101, Pub: *Zambian Ornithological Society Newsletter.* e-mail: zos@zamnet.zm
www.wattledcrane.com

INTERNATIONAL ORGANISATIONS

AMERICAS

PARTNERS

Argentina
Aves Argentina / AOP, 25 de Mayo 749, 2 piso, oficina 6, 1002 Buenos Aires. Pub: *Hornero; Naturaleza & Conservacion; Nuestras Aves; Vuelo de Pajaro.*
e-mail: info@avesargentinas.org.ar
www.avesargentinas.org.ar

Belize
The Belize Audubon Society, 12 Fort Street, PO Box 1001, Belize City. Pub: *Belize Audubon Society Newsletter.*
e-mail: base@btl.net
www.belizeaudubon.org

Bolivia
Asociacion Armonia, 400 Avenidad Lomas de Arena, Casilla 3566, Santa Cruz, Bolivia. Pub: *Aves en Bolivia.*
e-mail: armonia@scbbs-bo.com

Canada
Bird Studies Canada, PO Box/160, Port Rowan, Ontario N0E 1M0. Pub: *Bird Studies Canada - Annual Report; Birdwatch Canada.*
e-mail: generalinfo@bsc-eoc.org
www.bsc-eoc.org

Canada
Nature Canada, 1 Nicholas Street, Suite 606, Ottawa, Ontario, K1N 7B7. Pub: *Grass 'n Roots; IBA News Canada; Nature Canada; Nature Matters; Nature Watch News (CNF).*
e-mail: info@naturecanada.ca
www.naturecanada.ca

Ecuador
Fundación Ornitholó́gica del Ecuador, La Tierra 203 y Av. de los Shyris, Casilla 17-17-906, Quito.
e-mail: cecia@uio.satnet.net
www.cecia.org/

Jamaica
BirdLife Jamaica, 2 Starlight Avenue, Kingston 6, Pub: *Broadsheet: BirdLife Jamaica; Important Bird Areas Programme Newsletter.*
e-mail: birdlifeja@yahoo.com
www.birdelifejamaica.com

Panama
Panama Audubon Society, Apartado 2026, Ancón, Balboa. Pub: *Toucan.*
e-mail: info@panamaaudubon.org
www.panamaaudubon.org

Venezuela
Sociedad Conservacionista Audubon de, Apartado 80.450, Caracas 1080-A, Venezuela. Pub: *Audubon (Venezuela) (formerly Boletin Audubon).*
e-mail: audubon@cantv.net

PARTNERS DESIGNATE

Mexico
CIPAMEX, Apartado Postal 22-012, D.F. 14091, Mexico. Pub: *AICA's; Cuauhtli Boletin de Cipa Mex.*
e-mail: cipamex@campus.iztacala.unam.mx
http://coro@servidor.unam.mx

Paraguay
Guyra Paraguay,, Coronel Rafael Franco 381 c/ Leandro Prieto, Casilla de Correo 1132, Asunción. Pub: *Boletin Jara Kuera.*
e-mail: guyra@guyra.org.py
or guyra@highway.com.py
www.guyra.org.py/

United States
National Audubon Society, 700 Broadway, New York, NY, 10003 -9562. Pub: *American Birds; Audubon (USA); Audubon Field Notes; Audubon Bird Conservation Newsletter.*
e-mail: audubonaction@audubon.org
www.audubon.org

Chile
Union de Ornitologis de Chile (UNORCH), Casilla 13.183, Santiago 21. Pub: *Boletin Chileno de Ornitologia; Boletin Informativo (WATCH) (Chile).*
e-mail: unorch@entelchile.net
www.geocities.com/RainForest/4372

AFFILIATES

Bahamas
Bahamas National Trust, PO Box N-4105, Nassau. Pub: *Bahamas Naturalist; Currents; Grand Bahama Update.*
e-mail: bnt@batelnet.bs
www.thebahamasnationaltrust.org/

Cuba
Centro Nacional de Áreas Protegidas (CNAP). Calle 18 a, No 1441, e/ 41 y 47, Playa, Ciudad Habana, Cuba. e-mail: cnap@snap.cu
www.snap.co.cu/

El Salvador
SalvaNATURA, 33 Avenida Sur #640, Colonia Flor Blanca, San Salvador.
e-mail: salvanatura@saltel.net
www.salvanatura.org

Falkland Islands
Falklands Conservation, PO Box 26, Stanley,. or Falklands Conservation, 1 Princes Avenue, Finchley, London N3 2DA, UK. Pub: *Falklands Conservation.*
e-mail: conservation@horizon.co.fk
www.falklandsconservation.com

Honduras
Sherry Thorne, c/o Cooperación Técnica, Apdo 30289 Toncontín, Tegucigalpa.
e-mail: pilar_birds@yahoo.com

Suriname
Foundation for Nature Preservation in Suriname, Cornelis Jongbawstraat 14, PO BOX 12252, Paramaribo
e-mail: research@stinasu.sr
www.stinasu.sr

Uruguay
GUPECA, Casilla de Correo 6955, Correo Central, Montevideo. Pub: *Achara.*
e-mail: info@avesuruguay.org.uy
www.avesuruguay.org.uy/

ASIA

PARTNERS

Japan
Wild Bird Society of Japan (WBSJ), 1/F Odakyu Nishi Shinjuku Building, 1-47-1 Hatsudai Shibuya-ku, Tokyo 151-061, Japan. Pub: *Strix; Wild Birds; Wing.*
e-mail: int.center@wing-wbsj.or.jp
www.wing-wbsj.or.jp

Malaysia
Malaysian Nature Society, PO Box 10750, 50724 Kuala Lumpur. Pub: *Enggang; Suara Enggang; Malayan Nature Journal; Malaysian Naturalist.*
www.mns.org.my
e-mail: natsoc@po.jaring.my

Philippines
Haribon Foundation, Suites 401-404 Fil-Garcia Bldg, 140 Kalayaan Avenue cor. Mayaman St, Diliman, Quezon CIty 1101. Pub: *Haribon Foundation Annual Report; Haring Ibon; Philippine Biodiversity.*
e-mail: birdlife@haribon.org.ph
www.haribon.org.ph

Singapore
Nature Society (Singapore), 510 Geylang Road, #02-05, The Sunflower, 398466. Pub: *Nature News; Nature Watch (Singapore).*
e-mail: nss@nss.org.sg
www.nss.org.sg

Taiwan
Wild Bird Federation Taiwan (WBFT), 1F, No. 3, Lane 36 Jing-Long St., 116 Taipei, Taiwan, R.O.C. Pub: *Yuhina Post.*
e-mail: wbft@bird.org.tw
www.bird.org.tw

Thailand
Bird Conservation Society of Thailand, 43 Soi Chok Chai Ruam Mit 29, Vipahvadee-Rabgsit Road, Sansaen-nok, Dindaeng, Bangkok 10320 Thailand. Pub: *Bird Conservation Society of Thailand.*
e-mail: bcst@bcst.or.th
www.bcst.or.th

PARTNER DESIGNATE

India
Bombay Natural History Society, Hornbill House, Shaheed Bhagat Singh Road, Mumbai-400 023. Pub: *Buceros; Hornbill; Journal of the Bombay Natural History Society.*
e-mail: bnhs@bom4.vsnl.net.in
www.bnhs.org

AFFILIATES

Hong Kong
The Hong Kong Birdwatching Society, Room 1612 Beverley Commercial Building, 87-105 Chatham Road South, Tsim Sha Tsui, Kowloon, Hong Kong. Pub: *Hong Kong Bird Report.*
e-mail: hkbws@hkbws.org.uk
www.hkbws.org.hk

Indonesia
BirdLife Indonesia (Perhimpunan Pelestari Burung dan Habitatnya), Jl. Dadali 32, Bogor 16161, PO. Box 310/Boo, Bogor 16003, Indonesia.
e-mail: birdlife@burung.org
www.burung.org

Nepal
Bird Conservation Nepal, P.O.Box 12465, Lazimpat, Kathmandu, Nepal. Pub: *Bird Conservation Nepal (Danphe); Ibisbill.*
e-mail: bcn@mail.com.np
www.birdlifenepal.org

Pakistan
Ornithological Society of Pakistan, PO Box 73, 109D Dera Ghazi Khan, 32200. Pub: *Pakistan Journal of Ornithology.*
e-mail: osp@mul.paknet.com.pk

Sri Lanka
Field Ornithology Group of Sri Lanka, Dept of Zoology, University of Colombo, Colombo 03. Pub: *Malkoha - Newsletter of the Field Ornithology Group of Sri Lanka.*
e-mail: fogsl@slt.lk

EUROPE

PARTNERS

Austria
BirdLife Austria, Museumplatz 1/10/8, AT-1070 Wien. Pub: *Egretta; Vogelschutz in Osterreich.*
e-mail: office@birdlife.at
www.birdlife.at/

Belgium
BirdLife Belgium (BNVR-RNOB-BNVS), Natuurpunt, Kardinaal, Mercierplein 1, 2800 Mechelen, Belgium.
e-mail: wim.vandenbossche@natuurpunt.be
www.natuurreservaten.be

Bulgaria
Bulgarian Society for the Protection of Birds (BSPB), PO Box 50, Musagenitza Complex, Block 104, Entrance A, Floor 6, BG-1111, Sofia, Bulgaria. Pub: *Neophron (& UK).*
e-mail: bspb_hq@bspb.org
www.bspb.org

Czech Republic
Czech Society for Ornithology (CSO), Hornomecholupska 34, CZ-102 00 Praha 10. Pub: *Ptaci Svet; Sylvia; Zpravy Ceske Spolecnosti Ornitologicke.* e-mail: cso@birdlife.cz
www.birdlife.cz

Denmark
Dansk Ornitologisk Forening (DOF), Vesterbrogade 138-140, DK-1620, Copenhagen V, Denmark. Pub: *DAFIF - Dafifs Nyhedsbrev; Dansk Ornitologisk Forenings Tidsskrift; Fugle og Natur.*
e-mail: dof@dof.dk
www.dof.dk

Estonia
Estonian Ornithological Society (EOU), PO Box 227, Vesti Str. 4, EE-50002 Tartu, Estonia. Pub: *Hirundo Eesti Ornitoogiauhing.*
e-mail: eoy@eoy.ee
www.eoy.ee

Finland
BirdLife SUOMI Finland, Annankatu 29 A, PO Box 1285, FI 00101, Helsinki. Pub: *Linnuston-Suojelu; Linnut; Tiira.*
e-mail: office@birdlife.fi
www.birdlife.fi

France
Ligue pour la Protection des Oiseaux (LPO), La Corderie Royale, B.P. 90263, 17305 ROCHEFORT CEDEX, France. Pub: *Lettre Internationale; Ligue Francaise Pour La Protection des Oiseaux; Oiseau, L' (LPO); Outarde infos.*
e-mail: lpo@lpo.fr
www.lpo.fr/

Germany
Naturschutzbund Deutschland, Herbert-Rabius-Str. 26, D-53225 Bonn, Germany. Pub: *Naturschutz Heute (NABU) Naturschutzbund Deutschland.*
e-mail: nabu@nabu.de
www.nabu.de

Gibraltar
Gibraltar Ornithological and Nat. History Society, Jew's Gate, Upper Rock Nature Reserve, PO Box 843, GI. Pub: *Alectoris; Gibraltar Nature News.*
e-mail: gohns@gibnet.gi
www.gibraltar.gi/gonhs

Greece
Hellenic Ornithological Society (HOS), Vas. Irakleiou 24, GR-10682 Athens, Greece. Pub: *HOS Newsletter.*
e-mail: birdlife-gr@ath.forthnet.gr
www.ornithologiki.gr

Hungary
Hungarian Orn. and Nature Cons. Society (MME), Kolto u. 21, Pf. 391, HU-1536, Budapest. Pub: *Madartani Tajekoztato; Madartavlat; Ornis Hungarica; Tuzok.*
e-mail: mme@mme.hu
www.mme.hu

INTERNATIONAL ORGANISATIONS

Iceland
Icelandic Society for the Protection of Birds, Fuglaverndarfélag Islands, PO Box 5069, IS-125 Reykjavik, Iceland.
e-mail: fuglavernd@fuglavernd.is
www.fuglavernd.is

Ireland
BirdWatch Ireland, Rockingham House, Newcastle, Co. Wicklow, Eire. Pub: *Irish Birds; Wings (IWC Birdwatch Ireland).*
e-mail: info@birdwatchireland.org
www.birdwatchireland.ie

Israel
Society for the Protection of Nature in Israel, Hashsela 4, Tel-Aviv 66103. Pub: *SPNI News.*
e-mail: ioc@netvision.net.il
www.birds.org.il

Italy
Lega Italiana Protezione Uccelli (LIPU), Via Trento 49, IT-43100, Parma. Pub: *Ali Giovani; Ali Notizie.*
e-mail: lipusede@box1.tin.it
www.lipu.it

Latvia
Latvijas Ornitologijas Biedriba (LOB), Ak 1010, LV-1050 Riga, Latvia. Pub: *Putni Daba.*
e-mail: putni@lob.lv
www.lob.lv

Luxembourg
Letzebuerger Natur-a Vulleschutzliga (LNVL), Kraizhaff, rue de Luxembourg.L-1899 Kockelscheuer. Pub: *Regulus (WATCH); Regulus Info (& Annual Report) (WATCH); Regulus Wissenschaftliche Berichte (WATCH).*
e-mail: secretary@luxnatur.lu
www.luxnatur.lu

Malta
BirdLife Malta, 57 Marina Court, Flat 28, Triq Abate Rigord, MT-Ta' Xbiex, MSD 12, MALTA. Pub: *Bird Talk (WATCH) (Malta); Bird's Eye View (WATCH) (Malta); Il-Merill.*
e-mail: info@birdlifemalta.org
www.birdlifemalta.org

Netherlands
Vogelbescherming Nederland, PO Box 925, NL-3700 AX Zeist. Pub: *Vogelniews; Vogels.*
e-mail: info@vogelbescherming.nl
www.vogelbescherming.nl/

Norway
Norsk Ornitologisk Forening, Sandgata 30 B, N-7012 Trondheim, Norway. Pub: *Fuglearet; Fuglefauna; Var; Ringmerkaren.*
e-mail: nof@birdlife.no
www.birdlife.no

Poland
Ogólnopolskie Towarzystwo Ochrony Ptaków (OTOP), Ul. Hallera 4/2, PL-80-401 Gdansk, Poland. Pub: *Ptaki; Ptasie Ostoje.*
e-mail: office@otop.most.org.pl
www.otop.org.pl/

Portugal
Sociedade Portuguesa para o Estuda das, Aves (SPEA), Rua da Vitoria, 53-3° Esq, 1100-618, Lisboa. Pub: *Pardela.*
e-mail: spea@spea.pt
www.spea.pt

Romania
Romanian Ornithological Society (SOR), Str. Gheorghe Dima 49/2, RO-3400 Cluj. Pub: *Alcedo; Buletin AIA; Buletin de Informare Societatea Ornitologica Romana; Milvus (Romania).*
e-mail: office@sor.ro
www.sor.ro/

Slovakia
Soc. for the Prot. of Birds in Slovakia (SOVS), PO Box 71, 093 01 Vranov nad Topl'ou. Pub: *Spravodaj SOVS; Vtacie Spravy.*
e-mail: sovs@changenet.sk
www.sovs.miesto.sk

Slovenia
BirdLife Slovenia (DOPPS), Trzaska 2, PO Box 2990, SI-1000 Ljubljana, Slovenia. Pub: *Acrocephalus; Svet Ptic.*
e-mail: dopps@dopps-drustvo.si
www.ptice.org

Spain
Sociedad Espanola de Ornitologia (SEO), C/ Melquiades Biencinto 34, E-28053, Madrid. Pub: *Ardeola; Areas Importantes para las Aves.*
e-mail: seo@seo.org
www.seo.org

Sweden
Sveriges Ornitologiska Forening (SOF), Ekhagsvagen 3, SE 104-05, Stockholm. Pub: *Fagelvarld; var; Ornis Svecica.*
e-mail: birdlife@sofnet.org
www.sofnet.org

Switzerland
SVS/BirdLife Switzerland, Wiedingstrasse 78, PO

Box, CH-8036, Zurich, Switzerland. Pub: *Oiwvos Ornis; Ornis Junior; Ornithologische Beobachter; Der Ornithos; Steinadler.*
e-mail: svs@birdlife.ch
www.birdlife.ch

Turkey
Doga Dernegi, PK: 640 06445, Yenişehir, Ankarae, Turkey. Pub: *Kelaynak; Kuscu Bulteni.*
e-mail: doga@dogadernegi.org
www.dogadernegi.org/

United Kingdom
Royal Society for the Protection of Birds, The Lodge, Sandy, Bedfordshire, SG19 2DL.
e-mail: info@RSPB.org.uk
www.rspb.org.uk

PARTNERS DESIGNATE

Belarus
BirdLife Belarus (APB), PO Box 306, Minsk, 220050 Belarus. Pub: *Subbuteo - The Belarusian Ornithological Bulletin.*
e-mail: apb@tut.by
http://apb.iatp.by/

Lithuania
Lietuvos Ornitologu Draugija (LOD), Naugarduko St. 47-3, LT-2006, Vilnius, Lithuania. Pub: *Baltasis Gandras.*
e-mail: lod@birdlife.lt
www.birdlife.lt

Russia
Russian Bird Conservation Union (RBCU), Building 1, Shosse Entuziastov 60, 111123, RU-Moscow. Pub: *Newsletter of the Russian Bird Conservation Union.*
e-mail: mail@rbcu.ru
www.rbcu.ru/en/

Ukraine
Ukrainian Union for Bird Conservation (UTOP), PO Box 33, Kiev, 1103, UA. Pub: *Life of Birds.*
e-mail: utop@iptelecom.net.ua
www.utop.org.ua/

AFFILIATES

Liechtenstein
Botanish-Zoologische Gesellschaft, Im Bretscha 22, FL-9494 Schaan, Liechtenstein.
e-mail: broggi@pingnet.li or renat@pingnet.li

Andorra
Associacio per a la Defensa de la Natura, Apartado de Correus Espanyols No 96, Andora La Vella, Principat d'Andorra. Pub: *Aiguerola.*
e-mail: and@andorra.ad
www.adn-andorra.org/

Croatia
Croatian Society for Bird and Nature Protection, Gunduliceva 24, HR-10000 Zagreb, Croatia. Pub: *Troglodytes.*
e-mail: jasmina@hazu.hr

Cyprus
BirdLife Cyprus, PO Box 28076, 2090 Lefkosia, Cyprus.
e-mail: melis@cytanet.com.cy
www.birdlifecyprus.org

Faroe Islands (to Denmark)
Føroya Fuglafrødifelag (Faroese Orginithological Society) (FOS), Postssmoga 1230, FR-110 Torshavn, Faroe Islands.
e-mail: doreteb@ngs.fo

Georgia
Georgian Centre for the Conservation of Wildlife, PO Box 56, GE-Tbilisi 0160, Georgia.
e-mail: office@gccw.org
www.gccw.org/

MIDDLE EAST

PARTNERS

Jordan
Royal Society of the Conservation of Nature, PO Box 6354, Jubeiha-Abu-Nusseir Circle, Amman 11183. Pub: *Al Reem.*
e-mail: adminrscn@rscn.org.jo
www.rscn.org.jo

Lebanon
Society for the Protection of Nature in Lebanon, Awad Bldg, 6th Floor, Abdel Aziz Street, P.O.Box: 11-5665, Beirut, Lebanon.
e-mail: spnlorg@cyberia.net.lb
www.spnlb.org

PARTNER DESIGNATE

Palestine
Palestine Wildlife Society (PWLS), Beit Sahour, PO

Box 89. Pub: *Palestine Wildlife Society - Annual Report.* www.wildlife-pal.org
e-mail: wildlife@palnet.com

AFFILIATES

Bahrain
Dr Saeed A. Mohamed, PO Box 40266, Bahrain.
e-mail: sam53@batelco.com.bh

Iran, Islamic Republic of
Dr Jamshid Mansoori, Assistant Professor, College of Natural Resources, Tehran University, Mojtame Sabz, Golestan Shamali, Mahestan Ave, Shahrake Qarb, Phase 1, P.O.Box 14657, Tehran, I.R. of Iran.
e-mail: birdlifeiran@yahoo.com

Kuwait
Kuwait Environment Protection Society, PO Box 1896, Safat 13019, Kuwait.
e-mail: rasamhory@hotmail.com
www.keps74.com

Saudi Arabia
National Commission for Wildlife Cons & Dev, NCWDC, PO Box 61681, Riyadh 11575. Pub: *Phoenix; The.* e-mail: ncwcd@zajil.net
www.ncwcd.gov.sa/

Yemen
Yemen Society for the Protection of Wildlife (YSPW), 29 Alger Street, PO Box 19759, Sana'a, Yemen.
e-mail: wildlife.yemen@y.net.ye

PACIFIC

PARTNER

Australia
Birds Australia, 415 Riversdale Road, Hawthorn East, VIC 3123, Australia. Pub: *Australia Garcilla; Birds Australia Annual Report; Eclectus; Emu; Wingspan (WATCH) (Australia); from wingspan@birdsaustralia.com.au.*
e-mail: mail@birdsaustralia.com.au
www.birdsaustralia.com.au

AFFILIATES

Cook Islands
Taporoporo'anga Ipukarea Society (TIS), PO Box 649, Rarotonga, Cook Islands.
e-mail: 2tis@oyster.net.ck

Fiji
Dr Dick Watling, c/o Environment Consultants Fiji, P O Box 2041, Government Buildings, Suva, Fiji.
e-mail: watling@is.com.fj
www.environmentfiji.com

French Polynesia
Société d'Ornithologie de Polynésie "Manu", B.P. 21 098, Papeete, Tahiti.
e-mail: sop@manu.pf
www.manu.pf

Palau
Palau Conservation Society, PO BOX 1811, Koror, PW96940. Pub: *Ngerel a Biib.*
e-mail: pcs@palaunet.com
www.palau-pcs.org/

Samoa
O le Si'osi'omaga Society Incorporated, O le Si'osi'omaga Society Inc., P O Box 2282, Apia, Western Samoa.
e-mail: ngo_siosiomaga@samoa.ws

New Zealand
Royal Forest & Bird Protection Society of, PO Box 631, Wellington. Pub: *Forest & Bird; Forest & Bird Annual Report; Forest & Bird Conservation News.*
e-mail: office@forestandbird.org.nz
www.forestandbird.org.nz/

SPECIAL INTEREST ORGANISATIONS

AFRICAN BIRD CLUB.
c/o Birdlife International as below.
e-mail (general): info@hotmail.com
e-mail (membership and sales):
membership@africanbirdclub.org
www.africanbirdclub.org
Pub: *Bulletin of the African Bird Club*.

BIRDLIFE INTERNATIONAL.
Wellbrook Court, Girton Road, Cambridge, CB3 ONA, +44 (0)1223 277 318; (Fax) +44 (0)1223 277 200,
Pub: *World Birdwatch*. www.birdlife.net

EAST AFRICA NATURAL HISTORY SOCIETY see Kenya in preceding list.

EURING (European Union for Bird Ringing).
Euring Data Bank, c/o BTO, The Nunnery, Thetford, Norfolk IP24 2PU. 01842 750 050.
www.euring.org

FAUNA AND FLORA INTERNATIONAL.
Jupiter House, 4th Floor, Station Road, Cambridge, CB1 2JD. Call on +44 (0)1223 571 000; (Fax) +44 (0)1223 461 481. www.fauna-flora.org
e-mail: info@fauna-flora.org
Pub: *Fauna & Flora News; Oryx*.

LIPU-UK (the Italian League for the Protection of Birds).
David Lingard, Fernwood, Doddington Road, Whisby, Lincs, LN6 9BX, +44 (0)1522 689 030,
e-mail: david@lipu-uk.org www.lipu-uk.org
Pub: *The Hoopoe*, annually, *Ali Notizie*, quarterley.

NEOTROPICAL BIRD CLUB.
c/o The Lodge, Sandy, Bedfordshire, SG19 2DL.
Pub: *Cotinga*.
email: secretary@neotropicalbirdclub.org
www.neotropicalbirdclub.org

ORIENTAL BIRD CLUB.
P.O.Box 324, Bedford, MK42 0WG
Pub: *The Forktail; OBC Bulletin*.
email: mail@orientalbirdclub.org
www.orientalbirdclub.org

ORNITHOLOGICAL SOCIETY OF THE MIDDLE EAST (OSME).
c/o The Lodge, Sandy, Beds, SG19 2DL.
Pub: *Sandgrouse*.
www.osme.org

TRAFFIC International (formerly Wildlife Trade Monitoring Unit).
219a Huntingdon Road, Cambridge, CB3 ODL, +44 (0)1223 277 427; (Fax) +44 (0)1223 277 237.
Pub: *TRAFFIC Bulletin*.
e-mail: traffic@trafficint.org
www.traffic.org

WEST AFRICAN ORNITHOLOGICAL SOCIETY.
R E Sharland, 1 Fisher's Heron, East Mills, Hants, SP6 2JR. Pub: *Malimbus*.
e-mail bob@sharland2002.fsnet.co.uk
http://malimbus.free.fr

WETLANDS INTERNATIONAL.
PO Box 471, 6700 AL Wageningen, Netherlands, +31 317 478 854; (Fax) +31 317 478 850,
Pub: *Wetlands*.
e-mail: post@wetlands.org
www.wetlands.org

WORLD OWL TRUST.
The World Owl Centre, Muncaster Castle, Ravenglass, Cumbria, CA18 1RQ, +44 (0)1229 717393; (Fax) +44 (0)1229 717107,
www.owls.org

WORLD PHEASANT ASSOCIATION.
7-9 Shaftesbury St, Fordingbridge, Hants SP6 1JF. 01425 657 129; (Fax) 01425 658 053.
Pub: *WPA News*. www.pheasant.org.uk

WORLD WIDE FUND FOR NATURE.
Panda House, Weyside Park, Godalming United Kingdom. +44 1483 426 444;
(Fax) +44 1483 426 409,
www.panda.org

QUICK REFERENCE SECTION

Male Reed Bunting by Steve Knell

TIDE TABLES: USEFUL INFORMATION

BRITISH SUMMER TIME

In 2008 BST applies from 01:00 on March 30 to 01:00 on October 26.
Note that all the times in the following tables are GMT.

Shetland 42, 43
Orkney 44, 45

During British Summer Time one hour should be added.

Predictions are given for the times of high water at Dover throughout the year.

The times of tides at the locations shown here may be obtained by adding or subtracting their 'tidal difference' as shown opposite (subtractions are indicated by a minus sign).

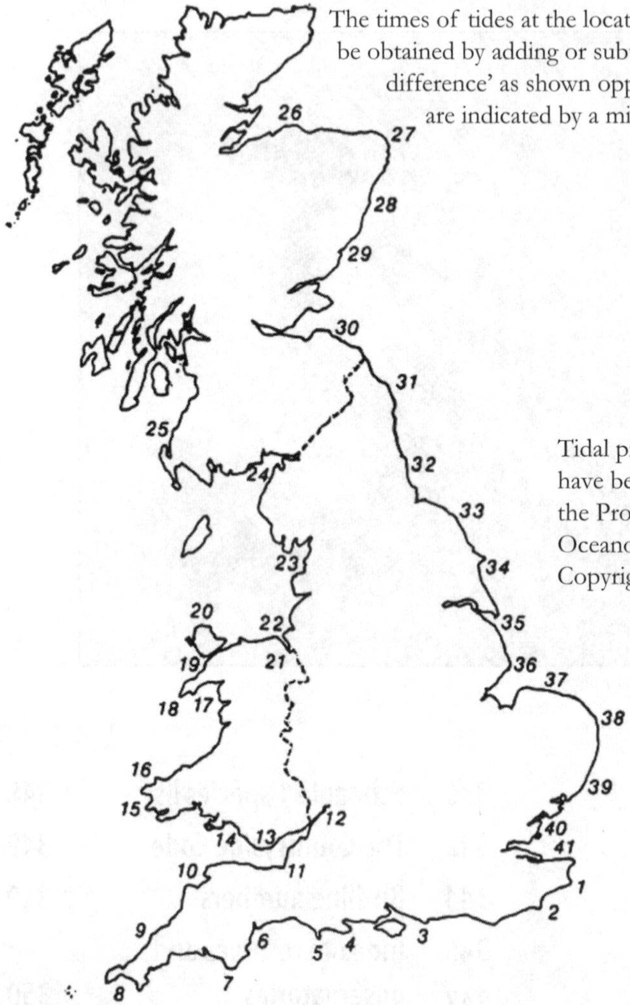

Tidal predictions for Dover have been computed by the Proudman Oceanographic Laboratory. Copyright reserved.

Map showing locations for which tidal differences are given on facing page.

TIDE TABLES 2008

Example 1

To calculate the time of first high water at Girvan on February 17

1. Look up the time at Dover (07 32)* = 7:32 am
2. Add the tidal difference for Girvan = 0.54
3. Therefore the time of high water at Girvan = 8:26 am

Example 2

To calculate the time of second high water at Blakeney on June 22

1. Look up the time at Dover (13 17) = 1:17 pm
2. Add 1 hour for British Summer Time (14 17) = 2:17 pm
3. Subtract the tidal difference for Blakeney = - 4.07
4. Therefore the time of high water at Blakeney = 10:10 am

*All Dover times are shown on the 24-hour clock. Thus, 08 14 = 08.14 am; 14 58 = 2.58pm Following the time of each high water the height of the tide is given, in metres.

(Tables beyond April 2009 are not available at the time of going to press.)

TIDAL DIFFERENCES

1	Dover	See pp 338-341		23	Morecambe	0	20
2	Dungeness	-0	12	24	Silloth	0	51
3	Selsey Bill	0	09	25	Girvan	0	54
4	Swanage (Ist H.W.Springs)	-2	36	26	Lossiemouth	0	48
5	Portland	-4	23	27	Fraserburgh	1	20
6	Exmouth (Approaches)	-4	48	28	Aberdeen	2	30
7	Salcombe	-5	23	29	Montrose	3	30
8	Newlyn (Penzance)	5	59	30	Dunbar	3	42
9	Padstow	-5	47	31	Holy Island	3	58
10	Bideford	-5	17	32	Sunderland	4	38
11	Bridgwater	-4	23	33	Whitby	5	12
12	Sharpness Dock	-3	19	34	Bridlington	5	53
13	Cardiff (Penarth)	-4	16	35	Grimsby	-5	20
14	Swansea	-4	52	36	Skegness	-5	00
15	Skomer Island	-5	00	37	Blakeney	-4	07
16	Fishguard	-3	48	38	Gorleston	-2	08
17	Barmouth	-2	45	39	Aldeburgh	-0	13
18	Bardsey Island	-3	07	40	Bradwell Waterside	1	11
19	Caernarvon	-1	07	41	Herne Bay	1	28
20	Amlwch	-0	22	42	Sullom Voe	-1	34
21	Connahs Quay	0	20	43	Lerwick	0	01
22	Hilbre Island			44	Kirkwall	-0	26
	(Hoylake/West Kirby)	-0	05	45	Widewall Bay	-1	30

NB. Care should be taken when making calculations at the beginning and end of British Summer Time. See worked examples above.

Time Zone **GMT**

Tidal Predictions : **HIGH WATERS 2008**

Datum of Predictions = **Chart Datum : 3.67 metres below Ordnance Datum (Newlyn)**

British Summer Time : **30th March to 26th October**

Units **METRES**

DOVER

January

DATE	DAY	Morning hr min	m	Afternoon hr min	m
1	Tu	04 42	5·7	17 24	5·3
2	W	05 47	5·5	18 33	5·2
3	Th	06 57	5·4	19 42	5·3
4	F	08 03	5·4	20 41	5·4
5	Sa	08 59	5·6	21 30	5·7
6	Su	09 47	5·8	22 11	5·9
7	M	10 25	5·9	22 46	6·1
8	Tu ●	11 00	6·1	23 20	6·3
9	W	11 34	6·2	23 55	6·4
10	Th	** **	* *	12 09	6·3
11	F	00 32	6·5	12 47	6·4
12	Sa	01 10	6·6	13 25	6·3
13	Su	01 48	6·5	14 04	6·2
14	M	02 27	6·4	14 48	6·1
15	Tu ☽	03 11	6·3	15 37	5·9
16	W	04 01	6·2	16 36	5·8
17	Th	05 03	6·0	17 44	5·6
18	F	06 13	5·8	19 00	5·5
19	Sa	07 31	5·8	20 23	5·7
20	Su	08 48	5·9	21 32	6·0
21	M	09 53	6·2	22 26	6·3
22	Tu ○	10 48	6·4	23 13	6·5
23	W	11 34	6·5	23 55	6·6
24	Th	** **	* *	12 16	6·5
25	F	00 34	6·7	12 56	6·4
26	Sa	01 11	6·7	13 31	6·3
27	Su	01 48	6·6	14 07	6·2
28	M	02 24	6·4	14 45	5·9
29	Tu	03 02	6·2	15 25	5·7
30	W ☾	03 44	5·8	16 14	5·4
31	Th	04 38	5·4	17 17	5·0

DOVER

February

DATE	DAY	Morning hr min	m	Afternoon hr min	m
1	F	05 52	5·1	18 46	4·9
2	Sa	07 21	5·0	20 07	5·1
3	Su	08 34	5·2	21 05	5·4
4	M	09 26	5·5	21 50	5·7
5	Tu	10 05	5·8	22 25	6·0
6	W	10 39	6·1	22 59	6·3
7	Th ●	11 13	6·3	23 34	6·5
8	F	11 48	6·5	** **	* *
9	Sa	00 11	6·7	12 26	6·6
10	Su	00 47	6·8	13 04	6·6
11	M	01 25	6·8	13 42	6·5
12	Tu	02 02	6·7	14 21	6·3
13	W	02 41	6·5	15 08	6·1
14	Th ☽	03 32	6·2	16 05	5·8
15	F	04 34	5·9	17 17	5·4
16	Sa	05 54	5·5	18 50	5·3
17	Su	07 32	5·4	20 27	5·5
18	M	08 58	5·7	21 32	5·9
19	Tu	09 58	6·0	22 19	6·2
20	W	10 43	6·3	23 00	6·5
21	Th ○	11 23	6·4	23 37	6·7
22	F	11 58	6·5	** **	* *
23	Sa	00 12	6·7	12 30	6·5
24	Su	00 46	6·7	13 03	6·4
25	M	01 18	6·6	13 34	6·3
26	Tu	01 48	6·5	14 03	6·1
27	W	02 19	6·2	14 34	5·8
28	Th	02 49	5·9	15 11	5·5
29	F ☾	03 32	5·4	16 04	5·1

DOVER

March

DATE	DAY	Morning hr min	m	Afternoon hr min	m
1	Sa	04 41	5·0	17 33	4·8
2	Su	06 30	4·8	19 21	4·9
3	M	08 00	5·0	20 33	5·2
4	Tu	08 58	5·4	21 19	5·6
5	W	09 39	5·8	21 57	6·0
6	Th	10 12	6·1	22 31	6·4
7	F ●	10 46	6·4	23 06	6·7
8	Sa	11 23	6·6	23 42	6·9
9	Su	** **	* *	12 01	6·7
10	M	00 20	7·0	12 39	6·7
11	Tu	00 57	6·9	13 18	6·6
12	W	01 36	6·8	14 00	6·4
13	Th	02 19	6·5	14 48	6·1
14	F ☽	03 12	6·1	15 49	5·7
15	Sa	04 21	5·6	17 06	5·3
16	Su	05 54	5·3	18 51	5·2
17	M	07 45	5·4	20 20	5·5
18	Tu	08 58	5·7	21 18	5·9
19	W	09 50	6·0	22 01	6·2
20	Th	10 28	6·2	22 38	6·5
21	F ○	11 00	6·4	23 11	6·6
22	Sa	11 31	6·4	23 45	6·7
23	Su	** **	* *	12 04	6·5
24	M	00 18	6·7	12 33	6·4
25	Tu	00 47	6·6	13 01	6·3
26	W	01 14	6·4	13 28	6·1
27	Th	01 39	6·1	13 56	5·9
28	F	02 07	5·8	14 30	5·6
29	Sa ☾	02 45	5·4	15 18	5·3
30	Su	03 50	5·0	16 41	4·9
31	M	05 40	4·8	18 23	4·9

DOVER

April

DATE	DAY	Morning hr min	m	Afternoon hr min	m
1	Tu	07 14	5·0	19 43	5·2
2	W	08 16	5·4	20 38	5·7
3	Th	09 01	5·8	21 19	6·1
4	F	09 39	6·2	21 57	6·4
5	Sa	10 15	6·5	22 34	6·7
6	Su ●	10 53	6·7	23 13	6·9
7	M	11 34	6·8	23 52	7·0
8	Tu	** **	* *	12 16	6·8
9	W	00 34	6·9	13 00	6·7
10	Th	01 18	6·7	13 48	6·4
11	F	02 09	6·4	14 41	6·1
12	Sa ☽	03 08	6·0	15 43	5·7
13	Su	04 21	5·5	16 59	5·4
14	M	05 59	5·3	18 37	5·4
15	Tu	07 34	5·4	19 55	5·6
16	W	08 35	5·7	20 49	5·9
17	Th	09 23	5·9	21 32	6·2
18	F	09 58	6·1	22 08	6·3
19	Sa	10 31	6·2	22 43	6·5
20	Su ○	11 03	6·3	23 17	6·5
21	M	11 37	6·4	23 51	6·5
22	Tu	** **	* *	12 08	6·3
23	W	00 22	6·4	12 37	6·3
24	Th	00 47	6·2	13 04	6·1
25	F	01 12	6·0	13 34	6·0
26	Sa	01 43	5·8	14 10	5·7
27	Su	02 26	5·5	14 59	5·5
28	M ☾	03 29	5·2	16 10	5·2
29	Tu	04 59	5·0	17 33	5·2
30	W	06 20	5·2	18 49	5·4

Time Zone **GMT**

Tidal Predictions : **HIGH WATERS 2008**

Units **METRES**

Datum of Predictions = **Chart Datum : 3.67 metres below Ordnance Datum (Newlyn)**

British Summer Time : **30th March to 26th October**

DOVER — May

DATE	DAY	Morning hr min	m	Afternoon hr min	m
1	Th	07 25	5·5	19 48	5·7
2	F	08 16	5·8	20 35	6·1
3	Sa	09 01	6·2	21 19	6·5
4	Su	09 43	6·4	22 01	6·7
5	M ●	10 25	6·6	22 45	6·9
6	Tu	11 11	6·7	23 30	6·9
7	W	11 59	6·7	** **	* *
8	Th	00 19	6·8	12 51	6·6
9	F	01 11	6·6	13 43	6·4
10	Sa	02 07	6·3	14 35	6·2
11	Su	03 08	5·9	15 33	5·9
12	M ☽	04 15	5·6	16 39	5·7
13	Tu	05 38	5·5	17 58	5·6
14	W	06 56	5·5	19 11	5·7
15	Th	07 55	5·6	20 07	5·8
16	F	08 42	5·8	20 54	6·0
17	Sa	09 23	5·9	21 36	6·1
18	Su	10 01	6·0	22 15	6·2
19	M	10 38	6·2	22 53	6·3
20	Tu ○	11 14	6·2	23 30	6·2
21	W	11 48	6·2	** **	* *
22	Th	00 02	6·2	12 22	6·2
23	F	00 33	6·1	12 54	6·2
24	Sa	01 04	5·9	13 28	6·1
25	Su	01 39	5·8	14 06	5·9
26	M	02 21	5·6	14 51	5·8
27	Tu	03 15	5·5	15 44	5·6
28	W ☾	04 19	5·4	16 48	5·6
29	Th	05 28	5·4	17 54	5·7
30	F	06 32	5·6	18 56	5·9
31	Sa	07 29	5·8	19 52	6·1

DOVER — June

DATE	DAY	Morning hr min	m	Afternoon hr min	m
1	Su	08 23	6·1	20 44	6·4
2	M	09 15	6·3	21 34	6·6
3	Tu ●	10 07	6·5	22 25	6·7
4	W	11 00	6·6	23 19	6·7
5	Th	11 54	6·6	** **	* *
6	F	00 15	6·6	12 46	6·6
7	Sa	01 10	6·5	13 36	6·5
8	Su	02 03	6·3	14 24	6·3
9	M	02 55	6·0	15 13	6·2
10	Tu ☽	03 50	5·8	16 07	6·0
11	W	04 52	5·6	17 09	5·8
12	Th	05 58	5·5	18 15	5·7
13	F	07 00	5·5	19 18	5·7
14	Sa	07 57	5·5	20 14	5·7
15	Su	08 49	5·7	21 06	5·8
16	M	09 36	5·8	21 51	5·9
17	Tu	10 17	6·0	22 34	6·0
18	W ○	10 55	6·1	23 11	6·1
19	Th	11 31	6·2	23 47	6·1
20	F	** **	* *	12 05	6·2
21	Sa	00 20	6·1	12 40	6·3
22	Su	00 54	6·1	13 17	6·3
23	M	01 31	6·0	13 53	6·2
24	Tu	02 09	5·9	14 31	6·1
25	W	02 52	5·8	15 15	6·0
26	Th ☾	03 41	5·7	16 07	6·0
27	F	04 41	5·7	17 04	5·9
28	Sa	05 42	5·7	18 09	5·9
29	Su	06 49	5·7	19 14	6·0
30	M	07 55	5·9	20 19	6·1

DOVER — July

DATE	DAY	Morning hr min	m	Afternoon hr min	m
1	Tu	09 01	6·1	21 22	6·3
2	W	10 01	6·3	22 21	6·5
3	Th ●	10 57	6·5	23 17	6·5
4	F	11 48	6·6	** **	* *
5	Sa	00 11	6·6	12 36	6·7
6	Su	01 01	6·5	13 19	6·6
7	M	01 46	6·4	14 02	6·6
8	Tu	02 28	6·2	14 44	6·4
9	W	03 13	6·0	15 29	6·2
10	Th ☽	04 01	5·7	16 19	5·9
11	F	04 57	5·5	17 19	5·7
12	Sa	06 02	5·3	18 27	5·4
13	Su	07 14	5·3	19 39	5·4
14	M	08 19	5·4	20 41	5·5
15	Tu	09 13	5·6	21 33	5·7
16	W	09 57	5·8	22 17	5·9
17	Th	10 36	6·0	22 53	6·0
18	F ○	11 10	6·2	23 26	6·1
19	Sa	11 45	6·4	23 59	6·2
20	Su	** **	* *	12 19	6·5
21	M	00 34	6·3	12 56	6·5
22	Tu	01 10	6·3	13 31	6·5
23	W	01 46	6·2	14 04	6·4
24	Th	02 23	6·1	14 42	6·3
25	F ☾	03 06	6·0	15 27	6·2
26	Sa	04 00	5·8	16 25	6·0
27	Su	05 04	5·7	17 34	5·8
28	M	06 19	5·5	18 51	5·7
29	Tu	07 45	5·6	20 14	5·8
30	W	09 04	5·9	21 26	6·1
31	Th	10 03	6·2	22 25	6·3

DOVER — August

DATE	DAY	Morning hr min	m	Afternoon hr min	m
1	F ●	10 52	6·5	23 14	6·5
2	Sa	11 35	6·7	23 59	6·6
3	Su	** **	* *	12 16	6·8
4	M	00 40	6·5	12 56	6·8
5	Tu	01 18	6·4	13 32	6·7
6	W	01 53	6·3	14 09	6·6
7	Th	02 31	6·1	14 47	6·3
8	F ☽	03 11	5·8	15 30	6·0
9	Sa	03 58	5·5	16 22	5·6
10	Su	05 00	5·2	17 35	5·2
11	M	06 25	5·0	19 04	5·1
12	Tu	07 49	5·1	20 20	5·2
13	W	08 51	5·4	21 15	5·5
14	Th	09 37	5·8	21 57	5·8
15	F	10 14	6·1	22 31	6·1
16	Sa ○	10 46	6·3	23 02	6·3
17	Su	11 19	6·5	23 33	6·4
18	M	11 52	6·7	** **	* *
19	Tu	00 06	6·5	12 26	6·7
20	W	00 41	6·5	13 01	6·7
21	Th	01 17	6·5	13 35	6·7
22	F	01 53	6·4	14 11	6·5
23	Sa ☾	02 35	6·2	14 56	6·3
24	Su	03 29	5·9	15 57	5·9
25	M	04 39	5·6	17 14	5·6
26	Tu	06 09	5·3	18 56	5·5
27	W	07 55	5·5	20 30	5·7
28	Th	09 05	5·9	21 33	6·1
29	F	09 56	6·3	22 21	6·4
30	Sa ●	10 38	6·6	23 02	6·5
31	Su	11 16	6·8	23 38	6·6

Time Zone **GMT**

Tidal Predictions : **HIGH WATERS 2008**

Datum of Predictions = **Chart Datum : 3.67 metres below Ordnance Datum (Newlyn)**

British Summer Time : **30th March to 26th October**

Units **METRES**

DOVER

September

DATE	DAY	Morning hr min	m	Afternoon hr min	m
1	M	11 52	6·9	** **	**
2	Tu	00 12	6·6	12 26	6·9
3	W	00 46	6·5	13 00	6·8
4	Th	01 17	6·4	13 32	6·6
5	F	01 49	6·2	14 04	6·3
6	Sa	02 23	5·9	14 38	5·9
7	Su ☽	03 01	5·6	15 20	5·5
8	M	03 56	5·2	16 35	5·0
9	Tu	05 24	4·9	18 25	4·8
10	W	07 08	5·0	19 52	5·1
11	Th	08 19	5·3	20 49	5·4
12	F	09 06	5·7	21 29	5·8
13	Sa	09 43	6·1	22 01	6·1
14	Su	10 15	6·4	22 31	6·4
15	M ○	10 48	6·6	23 02	6·6
16	Tu	11 20	6·8	23 37	6·7
17	W	11 55	6·9	** **	**
18	Th	00 13	6·7	12 30	6·9
19	F	00 50	6·7	13 07	6·8
20	Sa	01 29	6·5	13 48	6·6
21	Su	02 16	6·2	14 37	6·2
22	M ☾	03 13	5·9	15 44	5·8
23	Tu	04 31	5·5	17 17	5·4
24	W	06 13	5·3	19 12	5·4
25	Th	07 50	5·6	20 30	5·8
26	F	08 52	6·0	21 25	6·1
27	Sa	09 37	6·4	22 05	6·4
28	Su	10 15	6·6	22 39	6·5
29	M ●	10 49	6·8	23 10	6·6
30	Tu	11 23	6·8	23 42	6·6

DOVER

October

DATE	DAY	Morning hr min	m	Afternoon hr min	m
1	W	11 56	6·8	** **	**
2	Th	00 15	6·5	12 29	6·7
3	F	00 46	6·4	12 58	6·5
4	Sa	01 15	6·3	13 26	6·2
5	Su	01 45	6·0	13 56	5·9
6	M	02 20	5·8	14 34	5·5
7	Tu ☽	03 08	5·4	15 39	5·1
8	W	04 26	5·1	17 28	4·8
9	Th	06 06	5·0	19 04	5·0
10	F	07 28	5·3	20 06	5·4
11	Sa	08 21	5·7	20 48	5·8
12	Su	09 02	6·1	21 22	6·2
13	M	09 37	6·4	21 56	6·4
14	Tu ○	10 11	6·7	22 31	6·7
15	W	10 48	6·9	23 07	6·8
16	Th	11 24	7·0	23 48	6·8
17	F	** **	**	12 05	7·0
18	Sa	00 30	6·7	12 47	6·8
19	Su	01 17	6·5	13 35	6·5
20	M	02 10	6·3	14 34	6·1
21	Tu ☾	03 11	5·9	15 47	5·7
22	W	04 25	5·6	17 21	5·4
23	Th	05 58	5·5	19 01	5·5
24	F	07 24	5·7	20 09	5·8
25	Sa	08 23	6·0	20 59	6·0
26	Su	09 08	6·3	21 39	6·2
27	M	09 46	6·5	22 11	6·4
28	Tu ●	10 22	6·6	22 43	6·5
29	W	10 57	6·6	23 17	6·5
30	Th	11 31	6·6	23 51	6·5
31	F	** **	**	12 05	6·5

DOVER

November

DATE	DAY	Morning hr min	m	Afternoon hr min	m
1	Sa	00 23	6·4	12 34	6·3
2	Su	00 53	6·3	13 03	6·1
3	M	01 25	6·1	13 35	5·9
4	Tu	02 00	5·9	14 13	5·6
5	W	02 45	5·6	15 09	5·3
6	Th ☽	03 47	5·4	16 31	5·1
7	F	05 03	5·2	17 54	5·1
8	Sa	06 19	5·4	19 03	5·4
9	Su	07 22	5·7	19 55	5·7
10	M	08 11	6·0	20 38	6·1
11	Tu	08 55	6·4	21 19	6·4
12	W	09 36	6·7	22 01	6·6
13	Th ○	10 18	6·9	22 45	6·8
14	F	11 03	6·9	23 33	6·8
15	Sa	11 49	6·9	** **	**
16	Su	00 22	6·7	12 40	6·7
17	M	01 14	6·6	13 35	6·4
18	Tu	02 07	6·4	14 35	6·1
19	W ☾	03 04	6·1	15 40	5·8
20	Th	04 05	5·9	16 57	5·6
21	F	05 19	5·7	18 19	5·5
22	Sa	06 34	5·8	19 26	5·6
23	Su	07 38	5·9	20 20	5·8
24	M	08 30	6·0	21 04	5·9
25	Tu	09 15	6·2	21 43	6·1
26	W	09 56	6·3	22 21	6·2
27	Th ●	10 35	6·4	22 57	6·3
28	F	11 13	6·4	23 34	6·4
29	Sa	11 48	6·3	** **	**
30	Su	00 08	6·4	12 20	6·2

DOVER

December

DATE	DAY	Morning hr min	m	Afternoon hr min	m
1	M	00 40	6·3	12 53	6·1
2	Tu	01 14	6·2	13 25	5·9
3	W	01 49	6·1	14 02	5·8
4	Th	02 28	5·9	14 47	5·6
5	F ☽	03 13	5·8	15 41	5·4
6	Sa	04 10	5·6	16 48	5·4
7	Su	05 14	5·6	17 54	5·4
8	M	06 19	5·7	18 57	5·6
9	Tu	07 19	5·9	19 55	5·9
10	W	08 14	6·2	20 48	6·2
11	Th	09 08	6·5	21 41	6·4
12	F ○	10 00	6·7	22 34	6·6
13	Sa	10 52	6·8	23 27	6·7
14	Su	11 45	6·8	** **	**
15	M	00 19	6·8	12 39	6·7
16	Tu	01 08	6·7	13 32	6·5
17	W	01 56	6·6	14 24	6·3
18	Th	02 44	6·4	15 16	6·0
19	F ☾	03 34	6·2	16 12	5·8
20	Sa	04 32	6·0	17 16	5·6
21	Su	05 35	5·8	18 23	5·5
22	M	06 44	5·7	19 29	5·5
23	Tu	07 49	5·7	20 28	5·6
24	W	08 47	5·8	21 19	5·8
25	Th	09 37	5·9	22 03	6·0
26	F	10 21	6·0	22 42	6·2
27	Sa ●	10 59	6·1	23 19	6·3
28	Su	11 34	6·2	23 52	6·4
29	M	** **	**	12 06	6·2
30	Tu	00 26	6·4	12 39	6·2
31	W	00 58	6·4	13 11	6·1

Time Zone **GMT**

Tidal Predictions : **HIGH WATERS 2009**

Units **METRES**

Datum of Predictions = **Chart Datum : 3.67 metres below Ordnance Datum (Newlyn)**

British Summer Time : **29th March to 25th October**

DOVER

January

DATE	DAY		Morning hr min	m	Afternoon hr min	m
1	Th		01 31	6·3	13 43	6·1
2	F		02 04	6·3	14 19	6·0
3	Sa		02 41	6·2	15 01	5·8
4	Su	☽	03 25	6·1	15 53	5·7
5	M		04 19	5·9	16 55	5·6
6	Tu		05 24	5·8	18 04	5·6
7	W		06 34	5·8	19 17	5·7
8	Th		07 45	5·9	20 30	5·9
9	F		08 52	6·2	21 34	6·2
10	Sa		09 54	6·4	22 32	6·5
11	Su	○	10 50	6·6	23 23	6·7
12	M		11 44	6·7	** **	* *
13	Tu		00 11	6·8	12 33	6·7
14	W		00 56	6·9	13 18	6·6
15	Th		01 38	6·8	14 02	6·5
16	F		02 19	6·7	14 42	6·2
17	Sa		03 01	6·5	15 27	6·0
18	Su	☾	03 47	6·2	16 19	5·7
19	M		04 43	5·8	17 23	5·4
20	Tu		05 52	5·5	18 39	5·2
21	W		07 11	5·3	19 55	5·3
22	Th		08 23	5·4	20 56	5·5
23	F		09 20	5·6	21 46	5·8
24	Sa		10 07	5·8	22 25	6·0
25	Su		10 45	6·0	23 00	6·2
26	M	●	11 17	6·1	23 33	6·4
27	Tu		11 47	6·3	** **	* *
28	W		00 05	6·5	12 18	6·3
29	Th		00 36	6·5	12 49	6·3
30	F		01 07	6·6	13 18	6·3
31	Sa		01 36	6·5	13 50	6·2

DOVER

February

DATE	DAY		Morning hr min	m	Afternoon hr min	m
1	Su		02 09	6·5	14 27	6·1
2	M	☽	02 47	6·3	15 12	6·0
3	Tu		03 39	6·1	16 12	5·7
4	W		04 43	5·8	17 27	5·5
5	Th		06 05	5·6	18 58	5·4
6	F		07 35	5·6	20 28	5·7
7	Sa		08 55	5·9	21 36	6·1
8	Su		09 57	6·3	22 28	6·5
9	M	○	10 49	6·5	23 13	6·7
10	Tu		11 34	6·7	23 55	6·9
11	W		** **	* *	12 18	6·7
12	Th		00 34	7·0	12 56	6·7
13	F		01 12	6·9	13 32	6·5
14	Sa		01 48	6·8	14 07	6·3
15	Su		02 26	6·5	14 47	6·1
16	M	☾	03 06	6·2	15 30	5·7
17	Tu		03 54	5·7	16 26	5·3
18	W		05 02	5·3	17 47	5·0
19	Th		06 33	5·0	19 18	5·0
20	F		07 57	5·1	20 31	5·3
21	Sa		09 02	5·4	21 23	5·6
22	Su		09 49	5·7	22 03	5·9
23	M		10 24	5·9	22 36	6·2
24	Tu		10 52	6·1	23 07	6·4
25	W	●	11 20	6·3	23 37	6·5
26	Th		11 49	6·4	** **	* *
27	F		00 08	6·6	12 20	6·5
28	Sa		00 37	6·7	12 51	6·5

DOVER

March

DATE	DAY		Morning hr min	m	Afternoon hr min	m
1	Su		01 07	6·7	13 24	6·4
2	M		01 41	6·6	14 02	6·3
3	Tu		02 20	6·4	14 47	6·0
4	W	☽	03 12	6·1	15 49	5·7
5	Th		04 22	5·7	17 10	5·3
6	F		05 58	5·4	18 58	5·3
7	Sa		07 45	5·5	20 27	5·7
8	Su		08 59	5·9	21 27	6·1
9	M		09 54	6·2	22 14	6·5
10	Tu		10 38	6·5	22 53	6·7
11	W	○	11 17	6·6	23 33	6·9
12	Th		11 54	6·7	** **	* *
13	F		00 09	6·9	12 29	6·7
14	Sa		00 44	6·9	13 03	6·5
15	Su		01 18	6·7	13 35	6·4
16	M		01 52	6·4	14 10	6·1
17	Tu		02 27	6·1	14 49	5·8
18	W	☾	03 11	5·6	15 40	5·4
19	Th		04 15	5·1	16 53	5·0
20	F		05 51	4·8	18 32	4·9
21	Sa		07 25	4·9	19 52	5·1
22	Su		08 31	5·2	20 48	5·5
23	M		09 18	5·6	21 29	5·8
24	Tu		09 50	5·9	22 03	6·1
25	W		10 18	6·1	22 32	6·4
26	Th	●	10 46	6·3	23 03	6·6
27	F		11 17	6·5	23 34	6·7
28	Sa		11 51	6·6	** **	* *
29	Su		00 08	6·8	12 27	6·6
30	M		00 43	6·7	13 04	6·5
31	Tu		01 21	6·6	13 48	6·3

DOVER

April

DATE	DAY		Morning hr min	m	Afternoon hr min	m
1	W		02 06	6·3	14 40	6·0
2	Th	☽	03 06	5·9	15 47	5·7
3	F		04 26	5·5	17 13	5·4
4	Sa		06 09	5·4	18 54	5·4
5	Su		07 43	5·6	20 11	5·8
6	M		08 47	5·9	21 06	6·1
7	Tu		09 36	6·2	21 50	6·4
8	W		10 17	6·4	22 28	6·6
9	Th	○	10 52	6·5	23 06	6·7
10	F		11 27	6·6	23 42	6·8
11	Sa		** **	* *	12 02	6·5
12	Su		00 18	6·7	12 36	6·5
13	M		00 51	6·5	13 10	6·3
14	Tu		01 25	6·2	13 43	6·1
15	W		01 59	5·9	14 21	5·8
16	Th		02 40	5·6	15 08	5·5
17	F	☾	03 39	5·2	16 11	5·2
18	Sa		05 00	4·9	17 31	5·0
19	Su		06 30	4·9	18 54	5·1
20	M		07 39	5·2	19 56	5·4
21	Tu		08 27	5·5	20 41	5·8
22	W		09 04	5·8	21 18	6·1
23	Th		09 37	6·1	21 53	6·3
24	F		10 11	6·3	22 26	6·5
25	Sa	●	10 48	6·5	23 03	6·7
26	Su		11 27	6·6	23 44	6·7
27	M		** **	* *	12 11	6·6
28	Tu		00 27	6·7	12 57	6·5
29	W		01 15	6·5	13 50	6·3
30	Th		02 11	6·2	14 48	6·1

SUNRISE AND SUNSET TIMES

Predictions are given for the times of sunrise and sunset on every Saturday throughout the year. For places on the same latitude as the following, add 4 minutes for each degree of longitude west (subtract if east).

These times are in GMT, except between 01:00 on Mar 30 and 01:00 on Oct 26, when the times are in BST (1 hour in advance of GMT).

	London		Manchester		Edinburgh	
	Rise	Set	Rise	Set	Rise	Set
Jan 5	08 06	16 06	08 24	16 04	08 43	15 54
12	08 02	16 16	08 20	16 14	08 38	16 05
19	07 57	16 26	08 14	16 26	08 30	16 18
26	07 48	16 38	08 05	16 39	08 19	16 32
Feb 2	07 38	16 51	07 54	16 52	08 07	16 47
9	07 27	17 04	07 41	17 06	07 53	17 02
16	07 14	17 16	07 27	17 20	07 37	17 18
23	07 00	17 29	07 12	17 34	07 21	17 33
Mar 1	06 45	17 42	06 56	17 47	07 03	17 48
8	06 30	17 54	06 40	18 01	06 46	18 03
15	06 14	18 06	06 23	18 14	06 27	18 17
22	05 58	18 18	06 06	18 27	06 09	18 31
29	05 42	18 29	05 49	18 40	05 51	18 46
Apr 5	06 26	19 41	06 32	19 52	06 32	20 00
12	06 11	19 53	06 16	20 05	06 14	20 14
19	05 56	20 05	05 59	20 18	05 57	20 28
26	05 42	20 16	05 44	20 31	05 40	20 43
May 3	05 28	20 28	05 30	20 43	05 24	20 57
10	05 16	20 39	05 17	20 55	05 09	21 11
17	05 06	20 50	05 05	21 07	04 56	21 24
24	04 57	20 59	04 55	21 18	04 45	21 36
31	04 50	21 08	04 47	21 27	04 36	21 46

SUNRISE AND SUNSET TIMES

	London		Manchester		Edinburgh	
	Rise	**Set**	**Rise**	**Set**	**Rise**	**Set**
Jun 7	04 45	21 15	04 42	21 34	04 30	21 55
14	04 43	21 19	04 39	21 39	04 26	22 00
21	04 43	21 22	04 40	21 42	04 26	22 03
28	04 46	21 22	04 43	21 42	04 30	22 03
Jul 5	04 51	21 19	04 48	21 39	04 36	21 59
12	04 58	21 14	04 59	21 30	04 44	21 52
19	05 06	21 07	05 05	21 25	04 55	21 43
26	05 16	20 57	05 15	21 15	05 07	21 31
Aug 2	05 26	20 46	05 27	21 03	05 19	21 17
9	05 37	20 34	05 39	20 49	05 33	21 02
16	05 48	20 20	05 51	20 35	05 46	20 46
23	05 59	20 06	06 03	20 19	06 00	20 29
30	06 10	19 51	06 15	20 03	06 14	20 12
Sep 6	06 22	19 35	06 27	19 46	06 28	19 53
13	06 33	19 19	06 39	19 29	06 41	19 35
20	06 44	19 03	06 52	19 12	06 55	19 16
27	06 55	18 47	07 04	18 55	07 08	18 58
Oct 4	07 07	18 31	07 16	18 38	07 22	18 40
11	07 18	18 15	07 29	18 21	07 36	18 22
18	07 30	18 00	07 42	18 05	07 51	18 04
25	07 42	17 46	07 55	17 50	08 05	17 47
Nov 1	06 55	16 33	07 09	16 36	07 20	16 32
8	07 07	16 21	07 22	16 23	07 35	16 17
15	07 19	16 11	07 35	16 11	07 50	16 05
22	07 31	16 02	07 48	16 02	08 04	15 54
29	07 42	15 56	07 59	15 55	08 17	15 46
Dec 6	07 51	15 53	08 09	15 51	08 28	15 40
13	07 58	15 52	08 17	15 49	08 36	15 38
20	08 04	15 53	08 23	15 51	08 42	15 39
27	08 06	15 58	08 25	15 55	08 44	15 44

GRID REFERENCES

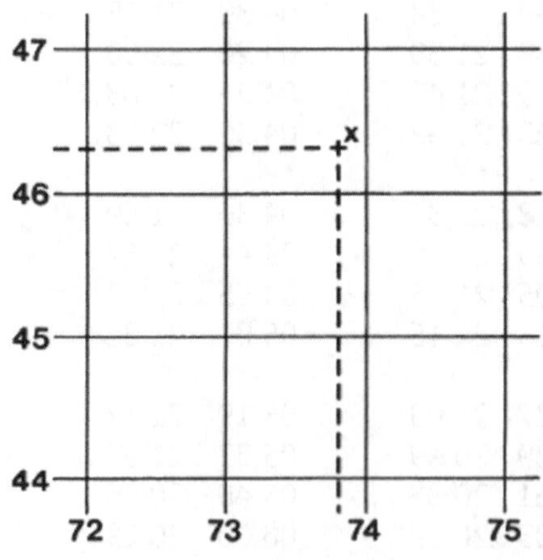

A grid reference is made up of letters and numbers. Two-letter codes are used for 100km squares on the National Grid (opposite) and single-letter codes on the Irish Grid (below).

The squares may be further subdivided into squares of 10km, 1km or 100m, allowing for increasingly specific references. On a given map the lines forming the squares are numbered in the margins, those along the top and bottom being known as 'eastings' and those along the sides as 'northings'. A reference number is made up of the relevant letter code plus two sets of figures, those representing the easting followed by the northing. According to the scale of the map they can either be read off directly or calculated by visually dividing the intervals into tenths.

For most purposes three-figure eastings plus three-figure northings are adequate.

The example above, from an Ordnance Survey 'Landranger' map, illustrates how to specify a location on a map divided into lkm squares: the reference for point X is 738463. If that location lies in square SP (see map opposite), the full reference is SP738463.

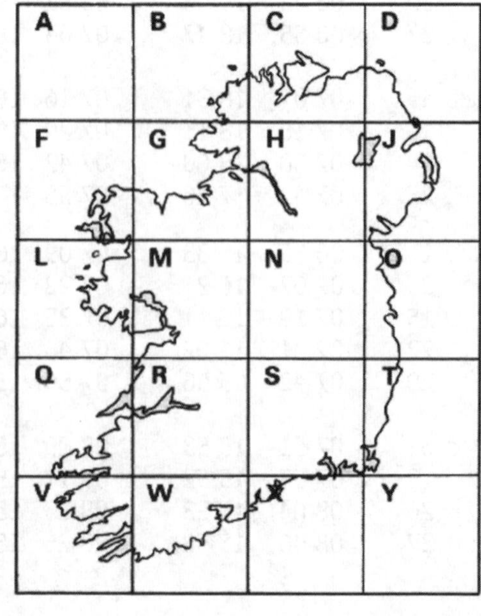

Letter codes for Irish grid 10km squares

GRID REFERENCES

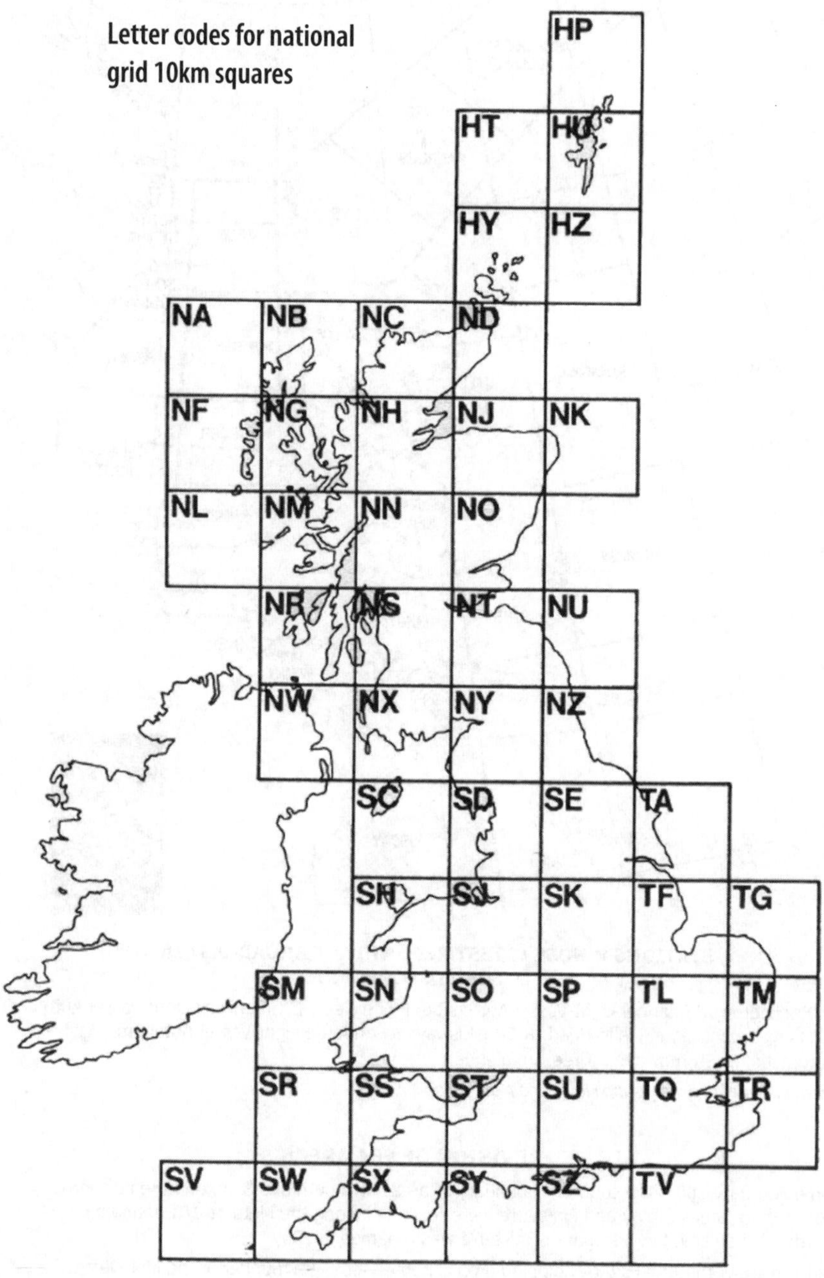

SEA AREAS

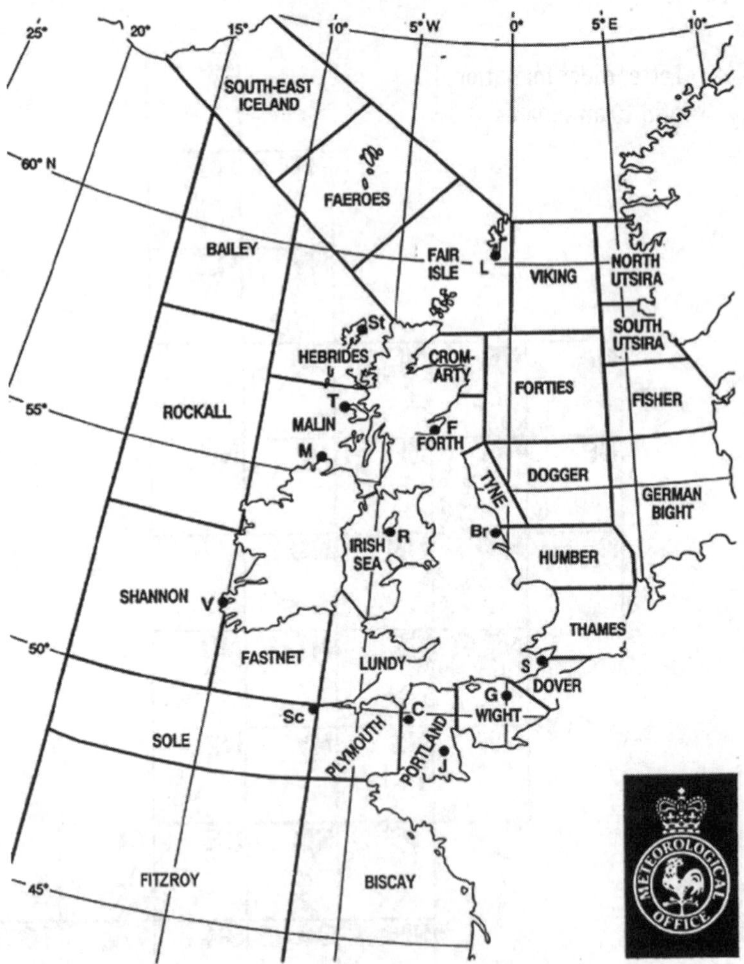

STATIONS WHOSE LATEST REPORTS ARE BROADCAST IN THE 5-MINUTE FORECASTS

Br Bridlington; C Channel Light-Vessel Automatic; F Fife Ness; G Greenwich Light-Vessel Automatic; J Jersey; L Lerwick; M Malin Head; R Ronaldsway; S Sandettie Light-Vessel Automatic; Sc Scilly Automatic; St Stornoway; T Tiree; V Valentia.

From information kindly supplied by the Meteorological Office

REVISION OF SEA AREAS

On 4 February 2002, the southern boundary of areas Plymouth and Sole, and the northern boundary of areas Biscay and Finisterre were realigned along the Metarea I/II boundary at 48°27′ North. At the same time, sea area Finisterre was renamed FitzRoy.

Did you know that the FitzRoy shipping area is named after the founder of the Met Office?

THE BIRDWATCHER'S CODE OF CONDUCT

Around three million adults go birdwatching every year in the UK. Following The birdwatchers' code is good practice, common sense and will help everybody to enjoy seeing birds.

This code puts the interests of birds first, and respects other people, whether or not they are interested in birds. It applies whenever you are watching birds in the UK or abroad. Please help everybody to enjoy birdwatching by following the code, leading by example and sensitively challenging the minority of birdwatchers who behave inappropriately.

1. The interests of the birds come first

Birds respond to people in many ways, depending on the species, location and time of year.

If birds are disturbed they may keep away from their nests, leaving chicks hungry or enabling predators to take their eggs or young. During cold weather, or when migrants have just made a long flight, repeatedly disturbing birds can mean they use up vital energy that they need for feeding.

Intentionally or recklessly disturbing some birds at or near their nest is illegal in Britain.

Whether you are particularly interested in photography, bird ringing, sound-recording or birdwatching, remember to always put the interests of the birds first.

- Avoid going too close to birds or disturbing their habitats – if a bird flies away or makes repeated alarm calls, you're too close. If it leaves, you won't get a good view of it anyway.
- Stay on roads and paths where they exist and avoid disturbing habitat used by birds.
- Think about your fieldcraft. You might disturb a bird even if you are not very close, eg a flock of wading birds on the foreshore can be disturbed from a mile away if you stand on the seawall.
- Repeatedly playing a recording of bird song or calls to encourage a bird to respond can divert a territorial bird from other important duties, such as feeding its young. Never use playback to attract a species during its breeding season.

2. Be an ambassador for birdwatching

Respond positively to questions from interested passers-by. They may not be birdwatchers yet, but good views of a bird or a helpful answer may ignite a spark of interest. Your enthusiasm could start lifetime's interest in birds and a greater appreciation of wildlife and its conservation.

Consider using local services, such as pubs, restaurants, petrol stations, and public transport. Raising awareness of the benefits to local communities of trade from visiting birdwatchers may, ultimately, help the birds themselves.

3. Know the Countryside Code, and follow it

Respect the wishes of local residents and landowners and don't enter private land without permission, unless it is open for public access on foot.

Follow the codes on access and the countryside for the place you're walking in. Irresponsible behaviour may cause a land manager to deny access to others (eg for important bird survey work). It may also disturb the bird or give birdwatching bad coverage in the media.

Access to the countryside

Legislation provides access for walkers to open country in Britain, and includes measures to protect wildlife. Note that the rules and codes are different in each part of Britain, so plan ahead and make sure you know what you can do legally.

4. The law

Laws protecting birds and their habitats are the result of hard campaigning by generations of birdwatchers. We must make sure that we don't allow them to fall into disrepute. In England, Scotland and Wales, it is a criminal offence to disturb, intentionally or recklessly, at or near the nest, a species listed on Schedule 1 of the Wildlife & Countryside Act 1981 (see www.rspb.org.uk/policy/wildbirdslaw for a full list). Disturbance could include playback of songs and calls. In Scotland, disturbing Capercaillie and Ruffs at leks is also an offence. It is a criminal offence to intentionally disturb a bird at or near the nest under the Wildlife (Northern Ireland) Order 1985.

The Government can, for particular reasons such as scientific study, issue licences to individuals that permit limited disturbance, including monitoring of nests and ringing. It is a criminal offence to destroy or damage, intentionally or recklessly, a special interest feature of a Site of Special Scientific Interest (SSSI) or to disturb the wildlife for which the site was notified.

If you witness anyone who you suspect may be illegally disturbing or destroying wildlife or habitat, phone the police immediately (ideally, with a six-figure map reference) and report it to the RSPB.

5. Rare birds

Mobile phones, telephone and pager services and the internet mean you can now share your sightings instantly. If you discover a rare bird, please bear the following in mind

•Consider the potential impact of spreading the news and make an effort to inform the landowner (or, on a nature reserve, the warden) first. Think about whether the site can cope with a large number of visitors and whether sensitive species might be at risk, such as breeding terns, flocks of wading birds or rare plants. The county bird recorder or another experienced birdwatcher can often give good advice.

- On private land, always talk to the landowner first. With a little planning, access can often be arranged.
- People coming to see a rare bird can raise money for a local reserve, other wildlife project or charity. Consider organising a voluntary collection at access points to the site.
- Rare breeding birds are at risk from egg-collectors and some birds of prey from persecution. If you discover a rare breeding species that you think is vulnerable, contact the RSPB; it has considerable experience in protecting rare breeding birds. Please also report your sighting to the county bird recorder or the Rare Breeding Birds Panel. (www.rbbp.org.uk). Also, consider telling the landowner – in most cases, this will ensure that the nest is not disturbed accidentally. If you have the opportunity to see a rare bird, enjoy it, but don't let your enthusiasm override common sense.

THE BIRDWATCHER'S CODE OF CONDUCT

In addition to the guidelines above:

- park sensibly, follow instructions and consider making a donation if requested
- don't get too close so that you can take a photograph – you'll incur the wrath of everyone else watching if you scare the bird away
- be patient if the viewing is limited, talk quietly and give others a chance to see the bird too
- do not enter private areas without permission
- not everyone likes to see an 'organised flush' and it should never be done in important wildlife habitats or where there are other nesting or roosting birds nearby. A flush should not be organised more frequently than every two hours and not within two hours of sunrise or sunset, so the bird has chance to feed and rest.

6. Make your sightings count

Add to tomorrow's knowledge of birds by sending your sightings to www.birdtrack.net This online recording scheme from the BTO, the RSPB and BirdWatch Ireland allows you to input and store all of your birdwatching records, which in turn helps to support species and site conservation. With one click, you can also have your records forwarded automatically to the relevant county recorder.

County recorders and local bird clubs are the mainstay of bird recording in the UK. Your records are important for local conservation and help to build the county's ornithological history. For a list of county bird recorders, look in the County Directory of *The Yearbook*, ask at your local library, or visit www.britishbirds.co.uk/countyrecorders

You can also get involved in a UK-wide bird monitoring scheme, such as the Breeding Bird Survey and the Wetland Bird Survey (see www.bto.org for details). If you've been birdwatching abroad, you can give your sightings to the BirdLife International Partner in that country by visiting www.worldbirds.org Your data could be vital in helping to protect sites and species in the country you've visited.

SCHEDULE 1 SPECIES

Under the provisions of the Wildlife and Countryside Act 1981 the following bird species (listed in Schedule 1 - Part I of the Act) are protected by special penalties at all times.

Avocet
Bee-eater
Bittem
Bittern, Little
Bluethroat
Brambling
Bunting, Cirl
Bunting, Lapland
Bunting, Snow
Buzzard, Honey
Chough
Crake, Corn
Crake, Spotted
Crossbills (all species)
Stone-curlew
Divers (all species)
Dotterel
Duck, Long-tailed
Eagle, Golden
Eagle, White-tailed
Falcon, Gyr
Fieldfare
Firecrest
Garganey
Godwit, Black-tailed
Goshawk
Grebe, Black-necked
Grebe, Slavonian
Greenshank
Gull, Little
Gull, Mediterranean
Harriers (all species)
Heron, Purple
Hobby
Hoopoe
Kingfisher
Kite, Red
Merlin
Oriole, Golden
Osprey
Owl, Barn
Owl, Snowy
Peregrine
Petrel, Leach's
Phalarope, Red-necked
Plover, Kentish
Plover, Little Ringed
Quail, Common
Redstart, Black
Redwing
Rosefinch, Scarlet
Ruff
Sandpiper, Green
Sandpiper, Purple
Sandpiper, Wood
Scaup
Scoter, Common
Scoter, Velvet
Serin
Lark, Shore
Shrike, Red-backed
Spoonbill
Stilt, Black-winged
Stint, Temminck's
Swan, Bewick's
Swan, Whooper
Tern, Black
Tern, Little
Tern, Roseate
Tit, Bearded
Tit, Crested
Treecreeper, Short-toed
Warbler, Cetti's
Warbler, Dartford
Warbler, Marsh
Warbler, Savi's
Whimbrel
Lark, Wood
Wryneck

The following birds and their eggs (listed in Schedule 1 - Part II of the Act) are protected by special penalties during the close season, which is Feb 1 to Aug 31 (Feb 21 to Aug 31 below high water mark), but may be killed outside this period - Goldeneye, Greylag Goose (in Outer Hebrides, Caithness, Sutherland, and Wester Ross only), Pintail.

THE COUNTRYSIDE CODE

Launched on 12 July 2004, this Code for England has been produced through a partnership between the Countryside Agency and Countryside Council for Wales.

The Countryside Code has been revised and re-launched to reflect the introduction of new open access rights (Countryside & Rights of Way Act 2000) and changes in society over the last 20 years.

• Be safe – plan ahead
Follow any signs, even when going out locally, it's best to get the latest information about where and when you can go; for example, your rights to go onto some areas of open land may be restricted while work is carried out, for safety reasons or during breeding seasons. Follow advice and local signs, and be prepared for the unexpected.

• Leave gates and property as you find them
Please respect the working life of the countryside, as our actions can affect people's livelihoods, our heritage, and the safety and welfare of animals and ourselves.

• Protect plants and animals, and take your litter home
We have a responsibility to protect our countryside now and for future generations, so make sure you don't harm animals, birds, plants, or trees.

The Countryside Code
RESPECT • PROTECT • ENJOY

• Keep dogs under close control
The countryside is a great place to exercise dogs, but it's every owner's duty to make sure their dog is not a danger or nuisance to farm animals, wildlife or other people.

• Consider other people
Showing consideration and respect for other people makes the countryside a pleasant Environment for everyone – at home, at work and at leisure.

BIRDLINE NUMBERS - National and Regional

Birdline name	To obtain information	To report sightings (hotlines)
National		
Bird Information Service	09068 700 222	
www.birdingworld.co.uk		
Flightline (Northern Ireland)	028 9146 7408	
Regional		
Northern Ireland	028 9146 7408	
Scotland	09068 700 234	01292 611 994
Wales	09068 700 248	01492 544 588
East Anglia	09068 700 245	01603 763 388
Midlands	09068 700 247	01905 754 154
North East	09068 700 246	07974 358 988
North West	09068 700 249	01492 544 588
South East	09068 700 240	01845 570 444
www.southeastbirdnews.co.uk		or 08000 377 240
South West	09068 700 241	0845 4567 938

Charges
At the time of compilation, calls to premium line numbers cost 60p per minute.

INDEX TO RESERVES

INDEX TO RESERVES

INDEX TO RESERVES